Psychopathology

of

Childhood

JANE W. KESSLER

Professor of Psychology,
Western Reserve University

PRENTICE-HALL, INC., ENGLEWOOD CLIFFS, NEW JERSEY

PRENTICE-HALL SERIES IN PSYCHOLOGY
John C. Wright, *Editor*

To

Morris and Martin

Current printing (last digit):

17   16

Library of Congress Catalog Card Number: 66:14359

Printed in the United States of America. C-73675

PRENTICE-HALL INTERNATIONAL, INC., *London*
PRENTICE-HALL OF AUSTRALIA, PTY., LTD., *Sydney*
PRENTICE-HALL OF CANADA, LTD., *Toronto*
PRENTICE-HALL OF INDIA (PRIVATE) LTD., *New Delhi*
PRENTICE-HALL OF JAPAN, INC., *Tokyo*

PREFACE

This book is addressed to people seriously interested in the general area of child psychopathology, with full appreciation of the fact that readers of different professions will find some sections more relevant than others to their particular interests. Concern about emotional disturbance in childhood, however, is shared by all professional practitioners who work with children. These practitioners come from a wide variety of backgrounds, and their training usually includes relatively little education in the problems and principles of psychopathology in childhood. The pediatrician is thoroughly trained in normal growth and development and problems involving physical pathology. The teacher's training also includes study of normal child psychology as well as methods and theory of education. The professional training for social workers and clinical psychologists encompasses more material in the area of childhood psychopathology, but again it is presented mainly in terms of their specific professional duties of diagnosis, case work, or therapy. The psychiatrist receives his training in clinical facilities for adult patients, and, unless he is one of the very few who enter the subspecialty of child psychiatry, his experience with children is minimal. After the completion of training, these professional workers are exposed to different journals and reading materials which often leave them ignorant of the potential contributions from other fields. Despite the varied and separate professional training and the differences in the nature of their professional relationship with children, practitioners in all these fields, and others, are keenly interested in methods for the detection, treatment, and prevention of emotional problems in childhood.

This book grew out of my experience with teaching a graduate course of the same title. I wanted to give the students an idea of the problems they would encounter in their work as teachers, psychologists, speech therapists, or social workers, so it covers the gamut from transitory nightmares to psychosis in childhood. The problems are considered in the context of normal child development with emphasis on psychological factors responsible for deviations. Some attention is given to organic and constitutional factors, but in my opinion empathy with disturbed children is achieved mainly through an understanding of the psychological conflicts and feelings. By stretching our memory and imagination most of us can recall some pale version of the feelings which beset and overwhelm the disturbed child. This kind of awareness takes away much of the mystery and provides a sound basis for communication between adult and child.

There are always so many people to thank in the preparation of a book. Students and professional colleagues at Western Reserve University have been generous with their suggestions. The children and parents I have known have taught me as much as anything I have ever read. The unique opportunity which I have had to work and study with Dr. Anny Katan and other child psychoanalysts of the Cleveland Psychoanalytic Society has greatly enriched and deepened my understanding of child development. And for the mechanics of transferring ideas onto paper, I am grateful to a succession of patient secretaries: Mrs. Nelcena Cunningham, Mrs. Gertrude Malloy, Miss Carol Dankowski, Miss Sally Hecker, Miss Kirsten Werrenrath, and Miss Ann Raffis. I am especially indebted to Jane Dixon who checked references, read and reread manuscripts, and assisted with the indexing. The staff at the Mental Development Center displayed great forbearance with a director who pummeled them with questions and ideas far removed from their pressing tasks of operating a clinic for retarded children. This forbearance was more than equaled by the devotion of my husband and son, who were willing time and time again to give this book priority over their personal wishes.

JANE W. KESSLER

CONTENTS

Contents

Contents

Contents

Contents

1

PERSONALITY THEORY AND PSYCHOPATHOLOGY

Most people interested in helping children usually have some ideas about why they act as they do, ideas suggested by their own childhood and by empathy. If the child has a special problem, however, one has to delve more deeply for the causes. The causes invariably are multiple, and they are thoroughly embedded in a matrix of inborn tendencies, unique past experiences, family relationships, and cultural forces which affect both the child and his family. At different times, different factors have been emphasized. In the 1960's the mental health professions have shifted emphasis away from individual, and toward social, factors. This change of focus came about for many reasons, including the civil rights movement, public concern about poverty and differential patterns of unemployment, and epidemiological studies showing that the grossly underprivileged suffer disproportionately from mental disease (*Hollingshead and Redlich, 1958*). But, although there is much evidence of the importance of those environmental factors which transcend the individual, nonetheless it is the individual who feels the impact of these forces. In general, an individual case approach will be maintained throughout this text, in the hope that it will help the reader to understand, relate to, and assist the particular children with problems who come to his attention.

It is not, however, feasible to consider every instance of problem behavior as an individual case. One has to find some general explanatory principles which apply to a large number of cases. And for this, one needs some theoretical frame of reference within which to organize observations about the origin, manifestation, and treatment of children's problems. Such a framework is not only necessary for the research investigator interested in cause-and-effect, but also for the practitioner who is trying to help children who are in emotional difficulty.

Function of a Theory

The dictionary defines "theory" in several ways, using, in some instances such words as "speculation," "hypothesis," "idea," "guess," and "conjecture." It tells us that "theory" may be opposed to "fact" in the sense that a theory is unproved. So it should not surprise us that, whenever some one sets forth a theory, criticism and controversy ensue. Any theoretical formulation is a mixture of facts and interpretation of these facts, and the minute one goes beyond the indisputable evidence of eyes and ears (which is not always so indisputable), alternative explanations can be advanced. Because of this, many conscientious scientists are chary of theory and limit themselves to the collecting and reporting of objective data. This would appear to be a way to avoid confusion or controversy, but it proves unsatisfactory, even in the physical sciences. One has to collect data for a reason; there is always a wish, or need, to piece things together and to make sense out of the observations. In other words, unexplained facts have little value and bring very little satisfaction to their collector.

The dictionary also defines "theory" as "the analysis of a set of facts in their ideal relation to one another." Theory provides the glue to stick facts together into some sort of cohesive whole. A theory integrates empirical data and poses crucial questions requiring further investigation. Without a unifying theory, each experimenter would function as a single individual; each little piece of research would have equal value; and any kind of investigation could be undertaken. So the theory is necessary to explain what has been observed before and to tell us what to look for next.

But this is the case for theory in the name of science. The person primarily interested in helping others may abjure theory as uselessly abstract, complicated, and controversial. He will object to wading through technical terms and pedantic logical systems, failing to see their practicality. As a practitioner, he wants to know what to look for and to say. Specifically in the field of child management, practical advice is handed out by child care experts with a minimum of theoretical explanation. The parent or teacher is cautioned against something, or directed to do something, simply because an authority says so. Many workers are intellectually impatient with the why of the advice and want only the prescriptions; the sophisticated practitioner, however, can detect the concepts which underlie the practical recommendations.

Many authorities choose to be eclectic, that is, to avoid commitment to any one theory by choosing the best parts of several approaches. This seems like the perfect way to avoid bias, but it does not really work out well. One reason is that it is a rare person who is equally familiar and expert with a number of theoretical systems. Every worker has his own preference, which usually reveals itself in greater knowledge of the preferred theory.

A survey of the contemporary literature on concepts of personality reveals a bewildering array of terms: "adience and self-actualization," "field theory," "humanistic psychology," "psychology of personal constructs," "phenomenology and personality," and others (*Wepman and Heine, 1964*). To relate all these to each other and examine their relevance to normal and deviant child development would be a Herculean task. Thus, the discussion that follows is limited to the major theories of child development, namely, those originating from psychoanalysis, learning theory, and maturational theory. Even narrowed to three, the expositions are by no means equal; the emphasis on psychoanalysis unavoidably reflects the author's background, preference, and area of competence.

Psychoanalysis as a Frame of Reference

In the author's opinion, psychoanalytic theories of personality development and structure of the mind are the most inclusive. It is true that the early psychoanalysts were primarily interested in investigating mental disorders; hence the reputation of psychoanalysis as a theory of neurosis. However, Freud hoped that in time the therapeutic aspect of analysis would be overshadowed by value as a science of human behavior. He was also aware of the need for reformulation of many aspects of psychoanalysis and of the tentative nature of some of his statements. Most of the recent developments in psychoanalysis have been in the direction of systematization, clarification of concepts, and integration with other scientific contributions; in an effort to achieve a theory comprehensive enough to encompass mental health as well as mental disease *(Rapaport, 1958; Hartmann, 1964)*.

Theoretical writings are unavoidably difficult to read and digest, and post-Freudian psychoanalytic writings have not permeated the literature. As a result, psychoanalysis is usually presented in its earliest form and suffers from a reputation of narrowness, oversimplification, and dogmatism. In the public mind, Freud explained everything in terms of sex, and professionals have made the same accusation in technical terms. For example, John Whitehorn remarked that "the original Freudian formulations were somewhat misleading in placing all motivational emphasis upon libidinal interests" *(1962, p. 198)*. The psychoanalytic theory of erogenous zones and the progression through oral, anal, phallic, and genital psychosexual stages is included in almost every text on child psychology, and many students are left with the impression that this is the sum theoretical total. But the ideas about infantile sexuality are an early development of psychoanalytic theory and a small part of the present body of psychoanalytic concepts.

Historical Development of Psychoanalysis

Psychoanalysis owes its origin to a single man, Sigmund Freud. Freud was a neurologist, interested in organic lesions of the brain and the functioning of the nervous system, before he turned to the psychology of behavior. He was 43 when his first work, *The Interpretation of Dreams*, was published, and he continued to write, and to revise his theories, until he died some 40 years later. Without guidance, it is hard for a student to educate himself about psychoanalytic theory. One does not know, on first reading the early publications, which parts of the theory remained ex-

tant to the end. And the later papers assume knowledge of the earlier ones. Moreover, the theory continued to develop and change after Freud's death in 1939. A further difficulty is that certain theoretical issues which have remained controversial have resulted in so-called schools of psychoanalysis. In some instances, the disagreement is really only a difference in emphasis; in others, the disagreement is a basic one.

As a physician practicing in Vienna, Freud's interest was aroused by his neurotic patients. He was impressed by the physical and mental suffering that could be caused by things thought and felt. He could readily see that these patients did not know why they suffered or even what was bothering them, and that the whole explanation did not lie in their objective circumstances. He soon discovered, however, that the patient resisted further knowledge of himself. Despite his suffering, the patient was loath to think about certain things, to remember certain past events, to recognize certain feelings. And these items, although the patient was unaware of them, often provided the key to his neurotic symptoms. Their uncovering led to relief of the suffering. This made Freud aware of the importance of the unconscious, and much of his early writing was designed to prove that feelings and events could be unconscious and yet determine behavior, a formulation with which there is today little disagreement.

His next question was: Why are certain psychological events made unconscious? Why does the patient ward off conscious knowledge of these important feelings and memories? Freud's answers were simple, and they have been generally accepted. A person does not think about those things which make him feel anxious or guilty, which are unpleasant feelings. It is a simple device of self-protection. Freud's next step was to study the general character of the feelings and memories walled off in the unconscious, and this was the first step which was repugnant to scientists of his time. He found that, with amazing regularity, the most painful thoughts, the ones requiring repression, had to do with sex. Apparently, his neurotic patients were more bothered about their sexual feelings than anything else.

Pursuing his inquiry, Freud wondered why a universal biological drive should present such special problems. Obviously there were many sexual taboos in the mores of his time, but the anxiety and conflict aroused seemed excessive nonetheless. Gradually, he began to focus his clinical investigations on origins, on childhood and the feelings emanating from this period of life.

At first, Freud took his patient's reports at face value and concluded that adult neurosis was the result of actual seduction experienced in childhood. Later, he rejected this idea on several grounds. For one thing, he could not believe that sexual attacks on young children could be so prevalent; it did not seem credible, for example, that so many fathers indulged in perverted acts with their daughters as the reports of hysterical women would suggest. This represented the first major change in psychoanalytic thinking.

If the memories painfully unearthed from the unconscious were not memories of actual events, they must be memories of childhood fantasies. The power of these fantasies hinted at the existence of internal forces which were as important as reality. Apparently a person could suffer long-lasting effects from imaginary experiences as well as from actual traumatic events. In order to explain psychopathology, one could no longer look only to events arising from the outside.

Next, Freud had to consider the origin of fantasies. They must have a source. If the source is not an external event, it must be some form of internal stimulation. He conceived of this internal stimulation as physical tension, a biological drive which found relief in

either physical or mental activity: "The force by which the sexual instinct is represented in the mind we call 'libido' —sexual desire—and we regard it as something analogous to hunger, the will to power, and so on, where the ego instincts are concerned" *(1917, 1955, p. 137).*

To view sexual longing as of equal psychological importance as hunger or the wish for power would probably have aroused little argument. But Freud used the term "sexual" to apply to activities which other people do not call "sexual." Also, he stated that even young children regularly experience sensations which should properly be termed sexual. The latter statement has particular relevance to child psychology, normal and abnormal, and deserves our special consideration.

Infantile Sexuality

The comment with which Freud began his *Three Essays on the Theory of Sexuality* is still a good beginning for this difficult subject:

Popular opinion has quite definite ideas about the nature and characteristics of this sexual instinct. It is generally understood to be absent in childhood, to set in at the time of puberty in connection with the process of coming to maturity and to be revealed in the manifestations of an irresistible attraction exercised by one sex upon the other; while its aim is presumed to be sexual union, or at all events actions leading in that direction.[*]

Popular opinion changes slowly, and people still find it hard to conceive that sexual feelings exist prior to adolescence. They reason that young children cannot have sexual thoughts or feelings because they are not capable of genital intercourse and reproduction. However, reality is no deterrent to fantasy.

---

[*]Quoted from Sigmund Freud, *Three Essays on the Theory of Sexuality* (1905). Standard Edition, ed. and trans. by J. Strachey (London: The Hogarth Press, 1953, VII, 135). © in U.S.A. by Basic Books, Inc. Reproduced by permission.

Young children are constantly dreaming about future, or even impossible, activities. A second line of attack questions the source of romantic fantasies. In part, fantasies owe their origin to reality in that they are elaborations of the child's experiences. These experiences may be real events which they witnessed, or imaginary events encountered in books, or on the movie or television screen. The question is, What are the external sources which stimulate sexual fantasies? In some unusual situations, the child is exposed to overt genital stimulation by seduction or by witnessing the primal scene, and the source of fantasy is clear. According to psychoanalytic theory, the more usual external sources of stimulation are regularly compounded by inborn sexual desires. The issues of controversy are first, the inherent nature of the child's sexual feelings, and second, the range of physical feelings which should be subsumed under the term "sexual."

When he first wrote on this subject, Freud had made virtually no direct observations of children. He arrived at his conclusions about the role played by sexual feelings in early childhood by three indirect routes. The first, already mentioned, was the repressed childhood fantasies of his adult patients. The second route was clinical consideration of homosexuality and of other variant sexual behavior. Such cases show that sexual pleasure can be obtained in various ways and provided Freud's justification for extending the concept of sexuality to other than strictly genital activities:

This gives us a hint that perhaps the sexual instinct itself may be no simple thing, but put together from components which have come apart in the perversions. If this is so, the clinical observations of these abnormalities will have drawn our attention to amalgamations which have been lost to view in the uniform behavior of normal people.[*]

---
[*]Freud, Sigmund, *op. cit.*, p. 162.

Further, Freud found that much neurotic anxiety and guilt surrounded fantasies regarding perverse sexual gratifications, activities which the patient would never permit himself in reality, and which he dreaded, yet could not suppress in fantasy. Apparently such wishes were not the exclusive property of a degenerate few. Further confirmation of the universality of nongenital sexual activities may be found in the looking, caressing, kissing, and so on which are customary accompaniments of normal love making. This, then, constitutes the third argument which Freud used to broaden the term "sexual" to include much more than genital activity.

Freud consistently maintained a developmental point of view: Nothing in the mental life of an individual arises spontaneously or without antecedent in his past experience. He was concerned with tracing psychological events back to their beginnings, and tracing back the sexual instinct led him to the nursery. The baby can be observed taking great pleasure in his body. He happily sucks, quite independently of his need for food. The toddler enjoys playing with his anus and, soon after, the boy discovers his penis and the girl her clitoris. Everyone knows that babies like to suck, that toddlers will stick their fingers or other objects into their anuses, that slightly older children will tug at their genitals, but such activities are commonly viewed as innocent. The idea that the child is in any way titillated by such activities is denied by some observers. Others see that these activities give the child pleasure, but divorce it from the kind of excitement a grown person might find in the same activity. They say, "They are just not the same thing. The child is just playing; it doesn't mean anything."

In psychoanalytic theory, there is a continuous line of development, deserving of the same name. The sexual instinct begins diffusely from the excitability of many erotogenic zones of the body. In describing the characteristics of such zones, Freud stated: "The example of thumb sucking shows us still more about what constitutes an erotogenic zone. It is a part of the skin or mucous membrane in which stimuli of a certain sort evoke a feeling of pleasure possessing a particular quality" *(1905, 1953, p. 183)*. The famous stages of psychosexual development, oral, anal, and phallic, are derived from those parts of the body which are, at the time, primary sources of erotic pleasure. As the child moves from one phase to another, he does not relinquish all pleasure in the earlier zone, but it recedes in importance.

Oedipus Complex

So far, the picture of sexual development in childhood is strictly a physical, sensual one, a question of body exploration. The child is not thinking about what he is doing. However, as he matures mentally as well as physically, a new dimension of fantasy comes into play. He, or she, begins to think about these feelings and pleasurable sensations. Shame or embarrassment may enter the scene because of the attitudes of the parents or other grownups. Thumb sucking is discouraged because it is babyish. Playing with the anus or the feces is discouraged because it is dirty. Tugging the genitals is discouraged, perhaps by distraction, frowns, or other signs that parents do not really like it, or perhaps by slaps or threats of the dire consequences which befall children who play with themselves. In any case, one can be sure that attempts have been made to discourage these infantile activities. Nevertheless, they are pleasurable and they die hard. The child may become more secretive, but some autoerotic activity usually continues. And as he gets smarter and socially more wise, more and more mental activity is likely to be associated with the physical habit.

But of what could the child of three, four, or five be thinking at such moments? What fantasies would ac-

company these activities? With such questions, we introduce the Freudian concept of the Oedipus complex. There is plenty of psychological material, reconstructed from patients and directly observed with children, to demonstrate that young children quite regularly entertain specific longings for their parents and that their longing is intertwined with their masturbation. It is not really so mysterious that this relationship should come about, as the reader will see in Chapter 3, where the Oedipus complex is discussed more fully. The concept has been raised here only because it bears on our understanding of infantile sexuality.

Like everything else connected with the theory of infantile sexuality, the Oedipus complex has been criticized, particularly the claim that it is universal. Anthropologists cite other cultures, and argue that the Oedipus complex is a cultural, not a biological phenomenon. And it must be admitted that the timing of the conflict, the strength of both the desire and the jealousy, the amount of ensuing anxiety, and the timing and success of its resolution are all modified by social and cultural circumstances. It will take a different shape in accordance with life experience.

It should be noted that the Oedipus complex, despite the inherent conflict and the possibility of fixation, is a cornerstone for further development. It is a kind of premature rehearsal for the future sexual role and, as such, is highly instructive in teaching tenderness, self-sacrifice, consideration for others, tolerance for frustration and other virtues incumbent on a civilized individual. The child's recognition of the futility of his infantile aspirations is a step toward realistic thinking and orientation to the world of childhood peers.

Schools of Psychoanalysis

Our discussion of dissident schools of psychoanalysis must be necessarily brief. The differences generally have to do with the concepts of infantile sexuality and the libido. Carl G. Jung reconceived the libido as a life force, a kind of Bergsonian *élan vital,* thus removing its distinctive sexual connotation. Jung differed from Freud in other important respects, also particularly in his belief that one inherits a racial *unconscious* which contains symbolic ideas from the past *(1916).* In direct contrast to Jung's extensive interest in unconscious processes, Alfred Adler *(1929)* concentrated on the conscious part of personality, the ego. He introduced the concept of *masculine protest,* suggesting that the prime motives of behavior are the quest for perfection and power. He emphasized the helplessness of the child as an original source of inferiority feelings, and did not consider sexual drives as especially important *(1929).* Otto Rank took the first moment of life as the crux of future personality problems in his theory of *birth trauma.* He postulated that the separation at birth was the basic source of anxiety, that man continues to yearn for the original intrauterine life and unconsciously strives to restore it *(1929).*

New names appeared in the 1930's and 1940's. The versions of psychoanalytic theory proposed by Karen Horney *(1939),* Erich Fromm *(1941),* and Harry Stack Sullivan *(1947)* are alike in minimizing the biological contribution to childhood sexuality and stressing the social, or learned, aspects of development. They seek, for example, to explain the Oedipus complex in terms of specific situations. Karen Horney states that fixations on the parents can be caused by various factors, including sexual stimulation by either a "gross sexual approach" or "sexually tinged caresses." The inference is that the Oedipus complex is preventable if the parents are sufficiently well adjusted. Although they added new words and shifted emphasis, these later reformers were essentially working with the ideas supplied by Adler and Rank. Neurosis was viewed as the outcome of conflict between human beings rather than between the environment and instinctual

drives (i.e., libido). In the author's opinion, such a view is similar to learning theory.

In the special area of child psychoanalysis, the psychoanalysts who studied with Melanie Klein (sometimes referred to as the "English school") follow the original Freudian principles, but with one crucial difference. They disregard the effect of reality almost entirely, and operate exclusively with the biological, innate factors. In this respect, their logic is reminiscent of Jung. Complicated psychological conflicts are attributed to the infant, and the Oedipus complex is considered to exist in the first year of life. Although the term is the same, the meaning is obviously different when one applies it to a baby rather than to a child of three to five.

We have taken this detour only to show that "you can't tell the players without a score card." The umbrella of psychoanalysis covers a variety of theories and therapies. It has been, and probably will continue to be, considered good form to acknowledge Freud's genius and then take off in any direction one sees fit. The confusing result is that almost any dynamic theory of personality is dubbed "psychoanalysis."

Later Modifications in Psychoanalytic Theory

As stated before, in the minds of many persons Freud stands for sex, and their knowledge does not extend beyond the libido theory and the psychosexual stages. At the time that Jung, Adler, and Rank took issue with Freud, this was indeed the main substance of his theories. However, important modifications and additions have been made within the framework of Freudian psychoanalysis, alterations which did not invalidate the early formulations but which changed the emphasis and brought a new perspective.

One major revision was the addition of aggression as a second basic drive *(1920, 1955).* The concept of drive is the most elusive abstraction in psycho-analytic theory. It is not synonymous with instinct, which commonly includes the specific behavior pattern of an animal. Drive includes only the human being's urge to act, not the form of the action. A drive cannot be seen nor measured; it can only be inferred from behavior. It is a concept which lies on the border between psychology and physiology, and Freud's great interest in it was undoubtedly a product of his background in neuroanatomy and his desire to explain mental phenomena in terms of organic functioning. He conceived of the drive as the source of the energy used in thinking, feeling, or acting, as analogous to physical energy, which is the capacity to do work.

It is impossible, from psychological data alone, to determine whether there are indeed two kinds of psychic energy (i.e., sexual and aggressive), or one kind, or many. However, there is no disputing the need to postulate some kind of internal driving force or forces which mobilizes the individual to action. Current psychoanalytic theory postulates two kinds of drives, which may operate at cross-purposes but which are normally fused. The aggressive instinct is akin to the death instinct proposed by Freud (1920, 1955), but many psychoanalysts have accepted the concept of a basic aggressive drive and at the same time, have rejected the idea that its aim is annihilation of the self (i.e., death).

Since the causes and management of aggression are paramount issues in normal and abnormal child psychology, the subject is discussed at length in a later chapter.

Freud's second major revision was the division of the functions of the mind into three parts: the ego; the id; and the superego (1923, 1961). This is termed "the structural hypothesis of the psychic apparatus." It is contrasted with Freud's earlier division of the mind into the conscious, preconscious, and unconscious, referred to as the "topographical theory" because of the image of layers of thoughts and feelings. The division of the mind into ego, id, and superego is not based on consciousness; the id largely consists of unconscious feelings, but aspects of the ego and superego may also be unconscious. The structural hypothesis is an attempt to group those mental processes and contents which are functionally related and to distinguish among the three groups on a functional basis.

The *id* is a broader concept than the unconscious, which supposedly consisted of thoughts and feelings which were once conscious and were then repressed. The id may be thought of as a deep reservoir of energy derived from the two primary instincts. It is completely unorganized, unreasonable, and unknowable in a direct way. The newborn baby is all id; and gradually, differentiation occurs and the rudiments of ego appear. The *ego* consists of all those psychological functions which have to do with the individual's relation to his environment: perception; motility; memory; judgment and reasoning; and language and thought. It is the ego which perceives the outside world, directs muscular action, remembers, compares present situations with old situations and makes decisions, and deliberates on problems or questions and expresses itself in words. The driving power for these activities is provided by the energy of the id.

As time passes, a further differentiation is made and the *superego* evolves. This structure comprises the moral precepts of our minds as well as our ideal aspirations; that is, our conscience, our guilt, and our ethical values. The superego, a latter-day development, is very complicated and is discussed in some detail when we consider delinquency.

The id-ego-superego division is useful in explaining internal conflicts which arise when a person has concurrent wishes which are incompatible. He may have a strong desire, rooted in the id drives, which is morally unacceptable to him (i.e., in conflict with his superego) or which is so unrealistic that the execution of his wish would cause trouble for himself (i.e., conflict with the ego). Thus, there may be, simultaneously, a push toward action and a resistance against that action (i.e., intrapsychic conflict). In early life, there is relatively little internal, or intrapsychic, conflict; most of the conflict is between the ego and the outside world. As the child matures, the possibilities of inner conflict increase and, by the time he is six or seven (by then the superego is an established internal governor), he is capable of the same kind of inner conflict as adults. In the numerous activities which we perform without conflict, the distinctions among id, ego, and superego cannot be made; all the agencies of the personality work together toward a common goal.

The introduction of the structural theory into psychoanalysis opened the door for new considerations, sometimes termed "ego psychology." Interest turned away from mere detection and uncovering of unconscious conflicts, toward the adaptive and defensive mechanisms which the ego employs to deal with internal demands and external reality. The ego was conceived of as being as important as the id in the genesis of neurosis and the development of personality. The sexual factor was not eliminated, but it became part of a larger whole.

Summation of Basic Psychoanalytic Tenets

In the foregoing historical narrative, a simplified one, many items have been omitted. Some—anxiety, defense mechanisms, the development of the superego, and principles of intellectual development and functioning—are discussed later in the book. The following is a list of the fundamental premises of psychoanalysis which have withstood changes in theory and which, in the midst of controversy, are beacon lights to the psychopathologist.

1. Psychic determinism is the *sine qua non* of *all* theories of personality development. Every thought, feeling, or action has a cause, and can be understood in terms of antecedent conditions.

2. It follows, then, that abnormal or irrational behavior is also explicable. O. H. Mowrer and Clyde Kluckhohn suggest that "perhaps the greatest single contribution of psychoanalysis has been to show the continuity of principles governing 'normal' and 'abnormal' behavior alike" *(1944, p. 69)*. In his *Psychopathology of Everyday Life (1901, 1960)* and *The Interpretation of Dreams (1900, 1953)*, Freud demonstrated that the same principles operate, under different conditions and to a different extent, in both normal and disturbed individuals. In special states which temporarily weaken the ego (e.g., toxicity, dreaming) the most normal individual is capable of thinking like a psychotic; under sufficient stress, the most normal individual will develop a neurotic symptom. The difference between the mentally ill and the normal is a difference of degree, not of kind. This precept is particularly important in the study of emotional disturbances of childhood.

3. Psychoanalysis established the tremendous power of repressed thoughts and feelings. Sometimes this power acts in the service of the individual and society, and we are grateful to it; sometimes this power operates against the rest of the person, and we try to give help. It should always be remembered that children also have an unconscious storehouse of memories and feelings.

4. Anxiety and the mechanisms of defense against it are a major cause of repression to unconsciousness and account for much of what seems irrational and unrealistic. The concept that anxiety can arise from inner conflict as well as from conflict with the outside world is necessary for the understanding of neurosis.

5. There is abundant evidence of the importance of past events in present behavior, but psychoanalytic investiga-

tions demonstrated the long arm of unconscious memory, reaching back to the first five years of life. We have few conscious memories of this early period and are therefore apt to underestimate its long-lasting influence.

6. Sexual feelings and conflicts in early childhood are particular sources of difficulty, whether the reasons for this be wholly biological, wholly environmental, or a combination of both. A blanket rejection of this idea inevitably results in a curtailed ability to understand the symptoms of psychopathology.

Common Misconceptions of the Application of Psychoanalysis

It might also be well to state what psychoanalysis is *not*. Most misconceptions about psychoanalytic theory have to do with what are thought to be the recommendations which proceed from it. In reality, the early psychoanalysts had relatively little advice to give. They were interested in the understanding and treatment of mental illness and were chary of recommendations, particularly in the area of child rearing. Many of the statements laid at Freud's door were made by practitioners eager to apply his ideas to other fields of work.

One common misinterpretation is that psychoanalysis proved that *frustration is bad*. If frustration of natural desires can cause neurosis, then the key to mental health would be lack of frustration. The fallacy here can easily be demonstrated by analogy. For instance, retrolental fibroplasia (a disease causing blindness in premature infants) is caused by administering an excessive amount of oxygen. This does not mean that the lack of oxygen (i.e., anoxia) is good for the brain. Far from it. But for a while the doctrine of permissiveness ran rampant, without consideration of the fact that a completely unfrustrated child would grow up uncivilized, uncontrolled, with no feeling for others, and in constant difficulty. Robert

Waelder concluded his list of common misunderstandings of psychoanalytic concepts with the following:

A psychoanalytic approach to education, finally, does not mean that children should get what they want when they want it; rather, it means an attempt to find for each situation the proper balance between satisfaction and frustration, in the light of the general principle that we have to search for the optimal mixture between two equally important but partly conflicting ingredients of healthy development, viz., love and discipline: how to love without pampering and how to discipline without traumatizing.*

Another misunderstanding, perhaps a variant of the first, is that *all defense mechanisms are bad*, i.e., that the healthy person never represses anything. The source of emotional trouble is in the unconscious. Therefore, if there is no unconscious, there is no trouble. In popular terms, the advice was to "Get things out of your system. Don't hold things in." Later proponents of this concept admitted that people cannot always be allowed to act on the basis of their wishes, but advise them to express their feelings in some socially acceptable manner. Again, there is a germ of truth in this idea; it harks back to one of the earliest forms of analytic treatment, which was essentially a form of catharsis. But it is an oversimplification, one which implies that we have volitional control over what will or will not be repressed. Those feelings which give us trouble are not readily accessible for conscious release. The operation of defenses is a silent one. The feelings which we could choose to vent are probably not sources of anxiety. To control and keep to oneself a conscious feeling is not neurotic.

Another related notion, which has made its way into child-rearing advice

---

*Quoted from Robert Waelder, *Basic Theory of Psychoanalysis* (New York: International Universities Press, Inc., 1960), p. 254. Reproduced by permission.

particularly, is that you can prevent conflicts and anxieties if you *tell the right things to the child*. Parents are charged with the task of preparing the child for traumatic events such as surgery, separation, or the birth of a sibling, and sometimes they are given to understand that if they prepare the child well, he will have *no* anxiety about surgery, *no* depression during separation, or *no* jealousy of a new baby. Similarly, many parents believe that a free-and-easy attitude toward sex will obviate anxiety on this score. Conscientiously, they seek to give the right information at the proper time and in the correct way. They leave the bathroom door open and are casual about nudity, assuming that the child will then have no inhibitions. The aim seems to be to prevent the child from having any uncomfortable feelings; to short-circuit feelings, rather than to permit their expression.

What is forgotten, in these simplified prescriptions for mental health, is that children grow and learn from conflict and frustration, in moderate doses. Some anxiety is necessary for mental health and social conformity. If a child had *no* fear of losing his parents' love, he would have little reason to accept their restrictions. And although depressed, angry, or anxious feelings are uncomfortable for the child, they are part and parcel of living with people and caring for them. Preparation or no, if a child feels no loss of love when a new baby comes, either he was not much loved in the first place or the baby is being shortchanged on love. The child with no anxiety about surgery has very little imagination. The child who feels nothing when his parents leave cares little for their presence. The child who experiences no Oedipal conflict has lost out on an experience of loving which serves most people well in later life. It is always tempting to offer parents a list of feelings and situations to be avoided; moderation is much more difficult to describe. Fortunately, most

parents feel their way to this middle road on their own, without recourse to doctrinaire philosophies of child rearing and education.

Historical Development of Learning Theory

Early in the twentieth century, Edward Lee Thorndike in the United States and Ivan Pavlov in Russia started to apply experimental techniques to the study of behavior. Like Freud, they tried to relate psychological findings to the operations of the nervous system (i.e., reductionism), but they drew their findings from laboratory experiments rather than from observations of life situations. Thorndike's main laws of learning, as formulated in 1913, were the *law of effect, the law of readiness,* and *the law of exercise.* Their relative importance is still a very live issue.

As Thorndike revised his thinking, he more and more rejected the law of exercise. Experimental data indicated that mere repetition of temporarily associated stimuli did *not* lead to learning. He emphasized the importance of the law of effect in learning, much as Freud emphasized the pleasure principle in relation to the development of the ego:

Of several responses made to the same situation, those which are accompanied or closely followed by satisfaction to the animal will, other things being equal, be more firmly connected with the situation, so that when it recurs, they will be more likely to recur; those which are accompanied by or closely followed by discomfort to the animal will, other things being equal, have their connection with the situation weakened so that, when it recurs, they will be less likely to occur. The greater the satisfaction or discomfort, the greater the strengthening or weakening of the bond. *(Thorndike, 1911, p. 244.)*

As Benjamin Wolman points out, the issue of reward still divides learning theorists into contiguity theorists and reward theorists: "The radical behaviorist-type theories, such as Watson's, Guthrie's, and others, reject the terms of 'satisfaction' and 'annoyance' and stick to 'contiguity of stimulus and response,' while Hull and others accept Thorndike's theory of reward" *(1960, p. 35).*

The next great push in learning theory came from the work of Ivan Pavlov, a pharmacologist and physiologist who never viewed himself as a psychologist. His experiments with animals began with innate, or unconditioned responses to stimuli. "Conditioning" occurs when two stimuli, one unconditioned and one new, are presented together enough times for the new stimulus to bring about the response which was initially evoked only by the original, unconditioned stimulus. The new stimulus then becomes the "conditioned" stimulus; the new response to it is the "conditioned" response. The best-known illustration of this is the salivary conditioning of dogs. The unconditioned stimulus is the presentation of food; the new stimulus may be a sound or a light. After a number of simultaneous presentations of the two, the dog salivates when he hears the sound, just as if it were the food itself. Like Freud, Pavlov consistently tried to relate behavior to neural mechanisms *(1928).* A central concept is reinforcement, that is, maintaining the conditioned response by again coupling the conditioned and unconditioned stimulus. Without reinforcement, Pavlov felt that the conditioned reflex was eventually extinguished, an idea somewhat related to Thorndike's concept of extinction by non-reward.

The school of behaviorism which flourished in the early twenties attempted to apply the laboratory principles of conditioning to all aspects of human development. Whereas Pavlov used conditioning to develop a theory of neurophysiology, the behaviorist used his conditioning principles to develop a theory of personality. The goal was to establish a purely objective, experimental science based on external facts, one that made no reference to introspective data about feelings and ideas. Behaviorism's chief exponent was John B. Watson, who consistently tried to reduce psychology to a generalized physiology. All unobservable data, such as thinking, feeling and perceiving, were interpreted as physiological facts (e.g., muscular tensions, glandular secretions) which he believed could be made observable by future laboratory techniques. His was an extremely environmental point of view and, with respect to child development, he promised a lot:

Give me a dozen healthy infants, well-formed and my own specified world to bring them up in and I'll guarantee to take any at random and train him to become any type of specialist I might select—doctor, lawyer, artist, merchant-chief, and yes, beggar-man and thief, regardless of his talents, penchants, tendencies, abilities, vocations, and race of his ancestors. *(1925, p. 82.)*

Learning versus Maturation

One of the most effective opponents of behaviorism in its heyday was Arnold Gesell, a pediatrician who also had a doctoral degree in psychology. He held that the orderly fashion in which the child's behavior developed, the consistent sequence of behavior patterns in children despite differences in their experiences, could not be explained by conditioning alone. He had the advantage of a considerable amount of new information about neural maturation. Gesell stated that the appearance of new abilities was "fundamentally determined by the ripeness of the neural structures," and introduced the term *maturation* into child psychology. One reviewer described the Gesell books as:

. . . mapping the emotional and behavior patterns of children from birth through ten years of age . . . Gesell experts found that children really are predictable, that they behave the way they do because they follow well-developed growth patterns from infancy through adolescence. They move from hill to valley to another hill—and their progress can be charted fairly accurately. In short, if a child is an angel at two, swears at four, obeys at five, and lies at six, he is probably just growing up in a normal way. *(Pollack, 1955.)*

There is no special attempt to explain why characteristic changes take place; it is enough to say that this is the normal course. Whatever explanatory attempts Gesell offered were couched in biological terms, relating the whole spectrum of child development to the kind of developmental principles established for embryology. The maturation theory might be described as *naturalistic*. Innate biological factors are maximized; environmental influences are minimized.

Naturalistic theory, which in large measure had been shaped by neurological studies, had a strong impact on child rearing and education. It did a service for child welfare in that parents and teachers were cautioned against forcing children to perform tasks for which their nervous systems were not yet equipped. From this theory came the idea of readiness, i.e., that there is a proper time to begin teaching children bladder control, motor coordination, and reading and writing. But the theory contributed relatively little to the understanding of deviant behavior; indeed, behavior problems were not studied as such. Problems were thought to be caused either by organic peculiarities of the nervous system or by pressure on the child to meet standards of behavior for which he was not ready.

The Gesell Study Center provided valuable data, and called attention to some innate features of child development which had been overlooked by the other schools. Psychoanalytic and learning theorists found room for these findings, but did not accept the theory that maturation alone can account for all the intricacies of individual development.

Later Modifications in Learning Theories

Just as psychoanalysis was revamped as time went on, so have learning theories become more sophisticated and more divergent. Watsonian dogmatism by no means represents the modern learning theorist; contemporary behaviorists place much less emphasis on neural mechanisms. In the words of Wolman, "Hull, for example, did to Pavlov what Horney did to Freud: Horney continued psychoanalysis without libido; Hull continued conditioning without the nervous system" *(1960, p. 62).*

Starting with theoretical constructs, Clark Hull developed elaborate mathematical formulae which could be experimentally tested. He believed that 121 of his 178 theoretical statements had been experimentally tested, and that 87 per cent had been validated *(1952)*. Hull stood firm on the importance of reinforcement, although he used the term "need reduction." He felt that conditioning was dependent on need reduction, in direct opposition to Edwin Guthrie's idea that association by contiguity in time is the most important principle of conditioning *(1935)*. Thus, although both Guthrie and Hull are learning theorists, the differences between them are no less great than between Anna Freud and Melanie Klein, both child analysts.

Although his approach is different, in that he goes from experiment to theory rather than the converse, B. F. Skinner is closer to Hull than to Guthrie. He acknowledges the complexity of human behavior, but sees its complications as extensions of basically simple processes. He differentiates two kinds of conditioning: classical, Pavlovian conditioning, in which stimuli are associated with an unconditioned response; and operant conditioning, in which the response itself *operates* on the environment to produce certain results. Like Hull, he subscribes to the law of effect:

"Instead of saying that a man behaves because of the consequences which are to follow his behavior, we simply say that he behaves because of the consequences which have followed similar behavior in the past. This is, of course, the Law of Effect, or operant conditioning" *(Skinner, 1938, p. 87).*

"Through operant conditioning the environment builds the basic repertoire with which we keep our balance, walk, play games, handle instruments, and tools." *(Ibid, p. 66).*

In other words, we repeat those acts which have, in the past, brought about the desired results.

Gregory Razran, another learning theorist, has introduced an evolutionary point of view, one which may lay the basis for the integration of the various schools of psychology. His developmental sequences in learning is parallel both to the stages of emotional development outlined by Freud and the stages of mental development outlined by Piaget. Briefly, Razran described three levels of learning. The simplest level follows the laws of classical conditioning, with contiguity a necessary, but not a sufficient, condition for acquisition of new responses. In the first stage, the animal, including man, is essentially passive; the environment acts to stamp in certain associations without his participation. In the second stage, he is more active. His operant responses do something to the environment, and instrumental or operant conditioning becomes a major mode of learning. His learning is based on the effectiveness of his operant responses. Razran calls this "reward and punishment learning," reserving "conditioning" for the simple associative learning of stage one:

This kind of learning takes place whenever the man or the animal acts and influences the environment, i.e., in the external motor actions of animals and in motor-verbal actions of men. . . . This learning does not apply to the viscera nor does it apply to the animals in the lower stages of evolution such as most of the invertebrates. This learning represents a higher level than conditioning. Experiments prove that this learning is more efficient, faster and more lasting than learning by conditioning. *(1957, p. 14.)*

At the highest level of learning, stage three, the learner's response no longer consists of external, observable actions, but rather of symbolic processes (i.e., thought). There is increasing experimental evidence to show the importance of such factors as attention, sets and attitudes, and cognitive styles in determining the individual's response to stimuli presented to him in traditional laboratory fashion.

Although Razran's viewpoint is more phylogenetic than ontogenetic, it is interesting to speculate on the relevance of his levels to child development. One would expect that the classical conditioning of phase one would predominate in the early months of life, and that the instrumental conditioning of phase two would become important in the second six months, when motor coordination has advanced to the point where the infant can manipulate his environment. The third type of learning would begin toward the end of the second year, when the child comes into possession of language. Such levelling does not mean that earlier, simpler modes of learning completely disappear. Like the developmental stages posited by Piaget and Freud, Razran's primitive levels are never lost, but simply overshadowed by later stages.

To this writer, who is admittedly not qualified to judge the relative merits of points of view in learning theory, the suggestions of Razran make a great deal of sense. Usually, when strong differences of opinion exist, all backed with supporting observations and experimental evidence, there is truth in all, and they must be combined into a larger truth. Razran suggests that the different learning theorists are all correct as far as they go, but that they have been too narrow. They have taken the "possible" to be the "only possible." "Neither cognition nor reward nor contiguity is the only type of learning. It all depends on whom you condition and how" *(Wolman, 1960, p. 157).* It is imperative to study the learning situation, the nature of the task, and the capacities and attributes of the learner, in order to determine which of the established principles are relevant.

The Critical Question of Motivation

Although Razran effected some rapprochement among learning theorists, he did not venture to relate learning theory to other theories of personality. Neal E. Miller and John Dollard *(1941)* and Mowrer and Kluckhohn have been especially concerned with the integration of learning theory and psychoanalysis. Their original position was that "the great unifying principle in learning theory is the proposition that all behavior is motivated and that all learning involves reward" *(1944, p. 79)*. However, Mowrer later came around to the idea that some learning does not require reward and some does, the two-factor learning theory *(1950)*. He then developed his own theory of neurosis, essentially based on the idea that neuroses form when education or training has been incomplete, so that the ego is dominated by the primitive, pleasure-seeking processes of the id *(1953)*. To an increasing extent, Mowrer has come to occupy a unique theoretical position. In the writer's opinion, his generalizations about psychopathology are not supported by clinical material. His point of view is discussed further in the chapter on psychotherapy.

Miller and Dollard have been more conservative in their theorizing. Like Hull, their basic premise is that all learning involves reward:

The learner must be driven to make the response and rewarded for having responded in the presence of the cue. This may be expressed in a homely way by saying that in order to learn one must want something, notice something, do something, and get something. Stated more exactly, these factors are drive, cue, response, and reward. *(1941, p. 2.)*

The concept that we learn that which is positively rewarding (i.e., pleasure is gained) or negatively rewarding (i.e., something painful is avoided) is almost identical with a basic psychoanalytic principle. "The pleasure principle states that the mind tends to operate in such a way as to achieve pleasure and avoid its opposite [pain]".*

The key issues here are: What constitutes pleasure? What constitutes pain? Psychoanalytic theory proposes that the essence of pleasure is relief of the id tension occasioned by the pressure of the two primary drives. Pain may be externally caused by outside reality, or internally caused by anxiety feelings. In learning theory, any strong stimulus which elicits a motor reaction is named "drive," and two sets of drives are proposed: primary and secondary. Hunger, thirst, sex, and avoidance of physical pain are innate, or primary. Then, through a complicated process of association with these primary drives (i.e., conditioning), a hierarchy of secondary drives is developed. Secondary, or learned drives, may be infinite in number and highly individualized, depending on individual past experience. Secondary drives include such things as the drive to acquire money, social status, parental approval, moral approval from the conscience, and so on. These drives motivate further learning which, in turn, results in new satisfactions. The question of drive, although probably the most important question, is still unsettled in the best theoretical circles.

Relationship of Psychoanalytic to Other Theories

Learning and psychoanalytic theories are far from jelling into a cohesive psychology of development. Although there are many important areas of agreement, the language is so different that it is difficult to move back and forth between the two. The starting points and fact-finding methods are at opposite extremes. Learning theorists concentrate on precise observations of single relationships; psychoanalysts make general observations of much

---

*Quoted from Charles Brenner, *An Elementary Textbook of Psychoanalysis* (New York: International Universities Press, Inc., 1955), p. 78. Reproduced by permission.

more complex phenomena. However, there does not appear to be a fundamental incompatibility, even if union seems difficult and far in the future. The principles of learning would have to do with ego functioning. The primary and secondary drives would be grouped differently and reduced to a few large categories.

Psychoanalysis does *not* omit the roles of external reality and learning, but it offers additional ways to understand the meaning of reality for the child and his motivation for learning. Reality, like time, is relative; it has different meanings at different ages and at different moments. A child becomes sensitized to specific aspects of the world about him and of the people in it, not only because of what has happened to him before (i.e., what he has learned) and because of his constitutional sensitivities (i.e., his heredity), but also because of his mental and emotional level. The younger the child, the more likely he is to misinterpret reality. And still another variable is the nature of anxiety and fantasies common to certain ages. Psychoanalytic theory describes some central conflicts which regularly appear as crises at different points in a child's life. During these crises, relatively insignificant events can assume psychological meaning and become incorporated in the child's personality as fantasies, inner conflicts, unconscious motivations, and sources of anxiety.

It is impossible, at least for this author, to discuss the full range of deviations in child behavior without making use of explanatory principles provided by psychoanalytic theory. However, in the chapters which follow there is an attempt to offer alternative explanations of the clinical problems under consideration. This will increase the difficulty for the reader but, without it, we run the danger of isolating our thinking and further delaying theoretical integration. It is regrettable that there exist rivalries among different approaches to the study of human motivation and behavior. The stress on differences has led to heat and division, rather than to light and synthesis. In the words of Douglas Bond:

It is high time, in my opinion, that we abandon such rivalrous behavior and face up squarely to the conclusion that man, in the many facets of his existence and meaning, is so complex that we need every reliable piece of evidence we can obtain about him, regardless of source, and that reliable information in any field is of interest and importance in every other field. No reliable piece of evidence from one field can be dismissed by another because of its source, and every field has the duty to understand, as far as is possible, information from another.*

All theorists agree that biological, cultural, and social forces are at play in every human being, and are at work in every normal and pathological process. The disagreements lie in the relative emphasis placed upon each. Child psychology is a young field, and no one is so brash as to believe that he has all the answers. The task of the future will be the revision and extension of existing theories to achieve a unified theoretical frame of reference within which clinicians, educators, and research investigators can operate together.

References for Chapter 1

Adler, Alfred, *The Practice and Theory of Individual Psychology.* London: Routledge & Kegan Paul, Ltd., 1929.

Bond, Douglas, "Psychoanalytic Theory and Empirical Research." Paper given at Social Work Conference, Cleveland, April, 1960.

Brenner, Charles, *An Elementary Textbook of Psychoanalysis.* New York: International Universities Press, Inc., 1955.

Freud, Sigmund, *A Difficulty in the Path of Psychoanalysis* (1917), Standard Edition, Vol. XVII, ed. and trans. by James Strachey. London: The Hogarth Press, Ltd., 1955.

———, *An Outline of Psychoanalysis* (1938),

---

*Quoted from Douglas Bond, "Psychoanalytic Theory and Empirical Research," Paper given at Social Work Conference, Cleveland, Ohio, April, 1960. Reproduced by permission.

Trans., James Strachey, New York: W. W. Norton & Company, Inc., 1940.

———, *A Short Account of Psychoanalysis* (1924), Standard Edition, Vol. XIX, ed. and trans. by James Strachey. London: The Hogarth Press, Ltd., 1961.

———, *Beyond the Pleasure Principle* (1920), Standard Edition, Vol. XVIII, ed. and trans. Press, Ltd., 1955.

by James Strachey. London: The Hogarth

———, *The Ego and the Id* (1923), Standard Edition, Vol. XIX, ed. and trans. by James Strachey. London: The Hogarth Press, Ltd., 1961.

———, *The Interpretation of Dreams* (1900), Standard Edition, Vols. IV, V, ed. and trans. by James Strachey. London: The Hogarth Press, Ltd., 1953.

———, *The Psychopathology of Everyday Life* (1901), Standard Edition, Vol. VI, ed. and trans. by James Strachey. London: The Hogarth Press, Ltd., 1960.

———, *Three Essays on the Theory of Sexuality* (1905), Standard Edition, Vol. II, ed. and trans. by James Strachey. London: The Hogarth Press, Ltd., 1953.

Fromm, Erich, *Escape from Freedom*. New York: Holt, Rinehart & Winston, Inc., 1941.

Gesell, Arnold, "The Ontogenesis of Infant Behavior," in Leonard Carmichael, *Manual of Child Psychology*. New York: John Wiley & Sons, Inc., 1946.

Guthrie, Edwin R., *The Psychology of Learning*. New York: Harper & Row, Publishers, 1935.

Hartmann, Heinz, *Essays on Ego Psychology*. New York: International Universities Press, Inc., 1964.

Hollingshead, A. B. and F. C. Redlich, *Social Class and Mental Illness*. New York: John Wiley & Sons, Inc., 1958.

Horney, Karen, *New Ways in Psychoanalysis*. New York: W. W. Norton & Company, Inc., 1939.

Hull, Clark L., *A Behavior System*. New Haven, Conn.: Yale University Press, 1952.

Jung, Carl G., *The Psychology of the Unconscious*. New York: Dodd, Mead & Co., 1916.

Klein, Melanie, *The Psychoanalysis of Children*, 2nd Edition. London: The Hogarth Press, Ltd., 1937.

Miller, Neal E. and John Dollard, *Social Learning and Imitation*. New Haven, Conn.: Yale University Press, 1941.

Mullahy, Patrick, *Oedipus, Myth and Complex: A Review of Psychoanalytic Theory*. New York: Grove Press, 1955.

Mowrer, O. H., *Learning Theory and Personality Dynamics*. New York: The Ronald Press Company, 1950.

———, *Psychotherapy: Theory and Research*. New York: The Ronald Press Company, 1953.

——— and Clyde Kluckhohn, "Dynamic Theory of Personality," in J. McV. Hunt, *Personality and the Behavior Disorders*, Vol. I. New York: The Ronald Press Company, 1944.

Pavlov, Ivan P., *Lectures on Conditioned Reflexes*. New York: Liveright Publishing Corp., 1928.

Pollack, Jack H., "The New Gesell Study on Child Behavior," *Collier's*, September 2, 1955. A review of *Child Behavior*, by Frances L. Ilg and Louise Bates Ames. Harper & Row, Publishers, 1955.

Rank, Otto, *Trauma of Birth*. New York: Harcourt, Brace & World, Inc., 1929.

Rapaport, David, "The Structure of Psychoanalytic Theory: A Systematizing Attempt," *Psychological Issues Monograph No. 6*. New York: International Universities Press, Inc., 1958.

Razran, Gregory, *The Psychology of Learning: Theory and Implications*. Boston: Teachers College, 1957.

Skinner, B. F., *The Behavior of Organisms*. New York: Appleton-Century-Crofts, Inc., 1938.

Sullivan, Harry S., *Conceptions of Modern Psychiatry*. Washington, D.C.: W. A. White Psychiatric Foundation, 1947.

Thorndike, E. L., *Animal Intelligence: Experimental Studies*. New York: The Macmillan Company, 1911.

Waelder, Robert, *Basic Theory of Psychoanalysis*. New York: International Universities Press, Inc., 1960.

Watson, J. B., *Behaviorism*. London: Routledge & Kegan Paul, Ltd., 1925.

Wepman, Joseph M. and Ralph W. Heine, eds., *Concepts of Personality*. Chicago: Aldine Publishing Co., 1964.

Whitehorn, John, "A Working Concept of Maturity of Personality," *American Journal of Psychiatry*, No. 119 (1962), 197–202.

Wolman, Benjamin B., *Contemporary Theories and Systems in Psychology*. New York: Harper & Row, Publishers, 1960.

2

RECIPROCAL RELATIONSHIP OF MENTAL AND EMOTIONAL DEVELOPMENT IN EARLY CHILDHOOD

In this chapter, we do not attempt to describe cognitive development completely, nor to discuss the controversial role of motivation in learning comprehensively. Our purposes are: to describe (1) the mental development of the preschool child; (2) how the child's mental growth leads to emotional problems and (3) how emotions goad the mind to work.

This review of normal development, a digression from problems of psychopathology, provides a basis for evaluating the clinical problems we will discuss later, for in general, abnormal psychological processes are drawn from psychological processes which are appropriate at younger ages. Abnormal behavior may appear as inability to master the next higher level of learning, or as a regression to an earlier stage. Emotional conflicts may produce, in the older child, the illogical thinking which is commonplace in the very young child. Primitive mental processes are involved in the formation of neurotic symptoms, and they invade the total personality of the psychotic person. The background material of this chapter also sets the stage for the consideration of learning problems (Chapter 9) and of the secondary psychopathology arising from mental subnormality (Chapter 8). The presenta-

tion which follows is descriptive rather than experimental, in order to help the reader empathize with the young child as he struggles to understand the meaning of what he observes in his world. But mental and emotional development interact, and difficulties on the one side usually affect the other. The reader must bear in mind, as we describe *mental development,* that growing attachments to people are equally important in the early years. The intellect does not develop in a vacuum; the environment must provide stimulation, security, and permanent love relationships. The intellectual effects of environmental deprivation are briefly touched on in discussions of pseudo-retardation (Chapter 8) and maternal deprivation (Chapter 15).

Preverbal Period

The preverbal period, or the sensori-motor phase of development, is here understood to cover roughly the first 12 to 18 months of life.

Birth of a Mind

Much of the available data on the infant's development comes from Jean Piaget's painstaking, round-the-clock observations of his three children. Piaget's observations were made at home; here, and throughout his extensive study of mental development of children, Piaget followed the general principle of observing their behavior without modifying or interfering with the environments.

The human infant has a number of patterns of behavior: (1) sucking, (2) looking, (3) listening, (4) vocalizing, (5) grasping, and (6) diffuse motor activity. Piaget calls these sensory motor activities "schemata." In the first two or three weeks, the need for homeostasis dictates behavior. The rising tension and pain of hunger disturbs the baby's rest; he responds with vocalations, diffuse motor activity, and by sucking; his sucking permits him to ingest the food which relieves his hunger; and he returns to a state of rest. Motility is greatest just before nursing and least immediately afterwards. Anna Freud has described this period as dominated by the alternation between pain and pleasure *(1953)*. The infant responds to pain with wakefulness and excitement; his response to pleasure is quiescence.

Because the infant cannot walk, talk, grasp objects, or otherwise show by directed behavior what he perceives and wants, his capacity for response is usually underrated. But experimental investigation shows that the infant will respond to auditory, thermal, and other stimuli, under special conditions. Robert L. Fantz found that even the newborn can differentiate patterned visual stimuli from plain field stimuli and prefer the former *(1963)*. Under ordinary circumstances, however, he sleeps most of the day and nurses a good part of the remainder; during these times he is inattentive to external stimulation. He does not use his sensory capacities initially, but within weeks, his behavior changes. Both his responses and the stimuli to which he responds become more varied.

Toward the end of the first month, something to look at will distract even a crying baby, and his gaze will stay fixed for many minutes. Piaget says that the images which capture the infants gaze "only constitute spots which appear, move, and disappear without solidity or volume. They are in short, neither objects, independent images, nor even images charged with extrinsic meaning" *(1936, 1952, p. 65)*. The baby stares simply for the sake of looking. During the second month the child will search with his eyes for the source of a sound, not because he knows that it is coming from a visible object, but because any stimulation elicits the response of looking. From the third month on, there is coordination between sight and hearing; the child recognizes that certain sounds come from objects of a particular appearance. During this same period, other coordinations (e.g., between hand movements and sucking), develop.

Everyone observing a baby in the first few months of life sees pretty much the same thing. A three-month-old can follow moving objects with his eyes. The psychologist records the behavior as a sign of intelligence; the psychiatrist or psychoanalyst, as a first sign of the developing ego; the pediatrician as an indication of a well baby with a good nervous system; Piaget, as the coordination of the schemata of looking and the motor activity of the eye and neck muscles. All observers are in agreement on what the baby is doing, but they interpret it as the beginning of different aspects of development. Actually, early mental, emotional, and physical development are inseparable; only later do they fan out in separate directions.

Emergence of the Ego as Part of the Psychic Structure

In the initial psychoanalytic formulation proposed by Freud, the mind of the newborn was described as consisting solely of *id*. The *ego* emerged out of the conflict between id drives and the frustration imposed by the environment. The ego was that part of the id which was modified by experience, a phenomenon of learning, forced into being because the basic drives could not be gratified without delays, detours, relinquishments, substitutions, and the like.

An important modification of this concept, proposed by Heinz Hartmann, has been generally incorporated in modern psychoanalytic theory. Hartmann suggested that "although the ego does grow on conflict [i.e., conflict between id drives and external reality], these conflicts are not the only source of ego development" *(1939, 1951, p. 364)*. Certain functions of the ego related to perception, motility, and so on have a "primary autonomy" and normally belong to a "conflict-free" sphere of the ego. He also postulated a kind of "secondary autonomy" of ego functions, (e.g., speech) which, once established, are automatic and become part of the conflict-free sphere. The introduction of these concepts changed the traditional formulation of the ego as arising from an "all-id" mind. Instead, the mind of the newborn is conceptualized by Hartmann and other ego psychologists as an undifferentiated matrix, out of which both ego and id evolve in the course of maturation and learning, with and without conflict.

By three to four months, the infant's behavior meets almost all the usual criteria of ego functioning. There is genuine *perceptual activity*, particularly visual. There is some *motor control* involved in getting the hand to the mouth for sucking. There is evidence of memory, both in the association between sounds and sights and in the child's pleasure in the preparations for his feeding. Willie Hoffer adds *reality testing*, demonstrated by the baby's meticulous choice of what he wishes to put into his mouth *(1950)*. There may be a competition between feeding and finger sucking, so that when he wishes to use his fingers, the baby will reject the spoon, pacifier, or breast. Admittedly, this is a rudimentary form of reality testing. At this early stage, only one of the functions usually ascribed to the ego, namely, the synthetic function, is missing.

Hypothesis of Wishful Hallucination in the Development of Reality Testing

This hypothesis, originally offered by Sigmund Freud in Chapter 7 of *The Interpretation of Dreams (1900, 1953)*, has been restated most clearly and simply by Anna Freud:

After the hungry child has been fed several times, the impact of these experiences will create something in him which did not exist before, namely, the image of the satisfying food. From then onward, whenever hunger arises, the image of the desired food will be evoked simultaneously. The hungry child will see inwardly a mental picture of the milk, or of the mother who brings the milk, or of the mother's breast, or of the bottle from which the milk is sucked. . . .

On the other hand, the hungry infant behaves in a peculiar manner toward its inner imagery. Since he has experienced many times that the actual appearance of the mother, or of her breast, has been followed by a stomach satisfaction, he expects his own mental image of her to produce a similar result. Naturally, this does not occur. The hallucination of the breast, or mother, leads to no relief. The need will not be satisfied until the distress signal is given and the real object has appeared. With frequent repetition of such experiences, the infant learns to distinguish between an inner image and the perception of a person in the outside world . . . This new ability to distinguish between the perception of reality, on the one hand, and inner mental images, on the other hand, is one of the most significant advances in the infant's mental development.[*]

[*]Quoted from Anna Freud, "Some Remarks on Infant Observation," *The Psychoanalytic Study of the Child* (New York: International Universities Press, 1953), VIII, 12–13. Reprinted by permission.

It is clear that this hypothesis can never be verified or disproved by direct observation; nor is it essential to the understanding of infant behavior. It was postulated as part of the attempt to explain dream images and the hallucinations of psychotic patients. Freud asks: How can hallucinations come about at all? If one assumes that hallucinations or dream images must materialize from prior experience, then the hypothesis of the wishful hallucination in infancy is a theoretically helpful one. Sigmund Freud's original statement was a cautious one:

"Nothing prevents us from assuming that there was a primitive state of the psychical apparatus [i.e., the mind] in which this path was actually traversed, that is, in which wishing ended in hallucinating" *(1900, 1953, p. 566).*

We know for a fact that somewhat older children have difficulty distinguishing fantasy from reality; it is probable that the younger the child, the greater is his confusion between imagery and perception. The distinction between wishful hallucination and perception of the real thing is traditionally viewed as the first step in reality testing, but this assumption is based on complicated logic rather than on direct observation.

Discovery of the Physical Self

While the observer sees the infant as a separate entity, the infant has no conception of where he ends and the environment begins. The first distinction between "self" and "not-self" is made on the basis of physical differences. One of the first parts of himself which the baby recognizes as such is his hands. Many times during the early months, he catches sight of his hands as they move across his field of vision; he follows their movement just as he follows any moving object which comes into sight. He learns also through touch. The fingers of one hand discover the fingers of the other, so that he touches himself and is touched simultaneously. Gradually he learns to do this in front of his eyes, and can watch, feel, and be felt. Sometime between the third and fourth months, he learns that his hands are always with him, in contrast to other things that come and go, and he derives a sense of the permanence and predictability of his hands. From this evolves the notion that these things are part of himself. This is a first lesson in self-discovery, crucial to the task of differentiating between the inner and outer worlds. One can observe children with profound ego retardation or regression, playing with their fingers in front of their eyes with the same absorption and fascination of a baby in this early stage of discovery.

In normal development, it is a quick step from viewing the hands as playthings to using them as tools. The eyes no longer follow the hands, helpless to intervene; they assume some control. The eyes take the lead, direct the hand in reaching and grasping. The obtained object goes directly to the mouth, because, at this point in the baby's life, his mouth is a major source of pleasure and knowledge about the world. Every new object is first given an oral trial. After six months or so, the baby begins to subject new objects to visual and tactile exploration, rather than to oral exploration only. And his growing ability to seize things and to examine them at his leisure provides him with yet another opportunity to learn what belongs to the self and what does not.

The baby does not become equally familiar with all physical boundaries of his body at the same time. He first becomes acquainted with the physical limits, capabilities, and sensations of his upper extremities; he must similarly discover his legs when he crawls and walks.

In the development of a sense of reality, the conception of one's own body plays a very special role. It takes the better part of a year for the baby to form a complete image of his body. Freud's statement that "the ego is first and foremost a body-ego" *(1923, 1961, p. 26)* assumes special significance when one views the disturbances of body awareness in the psychotic child.

Concept of Object Permanence

As the infant learns about his body, so does he learn about the outside world. In the first months, he does not perceive external objects as having substance, permanence, and constant dimensions. Things exist only as he perceives them. The baby's universe is a world of pictures, sounds, and so forth, each of which can be known and recognized but which disappear and reappear capriciously. He will show continued interest in an object which has disappeared by continuing to look at the place where it was, but if nothing reappears, he soon gives up. The vanished object is not yet a permanent object which has been moved; it is a mere image which enters the void when it vanishes and which re-emerges for no apparent reason.

A major change occurs early in the second half-year of life, or according to Piaget, at around nine or ten months. Briefly, the child demonstrates his knowledge that things continue to exist, even out of sight, by searching for them. He will pull off a cover which may be hiding the toy, he will look around corners, he will look under things. He leaves no doubt that he knows the object is somewhere. He is not easily distracted by substitutes and is really pleased only when he has found the lost object.

The child's play at this age provides ample evidence of his pleasure in reaffirming the fact that objects are permanent. He drops things out of the crib, playpen, and highchair simply for the pleasure of getting them back. As he becomes more skilled in visual-motor coordination, he will hide his toys and beloved objects in a box, bag, or other container, and then dump them all out again, only to repeat the procedure with unvarying glee. It seems as though he can never get quite enough proof of the happy thought that things and people never go away forever. He loves peekaboo, a game in which his parent hides his face behind his hands while baby waits breathlessly for the return of the beloved visage.

Stranger Anxiety

Even in the first six months, infants are distressed by radically altered versions of things they have come to recognize, but the reaction of anxiety to strangeness is much more prolonged and clear-cut in the second half-year. Strangers evoke this most dramatically. Sometime around eight months, the baby suddenly reacts with fear to the mere sight of a strange person. Dr. Benjamin Spock has described this vividly: "First, the prolonged 'freeze,' then the slow pucker, and finally the frantic crying, which may go on for 15 minutes after the stranger has disappeared" *(1953, p. 60)*. Spock says that this is a new feeling, one which emerges in relation to the recently acquired ability to discriminate between the familiar and the unfamiliar. The baby can contrast a new image with a remarkably clear memory of the familiar face, and he is genuinely frightened by the difference. Parents, on the other hand, are usually embarrassed and attribute the baby's fear to some real or hypothesized event which supposedly conditioned the baby against strangers. The differential reaction, however, is a result of cognitive and emotional maturation for which no single event can be held responsible. At this age, such fear is a healthy sign indicating appropriate attachments and discrimination powers.

There is evidence from many sources to indicate that the second six months is a critical period in terms of separation from parents and difficulty in acceptance of new people. Interestingly enough, animals may undergo a similar crisis. Fear of strange persons, or even of familiar persons in unfamiliar guise, appears in chimpanzees only after several weeks of contact with persons (*Hebb, 1946*).

Anna Freud and D. Burlingham reported that infants younger than seven or eight months did not suffer "separation anxiety" when they were separated from their families during the London blitz of World War II (*1944; also see Chapter 15*). There are two factors which prolong emotional reaction to separation at this early age. The first is the establishment of recognition of familiar persons and places; the second is the sense of permanence of objects and persons. The sense of loss, or mourning, is perpetuated by the infant's awareness that the vanished person exists somewhere. The exclusiveness of his attachment continues in proportion to his feeling that the person exists, even *in absentia*. Until the baby reaches this point of mental development, his interest in vanished objects and persons is short-lived, despite his pleasure when they reappear; essentially, out of sight is out of mind.

The baby's fear of strangers is a good illustration of the reciprocal relationship between the mind and the emotions. Progress in the perception of reality permits the baby to form more meaningful and lasting attachments to specific persons; the converse is also true—his attachment to familiar persons prompts him to think about them, remember them, search for them, reject substitutes, and wait for their return.

Pleasure in Recognition and Repetition

When we consider the whys of infant behavior, we face the critical questions about the kinds of rewards involved in learning new behavior which were mentioned in Chapter 1. The infant learns a great deal under the pressure of tensions caused by such drives as hunger. In a passive way, he learns many associations between the relief of hunger and the sights, sounds, and smells which portend food (i.e., classical conditioning). In a more active way, he learns to associate certain of his own acts such as crying, sucking, and grasping the bottle, with the desired relief (i.e., instrumental or operant conditioning). Much of his learning is readily understood in terms of the pleasure-pain principle of psychoanalyses or of the learning theory principle of reinforcement through reward or drive reduction. However, the infant evinces other behavior which also leads to learning, but which does not have any apparent physiological drive.

From the very first, the infant confronted by any new spectacle tries to reproduce it or make it continue. Initially, of course, the only way to make things last is to pay attention; the infant stares or listens hard in order to maintain the perception. Soon he becomes more active and searches for ways to perpetuate interesting sights and sounds. Over and over and with obvious pleasure, he repeats the same babbling sounds or the same activity. Moreover, he is delighted if someone else joins the game, and he recognizes the similarity between his own sounds and those imitated by the outside person.

Pleasure in making sights and sounds continue leads to pleasure in their reappearance. Familiarity becomes an important part of emotional attachments. The baby becomes attached first to the mother, who possesses many recognizable attributes, but concurrently, he becomes attached to toys which are left in his crib or playpen. He shows genuine pleasure in seeing them again, even though they have never served any purpose except to be looked at. Piaget has shown that the baby will smile in a wide variety of repeated situations, e.g., when a newspaper is repeatedly placed on the top of the bassinet, or when he repeatedly finds his nose with his hand.

The evidence of infant activity and pleasure in the absence of a primary need or drive has led theoreticians to postulate motivations such as "urge to mastery" *(Hendrick, 1943)* and "competence motivation" *(White, 1959)*. J. McV. Hunt postulated "motivation inherent in information processing and action," language borrowed from computer terminology *(1963-a)*. Edwin Guthrie describes much infant learning on the basis of contiguity in time, without seeking a motivational explanation *(1935)*. However, the infant's obvious pleasure in recognition and repetition conveys the strong impression they are highly rewarding. M.M. Kessler has suggested that the pleasure in repetition comes from the saving of energy which occurs from the physiological facilitation in a neuronal chain *(1955)*. The kind of facilitation to which he referred is the overcoming of resistance at the synaptic junction between neurons. Whatever theoretical explanation is advanced, the fact remains that the baby is pleased by recognition and repetition per se.

Derivation of Curiosity

In time, the infant becomes satiated by simple recognition and looks for novelty. The toddler is on the search for something new. Hunt has described the shift as follows:

I have noted Piaget's empirical generalization that "The more a child has seen and heard, the more he wants to see and hear" [*Piaget, 1936, 1952, p. 277*]. I have attempted to explain not only this generalization, but also several other commonly observed behaviors of infants and their role in development, with the notion that once children have been exposed to a given pattern of stimulation enough times to make it familiar, the emerging recognition of the pattern brings pleasure that motivates an effort to retain or re-elicit the pattern. I have further attempted to elaborate this explanation with the notion that, after a pattern has continued to be familiar for a time, it is variation in that pattern that brings pleasure and the effort to find that variation in either the child's own activities or in external stimulation. *(1963, p. 273.)*

The point is that the child must be quite familiar with something before he takes pleasure in a variation. The toddler of 12 to 14 months will be intrigued by new toys or new places to explore, but the same toddler will be distressed if a familiar nursery rhyme is altered in the reading. He is not yet sufficiently familiar with words to tolerate novelty in this area. Moreover, the toddler would have no wish to get into things unless he knew that objects are permanent. If things could not exist out of sight, there would be little purpose in climbing onto the table, opening handbags and boxes, or crawling into cupboards. It is the sense that there are things to be seen in all these places which prompts him to explore.

The toddler also needs a sense of ego identity, a recognition of his own independence, and an appreciation of the connection between his activity and the results achieved. His behavior becomes purposeful. He can have the important experience of deliberately separating himself from, and returning to, his mother; he can go away from her because he is sure of her permanence and confident of his ability to get back to her. Margaret Mahler terms this the beginning of the "separation-individuation phase" of personality development, a kind of second birth experience described as "hatching from the symbiotic mother-child common membrane" *(1955, p. 196)*. If, for some reason, the child does not take this step, he remains in a symbiotic relationship to his mother, and all his efforts are concentrated on maintaining the *status quo*. At the extreme is the child who is overwhelmed by anxiety at the smallest innovation, who displays no curiosity or exploratory behavior, and who has no sense of ego identity. This condition Mahler calls "symbiotic psychosis" (see Chapter 11).

Stages of Imitation

A discussion of the preverbal period must include some mention of imitative behavior. As we have observed, much of the baby's activity—staring, listening, and reaching—helps him to hold onto objects, to preserve images for longer and longer periods of time, and to postpone the helplessness of losing them. His ability to search for vanished objects also aids in this purpose.

Imitation gives the young baby yet another way to keep things going. By nine or ten months, he is quite a little imitator. Mother coughs or says "brrr," and he follows suit; she waves bye-bye or plays pattycake and he joins in. It is a social, delightful game. However, the baby is limited to the sounds and gestures with which he is already familiar; he cannot be taught to play pattycake before he can clap, for instance. The mother makes something out of his self-initiated behavior and gives it a new social significance, and the child learns that he can give his mother and himself pleasure by clapping in response to her signals. Failure to respond to this kind of social stimulation is often a first sign of the childhood psychosis known as "infantile autism." Some children are particularly deficient in their ability to relate to people, and the deficiency is often first apparent at this early juncture (see Chapter 11).

In his description of stages of imitative behavior, Piaget remarks that when the child becomes capable of repeating movements he has already made, but which he cannot see himself make (e.g., sticking out the tongue), he also tries to copy sounds and gestures to which he has hitherto been indifferent. Then he is imitating in a very real sense; everything he sees or hears another person do, he tries to do himself. When the child has advanced to the point of imitating what is brand new to him, he could be taught any number of simple performances by a patient model. However, few seriously consider providing the toddler with formal instruction; he is already a most thoroughly satisfactory student. His tremendous wish to do as others do enables him to teach himself every waking minute. His growing intellect requires only protection, living examples, and opportunity to explore.

Imitation is as much a cornerstone of personality as of intellect. The new skills the toddler acquires through imitation are obvious ones. But less obvious changes, which take place inside him, are the essential ingredients for the emerging personality. The child does not imitate indiscriminately; those who are near and dear are most frequently taken as models, and the mother most of all. Imitation is a precursor of *identification*. Imitation is the copying of another's specific actions; identification is based on a deferred and more comprehensive imitation. Gerald Pearson describes the evolution of infant's identification with his mother as follows:

He [the baby] combines all of the sensations he receives from his mother through the eyes, ears, and mouth, and through his senses of taste and smell, of touch, of equilibrium, of position, and of movement, into one whole in his mind, which becomes the memory of his mother. He can now recall this memory and perceive it when he is away from her, and at these times he strives to behave as he remembers she did, until eventually he finds himself automatically behaving like his mother. He has incorporated her and as a result has identified himself with her. To describe the same process another way, he has studied her, memorized her, and so learned her, and because he has learned her she exists as part of himself. *(1954, p. 135.)*

Acquisition of Language

Without language, an individual will inevitably be stunted, both intellectually and emotionally. If he has no understanding of words, he can have only a hazy idea of what others are saying; he is forced to rely on facial expressions, vocal inflections, and situational clues. He cannot make reference to absent persons or things; he cannot tell another person what has happened; he cannot inquire about future events. He cannot state his complaints, his wishes, or his feelings, except in actions which can be easily misinterpreted. He has to *do* things rather than think thoughts.

A child usually begins to talk between his first and second birthday, and this is probably the outstanding event of the preschool period. With the acquisition of speech, the son or daughter advances from infancy (which literally means "not talking") to childhood. But speech does not appear suddenly; there are many preliminaries. Speech development is two-sided: There is the receptive side, i.e., the ability to hear and understand what is said; and there is the expressive ability, i.e., the articulation of sounds which convey a message. Since a child must have some inner language before he speaks, the receptive side of speech development merits first consideration.

Passive Language Development

The human voice seems to be intrinsically meaningful, at least from a few weeks of age, and the language a baby hears is charged with feeling and presented in a context of facial expressions, gestures, actions, and objects. He seems to like to listen as much as look. Words first become significant because of the accompanying tone or gesture, and from the familiarity of their context. Toddlers quickly learn to recognize "no, no" or "hot," said in a special way, but they will ignore the words if the negative command voice is not used. Babies recognize the cue words which precede routine activities such as eating, bathing, or going to bed, but the cue words are recognized only in association with sights which remind them of what is about to happen.

Gradually, the baby differentiates sounds more precisely and responds to words. His first reactions are largely to commands and requests, such as "Give me" or "Show me" some object, and he shows his understanding by some appropriate gesture or action. At this stage, he has no understanding of words per se, but he becomes accustomed to the special form of the request and reacts to the whole situation rather than to the individual words. If someone other than the parent makes the suggestion, or if it is made in an unusual location, or if a different word, sequence, or tone is used, the verbal direction draws a blank. At this point, the baby is not far different from the well-trained dog that, signalled by cue words, can go through a repertoire of tricks. The child does not understand the words, but he understands what the person using them means and what he, or the adult, is going to do.

Soon the child learns to connect certain sounds with objects, rather than with actions. Often, the first meaningful words that refer to objects signify parts of his own body—eyes, ears, or hands. At first, the child must point these out in a certain order and a familiar person must do the asking. Then he makes a transfer of this knowledge and can point out the same parts of the body on a person other than himself, and in any order. At around 18 months, he takes another step in generalization and can point out the parts of a doll's body. At about two, he takes a truly giant step and can identify parts of the body on a two-dimensional representation, a drawing of a person. He now has the idea of what each word stands for and can associate it with anything which represents the real thing, even a colorless drawing on a piece of paper. His understanding of these words is now as abstract as that of an adult.

At the same time that the child is learning to differentiate sounds and their meanings, he is learning to make a similar differentiation between objects and their uses. In the first year, the child treats all objects as if they were the same, handling them in accordance with his latest achievement—mouthing, banging, throwing, or whatever. Early in the second year, he begins to discriminate: Food or eating utensils go to the mouth; the ball is thrown; the blocks are stacked; the pencil is used for scribbling. The recognition of objects and the recollection of their uses is a process parallel to the discrimination between words and the recollection of the associations between them and activities or objects.

Preverbal Communication

Before the child utters a single word, two processes which later coalesce into spoken speech go on concomitantly. One is the child's play with sounds; the other, his prelinguistic signals, his cries and gestures. The infant's vocal play reminds us that speech is a motor response. The expressive side of speech starts with babbling; which is the same in all cultures, Even deaf children start to babble, although they do not continue. The child is experimenting with the kinesthetic and tactile sensations of the oral apparatus, simply for the pleasure of feeling his lips and tongue move into different positions. This spontaneous, diffuse motor activity has two results: First, the infant realizes that his sounds produce an effect on his environment; second, when he realizes that the sounds are produced by himself, he listens to himself and tries to make the auditory perceptions persist by self-imitation.

Additional insight into this early phase of speech development was provided by the unhappy circumstances of war. Anna Freud and her co-workers observed a number of infants who were reared in residential nurseries because their homes had been destroyed *(1944)*. They found that the vocalizations of children under one year were normal in extent and kind, but that these same children were verbally backward by their second birthday. This suggests that vocalization in the first year is stimulated by different forces than in the second year. The desire for oral pleasure, like other early urges for self-gratification (e.g., sucking, rhythmic movements, and so on), may even be stronger when the child is left more to himself.

However, speech is more than the articulation of sounds. The primary purpose of speaking is to convey something to another person. Karl Buhler described three functions of mature language: expression, appeal, and description. He used the terms "symptom," "symbol," and "signal" *(1934)*. The expressive function appears first, in the form of a direct discharge of tension (i.e., screaming). Next, the infant, having developed perception and memory, links this expressive discharge with the relief of tension (i.e., food) which follows it. Then the screaming, or crying, becomes an appeal. The response of others to his vocal appeals teaches the infant the potentialities of special utterances and establishes the general notion of language as a communicative device.

First Words

It is not always easy to tell when the child begins to speak. It is traditionally thought that the child's first word is usually "mama" or "dada," but this is probably more in the ear of the parent than in the mind of the child. Many toddlers use a syllabic combination such as "mama" to convey all kinds of feelings and intentions. One child, of 15 months, could ask questions, say "no," express delight, and announce his hunger, by modifying his tone and the inflection with which he said "gaga." René Spitz refers to the appearance of global words toward the end of the first year and remarks that "the first global word is used by the child to communicate his needs to the libidinal object, that is to the mother, who is also his executive. It signifies indiscriminately hunger, boredom, discomfort, etc., and the wish to be relieved of them, just as it signifies biscuit, toy, mother and the desire for these" *(1957, p. 100).*

Some toddlers use a jargon, a stream of gibberish which has all the expressive intonations of genuine speech and which may contain some real words, but the jargon quickly disappears and the child settles down to one-word utterances. The first utterances are usually interjections and commands. "Hi" and "bye" are usually said at the urging of the parents; they may be appropriate, but their prime purpose is to please. Commands, including "no" and "hot," are clearly stimulated by the child's inner wishes to get something or to stop something. It is important to keep in mind that the only reason the child turns to speech as a way of making his wishes known is that he observes other people using speech for this purpose. Soon after he starts to walk, the child encounters the powerful meaning of "no," and often this is one of the first words with which he experiments. He has observed the consequences of this sound, and now he tries it himself. In this respect, as in so many others, the baby tries to meet life by imitating the models provided by the people around him.

Very soon, early in the second year, the child begins to utter another kind of word, the noun. He names objects. The motivation for this is not so obvious. In the words of Joseph Church:

Interjections and imperative statements are easily understood as part of the child's affective and pragmatic communication with his surroundings. Denomination, however, which seems a more abstract form of activity, deserves a further word. Some denomination seems purely reflexive—the object elicits its name. Sometimes the child names objects as a way of communicating with adults; he enjoys the adult's pleasure

and approval, and he enjoys the very fact of communication. Some of the child's naming activity seems to be a request for verification: 'Is this a . . .?' rather than "This is a. . . ." Finally the child names things to himself, just as though exercising a skill.*

Church also comments that "it seems likely that the toddler's insatiable hunger for names reflects the sense of possession and domination of the object that knowing its name gives him" *(1961, p. 74).* At this point, Buhler's third function of speech, description, is present and words have assumed symbolic meaning. The toddler has the general concept that everything has a name and either asks the adult for this label or picks it up silently by hearing words used in context. This has been termed the "Original Word Game" by Roger Brown: "In simple concrete terms the tutor says 'dog' whenever a dog appears. The player (i.e., the child who is learning) notes the equivalence of these utterances, forms a hypothesis about the nonlinguistic category (i.e., the external object or activity) that elicits this kind of utterance, and then tries naming a few dogs himself" *(1956, p. 285).*

This general concept is of a learning set which predisposes the child to discover the names of what he sees and hears. He is not a passive learner who must be spoon-fed each name by deliberate effort on his parents' part; he is active in making the connections between word and object or word and activity.

Acceleration of Language Development

There is a snowball effect in learning language. After a slow, labored start, verbal development accelerates rapidly in the second half of the second year. M. E. Smith found an average vocab-

---

*Quoted from Joseph Church, *Language and the Discovery of Reality* (New York: Random House, 1961), p. 62. Reprinted by permission.

ulary of 3 words at the age of 12 months; of 22 words at 18 months; and of 272 words at 24 months. That is, vocabulary increased about sevenfold in the first half of the second year and twelvefold in the second half. In the third year, the rate of growth slowed down, but was still high. The three-year-old knew three times as many words as the two-year-old *(Smith, 1926)*. There is a corresponding increase in loquacity; the child of two uses words much more frequently and reliably than the 18-month-old.

The third observable change is the combination of words into sentences of two or three words. The child has become able to divide the combinations of words which he hears into their components, and can understand each word separately. Now he can reassemble them into novel combinations. True, his verbal style is telegraphic, consisting of nouns, verbs, and adjectives. He has yet to learn grammar and shades of meanings, and his articulation is poor, but language has become a tool of communication for him. Church's view of the reasons for the ensuing phenomenal acceleration of verbal skill follows:

As we have seen, the child's first use of language is rather skimpy, but he almost immediately senses this new tool's power, which, at its highest development, becomes the power to capture the world in a net of symbols, to possess it, to manipulate it in new and wondrous ways, to master it, and to recreate it.*

Omnipotence of Words

We should consider what speech means to the child. It is easier to see what the ability to walk means to him, because he acquires it rather suddenly and shows his pleasure in it by wanting to walk all the time. Talking appears much more gradually. In the beginning, the child uses speech almost frugally,

as if he regards his few words with considerable respect. These sounds have the magic power of making something happen. The toddler is perhaps like the traveler in a foreign country. The sounds of a foreign language are mysterious, and the stranger usually hesitates to experiment with them. There is the danger of being misunderstood and of setting something undesirable in motion. Perhaps this is why so many travelers stick to "please" and "thank you," and do not risk asking questions or making requests.

Freud was one of the first to call attention to the tremendous power that the very young child ascribes to speech. "The child's earliest speech is a charm directed toward forcing the external world and fate to do those things that have been conjured up in words" *(Fenichel, 1945, p. 46)*. Church speaks of "word realism":

Word realism is sometimes interpreted narrowly to mean the child thinks of the name as somehow inherent in the thing named, but this is only one of its manifestations. Its central manifestation is in the power that words have over us, and the sense of power over reality that words give us.*

The child's first words are usually so effective that it takes some unlearning before he realizes that words, per se, do not reshape reality. He will try to change things by verbal fiat. A two-year-old, told he could not go out to play because "it is raining," put on his slicker, gazed outside at the rain, and declaimed firmly, "It is *not* raining."

There is an intimate connection between language and thought. Once language has been acquired, thought becomes more and more a matter of silent speech. The distinction between thinking to oneself and speaking out loud is fuzzy at first, and the child accords the same magic power to his thoughts as he does to his words. He expects even

---

*Church, *op. cit.*, p. 87.

*Church, *op. cit.*, p. 74.

his unspoken wishes to come true. It is, of course, a blow to find that this does not always happen. But there is also reassurance in the discovery: The primitive sense of power carries with it some frightening possibilities, particularly with respect to bad wishes. By the age of two, the youngster is certain to have experienced some frustration and disappointment and to be angry with his frustrator (i.e., the parent) and wish him no good. As he becomes conscious of his aggressive thoughts, he simultaneously fears that they might come true. His ambivalent feelings of love and anger produce an inner conflict, and it is a relief to learn the limitations of the power of his wishes.

Vestiges of this period of development can be seen in normal people as well as in neurotics and psychotics. Many people are superstitious about voicing an unpleasant possibility; they fear that to express a possible misfortune may make it more possible. So they avoid speaking of death, accidents, or illness and, if they happen to use one of these unlucky words, they promptly knock on wood in order to undo the damage which the words might cause. The primitive belief in the magic of thought and word is closely allied to *denial*, a psychological mechanism whereby painful sensations and facts are felt simply to not exist. If denial is applied wholesale to large segments of the outside world, the falsification of reality which follows reduces the person's competence, perhaps even to the extent of a psychosis.

Distortions in the use of words are frequently observed in obsessive-compulsive neurotics and in schizophrenics. The obsessive-compulsive individual like the young child, overvalues words. Certain words become taboo and other become talismans. Yet the obsessive-compulsive person remains aware of the usual meanings and has some insight into his idiosyncrasies. The schizophrenic patient lacks this insight, however, and may restructure his language

so that it loses its value as a form of communication.

Role of Verbalization in Behavior Control

We have observed that emotional factors—the child's wish to please and emulate his parents and his need to communicate—play a major role in the development of language. In turn, language has a profound effect on his subsequent educational development. The child has more control over his behavior. He can inhibit himself, using words in place of actions. Anny Katan, calling attention to a common omission in the education of the young child, has pointed out that, while parents usually encourage the child to learn the names of objects and answer his spoken or unspoken questions about the things he sees and hears, they do not usually teach him to express his inner feelings. She describes the situation as follows:

The child perceives his feelings, and expresses some of them without words, by crying or laughing, by facial expressions or body motility. In the very early stages of development, however, these feelings are not usually given names. Often they are not understood by the parents, so the means of communication, like pointing, etc., that exists with regard to wishes directed toward the outer world is non-existent for the expression of the child's feelings. . . . In my experience, feelings of pain or getting hurt are verbalized earlier than any other feelings; then follows the verbalization of feelings of fear, of being scared. Yet such feelings as sadness, excitement, happiness, and anger are often not verbalized for the child until a much later date. . . . If the child does not learn to name his feelings, a situation may arise in which there is a discrepancy between the strength and complexity of his feelings, on the one hand, and his modes of expression on the other. If the child could verbalize his feelings, he would learn to delay action, but the delaying function is lacking.*

Some of the parents' difficulty in rec-

---

*Quoted from Anny Katan, "Some Thoughts

ognizing and naming the emotions of their young harks back to their own childhood. This is particularly true of aggression. Many parents prefer to maintain an illusion of innocence, by denying any meanness; if their child hurts someone or destroys something, it is accidental. Some parents find it harder to tolerate the young child who verbalizes his defiance. The child seems smarter, more responsible, and thus more censurable. It is as if the child is not really angry unless he says so; an instance of adult belief in word magic.

Characteristics of Early Thought

One of the major differences between the two-year-old and the four-year-old is in the nature of his reasoning processes. It is hard to converse with a two-year-old. His attention span is short, he cannot explain himself, he does not listen well, he contradicts himself, and he tries to resolve difficulties by edict. He uses words which sound like ours, but somehow he does not use them in the same way, and he surely is not logical. As Church has remarked:

Parents who try to reason with young children often find themselves sinking in a quagmire of rapidly shifting premises, logical inconsistencies, unforeseen implications, word magic, and dissolving obviousness.*

Naive Assumptions: Egocentrism

The term "egocentrism," introduced by Piaget, embodies a concept invaluable to our understanding of the vagaries of childish thinking. Briefly, the idea is that the child's view of the world depends on his own activity. This does not imply selfishness, or even self-consciousness; on the contrary, it implies

the child's lack of awareness of the self as separate from the outer world. Egocentrism is the absence of both self-perception and objectivity. The child cannot conceive of anything beyond his own experience and his own feelings. He assumes that everyone and everything shares the identical experiences with him and at the same moment; he cannot detach himself from his particular vantage point and put himself in the position of another person. Freud stated the principle of egocentrism, but without using the term, as "a universal tendency among mankind to conceive all beings like themselves, and to transfer to every object those qualities with which they are familiarly acquainted and of which they are intimately conscious" *(1913, 1955, p. 77)*.

Piaget studied egocentrism in a number of contexts: stages of imitation, language and thought of the child, ideas of physical causality, and others. He suggests that the child is most egocentric at the age at which he imitates most, egocentrism being a failure to differentiate between the ego and the group, or a confusion of the individual's viewpoint with that of others.

The child often imitates without being aware of it, merely through confusion of his activity or point of view with those of others. If our definition of infantile egocentrism is accepted, we have here a typical manifestation of it. The child's egocentrism is essentially a phenomenon of undifferentiation, i.e., confusion of his own point of view with that of others or of the activity of things and persons with his own activity. *(1951, pp. 73–74.)*

Egocentrism is not outgrown all at once. The child may become conscious of himself and aware of the relativity of his own point of view in one area, yet remain subjective (i.e., egocentric) in another. Piaget demonstrated this with children of four to six. Each child was presented with a model representing three mountains in relief. He was then asked which of a number of

---

about the Role of Verbalization in Early Childhood," in *The Psychoanalytic Study of the Child* (New York: International Universities Press, 1961), XVI, 185-86. Reprinted by permission.

*Church, *op. cit.*, p. 77.

colored pictures showed the mountains from the point of view of a doll which was placed in successive positions on the mountains in the model. The younger ones did not understand that an observer sees the same mountains quite differently, depending on his vantage point, and they considered their own perspective absolute, the same no matter where the doll was placed. Similarly, a two-year-old playing hide-and-go-seek hides by simply closing his eyes, as if to say, "I can't see you; therefore I know you can't see me." A little later he gets the idea of hiding his head, but it is not until he is four or five that he can hide his whole person successfully.

Egocentrism is closely linked with animistic, or anthropomorphic, thinking. *Animism* is the belief that objects are alive and endowed with will; it means regarding objects and animals as having the same feelings and intentions as one has oneself. The child who bumps into a table feels that the mean table has hit him. A little girl of two, having punctured a piece of paper with her pencil, started to cry because the paper felt hurt. A little boy cried out, "Poor zwieback!" when the hard bread was broken into halves. Parents often subscribe to this way of thinking, seeking to reassure the child; and sometimes achieve the opposite result. For instance, a little girl of two, who had a great fear of vacuum cleaners, visited her grandmother and immediately asked where the vacuum cleaner was. Her grandmother replied that she need not worry, because "The vacuum cleaner is in the closet taking a nap, and sound asleep." After a moment's silent reflection, the child began to cry in terror. The fanciful explanation had not allayed her fears, because anything which can sleep can also wake up, anything which can wake up can walk around, and anything which can walk around can get very angry and become dangerous!

In accordance with the general principle of egocentrism, the child assumes that other people have identical bodies until he, or she, has some experience to the contrary. The first discovery of the difference between boys and girls is bound to come as a surprise. Some parents feels that the emotional impact of this discovery has been overrated by child psychiatrists, because their own child has not asked any questions regarding the sex difference. In such an instance, it is probable that the child did not ask about the difference because he believed that he knew the reason for it. The egocentric child is unaware of his ignorance and cannot imagine any explanation other than the one which spontaneously occurs to him.

It is open to speculation what explanation he might create for himself. The spontaneous explanation of a two-year-old would have to be in terms of his own very limited experience. In the life of most two-year-olds, there has been considerable emphasis on destruction. Favorite toys wear out, many household object. are taboo because of their fragility, and so forth. In view of this, we can deduce that a frequent spontaneous explanation for the absent penis would be that there has been a particularly unfortunate breakage. And the unhappy part of this notion is that what has happened once to one person can happen again to another. This particular misconception has a unique position in child psychology, because it is not one which can be dismissed lightly. Nor is it easy to correct, unless it comes out into the open. One might argue that a child would not think of such a thing unless he had been told something of this sort or had been threatened. But ideas are not formed passively; the normal child is not an inert being who registers only what people say to him. From the age of two, and perhaps even younger, he puts together one bit of experience with another bit, and out of these combinations he conceives original ideas. Castration anxiety can take many forms and have many causes, but fear has its genesis partly in the discrepancy between the knowledge of the young child and his direct observations.

As a mode of thinking, egocentrism is related to *projection*. Piaget remarks that egocentrism has two sides: suggestibility, which is a kind of unconscious identification with the behavior or feelings of someone else; and an unconscious projection of the ego into someone or something outside *(1945, 1951)*. Psychoanalysts reserve the term "projection" to describe a particular kind of defense mechanism whereby unpleasant feelings or repugnant wishes are attributed to someone other than the self, so that the individual can feel, "It is not I who thinks or feels in such and such a way; it is the other person." The paranoid patient, whose ability to test reality is severely distorted, produces the most extreme projective misinterpretation of reality. His narcissism, like that of the young child, is overwhelming. He interprets the universe as revolving around him, either to hurt him or to help him (i.e., megalomania), and he personifies all happenings in terms of his own projected wishes and fears. But his thinking, unlike that of the young child, is not open to correction by subsequent experience with reality.

Concepts Regarding Physical Possibilities

For the young child, anything is possible. All things imaginable are equally possible; the thought is father to the reality. The child takes no cognizance of differences between animate and inanimate objects nor of differences in size. Young children cannot see, upon inspection, that one object may be much too large to be contained within another. A two-year-old may repeatedly try to put his large fire engine into a tiny garage, sticking stubbornly to his purpose and becoming enraged by the lack of cooperation he gets. The child who stuffs things into the toilet has to do it over and over, exploring the possibility of flushing down every kind of household object, before he is satisfied that some things, including himself, are simply too large to disappear down the toilet. One experience does not immediately convince a two-year-old of any general fact; if this white shoe won't go down, maybe a red one will.

The same process can be observed as the child plays with his toys. The two-year-old, hard at work trying to put a round peg into a square hole, turns the peg upside down, turns the square hole around, takes the peg in the other hand, pushes harder. He tries to pull a bead over the knotted end of the string, despite repeated failures. He does not appreciate that the cause of his failure rests in the physical properties of the objects, so he attempts to accomplish the impossible by sheer determination. By the time the child is three he can perceive gross differences in size and shape at a glance, and adjust accordingly.

The two-year-old accords to dreams, make-believe, stories, or television programs, the same respect he accords to reality. And, if one considers the whimsies of television commercials, one can get a feel for the child's conception of the world. Picture animals on cereal boxes burst into song, glass bottles turn into muscular giants, and so on. The visual sights of television confirm any possibility. But the older the child grows, the more he becomes accustomed to paying attention to objective, factual signs; he checks his observations to see if they occur again.

Importance of Socialization

Progression from egocentrism requires that the child become aware that he thinks, feels, sees, and hears from a point of view unique to himself. The child needs a dual perspective, so that he not only perceives reality but is aware of himself as perceiving. Thus he is enabled, within limits, to discount and compensate for his own biases, blind spots, and restricted vision. He can only acquire this kind of awareness of self in contrast to something else, namely, the point of view of others.

A view of the world as it appears to someone else can only be achieved through the medium of language, but the mere possession of speech is not enough. Thoughts and experiences must be socially shared before the differences are exposed. The child must pit his own ideas against those of others. Discussing the functions of language, Piaget describes the central role of socialization:

Intelligence, just because it undergoes a gradual process of socialization, is enabled through the bond established by language between thoughts and words to make an increasing use of concepts; whereas autism, just because it remains individual, is still tied to imagery, to organic activity, and even to organic movements. The mere fact, then, of telling one's thought, of telling it to others, or of keeping silence and telling it only to oneself must be of enormous importance to the fundamental structure and functioning of thought in general, and of child logic in particular.*

In another context, the construction of reality in the child, Piaget comments:

It is by cooperation with another person that the mind arrives at verifying judgments, verification implying a presentation or an exchange and having in itself no meaning as regards individual activity. Whether conceptual thought is rational because it is social or vice versa, the interdependence of the search for truth and of socialization seems to us undeniable. *(1937, 1954, pp. 360–61.)*

The child must not only have the ability but also the desire and oppor-

---

*Quoted from Jean Piaget, *Language and Thought of the Child* (1926). Trans. by Marjorie Warden, Cleveland, Ohio: Meridan Press, World Publishing Co., 1955, p. 64. Copyright, Humanities Press. Reproduced by permission.

tunity to share his ideas. A child who is isolated or neglected may be deprived of the social context he needs to correct his subjectivity. A child who is very withdrawn, fearful, withholding, or chronically at odds with the people about him also will neither verbalize his thoughts nor listen thoughtfully to the utterances of others and, as a consequence, retains primitive modes of thought much longer than usual. A vicious circle may be perpetuated: Because of emotional difficulties, verbalization is inhibited. Primitive thinking, with all its attendant fears and anxieties, persists uncorrected, thereby perpetuating the emotional problems.

Normally, by listening and talking, the child discovers his mental self. In the first year of life, he had to learn to distinguish his own body from what was outside himself. A similar differentiation has to be made in respect to feelings and thoughts. The child must relinquish the naïve assumption of the identity of his feelings and those of other people and objects, and begin to wonder about the true nature of this outside world. The mental curiosity of the intelligent three- and four-year-old parallels the investigative curiosity of the toddler. For the toddler, the discovery that objects exist, even when they are not immediately visible, is a powerful reason to investigate the physical environment. Similarly, the older child is driven to ask questions to discover hidden knowledge. As long as he assumes that everyone and everything else thinks and feels exactly as he does, he has no need to ask questions.

Synthetic Function of the Ego

In describing the mental status of a four-month-old infant, we noted that his behavior reveals all ego functions except that of *synthesis*, which develops much later. By perceiving and remembering, the child brings together all kinds of past and present experiences, an early form of synthesis. But as he becomes capable of reflection, the synthetic process goes on in terms of his inner thoughts. Although Piaget does not use the psychoanalytic term "ego," he describes its synthetic function as:

. . . the tendency to unify one's beliefs and opinions, to systematize them with the object of avoiding contradictions. Up till the age of seven or eight, children make no effort to stick to one opinion on any given subject. They do not indeed believe what is self-contradictory, but they adopt successively opinions which, if they were compared, would contradict one another. They are insensible to contradiction in this sense, that in passing from one point of view to another they always forget the point of view which they had first adopted.*

Herman Nunberg describes the passionate eagerness with which all men seek explanations for the events which they observe. This need for causal explanation is the core of the synthetic function of the ego. Nunberg illustrated the need for causality by an adult's reaction to posthypnotic suggestion:

The hypnotized person in question was given the order to go to the corner of the room, to pick up an umbrella that had been placed there, and to open it five minutes after awaking from the hypnosis. When he had executed this order, he was asked why he opened the umbrella. He replied: "Because it is raining." (As a matter of fact it was not raining.) The need for causality is obviously so strong that when the cause is missing, it is invented. *(1955, p. 151.)*

Freud stated the problem thus:

There is an intellectual function in us which demands unity, connection, and intelligibility from any material, whether of perception or thought, that comes within its grasp; and if, as a result of special circumstance it is unable to establish a true connection, it does not hesitate to fabricate a false one. *(1913, 1955, p. 95.)*

_____
*Piaget, *op. cit.*, p. 91.

The younger, the less logical, the more primitive, or the sicker a person, the more easily will he find causes.

Ideas of Causality

A review of the cause-and-effect relationships in which children believe shows that they make many false connections. The first causal explanations, which are formulated without deliberation, are in terms of the child's over-evaluation of his own words and thoughts. When a child's efforts result in repeated disappointments, he is forced to conclude that his own powers are limited and that he cannot control everything by his words or wishes.

Although experience forces him to give up the idea that *he* is the sole cause of events, he finds another person to endow with the magic properties which he has renounced. This superior being is usually the parent. One three-year-old was infuriated by the refusal of his blocks to remain standing. Suddenly he turned to his mother and said, "Say 'stand up'!" It takes time for the child to forego the belief in the parent's omnipotence. It is, after all, a comfort to believe that even if one personally is helpless, there is someone else who *can* control what happens. Some of the irritation which children express against their parents probably stems from a mistaken belief in their parents' responsibility for disappointments and frustrations.

The child is driven to consider the problem of causality from every viewpoint. As a naïve believer in his own or his parent's omnipotence, the young child feels no uncertainty. But as he grows and becomes disillusioned on this score, he faces a totally unpredictable future. In his search for cause-and-effect relationships which will allow him to anticipate the future, he will undoubtedly consider the importance of temporal connections. Many times it is correct to explain a later event on the basis of an earlier one, but the young child overdoes it. He applies this *post hoc, ergo propter hoc* reasoning to all situations and makes no discrimination between chance circumstances and essential causes. This leads to the rigid conservatism typical of the two-year-old. Custom becomes law, and any departure from the usual routines is regarded with suspicion and alarm. Rituals are developed around all the everyday activities. From the child's standpoint, nothing is irrelevant; the whole sequence stands or falls as one piece. The child who insists on a glass of milk, one cooky, and one scraped carrot at his bedside is not necessarily hungry. It is as if he says, "When I had these things before and went to sleep, everything was all right. If I have these things again and go to sleep, everything will be all right again." The child's passion for sameness is more than a simple error in judgment; the determination behind it stems from his feeling of helplessness. It is an effort to make life predictable, and it involves a method which he will continue to use until he can predict on the basis of a more advanced comprehension. This mode of casual thinking is not entirely discarded by adult persons; it reappears in states of emotional distress or ignorance. The obsessive-compulsive individual is often as rigid as the young child, although he may have the insight to consider his habits "superstitious."

The four-year-old is famous for his persistent "why" questions, many of which are unanswerable. He believes that everything must have a reason and that his omniscient parents know all the answers. The idea of chance is absent from the child's thought. "Every event can be accounted for by its surroundings," or "Everything is connected with everything else"—such might be the tenets of this creed. He will find a justification at any price. As he expects an answer from others, so, if he is asked why, he will invent an answer. Acceptance of the answer, "One cannot know" comes only much later.

In a context far removed from child development, Eugen Bleuler echoes the same sentiment. He discusses the self-deception of physicians which results from their zealous desire to help patients, and concludes with the remark: "The clear and affect-independent statement, 'This I do not know,' requires a high level of relationship to reality" *(1922, 1951, p. 442)*. After the child has been introduced to religious concepts (around five or six years), God will become the *deus ex machina* to which everything is attributed. It is to God that he transfers the faith he invested first in his own, and later in his parents', omnipotence.

Topics of Concern

The young child seeks an explanation for everything, but certain subjects have great emotional meaning for both parent and child. The first of these, curiosity about the difference between the sexes, has already been mentioned. The child is also vitally interested in matters of life and death. As he learns to distinguish between animate and inanimate, he becomes aware of the distinction between living and dead. It will not be long before he realizes that there was a time when he himself did not exist. So where was he? This is not a casual question; underlying the curiosity is a concern lest he disappear back into the void.

It is even easier to understand the curiosity of the youngster into whose family a new baby is born. He has the intellectual problem of reconciling his observations of the mother and the coincidence of the baby's appearance, but his curiosity is further piqued by his jealousy. There is always the possibility that if one knew how this new baby arrived, one could effect a convenient disappearance, or at least prevent a recurrence. Freud was particularly impressed by the young child's concern with the birth of babies and suggested that this was the prototype of many of the child's questions *(1900, 1953).* Many times, when a child persistently asks about the origin of things, it represents his displaced curiosity about the genesis of human beings. Such curiosity is insatiable, one question leading to another ad infinitum. In view of their parents' difficulties in explaining where babies come from, many children give up asking direct questions and express their anxiety in many other forms of curiosity, never finding the answer they are seeking.

Death is only the other side of the birth question, but again the question is simple and the answer difficult. The child wants to know why it happens, in order to forestall it both for himself and his parents. The young child, observing a dead animal or plant, will ask plaintively, "Why did it die? What made it dead?" This might seem like a great surge of sympathy, but basically the child is trying to find the guilty party. Organic life is, for the child, a sort of story, well regulated according to the wishes and intentions of its inventor.

It is some time before children realize that death is irreversible *(Moellenhoff, 1939; Nagy, 1948).* The three-year-old who feels he can magically change the world around him can, in fantasy, destroy living things including people, and then revive them. Even five-year-olds think that the dead may come back to life and believe in ghosts. Most investigators agree with Maria Nagy that the child's notion of death does not become realistic, that is, based on biological principles, until about eight.

Two Principles of Mental Functioning

Everyone who has closely studied early mental development has come up with some idea of two planes of reality, two modes of thinking, or some kind of dichotomy in the mental process. The terms used to define the essential difference depend on the orientation of the observer. Suggested terms have been "concrete versus abstract," "prelogical versus logical," "irrational versus

rational," "magical versus realistic," and "primary processes versus secondary processes." Bleuler proposed "directed or intelligent thought," as opposed to "undirected, or autistic thought." With respect to autistic thinking, he remarks:

It has its own laws and these deviate from those of realistic logic. It is not after truths, but after the fulfillment of wishes; it does not operate with the experientially established associations of strict, realistic-logical thinking, but with incidental associations of ideas, vague analogies, and above all, *affective needs. (1922, 1951, p. 439.)*

This is very similar to Freud's distinction between the pleasure principle and the reality principle in mental functioning: primary processes operate according to the pleasure principle; secondary processes operate according to the reality principle. Freud believed that the substitution of the one for the other in the process of development is never complete or irrevocable. Freud described the primary processes in dreams where everything is possible and there is no coherence or logical sense. Freud, of course, emphasized the importance of dream interpretation as an adjunct in psychoanalytic treatment, but his observations on the psychology of dreams led to increased understanding of the structure of neurotic symptoms. The analysis of neurotic symptoms also reveals the operation of primary processes: a symptom originates from affective needs rather than logic, and it usually contains within it a kernel of irrational thinking, where forbidden wishes are treated by the ego as if they were real rather than imagined. Further, neurotic symptoms are usually symbolic, in that some object, place, or activity of the ego has become invested with all kinds of extra meanings beyond the realistic or logical. The dreamer and neurotic patient show that the capacity for primary process thinking is never completely lost; the potential for regression to infantile mental status is omnipresent.

Play and Imagination

It would be unfortunate to leave the impression that secondary processes are always good and primary processes are always bad. There is a time and place for both. Realistic or logical considerations matter little in the fantasies of children at play, or in later daydreaming. One never outgrows the need for the relief afforded by primary process thinking, but the importance of play and imagination is greatest in childhood.

In play, the child restructures reality to suit his wishes and, in most cases, it is easy to see how and why. He re-enacts events which were fun; he assumes grown-up roles; he bosses his toys and imaginary helpers to obey his every wish. It follows, then, that the child might be expected to forget or repress unpleasant memories rather than to reenact them in play. Yet he often does precisely this. Waelder describes a special kind of play where the pleasure is not immediately apparent:

... a child was taken to a dentist. It had been very apprehensive concerning the dentist, from whom it had previously suffered tormenting pain. According to the pleasure principle, we should offhand suppose that the highly disagreeable situation, once it was fortunately in the past, would have been set aside, and that the child would be only too glad to let the matter drop. The pleasure principle hardly prepares us to expect the return of the situation in play. Nevertheless, in reality, this often occurs. *(1933, p. 210.)*

The explanation is in the change of his role from a passive to an active one. In the original traumatic situation, the child was done to; in play, he is the doer. Not only does he take the part of the powerful, dangerous grownup, but also he can start the game and stop it whenever he chooses. Play can be a method of constantly working over and assimilating piecemeal an experience which was too large to be assimilated instantly at one swoop. A painful experience is repeated in play while it is still unmastered, and the playful repetition helps to gain mastery over the experience. Then the matter can be safely forgotten and the child loses his eagerness for the game. This use of play is closely related to the therapeutic concept of abreaction, discussed in Chapter 14. These ideas are mentioned here only to call attention to the fact that every child is subjected to a number of painful, anxiety-producing surprises. And that many children spontaneously find ways of liquidating their anxiety.

At four or thereabouts, the child stands at the threshold of adult modes of thought. He accepts the fact that there is an important difference between reality and imagination, although he will continue to confuse the two from time to time. In this respect, he is no worse off than the adult who substitutes his own thoughts and feelings for facts, especially in areas of ignorance or emotional involvement. At least, the child now knows the difference and can make some separation between the two. He can now appreciate the fanciful, the make-believe, and the humorous as belonging to the exaggerations and unrealities afforded by the world of play. On the other hand, he can appreciate the importance of information, the relatedness of facts, and the communication of ideas for verification. He is interested in the acquisition of knowledge as well as in pretending.

Already one can see, on a reduced scale, a number of ways in which personality can impede the full use of intellectual abilities. The major emphasis in the guidance of parents of pre-school children has been on emotional needs, and wisely so. Without emotional well-being, intellectual development cannot reach a maximum. However, it is useful, also, to consider the limitations of the child's powers of comprehension in order to understand the origin and nature of the fears and conflicts of this age. This is a two-way street: Out of misconceptions, fears arise, and too strong an anxiety can block further thought. In order to promote intellectual development, one has to consider the usefulness of intelligence at this early age. It should serve to diminish fear, to increase the sense of mastery, and to reinforce the child's indentifications with adults. If the child discovers the usefulness of thought at this age, the way is paved for his future education.

Incentives to Development and Means of Early Education

A tremendous amount of learning is facilitated by the emotions. But there are also things which run counter to his natural desires that the child must learn during the pre-school period. Learning to be clean, to share attention, and to tolerate disappointment or delay, for example, necessarily involve conflict.

We know that a one-year-old cannot be expected to know where the street is, so when he wanders off the lawn we view it as purely accidental. But what about the two- or three-year-old? He has the requisite knowledge, but this alone is not enough to deter him. He also has to learn that he will be happier if he obeys his parents. Many times, slowness to change behavior is attributed to intellectual factors when the fault actually lies in some slowness in emotional development. Certainly, learning is fastest and easiest when the task is intellectually comprehensible *and* compatible with the child's natural wishes. The other kind of learning, which is incompatible with his selfish wishes, is far more arduous and complex.

A great deal of social learning takes place in the first year but, if the mother is empathic and thoughtful, the frustrations can be so subtly introduced that she is not identified by the infant as frustrating. In the second year, the baby has advanced mentally and the unavoidable frustrations have multiplied, so that the hapless mother cannot totally escape the role of villain in the child's mind. Most mothers carry out their child rearing responsibilities with little conscious question; they use common sense, usually doing what their own mothers did and what they observe other mothers doing. They do not have a theoretical rationale for every step they take, and it is better for their self-confidence and the spontaneity of their relationship with the child that they do not. The professional, however, should consider the theoretical problems which confront the parent who is teaching the child to become more grown-up. What is the task of education? What are its basic methods? What are the sources of breakdown?

In 1909, Freud considered the education of the time to have as its goal controlling and suppressing the instincts without regard to the cost of the suppression. He suggested that the aim of education be redefined, that its goal be to "make the individual capable of becoming a civilized and useful member of society with the least possible sacrifice of his own activity" *(1909, 1955, p. 146)*. This emphasizes the two-sidedness of education: consideration both for society and for the individual. In some fashion, most parents and teachers have these twin goals in mind. Socially, they want a child to be acceptable, to do well, to cause no trouble, to be considerate of others, and so on. They also have objectives referrable to the inner state of the child: The child should be self-confident, spontaneous, and capable of enjoying himself in many ways.

There is less room for argument about the purposes than about the methods of pre-school education. Peller reviewed historical trends in child rearing theory in a thoughtful article in which she identified three major schools *(1946)*. The first is the "school of habit training" as represented by William

Blatz *(1944)*, R. I. Watson *(1951)*, and Leslie Hohman *(1943)*. According to this view, it is entirely up to the adults to recast the child's innate responses through consistent early training which anticipates the future. Like Watson, Blatz implies that parents can remake the child into the likeness of any image they choose. If they try and fail, "They should not blame the method but themselves; they should try again, be prompter in applying displeasure, be adamant in wiping out exceptions, and they will succeed *(Peller, 1946, p. 401)*.

The second major school of thought which influenced child rearing is that of maturation or, in Peller's terms, "developmentalism." Arnold Gesell softened the exhortations of the early habit trainers with the argument that training cannot transcend maturation. The early experiments of M. McGraw *(1935)* and others indicated that toilet training, for example, was much more efficient if it was started when the child was mentally and physically ready to learn. In some circles, the concept of readiness was taken to mean that the older the child, the more ready he was to learn new skills. Further research, particularly with animals, however, suggested that there may be critical periods for training and that training postponed beyond this point may become more difficult, rather than less. If buzzards are caged for ten weeks, their flying ability is permanently impaired *(Dennis, 1941)*. Similarly, if newly hatched chicks are isolated from the hen for more than eight days, they fail to respond to her call, and if they are prevented from pecking beyond eight days, they no longer peck at single grains *(Padilla, 1935)*. Comparable evidence may be found in the permanent, irreversible psychological damage which is done to children who are deprived of normal experiences in the first year of life. Apparently there is a right time for training. Earlier training is slow, effortful, and perhaps bewildering and frustrating to the child; delayed training is equally difficult for the child.

There is a system of pre-school education based primarily on the idea of critical periods, namely the Montessori method. This system, called by one author a "religion of childhood" *(Fisher, 1912)*, enjoyed some popularity in the first decades of this century, faded from sight, and was rediscovered in the sixties *(Edmonson, 1963)*. Maria Montessori, an Italian psysician, described sensitive periods, each with characteristic interests, sources of satisfaction, and sensitivities *(Walker, 1913)*. The child of 21 to 24 months shows a strong interest in odors; the child of five and six years, a concern for counting, and so on.

Dr. Montessori planned a program of education to offer those experiences which the child craves at various stages of his growth. Thus, she combined the ideas of training and maturation by instituting the one when the other was also there. It is probable that the method lost favor because too much was promised. Disciplinary problems could theoretically be settled by offering the right activities at the right time, so that the person in charge could efface herself. Anything of a coercive nature was to be avoided; all growth would be voluntary. The teaching materials were designed to encourage the child's independence; ideally, they would be so fascinating and self-correcting that no interference or instruction from the teacher would be needed.

In a sense, the modern interest in the teaching machines recapitulates this version of education: time the educational program correctly for the child; break it into small, assimilable steps; give it an interesting form in which the child is active; and prepare the material so that the child himself corrects his wrong answers. The teacher is the programmer who presents the material, and the child learns spontaneously, without fear of the teacher. Little is said about the importance of love for the teacher; the child's intellectual and moral growth are dependent on his natural desire to be good and self-controlled. In the view of the present writer, such desires are far more complicated and less natural in their development than first believed by Montessori devotees.

The third school of child rearing was labelled "psychoanalytic" by Peller:

According to the psychoanalytic view powerful stimuli from the social world come into alliance with his [the child's] innate tendency to develop. There is nothing automatic about the child's emotional, intellectual, and ethical progress. The main factors in his early development are his early attachment to his mother, his oedipal attachment to his parents, and the sequelae of this bond. *(1946, p. 407.)*

The child's love for his mother provides powerful leverage for his education. He becomes willing to forego infantile pleasures in order to win her love and also in order to establish himself as more like her, i.e., more grown-up. Modern learning theorists say the same thing when they emphasize the importance of reinforcement of learning new behavior and the power of the drive for love in the process of reward. The second part of the analytic view, the importance of the Oedipal constellation as an apprenticeship in human relations, is considered superfluous in learning theory.

Hopefully, we shall finally arrive at a well-integrated theory of child development which combines the truth of all these schools. Unfortunately, it is certain to be complicated and to lack the simplicity of single explanations. In our time, thoughtful students of child psychology are essentially agreed that the methods of early education include: (1) timing, in terms of the child's readiness; (2) gradualness; (3) teaching by adult example with which the child can identify; (4) imposition of frustration, made tolerable by the reward of parental love and approval; and (5) verbalization to increase self-control and understanding. Punishment cannot be relied upon to bring about the profound alterations in personality which enable the child to set standards for himself and to try and live up to them from the dictates of his own conscience. Internalization requires emotional attachments as well as experience and specific teaching.

The importance of communication between adult and child is frequently overlooked. Of course, it is not always possible to reason with a child. Objective reasons for self-control may sound weak to the young child who wants what he wants *when* he wants it. However, verbal explanations never hinder. And they give the child the example of putting things into words, which may enable him to put his own objections into words rather than actions. When there is an open channel of communication, the parent may become apprised of fantasies which are unnecessarily complicating the child's development. Verbal communication takes into account that a child is a thinking being, capable of insight and symbolic processes. Education which does not take this into account is no more than mechanical training not unlike that used by affectionate dog owners!

What are common sources of breakdown in the education process? On one side, the child may not be able to receive the training. Organic or constitutional defects may make it hard for him to learn or to comply. Or his ability to control himself may have been so weakened by anxiety that his ego control is insufficient. On the other side, the parents may not be able to give the proper education. They may be confused about their proper role, and so become indecisive or inconsistent. They may be too impatient and strict, or too passive and lenient. They may be so absorbed in their own problems that they have little energy to devote to the rearing of their children. Finally, they may be unaware of the inner mental life of their child and so lacking in empathy that child and parent are always working at cross purposes. There is no perfect parent and, normally, children are well able to withstand some degree of any of the above deterrents to growth. Seriously faulty education usually produces behavior problems, but it does not follow that faulty education is the *sine qua non* of childhood psychopathology. As we have observed earlier in this chapter, many emotional conflicts originate in the child's own fantasies.

References for Chapter 2

Blatz, William E., *Understanding the Young Child.* New York: William Morrow & Co., Inc., 1944.

Bleuler, Eugen, "Autistic-Undisciplined Thinking," (1922), in *Organization and Pathology of Thought,* ed. David Rapaport. New York: Columbia University Press, 1951, pp. 438–50.

Brown, Roger W., "Language and Categories," in Jerome S. Bruner, Jacqueline J. Goodnow, and George A. Austin, *A Study of Thinking.* New York: John Wiley & Sons, Inc., 1956.

Buhler, Karl, *Sprachtheorie.* Jena: Verlag von Gustav Fischer, 1934.

Church, Joseph, *Language and the Discovery of Reality.* New York: Random House, 1961.

Dennis, W., "Spalding's Experiment on the Flight of Birds Repeated with Another Species," *Journal of Comparative Psychology.,* Vol. XXXI (1941), 337–48.

Edmonson, Barbara, "Let's Do More than Look: Let's Research Montessori," *Journal of Nursery Education,* XIX, 1 (1963), 36–41.

Fantz, Robert L., "Pattern Vision in Newborn Infants," *Science,* CXL (April, 1963), 296–97.

Fenichel, Otto, *The Psychoanalytic Theory of Neurosis.* New York: W. W. Norton & Company, Inc., 1945.

Fisher, Dorothy Canfield, *A Montessori Mother.* New York: Holt, Rinehart & Winston, Inc., 1912.

Fraiberg, Selma H., *The Magic Years.* New York: Charles Scribner's Sons, 1959.

Freud, Anna, "Some Remarks on Infant Observation," in *The Psychoanalytic Study of the Child,* Vol. VIII. New York: International Universities Press, Inc., 1953.

——, and D. Burlingham, *Infants without Families.* New York: International Universities Press, Inc., 1944.

Freud, Sigmund, *Analysis of a Phobia in a Five-year-old Boy* (1909), Standard Edition, Vol. X, ed. and trans. by James Strachey. London: The Hogarth Press, Ltd., 1955.

——, *Totem and Taboo* (1913), Standard Edition, Vol. XIII, ed. and trans. by James Strachey. London: The Hogarth Press, Ltd., 1955.

——, *The Ego and the Id* (1923), Standard Edition, Vol. XIV, ed. and trans. by James Strachey. London: The Hogarth Press, Ltd., 1961.

——, *The Interpretation of Dreams* (1900), Standard Edition, Vols. IV, V, ed. and trans. by James Strachey. London: The Hogarth Press, Ltd., 1953.

——, *Two Principles of Mental Functioning* (1911), Standard Edition, Vol. V, ed. and trans. by James Strachey. London: The Hogarth Press, Ltd., 1953.

Guthrie, Edwin R., *The Psychology of Learning.* New York: Harper & Row, Publishers, 1935.

Hartmann, Heinz, "Ego Psychology and the Problem of Adaptation" (1939), in *Organization and Pathology of Thought,* ed. and trans. by David Rapaport. New York: Columbia University Press, 1951.

Hebb, D. O., "On the Nature of Fear," *Psychological Review,* LIII (1946), 259–76.

Hendrick, Ives, "The Discussion of the 'Instinct to Master,'" *Psychoanalytic Quarterly,* XII (1943), 561–65.

Hoffer, Willie, "Development of the Body Ego," in *The Psychoanalytic Study of the Child,* Vol. V. New York: International Universities Press, Inc., 1950.

Hohman, Leslie B., *As the Twig Is Bent.* New York: The Macmillan Company, 1943.

Hunt, J. McV., "Motivation Inherent in Information Processing and Action," in *Motivation and Social Interaction,* ed. O. J. Harvey. New York: The Ronald Press Company, 1963-*a*.

——, "Piaget's Observations as a Source of Hypotheses Concerning Motivation," *Merrill-Palmer Quarterly,* IX, (1963-*b*), 263–75.

Katan, Anny, "Some Thoughts about the Role of Verbalization in Early Childhood," in

The Psychoanalytic Study of the Child, Vol. XVI. New York: International Universities Press, Inc., 1961.

Kessler, M. M. "Extensions of Certain Parts of Freud's Instinct Theory." Unpublished paper presented at the Cleveland Psychoanalytic Training Center, Cleveland, Ohio, December, 1955.

McGraw, M., *Growth: A Study of Johnny and Jimmy*. New York: Appleton-Century-Crofts, 1935.

Mahler, Margaret S. and Bertram J. Gosliner, "On Symbiotic Child Psychosis: Genetic, Dynamic and Restitutive Aspects," in *The Psychoanalytic Study of the Child*, Vol. X. New York: International Universities Press, Inc., 1955.

Moellenhoff, F., "Ideas of Children about Death," *Bulletin of the Menninger Clinic*, III (1939), 148–56.

Nagy, Maria, "The Child's Theories concerning Death," *Journal of Genetic Psychology*, LXXIII, (1948), 3–27.

Nunberg, Herman, *Principles of Psychoanalysis*. New York: International Universities Press, Inc., 1955.

Padilla, S. G., "Further Studies on the Delayed Pecking of Chicks," *Journal of Comparative Psychology*, XX (1935), 413–43.

Pearson, Gerald, *Psychoanalysis and the Education of the Child*. New York: W. W. Norton & Company, Inc., 1954.

Peller, Lili E., "Incentives to Development and Means of Early Education," in *The Psychoanalytic Study of the Child*, Vol. II. New York: International Universities Press, Inc., 1946.

Piaget, Jean, *Judgment and Reasoning in the Child* (1928), trans. Marjorie Warden. Paterson, N.J.: Littlefield, Adams and Co., 1959.

–––, *Play, Dreams and Imitation in Childhood* (1945), trans. C. Gattegno and F. M. Hodgson. New York: W. W. Norton & Company, Inc., 1951.

–––, *The Construction of Reality in the Child* (1937), trans. Margaret Cook. New York: Basic Books, Inc., 1954.

–––, *The Language and Thought of the Child* (1926), trans. Marjorie Gabain. New York: Meridian Books, Inc., 1955.

–––, *The Origins of Intelligence in Children* (1936), trans. Margaret Cook. New York: International Universities Press, Inc., 1952.

Smith, M. E., "An Investigation of the Development of the Sentence and the Extent of Vocabulary in Young Children," *University of Iowa Studies in Child Welfare*, Vol. III, No. 5 (1926).

Spitz, René A., *No and Yes: On the Genesis of Human Communication*. New York: International Universities Press, Inc., 1957.

Spock, Benjamin, discussion following "Emotional Development in the First Year of Life," Escalona, Sibylle, in M. J. E. Senn, *Problems of Infancy and Childhood*, Transactions of the Sixth Conference, New York, March 17 and 18, 1952. New York: Josiah Macy, Jr., Foundation, 1953.

Waelder, Robert, "The Psychoanalytic Theory of Play," *The Psychoanalytic Quarterly*, II (1933), 208–24.

Walker, Jane, "The Montessori Method of Education," *Educational Review*, XLVI (1913), 300–307.

Watson, R. I., *The Clinical Method in Psychology*. New York: Harper & Row, Publishers, 1951.

White, R. W., "The Concept of Competence," *Psychological Review*, LXVI (1959), 297–333. Reprinted in *Functions of Varied Experience*, ed. Donald W. Fiske and Salvatore R. Maddi. Homewood, Ill.: The Dorsey Press, 1961.

3

ANXIETY, AGGRESSION, AND GUILT

The Problem of Anxiety

Definition

Psychoanalytic theorists view anxiety as central to the study of psychopathology. The part played by anxiety as the force behind repression and the formation of neurotic symptoms was established at the outset. Its survival value for normal development was also acknowledged:

Freud considered anxiety to have a biological, inherited basis. In other words, he believed that the human organism is congenitally endowed with the capacity for reacting with the psychological and physical manifestations which we call anxiety . . . If a human being, without the protection of his parents, could not be frightened by anything, he would soon be destroyed.*

Anxiety is a feeling, or affect, of a particularly unpleasant, painful nature. In addition, it is an emotion which has distinctive physiological features. In an anxious state, the body is prepared for fight or flight (*Cannon, 1932*). The stimulation of the sympathetic nervous system and the release of adrenalin results in a faster heart beat, quicker res-

piration, peripheral vasoconstriction, and higher blood pressure. Anxiety also produces pilomotor effects which account for the prickly sensation of the skin, alterations of muscle tension, and excretory reactions. All this may result in a surge of physical strength and speed, but there is little, if any, improvement in mental efficiency.

Many authors have proposed that anxiety be distinguished from fear, on the basis that anxiety is a response to subjective danger and fear is a response to objective danger. However, there is no difference in the psychological experience. It feels the same; the same somatic mechanisms are activated; and, besides, it is sometimes difficult to distinguish a real danger from an imagined one. For example, if a young child is afraid a dog will bite him, his fear has a real basis if the dog is vicious, an imagined basis if the dog is friendly. If a child is afraid a bridge will fall down as he passes over, and the bridge is flimsy and rickety, his fear has a real basis. But it has an imaginary basis if the bridge is sturdy. Fears about traveling are justified when one considers the number of auto or airplane accidents, but most of us dismiss such fears and take the trip nonetheless.

In almost every instance, anxiety about external danger is at least compounded by the child's imagination. And the converse is also true: Fears

---

*Quoted from Charles Brenner, *An Elementary Textbook of Psychoanalysis* (New York: International Universities Press, Inc., 1955), p. 83. Reprinted by permission.

which take on phobic dimensions can be rationalized in some small measure by objective considerations. Thus, the terms "anxiety" and "fear" are used interchangeably. But a distinction may be made between pathological and normal anxiety on the basis of (1) the intensity of the reaction; (2) its persistence; (3) its imperviousness to objective reassurance; and (4) the extent to which it limits the individual's freedom of action.

Psychoanalytic Theories: Old and New

Sigmund Freud's earliest discussions of anxiety are contained in his first paper on the anxiety neurosis (1895, 1962). At that time, he adhered firmly to a neurological frame of reference and attempted to formulate physiological bases for psychological data. He accepted Fechner's principle of constancy, which postulated an inherent tendency of the nervous system to keep constant the amount of excitation present in it. From clinical experience, he discovered that patients with anxiety neurosis had in common some form of inhibition of the sexual act which resulted in a damming up of sexual tension. His first view was that this excitation acted like a toxin (by virtue of its accumulation and lack of discharge) and was subsequently transformed into the psychological and physical manifestations of anxiety. Freud felt that this concept of anxiety was a basic one:

One of the most important results of psychoanalytic research is this discovery that neurotic anxiety arises out of libido, that it is a transformation of it, and that it is thus related to it in the same kind of way as vinegar to wine.*

The fact that the affect aroused by

external danger was identical to the affect aroused by anxiety was one of the considerations that eventually led Freud to re-examine his view; clearly, the reaction to external danger could have little to do with the toxic effect of dammed-up libido. The original concept was radically modified in a monograph on anxiety (1926, 1959), in which he regarded anxiety as a reaction of the ego to danger, no matter what the source or kind of danger.

In a traumatic situation, the ego is flooded by stimuli which are overwhelmingly suprising and painful. The essence of the traumatic situation is the experience of helplessness and lack of preparedness. By "traumatic" Freud meant situations which are (1) overwhelming, flooding the child with excessive stimulations from internal or external sources; (2) shocking, coming as a surprise with no forewarning; and (3) overpowering, in that the child has no avenue of flight or fight. Freud considered the act of birth the first trauma, and thus the source and physiological prototype of anxiety. The newborn is suddenly exposed to a massive dose of external sensations which evoke an automatic, reflex-like response, physiologically similar to fear. It is the suddenness of the change in environment which made birth traumatic in Freud's special sense; he did not consider the newborn to have fantasies or memories in connection with birth.

Freud distinguished between anxiety as a direct and automatic reaction to a trauma (which he termed "traumatic anxiety" or "automatic anxiety") and anxiety aroused in anticipation of trauma ("signal anxiety"). The younger the child, the more susceptible he is to automatic anxiety. The infant is not born with experience which would permit him to prepare himself for dangerous situations; he reacts to the immediate situation. In addition, the infant has relatively little capacity for assimilation; he has little understanding and few mechanisms for coping with pain-

---

*Quoted from Sigmund Freud, *Three Essays on the Theory of Sexuality* (1905). Standard Edition, ed. and trans. by J. Strachey (London: The Hogarth Press, 1953.) VII, 224. © in U.S.A. by Basic Books, Inc. Reproduced by permission.

ful surprises. As he grows, the difficult experiences of the past function as preparation for future tolerance.

The difference between automatic and signal anxiety does not depend on the source of the danger, but on the timing. Traumatic situations arise from impulses as well as from outside stimulation. In this sense the first orgasm a person experiences is a trauma, because of its newness and its overpowering character. There are differences of opinion among child psychologists as to the age at which a child can experience such feelings, but it is generally recognized that adolescents are fearful of the arousal of sexual feelings, a fear quite independent of possible objective consequences. The experience of rage, of losing one's temper, can have the same terrifying effect, partly because of fear of punishment or disastrous results, but partly also because of the disintegrating effect of the aggression on the self. When a tremendous rage takes over the ego and makes it inoperative, one becomes a stranger to oneself, helpless in the grip of sudden, strong emotion. This is expressed by children, as well as others, as a fear of being out of control, and it is in part engendered by the basic fact of helplessness.

The young child learns to anticipate the advent of traumatic situations and to react with anxiety before they occur (i.e., signal anxiety). Its production is a function of the ego and serves to mobilize the forces at the command of the ego to meet or to avoid the impending danger. The child develops this capacity to experience signal anxiety as he becomes able to anticipate the future. He is able to imagine how he *would* feel *if*, and how he *will* feel *when*. He sees his mother preparing to leave, and he knows how he will feel after she is gone.

It might appear that it is disadvantageous and painful to the child to anticipate future unpleasantness, some parents, with this thought in mind, and hoping to spare the child unnecessary worry, fail to prepare their child for such an event as a tonsillectomy. And part of signal anxiety does appear to be designed to avoid or postpone the dreaded event. But anticipatory anxiety helps the child to master the actual experience when it comes. And if he anticipates an event, he can also be helped to anticipate when it will be over. To be taken by surprise is one of the prime features of the traumatic situation. Advance preparation, provided by the child or by the parents, helps to dilute the shock of the actual situation.

Anxiety as a Learned Drive

Psychoanalysts and learning theorists agree that the potential for becoming anxious must be physiologically innate. One does not learn how to be anxious; one learns when to be anxious and about what. N. E. Miller has stated that "fear [or anxiety] is called *learnable* because it can be learned as a response to previously neutral cues; it is called a *drive* because it can motivate the learning and performance of new responses in the same way as hunger, thirst, or other drives" *(1951, p. 436)*. Laboratory experimentation has shown that an animal can be conditioned to fear a situation in which he has experienced an electric shock and that he will be motivated to learn how to escape even if the painful stimulus is inactive. He expects a repetition of pain; he is anxious. Further experiments, particularly by Miller and others of the Yale school, have demonstrated that learning motivated by reduction of anxiety follows the same principles as learning rewarded by reduction of tension from innate, or primary drives.

In these experiments, the anxiety is aroused by association with physical pain. The connection between pain and fear is presumably innate. P. H. Mussen, J. H. Conger, and J. Kagan illustrated learned anxiety in an infant by positing a hypothetical associative pairing of a physically painful experience (a pinprick) with a specific visual stimulus (older brother who does the pricking). Future appearances of the brother will evoke fear until it is extinguished by the infant's learning a new pair: visual stimulus (brother) with*out* pain *(1963, p. 145)*. There is no argument with this example. It is simple, straightforward, and has a common-sense and everyday quality. Many anxieties can be explained by this formula.

The problem is *what constitutes pain,* which is agreed to be "innately capable of arousing the response of fear." Freud wrestled with this problem many times. In accordance with the principle of constancy mentioned earlier, he postulated that unpleasure (or pain) corresponded to an increase in the quantity of excitation in the nervous system, and that pleasure corresponded to its diminution. Pain is experienced when there is no outlet for excitation. In the case of the pinprick, the pain is easy to define and locate. It is easy to locate the pain when the infant experiences hunger contractions. But if an infant is well cared for, there is no physical source for the pain and anxiety he feels when he is separated from his mother. And, as a youngster grows older, he does not lose his anxiety about physical pain and situations which contain a threat of physical danger, but psychological pain becomes more important. For example, as the child begins to love others, he is susceptible to a new kind of danger, the danger of losing the loved person. Through learning, the child has acquired the drive, or need, of dependence and this drive, if frustrated, can cause pain. Anxiety can be grafted onto any secondary drive, in the same fashion as it was grafted onto the primary drive of physical pain in the pinprick example.

Age Trends in Children's Fears

The external manifestations of childish anxiety have been extensively studied by A. T. Jersild and his coworkers. In the 1930's, several investigations of reported and observed fears in children of different ages were made. The studies included direct observation of pre-school children in experimental situations, interviews with older children, reports of parents and teachers on pre-school children, and retrospective reports of childhood fears by adults.

In the group of normal pre-school children, fears of concrete and tangible stimuli (noises or objects, agents and events associated with them, sudden unexpected movements, and strange objects, situations and persons) declined between one and six years. On the other hand, their fears of imaginary, anticipated, and supernatural dangers (e.g., dreams, robbers, imaginary creations, the possibility of accidents and events associated with the dark) increased over the same age span. "Fear scores" correlated positively with the intelligence quotient, the relationship being most marked (.53) in those between two and three years old. With regard to these findings, Jersild remarked, "As the child matures, new things affect him by virtue of his keener perceptions and fear is likely to arise when the individual knows enough to recognize the potential danger in a situation but has not advanced to the point of a complete comprehension and control of the changing situation" *(1960, p. 257)*. This recognition of potential danger is synonymous with signal anxiety.

H. Angelino and his associates asked groups of youngsters, of 9 to 18 years of age, to "list the fears and worries you think persons of your own age group have." In this age range, there was a decline in fears for personal safety and in fear of animals. On the other hand, fears pertaining to school (worries about grades, fears of teachers, and stage fright) increased between 9 and 12, and there was some increase in fears pertaining to social relationships and fears classified as "economic and political" *(Angelino, Dollins and Mech, 1956, p. 264)*. It is interesting to note that childhood fears recalled by adults correspond quite closely to fears reported by children of 11 to 12. Apparently earlier fears are forgotten or superseded by the fears of later childhood.

Not only does the content of children's fears change with age, but also the form in which they are expressed. As the child grows older, there is a decrease in obvious signs of fear (e.g., crying, trembling, or clinging to an adult). Partly this is because children become more controlled in all respects, and partly because most children are discouraged from showing their anxiety. Children are praised for courage, which is usually defined as "having no fear." It would be more helpful for children if they were praised for their ability to tolerate anxiety, to proceed to a certain objective despite fear. However, as it is, many children have a fear of showing fear, and anxiety assumes many disguises. Jersild comments that fear may be expressed in innumerable forms, "ranging from an obvious show of fear to a show of complete confidence, and from extremely good and compliant conduct to stubbornness, resistance, unwillingness to 'see the point,' and outright rebellion and defiance that look more like anger than like fear" (1960, p. 258).

Such disguises would be called "defense mechanisms" by a clinician. Two of the most common, and misleading, mechanisms whereby children hide their anxiety are: (1) counter-phobic behavior; and (2) identification with the aggressor. In the first, the child is fascinated by the very thing or object of which he is most afraid, as if he cannot forget it for a moment. The fear masquerades as strong interest. By dint of the second mechanism, the child becomes the imagined dangerous person (or sometimes animal) by identification. He appears to be absolutely bold and fearless as he sets about to do unto others what he fears might be done to him. The casual observer is easily misled by the apparent lack of fear.

Danger Situations

It has been said that anxiety is a reaction of the ego to danger or to the threat of danger, danger causing physical or psychological pain. The next question is: What kind of dangers does the child experience in the process of growing up? Although psychoanalytic theorists have been concerned with the kernels of infantile anxieties, rather than with the specific forms and shapes which they may take, Freud outlined a series of typical danger situations which may be expected to occur in sequence in the child's life. The first of these is fear of losing a loved person or fear of abandonment. In psychoanalytic literature, this is referred to as "loss of the object" ("object" meaning the object of a drive, usually a person to whom the child has become attached). The next typical danger situation is the loss of the love of that person, "loss of object love." The basic anxiety centers around psychological separation in feeling, rather than around physical separation in body. These may be considered the focal anxieties of the first two-and-a-half to three years of life, and there is little controversy about their importance. In their accounts of anxiety, both Harry Stack Sullivan (1947) and Karen Horney (1939) emphasize the child's dependence and helplessness and the difficulties he faces if there is a disturbance in his relationships with persons who are important to him. Learning theorists have great respect for the need for love and approval as a means of reinforcement of behavior, and for the pain which ensues when they are withdrawn.

The third danger situation is unique to Freudian theory and is disputed by others. Briefly, it is the castration anxiety of the three- to five-year-old. R. Waelder has described this danger situation as it occurs for boys and girls as follows:

In boys, it is fear of losing the penis or of damage to it; or fear of being overpowered by the stronger male and thereby forced into the feminine position, or being put into a lower place in the scale of 'relative sexuality,' a fear that can, in the last resort, be traced back to the fear of losing the penis; or fear that, on comparison with one's peers, one will turn out to have the smaller membrum, to be less virile.

In girls, castration fear is originally the fear of repetition, or symbolic repetition, of the violent intervention that had made them females in the first place; and later, after a successful development along the feminine line, i.e., after acceptance of their femininity, the fear of being deprived of the very qualities or possessions of femininity, particularly the integrity of the female organs, attractiveness as women, and satisfactory children.*

The above statement shows the ramifications of this particular danger situation. It is not only, for boys, fear of actual loss of the penis, or for girls, anxiety about its nonexistence; there is also, for both, anxiety about adequate sexual functioning.

The fourth danger situation namely, the anxiety of guilt, or disapproval and punishment by the superego or conscience, brings us back to common, uncontested ground. This anxiety is not lost in the process of growing up and all of us are conscious of it. In a sense, because the conscience is the internal representative of the parents, it is a development of the fear of losing their love. A fifth danger, the possibility of losing control, has already been mentioned.

Anxiety can be aroused, therefore, by five root dangers: loss of object, loss of love, emasculation, loss of self-love, and ego disintegration. The strength of these anxieties varies greatly in different individuals and at different times. Waelder has remarked that "the fear of losing love is particularly marked in depressives, castration fear in phobics,

the fear of psychic disintegration in incipient schizophrenics or in people who sense in themselves a threat of psychosis."*

Let us consider the way in which these anxieties may appear in overt behavior and use as an illustration the development of a fear of an animal. In an experimental situation, Jersild found that children up to the age of two showed no fear when a large, harmless snake was placed near them. Children of three and four tended to be cautious, and definite fear was displayed by children over four (1935). One might say that the child develops such a fear because someone has told him that snakes are to be feared or because he has seen someone act afraid of a snake. This is, of course, possible, but it also happens that a child fears an animal which he has been told not to fear. One must consider the possibility that the child has a fantasy about the snake. According to the schedule of danger situations, one would not expect a child under two to be afraid of an object unless it came as a substitute for the mother (fear of object loss) or unless it was associated with the mother's anger or disapproval (fear of loss of object love). A snake doesn't seem to meet the requirements. In the next period, the fear should develop on the basis of the object's potential for inflicting bodily injury on the child; the child is not afraid of the animal as such, but rather of what he thinks it can do to him. Interestingly enough, a snake, with its particular characteristics, is especially suitable for the projection of castration anxiety.

Aggression

Definition

It is even more difficult to define "aggression" than to define "anxiety." The dictionary offers two definitions of the verb "aggress": "to step forward, to approach" and "to make an attack." A

---

*Quoted from Robert Waelder, *Basic Theory of Psychoanalysis* (New York: International Universities Press, Inc., 1960), p. 159. Reprinted by permission.

---

*Waelder, *op. cit.*, p. 162.

similar duality of meaning is encountered in professional usage. Often the term "aggressive" is used in a general way, meaning "active, energetic, taking the initiative," yet omitting the destructive intent. More commonly it is used in the more restricted sense. For example, J. Dollard defines aggression as "an act whose goal response is injury to an organism" *(1939, p. 9)* and R. Waelder *(1960)* and C. Brenner *(1955)* use "aggression" and "destructiveness" interchangeably.

Anger and hatred refer to feelings which usually accompany aggressive behavior. We know that anger and fear are closely related. Similar factors are involved in their instigation, and either emotion may accompany or give rise to the other. The effects of anger on the body chemistry are not as clear-cut as those of anxiety, but the physiology is close. In anxiety, the body is made ready for fighting as well as for fleeing. The sharpest difference between the response of anger and the response of anxiety is the way that the person feels. If he wants to attack, it is anger; if he wants to run, it is anxiety. Often he wants to do both, and experiences the resulting conflict as additional discomfort.

Aggression as a Basic Drive

The problem of aggression did not come into the forefront of psychoanalytic theory until relatively late. Freud always maintained a dualistic theory of drives, but it was not until the publication of *Beyond the Pleasure Principle* that the dichotomy was established in terms of sexual and aggressive drives *(1920, 1955)*. Before this turning point in theory, aggression was viewed as either (1) a manifestation of pregenital sex urges (related to the concept of sadism); or (2) a function of the ego instincts in response to frustration. In this formulation, aggressive impulses were at the disposal of the ego for the purposes of preserving life and safe-

guarding the gaining of instinctual satisfaction. When Freud abandoned the dichotomy of ego instincts and libido, he viewed aggression as a drive equal in importance to the sex drive. From this, he evolved his theory of the life and death instincts as in fundamental opposition to each other. In 1930, Freud stated his position as follows:

In all that follows I adopt the standpoint, therefore, that the inclination to aggression is an original, self-subsisting instinctual disposition in man, and I return to my view that it constitutes the greatest impediment to civilization . . . Man's natural aggressive instinct, the hostility of each against all and of all against each, opposes this programme of civilization. This aggressive instinct is the derivative and the main representative of the death instinct which we have found alongside of Eros and which shares world-domination with it." *(1930, 1961 p. 122).*

Both R. Waelder and C. Brenner have pointed out that the concept of an inborn aggressive drive does not require allegiance to the concept of the death instinct. The postulate of innate aggression is a clinical, or psychological one which will stand or fall on clinical grounds alone. The death instinct introduces biological problems, and many feel that Freud's argument was based on biological facts which are now obsolete (i.e., the idea that living matter contains within it catabolic processes which inevitably lead to its own death). Many, if not most psychoanalysts do not accept the concept of a death instinct but nevertheless find it useful, on the clinical level, to consider instinctual manifestations to be composed of admixtures of sexual and aggressive drives.

Aggression in Learning Theory

Since learning theory proposes a formulation of drives radically different from that of psychoanalysis, one would expect to find aggression viewed as another secondary, or learned drive, And Dollard *et al.* presented a comprehensive account of the arousal of anger as the result of frustration created by the intervention of another individual or some sort of physical obstacle *(1939)*. This tie-in between frustration and aggression is similar to that between pain and anxiety. The frustrated child learns to behave aggressively because this helps him to accomplish his purpose:

[Aggression] develops because the child discovers that he can secure compliance with his wishes, i.e., rewards from the social environment, by hurting. [Also, his physical attack on physical obstacles would get them out of his way.] As his knowledge of others' motivations increases, he becomes more and more skilled at utilizing this method of control. The devices he learns are a function of what the parents and others respond to, and the extent or degree to which he develops such a motive is a function of their rewarding responsiveness when he behaves injuriously —i.e., aggressively. *(Sears et al., 1953 p. 179)*.

According to this theory, the more frequently aggressive responses are elicited and rewarded, the stronger the aggressive drive will be. The converse should also be true: That is, aggression should be least when there is little provocation (i.e., reduction of frustration) and when aggressive responses are punished instead of rewarded. But, while it is true that rewarding aggression tends to perpetuate it, punishment may have the same effect. The punishment may arouse further anger (and further frustration because the anger at the punisher cannot be expressed), or the child may have been seeking punishment in order to relieve a feeling of guilt.

In discussing the case for a separate, basic aggressive drive, Waelder describes instances of "essential destructiveness" which are so vast in intensity or duration, that they cannot be explained as reaction to provocation. They seem to serve no purpose and

they seem devoid of any pleasure or sexual excitatory value. Psychotics, epileptics, and severely defective individuals have extraordinary outbursts of rage for no apparent reasons, outbursts which appear to be an organic release of pure aggression. Such extreme cases do not ordinarily come within the purview of learning theorists, and whether this is a valid argument for postulating a separate drive is primarily a theoretical question. It is agreed that the potential for the arousal of aggression, like the potential for anxiety, is innate, and necessary for survival. The developing child learns when to be angry, about what to be angry, and what to do when angry.

Situations Arousing Aggression

There is no sequence of typical frustration situations similar to the danger situations described in our discussion of anxiety. Waelder suggested an outline of the causes of aggression which may be used as a basis for discussing typical frustrations experienced by the young child.

A destructive attitude, action or impulse may be

I. A by-product of an ego activity such as
   (a) the mastery of the outside world, or
   (b) the control of one's own body or mind. Or
II. [It may be] the reaction to
   (a) a threat to self-preservation or, more generally, to purposes usually attributed to the ego; or the reaction to
   (b) the frustration, or threatened frustration, of a libidinal drive. Or
III. It may be a part or aspect of a libidinal urge which in some way implies aggressiveness against the object [person], such as, e.g., incorporation or penetration.* (We have taken the liberty of reversing I and II to present the situations chronologically.)

---

*Waelder, *op. cit.*, p. 139–40.

In the normal course of development, aggression is part of the infant's exploration of the world about him. In the second half of the first year, he hits, bites, scratches, pulls, and kicks as he manipulates things, be they inanimate or human. This manipulation serves many purposes, primarily those of perceptual coordination and manipulative mastery, but the behavior is aggressive in effect whether or not it is aggressive in intent. The infant and toddler are experimenting with their body mechanics as well as with the properties of things. It is great fun to kick, bite, pinch, throw, and spit, for the pure pleasure of doing it. But the child soon learns from his mother whose hair is pulled or breast bitten in nursing, that this behavior hurts her. Indeed, one of the first educational tasks is to teach the child the aggressive significance of such activities and to put them in a different category from kissing, hugging, eating, playing, or running. At this stage most of the aggression is an incidental byproduct of exploratory behavior (I*a* and *b*).

In his second year, the child becomes acutely vulnerable to frustration, and aggression takes on an intentional character. As his behavior becomes more purposeful, he becomes more aware of interference and of its source. There is a painful process of devaluation as he loses his sense of omnipotence. He is blocked by people (parents, primarily) and by physical reality. Negativism and resistiveness are considered characteristic of children from one and a half and two and a half. In her study of anger, F. L. Goodenough found that outbursts of anger reached a sharp peak at 18 months, and then declined markedly until the age of five, after which they reached a plateau (*1931*). R. Stutsman, who standardized the Merrill-Palmer test of intelligence for preschool children, reported that the height of resistance occurred between 24 and 27 months (*1932*). Psychoanalysts have observed that the peak

period of aggressiveness coincides with the anal stage of sexuality. On this level of instinctual development, the wishes to harm or to destroy things or people, and to make sadistic attacks on loved persons, assume equal importance with the anal interests themselves. This preponderance of aggressive tendencies during the anal stage led to the combined term, "the anal-sadistic phase."

The part played by toilet training deserves special mention here. Such training normally given within the first three years of life, is an obvious example of the parents' interference with the child's natural urge to relieve himself as he chooses. Very few children, if any, have an innate wish to be clean; on the contrary, most young children are delighted with their excretions. Feces are highly regarded as an achievement or even a plaything (for smearing). But this attitude is not socially acceptable, and the child must relinquish his pleasure.

Toilet training is more than the substitution of a convenient response for an inconvenient one in order to win mother's approval. There are several aspects of the situation which can be anxiety-provoking, aside from the fear of loss of love. Two of these are well described by Selma Fraiberg:

He regards this b.m. as part of his body. We say that's ridiculous and how could he imagine that a body's waste product was part of the body? But he doesn't know that and we could never explain it to him at this age either. No, the best he can do in explaining this phenomenon with the type of thinking he has at his disposal is this: it is like an appendage to the body, it is part of his body and as part of himself he values this product. And since he produces his b.m.'s on the toilet to please his mother, he comes to regard this act in the same way that an older child regards a gift to a loved person . . . We accept this gift of love with demonstrations of approval—after which we indifferently flush it down the toilet! From the point of view of the child in the second year, this is one of life's great mysteries. When he values an object he wants to keep it and see it . . . The fate of his gift, its disappearance into the cavern of noisy, rushing waters, strikes him as a strange way to accept and dispose of an offering of such value. *The toilet itself adds to the madness and mystery* of this operation, in the eyes of the second-year child . . . The most superficial observation will reveal that it swallows up objects with a mighty roar, causes them to disappear in its secret depths, then rises again thirstily for its next victim which might be—just anyone.*

Toilet training is a frustration situation which is fraught with complicating fears. In successful training, the mother has scored a major victory over the natural impulses of the child. Usually, at the completion of this skirmish, everyone is happy. The mother is pleased for obvious reasons; the child is pleased because (1) he could give his mother this special pleasure; and (2) this takes him nearer to his goal of being grown-up. He has participated in a learning situation which has taught him to postpone one kind of gratification in order to obtain a later, different kind of gratification or reward.

Returning to Waelder's outline of causes of aggression, we see that most of the aggressions of the second and third year have been reactions to those who thwart our ego ambitions (II*a*). In the same period of time, the child is undoubtedly aroused to anger by jealousy. He feels hostile to people or children who compete for his mother's love and attention (II*b*). His hostility may be aroused by a sibling, particularly by a younger child who comes into the family as a stranger, or it may be a milder reaction, perhaps to his father, other relatives, or other children. Children this age have great difficulty in sharing and are insatiable in their demands for attention. Gradually, experience with reality tones down their de-

mands and their aggressive responses are mitigated.

Finally, aggression may be part and parcel of a libidinal urge, or an aspect of it, as in oral biting, oral incorporation, phallic penetration, or vaginal retentiveness (III). Aggression is necessary to lend force to the expression of the child's love life. Without some admixture of aggression, the sex impulses remain unable to reach any of their aims. Anna Freud states the problem as follows:

The fusion of sex with aggression makes it possible for the child to assert his rights to the possession of his love objects, to compete with his rivals, to satisfy his curiosities, to display his body or his abilities,—even to obtain possession of his food and destroy it by eating it. Equally, in normal adult sex life, the carrying out of the sexual act presupposes on the part of the male sufficient aggression to obtain mastery over the sexual partner. Where in abnormal cases, through repression or inhibition of aggression, this admixture from the side of the destructive forces is lacking, sexuality becomes ineffective. In adult genital life this results in impotence.*

Consideration of the sexual act shows the greater need for aggressiveness in males than females, and society expects boys to be more aggressive than girls. Fortunately, one need not rely on social learning alone. Goodenough's study showed that girls consistently had fewer outbursts of anger, and it is doubtful that, in the ages from one to seven, the difference is solely the result of training.

Aggression and Anxiety

It has already been observed that anger and fear are closely related. After a time, the young child usually experiences anger and anxiety simultaneously. The experience of anger exposes him to all the danger situations discussed in the

---

*Quoted from S. Fraiberg, *The Magic Years* (New York: Charles Scribner's Sons, 1959), pp. 93–94. Reprinted by permission.

*Quoted from Anna Freud, "Notes on Aggression," *Bulletin of the Menninger Clinic*, XIII, No. 5 (1949), 147. Reproduced by permission.

section on anxiety. Unfortunately, the very people who bring joy to a child are the source of his greatest frustrations and anger. He becomes caught in an inner conflict between love and hate and suffers from the ambivalence of his feelings. His aggressive hate culminates in death wishes against the very people whose living presence is of the utmost importance for his well-being.

The intense anxiety about separation which usually makes a sudden appearance between one-and-a-half and two-and-a-half illustrates the conflict. The first part of this is signal anxiety, the child's distress as he watches his parents get ready to leave, and he goes to great lengths to stop them. As he works himself up, it is sometimes difficult to tell whether he is only frightened, or angry as well, but often, in the midst of tears and clinging, he screams, "I hate you, Mommy!" His ire is aroused by the pain his mother is about to cause him. But then his own hostility exposes him to a new set of anxieties; with his magic thinking he is deeply afraid that his destructive wishes might actually come true and that his mother might permanently disappear. And even should that not happen, she might be so angry at him for his anger that she would retaliate by not returning.

If a parent attempts to handle this particular problem by spanking or scolding, the punishment seems to the child to justify his apprehensions. His fantasies are further confirmed if he has in the past been threatened with separation for bad behavior, a not uncommon threat because parents find it brings children into line so quickly. Sometimes, when the parent returns, the child treats her with studied neglect, as if the separation had meant nothing whatsoever to him. He is giving her the treatment which he finds most devastating, namely, to be ignored, and in this way expressing his resentment. Sufficiently reassured by her physical presence, he can afford to express the anger he may have repressed during her absence. If the separation was lengthy, e.g., the mother's hospitalization for a new baby, or the child's own hospitalization for some reason, his reactions may be quite intense and lead to a serious estrangement between the bewildered mother and the angry, unhappy child.

Aggression and Anxiety in Relation to the Oedipal Conflict

There is no place where the agony of ambivalence is more keenly felt than in the life situation which Freud called "the Oedipus complex." The Oedipus complex is strongest between the ages of three to five, but one should first consider its origin. For both the boy and the girl, it starts with a strong attachment to the mother. They claim as much of her attention as they possibly can. Hence the demandingness, possessiveness, and jealousy of the child of one to three. Hand-in-hand with this desire for love and attention is a tremendous wish to be grown-up, to be the same as these marvelous beings, the parents. This wish is demonstrated in the child's imitation of and identification with his parents, and in his play and fantasies. The young boy loves nothing better than to act the part of a man. There is no particular joy in being just a little girl or boy. As one four-year-old said sadly, "I have to pretend I am just me."

One of the most interesting grown-up activities which they perceive is that of marriage, and "playing house" is a favorite game. As they become aware of the sex difference, the little girl will be "mommy" and the little boy will be "daddy." This game, or fantasy, is more real and meaningful than any other such game, because it represents the situation with which they have had the most experience. But completely successful identification with the mother or father, would be tantamount to replacing that parent. If mother is replaced by the little girl, or father is replaced by the little boy, the parent ceases to exist. This eventuality, an unhappy one in view of the child's continued love and dependence on this very same person, is one source of the ambivalence inherent in the Oedipus complex.

The discussion that follows focuses mainly on the conflict within the boy rather than the girl. The two run a parallel course, except that the girl must make a shift in love object, from mother to father. She does this as the result of the discovery of the sex difference and the identification with her mother. The development of the little girl's Oedipal phase depends on her acceptance of herself as a girl. Usually, she is compensated for what she does not have (i.e., the penis) by the thought of what she can have (babies). In order to obtain the gift of babies, the little girl turns to the father as the source, which thus ushers in her Oedipal feelings.

Ambivalence pervades the child in the Oedipal stage. The boy actively wishes for the disappearance of his father because he is a rival for the affections of the mother. In his wishes to be grown-up, he yearns to have his mother in the same way as his father has her. He wants everything that daddy has, and to do everything that daddy does. Just what it is that the father does in marriage, he does not know, but from his own physical reactions, regardless chance observation, he may well relate his fantasies to exciting sensations in the genital region, including the experience of erection. He has, however nebulous, some sense of a connection between sexual excitement and marriage. The fact that his Oedipal wishes may be impossible of realization does not diminish the strength of the child's feelings, which has been eloquently described by Brenner:

The most important single fact to bear in mind about the oedipus complex is the strength and force of the feelings which are involved. It is a real love affair. For many people it is the most intense affair of their entire lives, but it is in any case as intense as any which the individual will ever experience [Any] description . . . cannot begin to convey what the reader must keep in mind as he reads it: the intensity of the tempest of passions of love and hate, of yearning and jealousy, of fury and fear that rages within the child. This is what we are talking about when we try to describe the oedipus complex.*

So far we have presented the ideas that the child identifies with the parent of his own sex and that he also wishes to exterminate this parent as a rival. His ambivalence is similar to that felt by the younger child who fears separation. But whereas anxiety about separation is allayed by the mother's return, Oedipal feelings go on for some time, relatively untouched by what happens outside. The situation grows even more complicated as he grows a bit older. The child of three will blithely state his intentions to marry mother and "Daddy can be the grandfather." At this age, he is not bothered by contradictions; he can shift opinions with alacrity and tolerate all sorts of mutually incompatible beliefs and wishes. But the child of four or five is more logical. He recognizes that he can't have his cake and eat it, too. There comes a point in mental development when he knows that his mother can have only one husband and that his father cannot be killed off and yet remain his loving father. The Oedipal wishes go underground; the child becomes silent about his desires, giving the casual observer little hint of what is going on inside.

The aggressive component of the Oedipus complex is the wish to get rid of the rival parent. This engenders anxiety for three related, but slightly different, reasons. The child fears (1) that his wishes will come true and that he will actually lose the parent he simultaneously loves and hates; (2)

---

*Brenner, op. cit., p. 121.

that the rival parent will cease to love him if he detects his child's hostility; and (3) that there will be retaliation.

The retaliation feared may be castration, death, abandonment, and so on. Retaliation is anticipated on the basis of talion law: an eye for an eye, and a tooth for a tooth. The child expects the same thing to be done to him as he would like to do to another, so that the specific form of the expected revenge depends on the form of his angry wishes. And, since so many fantasies and wishes are connected with the genitals, it is more than likely that his angry thoughts are directed at this part of his father and that retaliation is conceived in terms of genital attack and possible permanent injury.

The Oedipus complex and its attendant anxieties demonstrate the role of fantasy in the mental life of the child. The boy's contemplated aggression toward his father is in proportion to his love for the mother. His fear of his father is related to the kind and amount of aggression he feels, not to the father's tolerance or kindness. That the father will not retaliate in any cruel way does not relieve the child's anxiety. He knows how *he* sometimes feels and he suspects that if his father knew about these inside bad feelings, he would retaliate. In the child's mind, the father is kind only because he does not know the unworthiness of his son and, of course, the son won't tell him.

Barring seductive circumstances which keep hope alive, the fire finally burns out. Fraiberg described the process of resolution very simply:

It's a daydream without any possibility of fulfillment, now or ever . . . It ends in renunciation of the impossible wishes and, normally, in the resolution of the conflicts engendered by them. The rivalries subside and the personality reintegrates in the most promising fashion. For we find that the rivalry with the parent of own sex is finally overcome by the strength of the positive ties.°

°Fraiberg, *op. cit.*, p. 204.

The conflict is resolved for the time being, but is destined to reappear in adolescence before its final resolution is achieved by emancipation from the family and attachment to new love objects of the opposite sex. In the interval, the latency period, the child avoids passionate ties with the opposite sex and sticks closely to peers of his own sex. In identifying with the parent of the same sex, the child omits one feature, namely, that parent's interest in the other parent.

Fate of Aggression

The quotation regarding the resolution of the Oedipus complex contains one of the answers as to what happens to aggression: It is overcome by the strength of the positive ties. In psychoanalytic terms, aggression fuses with libido. If the young child was deprived of love, the normal fusion between erotic and destructive urges does not take place, and aggression manifests itself as pure, independent destructiveness. This can be seen in the so-called psychopathic personality of the delinquent on whom control, punishment, admonitions, and so forth have no effect (see Chapter 12).

By social learning, aggression becomes more controlled and inhibited. Hostile acts become hostile words, which in turn become hostile thoughts, first unspoken and then unconscious. The factors which tend to inhibit aggressive behavior favor the development of certain defense mechanisms such as reaction formation, undoing, displacement, and projection, in addition to repression. A mechanism unique to the problem of aggression is turning against the self. The toddler who has learned not to bite his mother may bite himself or bang his head in impotent fury. As he grows older, signs of physical self-aggression become more subtle, for instance, teeth grinding, nail biting, or scratching at scabs. Also, aggression turned inward usually changes from direct physical to indirect mental manifestations, for instance, the unconscious courting of injury, humiliation, or failure. The formation of conscience is very much dependent on aggression directed against the self. If this aggression is not satisfactorily fused with love and admiration for the self, the demands of conscience stand out as cruel and relentless.

As with anxiety, the defenses make overt behavior an unreliable indicator of the amount of aggression that a child feels. A. F. Korner obtained low correlations between real and fantasy aggression *(1949)* and R. R. Sears found that pre-school children severely punished for aggression tend to commit few aggressive acts in school but play very aggressively with dolls *(1951)*. Outward appearances may be deceiving because aggression can be stimulated by anxiety (i.e., identification with the aggressor in self-defense) or love (i.e., an attention-getting mechanism), rather than hatred.

Guilt

Definition

Guilt is a painful affect which stands somewhere between anxiety and aggression. It is aroused by the conscience, or superego. Freud coined the term "superego" *(1923, 1957)*, and related it to the passing of the Oedipus complex. He remarked that before the final internalization of socially acceptable standards we should not speak of a sense of guilt or of conscience; there is only dread of discovery.

The timing of the formation of the superego is an issue of controversy even among orthodox child psychoanalysts. In her paper "On the Development of Mental Functioning" *(1958)*, Melanie Klein placed the beginning of the superego in the second quarter of the first year. Her account of its formation has to do with the projection of the death instinct into the outside

world for the sake of self-preservation. In her view, there exists in the child a full superego of the utmost harshness and cruelty, before the resolution of the Oedipus complex. Anna Freud, however, holds very different views. Klein's assumption of an intricate psychic system elaborated soon after birth and capable of highly sophisticated fantasies is at variance with what we think we know about the infant's mental and emotional capabilities. However, there is no doubt that there are important precursors to the superego which predate the Oedipal period.

Precursors of Conscience Development

For purposes of discussion, the development of a conscience can be divided into two periods: (1) precursors, in the first four years of life; (2) internal conscience, which starts around four and continues throughout life. The conscience begins to develop, as do the intellect and personality, in the first year. The early mother-child relationship has to be sufficiently strong to bear the weight of the inevitable frustrations of the ensuing years. K. Friedlander has written a graphic description of the moral status of the two to three-year-old:

Feelings of shame, disgust or pity seem to be wholly absent; the toddlers are intent only on doing what gives them the greatest pleasure for the moment. And this pleasure is gained by activities which, if present in the adult, would be classified as criminal, insane or perverse . . . They certainly are not socially adapted, for they have no regard for the desires of other people and do not submit of their own free will to demands made upon them. Looked at from another angle, we might say that they do not yet show any signs of conscience . . . It seems really much more astonishing that so many of these little "savages" develop into socially adapted human beings than that some of them do not reach that stage. *(1951, p. 13)*.

In the first period, the child learns to comply with his parents' wishes.

Gradually he learns to obey their prohibitions automatically. He does not need constant reminding, and he establishes good habits of cleanliness, obedience, avoidance of aggression, and so on. In this phase, however, the child treats the moral demands which are made upon him as a part of his environment. If mother is present, and if the child wants to please her, he will refrain from transgression. If he is alone, or if he is angry at mother, he will either deliberately displease her or do as he wishes, restrained only by fear of punishment (as opposed to fear of loss of love). Moral development, in this phase, consists of simple learning situations in which socially acceptable behavior is rewarded by love and approval. The term "sphincter morality" was coined by Ferenczi to describe compliance in the training situations of early childhood (1926). The first stage of conscience development differs from the second stage in four ways:

1. The child's goodness is motivated by the reward of approval, or fear of punishment, rather than by the pain of guilt feelings.
2. The child's goodness is dependent upon an external person.
3. The good behavior is defined in terms of concrete, specific behavior rather than general ethical principles.
4. The goodness is in terms of prohibitions —activities which one must not do rather than activities which one should do.

If this early situation persisted, it would be necessary to have vigilant authorities keeping an eagle eye on the activities of all. Fortunately, most mature individuals do not require such vigilance. One of society's major goals is to produce adults capable of self-control and ethical behavior without external pressure and every serious type of education tries to induce in the child the desire to adapt to social standards, not because he is continually urged to do so but because he has made these standards his own.

Internalization of Conscience

Between the ages of four and six, morality begins to be an inner concern. The child begins to feel that wrongdoing must be punished, repented, and undone, and he will do this by himself if he is not punished by someone else. W. Allinsmith has described the superego in terms of learning theory:

Superego refers to certain learned needs in a person that provide internal reward and punishment regardless of whether the person's actions also provoke negative or positive reactions from other people . . . In most actual life situations, there is usually a good possibility that an antisocial action will have environmental as well as internal repercussions. As a result we usually cannot tell from observation of a man's behavior how much his inhibitions are motivated by fear or wish for praise and how much by inner moral forces. Similarly, we cannot tell to what extent his disturbance following a misdeed is caused by fear rather than guilt feelings. For the superego, we need evidence of conformity to a standard regardless of real pressures, or of guilt following a violation regardless of reality pressures. (1957, p. 469.)

To some extent, also, internalization is a function of mental development. The child develops concepts of time, of future gratifications, or consequences, of right and wrong, of values and ideals, and he becomes increasingly aware of the effects of his actions. His perception of the feelings of others becomes more acute. He learns that his interests are best served by a spirit of cooperation and the application of the golden rule: "Do unto others as you would be done by." The scope of his imagination widens, so he can have a much broader concept of consideration for others than that based on the specific do's and don't's offered by his parents.

However, the changes in intellectual powers do not seem sufficient to explain the amazing strength of the superego to control behavior. Not only bad actions, but even bad thoughts and wishes are prohibited by this internal governor. The energy required to counter the natural pleasure-seeking impulses of the child is, according to psychoanalytic theory, derived in part from the resolution of the Oedipus complex, and in the following sequence:

1. The child renounces the incestuous and aggressive wishes which constitute the Oedipus complex because of their futility and anxiety associated with them.
2. The greatest anxiety is aroused because of the expected retaliatory aggression of the rival parent.
3. In order to protect himself against retaliation, the child assumes the same attitude toward his Oedipal wishes as he believes his parents would, if they but knew. He scolds himself for such bad thoughts.
4. The child goes further than identifying with the parents' imagined attitudes towards the Oedipal wishes only. The boy incorporates the whole of the conscience structure of his father; the girl, of her mother.

The third step in this sequence involves identification with the aggressor, an aggressor half-imagined and half-real. The aggression is no longer outwardly directed, but directed against the self in the form of guilt. This is the source of energy which the superego has at its disposal for internal government. In Brenner's theoretical exposition, he states:

. . . we may say that it is the intensity of the child's own hostile impulses toward his parents during the oedipal phase that is the principal factor in determining the severity of the superego, rather than the degree of the parents' hostility or severity toward the child . . . Thus the aggressive energy at the disposal of the superego derives from the aggressive energy of the oedipal object cathexes and the two are at least proportional, if not equal in amount.*

---

*Brenner, op. cit. pp. 132–33.

This concept is most useful when we are trying to explain abnormalities in superego functioning, for instance, in psychotic depressions or obsessive-compulsive neuroses. In such illnesses, the superego is so relentless that the patient cannot escape his feeling of guilt, no matter how exemplary his behavior or how unjustified is his self-reproach. These patients have unconscious murderous wishes which are anathema to their self-regard. They have a psychological right to feel guilty, but the real reason is unknown and another reason is manufactured as a rationalization. For the understanding of normal personality, simpler explanations of conscience development appear to suffice.

However, children with excessive superego development usually show a corresponding inhibition of aggression. Parents may unwittingly create this situation by treating even the child's earliest aggressive acts as if they were crimes. Such over-reaction makes Oedipal aggression totally intolerable to the child. Or they may fail totally to recognize any aggression in the child. Such denial is ordinarily prompted by the parents' own problems with regard to aggression, and the child correctly detects their anxiety. But if aggression is totally blocked, there is no place for it to go except inward.

The strength or weakness of a child's conscience corresponds closely to that of his parents. This is partly the direct result of the child's inward acceptance of the directives of his parents, but the resemblance is not solely a reflection of the parents' deliberate educational efforts. One might conclude, about a child who is perfectionistic and self-critical, that his parents have insisted on excellence. And this might be so, but not necessarily. It might be that one of the parents is perfectionistic about himself and that the child has observed this and has incorporated into his own ego the overstrict superego of that parent (step four in the derivation sequence). He observes his parents in a very perceptive way—a perfectionist parent may be quite lenient with his child, but the child acquires the perfectionism from observation. An antisocial parent may be strict, but the child may acquire the parent's antisocial behavior. This is discussed later, in connection with juvenile delinquency. Children internalize the practices, rather than the preachments, of their parents.

Internalization continues throughout life. Although the resolution of the Oedipus complex is thought to give the internal forces of conscience tremendous new strength, the superego neither begins nor ends here. New figures of authority influence the child's system of values. A kind of reexamination and integration of the superego takes place in adolescence; childish standards are reevaluated, and some are discarded. The content of the superego remains susceptible to external influence.

In contrast to anxiety and aggression, the capacity to feel the affect of guilt is *not* innate. By the conclusion of the Oedipal period (i.e., six or seven) the child has acquired the capability of feeling guilt. The standards he sets for himself, and the particular causes for guilt, will change as he grows older.

Manifestations of Guilt

The conventional manifestation of guilt is remorse. The person hates himself, at least temporarily, perhaps for a specific reason or, if he is a depressive, for no known reason.

Guilt can be expressed in the form of proneness to accident or seeking of punishment. The child misbehaves with flagrant disregard of consequences. He takes no precautions against detection or leaves obvious clues. A 12-year-old who was in constant difficulty at home and in school finally demonstrated his need for help in the following way: The father, because his son so often misplaced borrowed tools, purchased a set for the boy and locked up his own. One day the father found his toolbox open and a tool missing and, although the son disclaimed any responsibility, the key was lying on his bureau. The boy had gone to all the trouble of locating the key, taking a tool identical to his own, leaving the box open, and laying the key down in plain sight so that apprehension would be certain. Then he showed no remorse. A careful review of his difficulties showed that he had repeated this pattern over and over; he was an intelligent boy, parading his badness so that he was perpetually being punished.

In depressed adult patients, one sees guilt as aggression directed against the self, but depressions are rare in children. They usually express their inwardly directed aggression in unwarranted feelings of inferiority: "No one likes me," "I am stupid," or "I can't do anything right." This may be an instance of "reflected appraisal," to use Sullivan's term, i.e., the child views himself according to someone else's opinion of him. But it is also possible that his low self-esteem is not shared by others, that he has concocted it out of a sense of badness. The reason for the badness may be quite unknown to the child, and understandable only in terms of unconscious wishes. To the eye of the conscience, however, there is no distinction between a wish and a deed; the thinker is as culpable as the doer.

Finally, guilt may masquerade as an irrational fear. Disapproval by the superego was given as the fourth and final danger situation to which the ego reacts with anxiety, but a child may experience this as a morbid fear of something outside, rather than as a fear of guilt feelings. A child who feels chronically bad considers himself deserving of punishment, and he anticipates it. He deserves to be sick, hurt, or even killed by the menaces of his environment. This is why he fears he would be the unlucky one who would be attacked by the escaped circus lion, or killed by the tornado, and so on.

Concept of "immanent justice."

Jean Piaget described a type of logic which is of relevance in this context. During the early years, the child believes in punishments which emanate from things themselves, "immanent justice." Somehow, events conspire so that one gets what one deserves. One hundred sixty-seven children, 6 through 12, were asked the following question.

Once there were two children who were stealing apples in an orchard. Suddenly a policeman comes along and the two children run away. One of them is caught. The other one, going home by a roundabout way, crosses a river on a rotten bridge and falls into the water. Now what do you think? If he had not stolen the apples and had crossed the river on that rotten bridge all the same, would he also have fallen into the water? *(Piaget, 1932, pp. 250–51.)*

Some 86 per cent of the six-year-olds maintained that if the child had not stolen, he would not have fallen. In contrast, 66 per cent of those over 11 felt there was no connection between the accident and the theft. The younger the child, the stronger his belief that in some unknown way the physical universe functions like a policeman. "In short, there is life and purpose in everything. Why then should not things be the accomplices of grown-ups in making sure that a punishment is inflicted where the parents' vigilance may have been evaded?" *(Piaget, 1932, p. 255).* This conviction is never entirely dissipated. Adults also often interpret their misfortunes as justified or unjustified punishments.

Functions of the Superego

In *The Ego and the Id (1923, 1957),* Freud listed as the following functions of the superego: self-judgment; prohibi-

tions and injunctions; a sense of guilt; and social feelings. These functions fall into two groups: those which prevent the expression of forbidden drives; and those which define the ideals and values of man. Discussions of guilt usually focus on the aggressive potentiality of the superego for self-criticism, but there is also a loving side of the superego. The conscience can be admiring, and raise one's self-esteem. When it functions punitively, the superego transforms aggression into self-hate; when it functions benignly, the superego transforms love for others into that aspect of self-love or narcissism which is felt as pride and security. Most children, most of the time, are on good terms with themselves; their good behavior is constantly reinforced by self-satisfaction. The two aspects of conscience are well described in Freud's summing up in the last chapter of his last book:

The torments caused by the reproaches of conscience correspond precisely to a child's dread of losing his parents' love, a dread which has been replaced in him by the moral agency. On the other hand, if the ego has successfully resisted a temptation to do something that would be objectionable to the superego, it feels its self respect raised and its pride increased, as though it had made some precious acquisition. In this way the superego continues to act the role of an external world although it has become part of the internal world. During the whole of a man's later life it represents the influence of his childhood, of the care and education given to him by his parents, of his dependence on them—of the childhood which is greatly prolonged in human beings by a common family life. And in all of this what is operating is not only the personal qualities of these parents but also everything that produced a determining effect upon themselves, the tastes and standards of the social class in which they spring.[*]

---

[*]Quoted from Freud, S. *An Outline of Psychoanalysis* (1938). New York: Copyright 1949 by W. W. Norton & Company, Inc., pp. 122–23. Reprinted by permission.

Mechanisms of Defense

Definition

In the preceding sections, we have described many conflicts which are capable of arousing anxiety, aggression, and guilt. Such conflicts are originally external; the child's wishes are opposed by his parents or by reality. As he grows older he takes the wishes of his parents for his own, and the potentiality for internal conflict arises. Growing up is gratifying, but it is also painful. In order to avoid conflict and the attendant anxiety, the child learns to control his behavior by subordinating his desires to the demands of others. More and more this process becomes automatic. The child's basic drives are nipped in the bud, so to speak, so that he is unaware of making a deliberate choice between his way and the way of the world.

Much of the child's acquired goodness can be interpreted in terms of secondary drives or learned motives. In the field of child psychopathology, however, it is common and in the author's opinion, helpful, to consider behavior in terms of anxiety and the mechanisms used to ward it off. Particularly in childhood neurosis, it is important to ask two questions: "Of what is this child afraid?" and "When he is afraid, what does he do?"

The term *defense* was first used by Freud in 1894 to describe the ego's struggle against painful or unendurable ideas or affects. For a long time, he concentrated on the part played by repression. In *Inhibitions, Symptoms, and Anxiety (1926, 1959)*, he remarked on the concept of defense and suggested that repression was only one example of a defense mechanism, but it was only with Anna Freud's *The Ego and Mechanisms of Defense (1946)* that these mechanisms achieved the importance they deserve in both theory and ther-

apy. This is the real beginning of what is loosely called "ego psychology." Psychoanalysts no longer concentrated solely on making "the unconscious conscious" to the patient. Equal concern was given to discovering and interpreting the various maneuvers which the patient used to avoid the feeling of anxiety, no matter what its specific source.

All sorts of defensive operations are possible, but some, because of their frequent appearance, have been separately identified. We have already mentioned some in passing. What follows is a glossary of these technical terms which come up over and over again, both in this text and in the clinical literature pertaining to childhood disturbances.

Introjection and Identification

These two mechanisms belong together because they are operative from a very early age and continue, to some extent, throughout life. Both have to do with taking into the self something from the environment. Both are basic ingredients of the learning process and an essential part of normal development.

Introjection (which is roughly synonymous with incorporation) is the psychological analog of a physiological process, i.e., eating. This analogy is attested to by vestiges which remain in the symbolic meanings attached to specific foods in various dietary and religious observances. One accepts sacramental food or drink in order to achieve a spiritual union, for example. Food advertisements are often based on the principle of introjection, as for example, when spinach magically restores Popeye's strength. Swallowing represents a positive interest in an external object and is a primitive way of relating to it. However, swallowing has the secondary consequence of destroying the object. This dilemma was clearly expressed in an argument between two three-year-olds as to who had the greater liking for an ice-cream cone, the one who ate it up quickly or the one who saved it and tried to make it last. Ordinarily, the two-sided nature of eating presents no conflicts, but the study of feeding difficulties as we shall see, reveals that fantasies can be built up around particular foods and around the processes of biting, swallowing and digesting.

In a theoretical sense, one might say that perception is a kind of introjection, a taking in of the outside world and an absorption of it in the form of memories. *Imitation* is somewhere midway between introjection and identification: the behavior of someone else must first be taken in as a perception before it can be imitated.

Identification is a more general process, partly based on deferred imitation. Identification is part and parcel of normal development, and it brings pleasure and security to the child as he feels himself closer to the grownups to whom he is so attached. But it is pathological when identification goes so far that his own identity is lost, when the child's personality melts into that of the mother. Such total fusion renders the child helpless, totally dependent, unable to tolerate separation from his other half. He does not know what he thinks and feels, what he can and cannot do, except as it is reflected by his mother. Fear of loss of the other person is the particular kind of danger situation which would ordinarily lead to pathological identification.

Denial and Repression

Denial and repression are alike in that they both serve to make something unconscious. They are both basic mechanisms which underlie more involved mechanisms of defense.

Denial is perhaps the more primitive of the two. It is related to faith in the magical power of thoughts and words. The child acts as if he can alter reality by dint of his wishes; that which he does not want to see or acknowledge ceases to exist. This is normal in the young child (see page 29) but, if it's not outgrown it can become a serious handicap. And not only external events, but also internal feelings, may be denied. For instance, an eight-year-old girl in obvious emotional difficulty was talking with her mother, sobbing all the while, and saying, "I am not unhappy." At no time was this obviously unhappy girl able to admit her feelings, despite encouragement to do so; she denied her affect as completely as the younger child quoted in Chapter 2 denied the rain.

Repression, a derivative of denial, is more complex. Assume that our sobbing eight-year-old might be able to admit her sadness (i.e., no denial) but be unable, 15 minutes later, to recall either her tears or her admission (i.e., repression). Repressing is making unconscious an unwanted feeling, memory, or fantasy. A repressed memory is a forgotten one. But it can return when the guard is down, as in illness, fatigue, intoxication, and sleep.

A rather special mechanism, which is halfway between denial and repression, was termed "negation" by Freud. Here the person makes a special point of saying that something is not so. A child who is consistently losing in a game may suddenly remark to his opponent, "Don't think I am angry that you are winning all the time." He feels himself in danger of expressing his anger (and perhaps losing a friend), so he throws in a sop in advance of the actual danger. Negation is a kind of compromise between repression and denial; in our example, the child brings up the possibility of feeling anger (a relief of repression) but denies the affect in advance. This does not mean that all children mean the opposite of what they say, but it does require empathy and intuition to detect their true meaning. One has to think, "If I were in his place, how would I feel?" and be ready to suspect gratuitous statements which express the contrary of what one would expect.

Projection and Displacement

These are both mechanisms which alter the source of the danger. The affect is acknowledged, but attributed to someone else (i.e., projection) or to some other cause (i.e., displacement). In *projection,* the child says "It is not I who am angry; it is the teacher," or, "It is not I who don't like the other children; they don't like me." However, if the other people are viewed as hostile (by projection), then the child's angry feelings are justified and become self-perpetuating. Projection is derived from primitive thought processes previously described as egocentrism. The very young child does not distinguish between his thoughts and the thoughts of others. In projection, he rids himself of anxiety-provoking affects by giving them to someone else: "Let him worry, not me." This may be carried so far as to distort the person's perception of reality. Paranoid patients interpret ordinary events in terms of themselves, ascribing all kinds of malicious purpose to the most innocent circumstances.

A certain measure of projection is usually involved in a special kind of identification, "identification with the aggressor," first described by Anna Freud. "By impersonating the aggressor, assuming his attributes or imitating his aggression, the child transforms himself from the person threatened into the person who makes the threat" *(1950, p. 121).* The child may make this transformation as a prophylactic measure, on the basis that the best defense is a good offense. But sometimes the aggressiveness of others is more assumed than real. Still the child expects attack; he has, by projection, attributed his own hostile intention to the other person. The operation of these mental processes was described in connection with the Oedipal conflict. Identification with the aggressor is an extremely important mechanism for the clinician to recognize. Sometimes, the most effective way of dealing with an aggressive child is by repeated assurance: "You may be angry with me, but I am not angry with you. I will not fight you or hurt you." This puts the feeling back where it belongs and eliminates the child's need for counterattack.

In *displacement,* the child feels the affect about the wrong thing. One idea or image may be substituted for another which is associated with it, or one source of anxiety may be substituted for another. For instance, a child who is afraid of his mother's disapproval may be unaware of this fear, that is, he may have repressed it, and he may have replaced it with a morbid fear of the teacher's disapproval. Projection and displacement go hand-in-hand in the formation of phobias. Displacement is the same kind of behavior as that described by the learning term of "generalization": "the tendency to make the response learned to one stimulus to another similar stimulus." However, displacement is a defensive substitution. By simple generalization, the child might be angry at his mother and every other woman as well; if displacement has occurred, he is angry at the teacher *instead* of his mother.

Reaction Formation, Undoing, and Isolation

These are put together because they so often occur in conjunction with one another, particularly in obsessional-compulsive neurotics. They are directed against internal feelings which are, first, repressed. Then an extra defense is constructed in order to guard against the return of the repressed wish.

Reaction formation is frequently observed during toilet training. As the child's pleasure in dirt is repressed, he sometimes takes a further step and is repelled by dirt. He becomes more offended by messiness than his parents;

he outdoes them in his fastidiousness, so that he won't be tempted back to the old dirty ways. This same mechanism may be invoked against other unwelcome impulses. An impulse to hurt others may be warded off by excessive sympathy and gentleness, to the point that a child cannot bear to have a housefly swatted down.

In reaction formation, then, an attitude is taken that counters the original, feared impulse. In *undoing*, one more defensive step is taken. Something positive is done which, actually or by magic, is the opposite of something which was done before. The compulsive patient has to perform some particular act in order to avoid a feeling of anxiety. To the patient's knowledge, the anxiety has no cause, but it is relieved by the act. The child who has repressed his delight in messing and who has set up a reaction formation of great cleanliness may find that this is not enough. He may still feel unconsciously dirty and get relief only by constantly washing his hands. An aggressive person may find that excessive sympathy for others is not enough. He may have to go to unreasonable lengths to perform kind acts, acts perhaps undesirable to the recipient, in order to assure himself of his kindliness.

Isolation is a rather specialized mechanism of defense, and hard to detect. It may be manifested as compartmentalized thinking. The person fails to see obvious connections; he keeps things apart, separated. He may separate the appropriate feeling from the actual event. Such a child may recall an emotional experience in detail, but feel no emotion about it. He talks about it as if it had happened to someone else.

Other children try to solve conflicts by isolating certain spheres of their lives from one another. They may think of themselves as two people. Perhaps the good one goes to school and the bad one stays at home, or vice versa. Children may worry that they have bad thoughts or think bad words, and they may disown the part of them that does such things. Sometimes they even have a name for this other self, for which they feel no responsibility. The phenomenon of isolation is related to anxieties about touching. Things that are to be kept apart must not touch each other and children who are compulsive neurotics have complicated rituals involving touching or not touching.

Regression and Fixation

These mechanisms are alike in that they are more pervasive and have the effect of retarding development. In *fixation*, a child does not move ahead because something about the forward step makes him anxious. In *regression*, the child moves backward; he gives up something which has proven painful and regresses to an earlier stage. Whenever a person is frustrated, he tends to long for "the good old days," the easier times before trouble set in. Both of these reactions are considered again in the section dealing with immaturity.

Defense Mechanisms of Adolescence

Adolescence is a period of extra psychological stress and, as a consequence, a time requiring the mobilization of defenses. An adolescent may use any one or all of the mechanisms already mentioned but, in addition, there are some rather special means which are evoked to cope with the increased drives. Anna Freud described two characteristic mechanisms of the adolescent: asceticism and intellectuality *(1946)*. In *asceticism*, the adolescent goes further than repressing only sexual wishes; he mistrusts enjoyment in general and subjects himself to all kinds of stringent hardships. The renunciation is extended to all kinds of things which are harmless and even good for him.

Intellectualization is another defense against adolescent drives. The youngster tries to make everything impersonal, abstract, theoretical and unemotional. Emotions as such are scorned;

he tries to rule his life by reason alone. This defense against affects may persist, but it rarely appears prior to adolescence.

Summary

All the defense mechanisms discussed above have their good sides and are a necessary part of personality development. They become pathological only when they are overworked, and then they may produce any combination of the following bad effects: (1) they may seriously restrict the functions of the ego and the freedom of the child; (2) they may impede further development; (3) they may alienate the child from other people; (4) they may distort his view of reality.

The whole field of psychopathology, including the formation of symptoms, is greatly illuminated by an understanding of the value of defenses in warding off anxiety. Despite their possible long-range disadvantages, defenses and symptoms immediately reduce anxiety. Because of this, they tend to persist and become more and more ingrained until they become second nature. Any effort to modify behavior must take into account the usefulness, to the patient, of the pathological development. And this brings us around full circle, back to the problem of anxiety with which this chapter began.

References for Chapter 3

Allinsmith, W., "Conscience and Conflict: The Moral Force in Personality" *Child Development,* XXVIII (1957), 469–76.

Angelino, H., J. Dollins, and E. V. Mech, "Trends in the Fears and Worries of School Children as Related to Socio-economic Status and Age," *Journal of Genetic Psychology,* LXXXIX (1956), 263–76.

Brenner, C., *An Elementary Textbook of Psychoanalysis.* New York: International Universities Press, Inc., 1955.

Cannon, W. B., *The Wisdom of the Body.* New York: W. W. Norton & Company, Inc., 1932.

Dollard, J. *et al., Frustration and Aggression.* New Haven, Conn.: Yale University Press, 1939.

Ferenczi, S., *Psychoanalysis of Sexual Habits: Further Contributions to the Theory and Technique of Psychoanalysis.* Trans. Jane I. Suttie. London: The Hogarth Press, Ltd., 1926.

Fraiberg, S., *The Magic Years.* New York: Charles Scribner's Sons, 1959.

Freud, Anna, "Aggression in Relation to Emotional Development, Normal and Pathological," in *The Psychoanalytic Study of the Child,* Vols. III, IV. New York: International Universities Press, Inc., 1949.

———, "Notes on Aggression," *Bulletin of the Menninger Clinic,* XIII (1949), 143–51.

———, *The Ego and the Mechanisms of Defense* (1946). Trans. Cecil Baines. New York: International Universities Press, Inc., 1950.

Freud, Sigmund, *An Outline of Psychoanalysis* (1938), trans. James Strachey. New York: W. W. Norton & Company, Inc., 1949.

———, *Beyond the Pleasure Principle* (1920), Standard Edition, Vol. XVIII, ed. and trans. by James Strachey. London: The Hogarth Press, Ltd., 1955.

———, *Civilization and its Discontents* (1930), Standard Edition, Vol. XXI, ed. and trans. by James Strachey. London: The Hogarth Press, Ltd., 1961.

———, *Inhibitions, Symptoms, and Anxiety* (1926), Standard Edition, Vol. XX, ed. and trans. by James Strachey. London: The Hogarth Press, Ltd., 1959.

———, "On the Grounds for Detaching a Particular Syndrome from Neurasthenia under the Description of 'Anxiety Neurosis' " (1895), Standard Edition, Vol. III, ed. and trans. by James Strachey. London: The Hogarth Press, Ltd., 1962.

———, *The Ego and the Id* (1923), Standard Edition, Vol. XIX, ed. and trans. by James Strachey. London: The Hogarth Press, Ltd., 1957.

———, *The Neuropsychoses of Defense* (1894), Standard Edition, Vol. III, ed. and trans. by James Strachey. London: The Hogarth Press, Ltd., 1962.

———, *Three Essays on the Theory of Sexuality* (1905), Standard Edition, Vol. VII, ed. and trans. by James Strachey. London: The Hogarth Press, Ltd., 1953.

Friedlander, K., *The Psychoanalytic Approach to Juvenile Delinquency.* New York: The International Universities Press, Inc., 1951.

Goodenough, F. L., "Anger in Young Children," *Institute of Child Welfare Monographs*, No. 9. Minneapolis: The University of Minnesota Press, 1931.

Horney, Karen, *New Ways in Psychoanalysis.* New York: W. W. Norton & Company, Inc., 1939.

Jersild, A. T., *Child Psychology*, 5th ed. Englewood Cliffs, N. J.: Prentice-Hall, Inc., 1960.

———, and F. B. Holmes, "Children's Fears," *Child Development Monographs*, No. 20. New York: Bureau of Publications, Teachers College, Columbia University, 1935.

Klein, M., "On the Development of Mental Functioning," *International Journal of Psychoanalysis*, XXXIX (1958), 84–90.

Korner, A. F., *Some Aspects of Hostility in Young Children.* New York: Grune & Stratton, Inc., 1949.

Miller, N. E., "Learnable Drives and Rewards," in *Handbook of Experimental Psychology*, ed. S. S. Stevens. New York: John Wiley & Sons, Inc., 1951.

———, "Studies of Fear as an Acquirable Drive: I. Fear as Motivation and Fear-Reduction as Reinforcement in the Learning of New Responses," *Journal of Experimental Psychology*, XXXVIII (1948), 89–101.

Mussen, P. H., J. H. Conger, and J. Kagan, *Child Development and Personality*, 2nd ed. New York: Harper & Row, Publishers, 1963.

Piaget, Jean, *The Moral Judgment of the Child*, trans. Marjorie Gabain. London: Kegan Paul, Trench, Trubner & Co., Ltd., 1932.

Sears, R. R., "A Theoretical Framework for Personality and Social Behavior," *American Psychologist*, VI (1951), 476–83.

———, *et al.*, "Some Childrearing Antecedents of Aggression and Dependency in Young Children," *Genetic Psychology Monographs*, No. 47 (1953), 135–234.

Stutsman, R., *The Mental Measurement of Preschool Children with a Guide for Administration of the Merrill-Palmer Scale.* New York: Harcourt, Brace & World, Inc., 1932.

Sullivan, H. S., *Conceptions of Modern Psychiatry.* Washington, D.C.: William Alanson White Psychiatric Foundation, 1947.

Waelder, R., *Basic Theory of Psychoanalysis.* New York: International Universities Press, Inc., 1960.

———, "The Psychoanalytic Theory of Play," *Psychoanalytic Quarterly*, II (1933), 208–24.

4

REFERRAL AND DIAGNOSTIC PROCEDURES

Concept of Normality

The question: "What is normal?" plagues researchers as much as it plagues the parents and teachers who are seeking a standard by which to judge the behavior which they observe daily. The mental hygiene movement has emphasized the value of early detection and treatment of emotional disorders but, while this imposes a feeling of responsibility on those who care for young children, there is still a natural reluctance to seek professional aid unless there is a real problem. Parents, pediatricians, and teachers are on the firing line, so to speak; the decision about referral for special help is in their hands. The clinician ensconced in a clinic or agency is in a much more comfortable position; he can assume that the child who gets to his office probably needs help. Someone else has taken the first difficult step of identification, and he can proceed from this point.

Prevalence of Emotional Disorders in Childhood

Statistics about the number of children with personality disorders have little meaning, because they depend so much on the researcher's criteria for adjustment and on the information gathered. A perfectionist might include all children who have persistent, unreasonable worries or fears, and obtain a figure close to 50 per cent of all children (*Jersild, 1960, p. 454*). Another worker might include only those children who are so atypical that they are immediately conspicuous in any group, and obtain a figure of perhaps 1 to 2 per cent. A frequently quoted estimate is that 10 per cent of all children have emotional problems. In part, this is a compromise between the two previous figures; in part, it is calculated retrospectively from the prevalence of mental disorders in adult life. As of 1953, H. Goldhamer and A. Marshall estimated that one person in every ten who live to be 75 years old will be hospitalized for mental illness. It is likely that some acquire their mental illness late in life without precursors in childhood; but it is also true that many of the mentally ill are never hospitalized and never counted. In the absence of better data, it is assumed that these inaccuracies cancel each other, and that some 10 per cent of children have emotional problems sufficiently severe to disable them in adult life. Admittedly, this is a very rough way of figuring, but it is not likely to be improved on as long as we use such general terms of "mental illness."

Statistical Norms for Defining Normality

One of the most common criteria of normality is the statistical norm: Normality is that which the largest group of the population has or does. This approach may be effective in classifying intelligence, but several problems are created when it is extended to other personality variables.

One major difficulty is the lack of an evaluative measure which will separate desirable deviations from undesirable ones. "The criteria for mental health must be such that they do not automatically exclude everything but the average" *(Jahoda, 1955, p. 302)*. In the field of mental health, generally, there is an attempt to evaluate behavior in terms of its adaptivity to society. Adjustment implies a workable arrangement between personal needs and social conditions. But this is a sufficient criterion only if one accepts the existing social order as the best possible one. One does not like to say that simply being the same as one's fellow is mental health, but there is as yet no simple standard by which to judge whether deviations are good or bad.

A statistical approach entails the use of age norms, because one of the criteria of abnormality of child behavior is that it has persisted beyond the usual age. A ten-year-old behaving like a normal two-year-old would soil, wet, display cruelty, have little ability to tolerate frustration, display outbursts of temper, speak little and indistinctly, and think illogically. This is undeniably abnormal at ten, but not at two. So, before considering disorders in development, it is imperative to know what normal development is. One must know children, know how they look, how they talk, what their abilities and limitations are at different ages, what their typical reactions are, and so on. There is no abnormal behavior which cannot be found in normal individuals at certain ages and under certain conditions.

Behavior becomes abnormal when it is too easily aroused or is inappropriate to the individual's age and situation.

The statistical approach has been used to prove the normality of isolated bits of behavior such as nightmares, nail biting, and thumb sucking, on the basis of their frequency in the population. In Great Britain, C. W. Valentine wrote *The Normal Child and Some of His Abnormalities* with the avowed purpose: "To stress individual differences as normal and to show that many things thought by some (psychiatrists especially) to be signs of serious abnormality are not so" *(1956, Preface, p. xii)*. He cites J. E. Cummings' survey of 239 children, aged two to seven, in which practically every child had 2 or more of some 18 symptoms, such as daydreaming, laziness, and restlessness, *(1944)*. "Paradoxically, then, it would seem quite normal in the statistical sense for a child to be apparently maladjusted and, as some would say (in another sense), 'abnormal' " *(Valentine, 1956, p. 33)*.

In this country, L. Kanner has written in a similar vein on "Everyday Problems of the Everyday Child." He is concerned that "in the clinic statistics [of child psychiatry facilities] . . . symptoms figuring among the 'traits' found in the histories of 'problem children' are apt to be given too prominent a place, far out of proportion to their role as everyday problems or near-problems of the everyday child" *(1961, p. 49)*. He quotes a survey, by R. Lapouse and M. A. Monk, of the behavior of children aged 6 to 12. The information was obtained by interviewing 482 mothers of 733 children. Their general conclusions were as follows:

"This preliminary study, designed as a testing device for a larger project, has presented two significant findings. The first is that for a representative sample of children, mothers report a high percentage of behavior characteristics commonly thought of as pathological. The second is that mothers' reports (as checked by interviews with the children themselves) tend to err in the direction of under-enumeration, suggesting that the prevalence of the reported behavior may be even higher than the data disclosed. This raises for serious consideration the question whether these characteristics are truly indicative of psychiatric disorder or whether they occur as transient developmental phenomena in essentially normal children."*

In another paper Kanner uses a second line of argument to demonstrate the normality of behavior symptoms in childhood; namely, that normal adults report a history of such behavior. He quotes "one of the country's leading pediatricians," who asked if he could be considered normal despite a history of enuresis until the age of 13. Despite this childhood symptom, "he grew up to be a sane, superbly adjusted, emotionally stable, highly respected and well-liked member of society" *(1960, p. 17)*. The inference seems to be that the enuresis was of no significance. Should we be concerned only with children obviously destined to be failures and misfits?

One aspect has been entirely ignored, namely, how the person feels. Perhaps the doctor of whom Kanner writes was an embarrassed and ashamed child. Possibly he never got over a gnawing feeling of difference and inferiority; perhaps he drove himself mercilessly to achieve perfection. Possibly his love life was inhibited and unsatisfactory, something he would hardly report in a casual conversation. These are only conjectures, but they are not at all unreasonable. In evaluating mental health, either of children or adults, it is not satisfactory to use only external criteria. Feelings, which are admittedly more difficult to evaluate, are nonetheless important.

Kanner and Valentine seem to make the unwritten assumption that there are two kinds of children, normal and

*From Leo Kanner, *Child Psychiatry*, 3rd Ed., 1957, p. 49. Courtesy of Charles C Thomas, Publisher, Springfield, Illinois.

abnormal. They argue that these many children cannot be called abnormal simply because of some bit of behavior. But problem behavior is not explained by saying that "a lot of children do it." Children bite their nails, wet their beds, and so on for a reason, even though it may be a transitory one. When the behavior persists, the child has a feeling about it, and his feeling may be more disturbing than the symptoms themselves.

Attention should not be restricted solely to children who seem destined for a mental institution. Perhaps the mental health propaganda has overemphasized this danger. Perhaps any child labelled "emotionally disturbed" is viewed as a candidate for this fate. If so, it is an unfortunate consequence of a laudable cause. Does the medical profession ignore the usual childhood diseases because all children have them and they ordinarily run their course without permanent aftereffects? Physicians do pay attention to these common physical disorders. First, because the child is temporarily very uncomfortable; second, in some instances, there may be serious aftereffects; and third, although rarely, these familiar symptoms may be signs of a more serious condition. No one attempts to divide children into two categories: the physically healthy and the physically unhealthy. Children's mental or emotional problems, however common, need to be taken as seriously as their physical illnesses.

Indications for Referral

The analogy given above is not a perfect one. Most Americans have routine access to medical care, but very few have access to psychiatric or psychological care. It is impractical even to expect that the day will come when parents or teachers can call on a child care expert to report some behavior in the way they might report the sniffles. Therefore, it is necessary to identify those children in need of specialized help. The following criteria are suggested as guidelines for consideration of referral.

1. *Age discrepancy* has already been mentioned. There are ages by which most children have outgrown particular habits and behavior.

2. *Frequency of occurrence of the symptom* must be considered. No one would become exercised should a child occasionally wet his bed, even after the age of five or six. Under special emotional or physical stress, any child will regress to previous patterns of behavior, and isolated regressions are not pathological as long as the child can recover quickly. One should be concerned when the symptomatic behavior is aroused under minimal stress, which means it occurs very often.

3. *The number of symptoms* is an obvious consideration. The more symptoms, the more the child is disabled. However, one should not rely exclusively on the criterion of multiplicity of symptoms to judge the extent of psychopathology. It is possible for a single symptom to work so efficiently that all the child's anxieties are taken care of at once. A good example is that of school phobia. Such a child may appear completely happy and well adjusted if he is allowed to remain home. All his problems may be bound up in the one phobic situation so that there is no spillage into other areas.

4. *The degree of social disadvantage* is an inevitable determinant of parental concern about children's symptoms. School phobia is obviously serious because it prevents the child from receiving an education. Behavior, such as aggressiveness or day wetting and soiling, which alienates the child from others has in reality serious secondary consequences for the child. It is easy to see a vicious circle at work where the effects of symptom may tend to perpetuate the symptom. After a while,

the school phobic child will be even more fearful of returning to school because he will be so far behind in his classwork. The aggressive child will make so many enemies that he has no choice but to continue to fight.

5. *The child's inner suffering* is often overlooked. It is often assumed that the child's opinion of himself is based solely on the spoken statements of others. So, if the parents are tolerant, and outsiders do not know about the symptom, the parents may feel that the child will not be upset about it. But children are quite capable of judging themselves. A child may feel embarrassed and inferior because of a habit which he cannot stop, even if it is a secret habit. And though he may not verbalize his inner distress, he often reveals it to someone who knows him well. The obvious pride in the occasional dry night demonstrated by a chronic bed wetter, for example, also reveals his hidden shame about wetting.

6. *Intractability of behavior* is implied, in part, in the criterion of frequency. It is conceivable that a child persists in behavior which is abnormal for his age, simply because no one has suggested that he change. But usually, efforts to discourage the behavior have proven futile. The persistence of symptoms, despite the efforts of the child and others to change them, is the hallmark of so-called behavior disorders.

7. *General personality appraisal* is the most important criterion, and the most difficult. The first six criteria have to do with the symptom as such: Suitability to the age, frequency, number, secondary effects on the child, and persistence. This criterion has to do with the child's general adjustment, rather than with isolated symptoms.

Freud defined emotional adjustment in adulthood in terms of the ability to love and to work (*Lieben und Arbeiten*), and this applies equally well to children. The child's relationships with his family, with outside authority, and with his peers should contain affection and give him pleasure. Mere compliance is not enough. Also important, particularly in relation to the adult love life to come, the girl should be happy to be a girl and the boy pleased to be a boy. The child's work is his schooling, and here one would like to see the flowering of ambition, responsibility, and gratification in work well done. Whether such attitudes result in academic excellence depends on other factors, which are irrelevant. To judge a boy's mental health by his grades would be like judging his father's mental health by his salary.

The criteria for judging whether a child needs help can be conceptualized in terms of progression, fixation, and regression. The child is growing and developing and, as a consequence, his behavior is constantly changing. If he is at a standstill in some respect, he is soon out of step with his peers. In severe cases, he goes backward. If he is constantly progressing, moving toward maturity, the outlook is good. In her book, *Normality and Pathology in Childhood*, A. Freud evaluates disturbances of childhood in terms of their interference with normal development processes *(1965).*

"The capacity to develop progressively, or respectively the damage to that capacity, are the most significant factors in determining a child's mental future. Accordingly, it becomes the diagnostician's task to ascertain where a given child stands on the developmental scale, whether his position is age adequate, retarded or precocious, and in what respect; and to what extent the observable internal and external circumstances and existent symptoms are interfering with the possibilities of future growth." *(Freud, 1962, p. 150.)*

A diagnostic procedure has been proposed by the Diagnostic Research Group at the Hampstead Clinic (London) in the form of a Developmental Profile which contains such headings as Drive Development (Sexual and Aggressive); Ego and Superego Development; Task Mastery; Regression and Fixation Points; Conflicts; Defenses; Response to Anxiety and Frustration *(Nagera, 1963).* The Diagnostic Profile thus serves as a frame of reference for evaluating a given child on a great number of personality features. "In the Profile pathology is seen against the background of normal development and its possible variations. This is, of course, of particular importance in child diagnosis, because the child, unlike the adult, is not yet a finished product" *(Nagera, 1963, p. 512).*

The Process of Referral

Preparation of parent

The process of referral begins after the child has been recognized as in need of help. Let us assume that the detection has been done by someone other than a parent, and that this person, perhaps a teacher or physician, must first convince the parents.

The preparation of the parents involves three steps. The first is the explanation of why the child needs help. The referring person must describe the emotional difficulties which have been observed, and must describe in what ways the child differs from others. Presumably, he knows the child and has significant information to offer. However, the information must be presented tactfully and emphatically, so that the parents do not feel that the person is merely criticizing and rejecting their child.

It is important to communicate a feeling of genuine concern for the child's welfare. For instance, if a school officer wanting to refer a hyperactive, aggressive child stresses his disruptive effect on the group, the parent might think, "Oh, you just want to get rid of him somehow, because he is a nuisance to your school." It is better to talk about the effect of the child's behavior on himself, to point out that he has no friends and that he suffers from social isolation. If a doctor who can find no organic reason for persistent stomach aches should try to initiate a referral by saying, "There's nothing really wrong with him; it's all in his head," he conveys the impression that the child is malingering. Again, it is better to discuss the symptom in terms of the child's suffering, to say that his stomach aches are an expression of painful feelings which are hard to see. An approach which emphasizes the child's inner feelings is apt to convince the parent that the referring person is not simply trying to rid himself of the child.

The second step in preparing the parents is to deal with their resistances and objections to referral. Some of these arise from ignorance about psychiatry or clinical psychology; even some sophisticated people believe that such services are reserved for the crazy or the obviously handicapped. They need to be told that normal children can have emotional problems. Some parents may fear that the child will be stigmatized for life if he has a record with a child guidance clinic. They need to be assured of the confidentiality of such records.

Another source of resistance is the parents' sense of guilt. Parents commonly feel that they are entirely responsible for their children's personality and behavior. If the child has problems, it reflects on them. Often they feel that it must mean that the child is insecure because they did not give him enough love, or else that they made some serious mistake. It is vitally important that the referring person realize that children can develop emotional problems from traumatic events which were fortuitous or completely unintended by the parents. The referring person must be familiar with the part played by fantasy and unconscious inner conflicts in the creation of emotional disorders. It is not appropriate, in the referral process, to give a complete lecture about child development, but there are ways of getting this idea across. One can explain that the child may be nervous about some accidental event which happened a long time ago, or even about something which he has only imagined. The main task is to meet the parent's defensiveness with explanation rather than argument. When he says, "It must be something I am doing wrong," one should be quick to reply, "There are undoubtedly other important reasons."

The third step in the preparation of the parents is to try to convey a realistic understanding of what a referral can accomplish. Sometimes, in his zeal to convince parents, the referring person will endow a visit to an agency or clinic with almost magical powers. The parents get the idea that you just walk into the psychiatrist's office and come out cured. A referral for diagnosis should be described in some such way as, "These specially trained people can give you some ideas of what to do next." The referring person should avoid promising that the clinic, or whoever, will "fix the child up." Equally, he should avoid dire predictions about what will happen if they do not go. The objective is *not* to get the parents to the agency no matter what, but to start them thinking along certain lines so that they will want to study the child's problem *with* someone.

Preparation of the child

The next major part of the referral process is the preparation of the child. Usually the child care agency helps the parents with this aspect, but the outside referring person should know something about it, too. Candor and honesty are of the greatest importance.

The child has a right to know where he is going and why. As to why, he should know what is meant by his "problem." Sometimes his problem has never been identified for him or has never been discussed frankly for fear of shaming him. On the other hand, perhaps it has been talked about too much, and always negatively: "I don't know what will become of you," or, "I don't know what we will do with you" or "Why don't you just quit that baby stuff?" The child may assume that the psychologist will say more of the same, and his parents will have a difficult time convincing him that the therapist will be for him, not against him.

It is impossible for a child to visit a psychiatrist, clinic, or social agency without knowing that something is up. Subterfuges never work. He soon realizes that this is no "old friend of mother's." The explanation has to be tailored to his age and level of understanding, but it should be completely honest. He should know whom he is going to see, and what interviews, tests, and procedures to expect. Right from the beginning, even with a young child, one sets a pattern of honest communication, hoping that the child can respond with equal honesty.

Preparing the referral service

The third step in referral is choosing the proper agency and paving the way for the parents. It is common practice to insist that a parent call to make the appointment, but it is helpful to call ahead to make sure that this is the kind of problem the agency is concerned with and that they will accept the case. The demand for child psychiatry facilities, private or public, and for child agencies of any professional description far exceeds the supply. Waiting lists are common, and many clinics simply close their doors to new applicants when the list becomes too long.

Making a referral is much more than calling a parent in and saying, "Your child is sick, go here." It takes time, and a lot of understanding. But it is a crucial first step in the treatment of the child, and well worth the effort.

The Process of Diagnostic Evaluation

The team approach

Many professional workers in the field of child psychopathology received their clinical training in a child guidance clinic. Child guidance clinics differ in theoretical orientation, but the one thing which they have in common is the team approach. The usual team consists of three professionals: child psychiatrist, clinical child psychologist, and psychiatric social worker. Traditionally, the social worker works with the parents, the psychologist tests the child, and the psychiatrist makes the formal diagnosis, supervises the treatment, and recommends necessary medical treatment. In many clinics, however, there is considerable overlapping of function, without a sharp division of responsibility. In the following description of the diagnostic process, therefore, the functions are emphasized rather than the specific person who might perform them.

Parental interviews

The first phase of the diagnostic process consists of the parental interviews, which may be with the mother, the father, or both together. There is usually a minimum of two one-hour interviews. The information which is sought in these interviews belongs to six categories: the "presenting problems"; the current functioning and personality of child; the history; parental attitudes; family relationships; and the history of the parents. A skilled interviewer will probably not take up these topics one after another, but will seize natural conversational opportunities to get information, sorting it out in his mind for systematic recording later. He may very well take notes of identifying data and important dates, but it is impossible, and unwise, to record everything as it is said.

The "Presenting Problems." A natural starting point is an inquiry about the "presenting problem," that is, what brought the parent to the point of seeking help for the child. The parent's exact words should be recorded. Her initial description may reveal a good deal about her attitude and degree of understanding. For instance, consider aggressiveness. A parent might say, "My boy is very mean and has a hateful disposition." Another might say, "The teacher at school says she can't manage my boy and told me to come here." Still a third might say, "I think my boy is frustrated because he is the middle child." They may all be equally concerned about the same behavior, but the first parent sounds angry at the child, the second may be angry at the teacher, and the third is attempting to diagnose.

Next, one tries to find out the duration of the symptom. Often, this is very hard because the onset has been insidious: "He was always this way, but I didn't worry until this year." Or, "He was always sensitive, but it seems to be getting worse." There are however, some symptoms, particularly phobias or other anxiety reactions, which may have had a sudden onset. The circumstances surrounding the onset may be very important to an understanding of the symptom.

It is also important to get specific details about the problem behavior. What does the child do or say? When? How often? Under what provocation? What happens afterwards? What has been said to the child about it, either by his parents or others? Previous efforts at treatment should be carefully recorded. Such efforts may have ranged from punishment, shaming, offering rewards for change, ignoring, physical examinations, and mechanical gadgets (for thumb sucking or enuresis), to previous visits to other agencies. This information is particularly valuable in predicting the child's reaction to the imminent clinic visit.

Current Functioning. It is usual to inquire about the more common nervous habits and other symptoms of childhood psychopathology. It is remarkable, how often parents will come to a clinic because a child is failing at school and never volunteer the information that he is also an enuretic, suffers from recurrent nightmares, and has chronic constipation or severe feeding problems! Because they are unaware of the possible connections, they fail to mention problems which do not bother them.

One also tries to get a picture of the child's personality as the parents see it. This includes his adjustment in the family, with other children, and in school; his likes and dislikes; and so on. One also searches for character traits, not so much for moral character (e.g., honesty or truthfulness), as for habitual ways of responding to situations. We are interested, for example, in the child's reaction to responsibility. Some children are overly conscientious, but the child referred to a guidance clinic is likely to be passive about responsibility. He dawdles and procrastinates, until he is forced to dress, make his bed, do his homework, go to bed, or whatever. The child's reaction to competitive situations is also interesting to us. Some children are afraid of success and scrupulously avoid achieving a top rating; others fear failure and avoid any situation where success is not guaranteed. The child's reaction to physical risk is also important. No child likes to be hurt, but some go to extraordinary lengths to keep out of any ruckus or any games involving bodily contact. Such children may appear simply disinterested. The key word here is "always"; the fixed nature of the response reveals a need to avoid certain situations.

One inquires of the parents what the child does when he is angry or frightened. Their replies are of interest not only because they contain information about the child, but also because they reveal something about their own perceptiveness. It is surprising how often such questions draw a blank; they can't remember when the child was angry or frightened about anything. Since one can be sure that the child has experienced both emotions, either the child is extraordinarily inhibited or the parents are extraordinarily good at forgetting.

History. There used to be a great deal of emphasis on the child's history, and most of the interview would be devoted to the details of his early development. Such items as the age and manner of weaning, age and method of toilet training, early development, questions about and reactions to new babies, and other matters related to infancy and early childhood adjustment were dutifully investigated. One usually inquired about the mother's attitude toward the pregnancy and about her sex preference. The concept that present behavior is determined by past events is as valid as ever, but clinicians have found that developmental details are hard to get in initial interviews. E. K. Beller found that:

. . . information was more complete about events which were less removed from the time of the interview, and more meager for most events which occurred further back in time . . . parents failed to recall events in the child's infancy, particularly their own feelings and attitudes toward the child, in contrast to their full reporting of the child's current functioning and problems.[*]

Beller felt that there were two reasons for this: First, the parents did not see the relevance of such information; and second, they were anxious to avoid acknowledging their own contribution to the child's problem and fearful that it would emerge in a discussion of their early attitudes and feelings. In part,

they deliberately suppress information; in part, they have forgotten it.

Clinicians now rely more on early history volunteered by, rather than directly elicited from, the parents. The parents are asked if they recall anything special during infancy, regarding feeding, toilet training, early fears, persistent habits, discipline difficulties, slowness of development in any respect, and so on. Factual data, such as separations from home, serious parental illnesses, hospitalization of the child, surgery, and subsequent births are usually recalled with fair accuracy.

The parents' attitudes toward the child are obviously important, but they are difficult to ascertain. An occasional parent can verbalize his feelings, but more often he does not and cannot. Throughout, however, the interviewer is looking for cues, some of which have been mentioned already. Sometimes, in the questioning about family relationships, attitudes are expressed indirectly. As the parent discusses the other children, preferences or incompatibilities may become apparent. The parent is also asked to contrast his (or her) attitude toward the child with that of the other parent, and this question sometimes illuminates the ephemeral area of attitude and feeling.

Family Relationships. One is interested in the role played by the child with his siblings, and parents usually can describe this well. One is also interested in the husband-wife relationship, and sometimes the parents voluntarily relate their disagreements. But discussion is usually highly guarded, especially when the marriage is stressed. A joint interview sometimes reveals conflicts which neither parent would discuss alone. In case work agencies, there has been some experimentation with "family diagnosis" where the total family unit is interviewed as part of the initial diagnostic exploration. F. H. Scherz reported that "certain types of diagnostic material emerge quickly and

---

[*]Quoted from E. K. Beller, *The Clinical Process* (New York: The Macmillan Company, 1962), pp. 57–58. Reprinted by permission.

clearly in various types of joint and family-unit interviews: client attitudes toward using help, family members' expectations of each other, their capacity to give and take, their closeness or distance, their ability to assume their share of the responsibility for the problem, their patterns of communication, and family roles" *(1964, p. 213).* Usually, these techniques are used as a preliminary to family-group treatment (see Chapter 15).

Parental History. The history of both parents provides material which helps us to understand them. A mother may be overly indulgent because her parents were rigid. A parent who was too good as a child may derive vicarious satisfaction from her rebellious, aggressive son. Sometimes, a parent has had the very symptom his child is now displaying.

Repetition and continuity of conflict and pathology in successive generations suggests that deeply rooted experiential determinants and biological predispositions are complicating the present picture. No one questions the significance of such data, but they are hard to obtain. The interviewer wants to build a good relationship with the parent, and direct questioning on these scores may sound inquisitory. It is of no value to get the facts and lose the case. In Beller's evaluative studies of the clinical records of the Child Development Center of New York, he found an even greater dearth of information about family history than about the developmental history of the child. This does not reflect the clinicians' ignorance of the importance of such information but, rather, its inaccessibility on short acquaintance.

Child interviews

The difficulty of obtaining information from the parents is as nothing compared to the difficulty of obtaining information from the child. The second stage of the diagnostic evaluation is usually an interview with the child. Anna Freud described the situation as follows:

Whoever has dealt with school children will tell you they betray very little. They are resentful usually of being brought to the clinic. They are suspicious, the more normal they are, the less they like strangers prying into the intimacies of their lives. It is so rare that we get deeper diagnostic material in the first interview that I selected the very few cases where this happened in our clinic . . . I saw a boy of ten who was most restless, he fidgeted, touched everything, did not say a thing. I asked him about the semi-delinquent symptoms for which he had been sent, the circumstances of his family and so on, but all he said was, 'I would not like to give you wrong impressions' by which he gave me *no* impressions at all. Finally he found a tape measure (spring type) and he began to play with it and did not stop until he broke it. Then he changed completely. He became most cooperative, nearly cringing in his appeals, asking me over and over whether I could not mend it again. His worries evidently centered around masturbation, his fears were that he would damage himself, and the change in his behavior from distrust and suspicion to passive appeals whenever he found he had damaged something told us a lot.[*]

Such a revelation in an initial interview is indeed exceptional. The child is less able to verbalize his feelings and his complaints, partly because he lacks the skill and experience to do so and partly because he rarely seeks help of his own accord.

Age makes a difference, however. The author interviewed the same boy over a period of six years. At 10, Jay denied that he had any problems or needed help of any kind, and said his mother was crazy to think otherwise.

---

[*]Quoted from Anna Freud, "Diagnosis and Assessment of Early Childhood Difficulties." Paper presented at the Philadelphia Association for Psychoanalysis, Philadelphia, Pa., May, 1954, p. 5. Reprinted by permission.

At 14, Jay said he had some worries, but he insisted that they were the fault of his parents (who were, in fact, very disturbed). He felt that the remedy lay in their changing their behavior toward him. At 16, he came in to tell me that he was worried about himself and wanted some kind of help, that his problems were 'inside" and that a change in his parents would not help him. At 16, he had insight and a desire to cooperate in an adult way; the only obvious sign of his immaturity was his insistence that his parents not know he was seeking help.

There are other reasons for the child's lack of verbalization. He is understandably reluctant to confide anything which might appear hostile to his parents. It might get back to them. Even if he has no fear of recrimination, his loyalty will make him hesitant about being more intimate with a stranger than he has been with his own parents.

Still another inhibiting factor is a superstitious dread of verbalizing something painful or frightening. Putting something into words gives it added reality, makes it seem more likely to come true. One boy, visiting a psychiatric clinic in a hospital, thought that his tonsils were going to be removed. Although he was in panic during the interview, he never said a word about his fear; that would be reminding these people to go ahead with their cutting. Children are likely to be silent about the very things which cause them the greatest anxiety.

The Play Interview. In view of the child's inability and reluctance to talk about himself, the verbal interview often yields only superficial observations about appearance and social behavior. A play interview, with no attempt at formal inquiries, works well with pre-school children. They are intrigued by the new toys and play readily. Once they are assured that this is all that is going to happen to them, and that they are going to rejoin their moth-

ers, they soon become absorbed in play and it seems that everything is open to view. But, although their defenses against showing worries and conflicts are fewer, it is nonetheless difficult to evaluate the *degree* of abnormality of very young children. Fears, anxieties, emotional outbursts, restlessness, and so on are common, and it is hard to measure the significance of such behavior in a single play session.

Psychological testing

Partly because communication with children is so difficult to establish quickly, psychological tests are widely used in child guidance clinics. They are considered a short cut to the understanding of personality. The child is faced with a standardized situation (e.g., questions, pictures, specially selected toy materials) in which he has to do something, and his responses are then compared with those of other children in the identical situation. Testing procedures vary; some clinics use tests routinely, others only for special reasons. There are numerous tests, many more for children than for adults, but there has been no survey to establish the frequency with which various methods or tests are employed.

Intelligence Testing. The individual intelligence tests which are used most commonly are the Stanford-Binet *(Terman and Merrill, 1960)* and the Wechsler Intelligence Scale for Children, known as the WISC *(Wechsler, 1949)*. Although these tests overlap in their ranges, the Binet is most appropriate for young children and the WISC for adolescents. Other individual tests have been constructed for special purposes such as testing the non-verbal child *(Leiter International Performance Scale, Leiter, 1952; Progressive Matrices, Raven, 1947)* and obtaining quick evaluations for screening purposes *(Peabody Picture Vocabulary Test, Dunn, 1959)*. In order to properly select and interpret tests, the psychologist must consider the child's age, the nature of his problems, and he must also be familiar with the standardization features of the particular test. Buros publishes a yearbook in mental measurements which reviews the standardization data and published reports of most currently available psychological tests *(Buros, 1959)*.

The quantitative result (e.g., IQ) has obvious diagnostic significance when it is subnormal (See Chapter 8). Beyond this, the score is of interest when it reveals a wide discrepancy between performance in school and the test score, in either direction (See Chapter 9). There are qualitative features which are equally important. The Stanford-Binet test involves the greatest amount of social interaction between the examiner and the child, and this gives many opportunities to make observations about personality functioning. In the testing situation, demands are being made of the child; he is in a situation where he can be right or wrong, and his reactions to this situation and to the examiner may be very different than in the play, or unstructured, interview. The child can be labelled "cooperative" or "uncooperative," but the examiner-child relationship is susceptible of much deeper analysis than this. If one gives some thought to the situation, it becomes clear how much more is involved. The child must adjust to a stranger, a stranger who for 50 or 60 minutes requires him to do first one thing and then another, who asks to be shown all that he knows and can do, who is writing all kinds of things down on a paper, and so on. A child of two or three may tire of this giving and never getting, and may finally balk, perhaps being willing to return to the task if the examiner can contrive some reward. A slightly older child, four or five, may tire of the passivity of his role and decide to start asking some questions himself. His questions will show how he visualizes the tests. If he gleefully chooses questions which he con-

siders impossible to answer, and then plans to tell everyone of the examiner's failure, it is clear that he sees the examiner as an aggressive figure. Another common reaction of young children is to regard the testing as some sort of contest in which the examiner holds all the trump cards. They may refuse to copy the examiner's model of a bead chain, a series of numbers, and the like. They are unwilling to play by the rules, and insist that they can make a much longer chain, can count to 100, or in some way do something much better.

These reactions, to some degree normal in the pre-school child, become diagnostically important when demonstrated by a school child. Perhaps the clearest examples are provided by children with obsessional characteristics. These children may do much better in their school work and in group tests of mental ability than in an individually administered Stanford-Binet. The direct person-to-person situation reactivates their tendencies to resist authority. Rather than give answers, they quibble, refuse to accept the obvious and hunt for hidden or farfetched interpretations of the questions, or become immersed in the concrete meanings of words or in other irrelevant aspects of the test material.

Other children may do better in the individual situation and still behave in a way that is diagnostically significant. For instance, a child who is essentially disinterested in his ability to perform may tolerate the demands of the examiner as a personal favor or in anticipation of a reward—a treat at the soda fountain, a chance to play with the toys glimpsed in the playroom, or the like. This attitude, typical at two or three, has an obvious deleterious effect on a child's intellectual performance in school, where tangible rewards are lacking.

Although intelligence test items are designed to evaluate problem-solving ability, emotional problems often intrude. For instance, the Stanford-Binet questions for age levels four to six contain a number of items which deal, directly or indirectly, with sex differences: Opposite Analogies, Pictorial Likenesses and Differences, Mutilated Pictures, and Draw-a-Man. When such items are failed as a group and other items of equal difficulty are passed, it becomes apparent that the child is coping with an inhibition in this area—frequently by denying the perception of any differences or of any missing parts.

For more advanced age levels, there are several questions in the Verbal Absurdities series of the Stanford-Binet which deal with the permanence of death or bodily injury. Some children fail to appreciate the illogicality contained in the absurd statements because of their need to moralize about the accident; others refuse to accept the statement even as a hypothetical case. Children's efforts to name similarities between various objects may also be revealing, particularly when they continually use the same basis of comparison (e.g., the ability of objects to hurt a person, the relative size of the objects, or the fragility of the objects to be compared). There are Comprehension questions which require the child to tell what he would do in various situations which have in them a hint of danger or conflict (e.g., if he is hit by another child or in danger of being late for school). His replies may reflect an inordinate dependency on his mother; the solutions may be phrased in moral or religious terms, as if a serious crime were under discussion; or violent retributions may be fantasied and no solution seen as available.

At the older age levels, the questions are less provocative of emotional reactions, although one unhappy 13-year-old boy made his bitterness obvious throughout the test. For example, in forming a sentence which contained certain key words, he used them negatively: "You do not make an impression on me—your dignity is unbearable in its ceremonial." When he was asked to repeat the general idea of a passage on the value of life, he interjected the thought that "our life is no better than an animal's life."

No prediction can be made that any intelligence test question will provide psychologically valuable material; the recognition of the uniqueness of an answer or a reaction rests on the examiner's alertness. However, the child's reaction to the total situation is always meaningful. If he responds well, he is showing a measure of healthy functioning, a fact which is sometimes overlooked in the zeal to study his pathological functioning.

Projective Testing. The projective testing techniques are usually regarded as diagnostic instruments which penetrate the surface and reveal the underlying personality pattern and psychodynamics. The Rorschach inkblot test, historically the first, remains the most popular. R. I. Watson *(1951)* considers the Rorschach appropriate for children over eight, and the clinics responding to one survey *(Klopfer, 1956)* generally agreed that the minimum age at which it is useful is around seven, about the time when play sessions become inappropriate. There are numerous studies which show that so-called disturbed children can be reliably differentiated from so-called normal children on the basis of their Rorschach responses *(Beck, 1931; Krugman, 1942)*. Analysis of responses for indications of anxiety and hostility revealed more such indications in the responses of delinquents than of nondelinquents *(Gorlow, Zimet, and Fine, 1952)*. In a child guidance clinic setting, Miriam Siegel found that diagnoses based on the Rorschach agreed closely with the final diagnoses formulated by the psychiatrist after a period of therapy *(1948)*. Jane Kessler and C. M. Wolfenstein compared Rorschach test-and-retest results in a group of emotionally disturbed children in residential treatment. They found that the amount of change indicated by the Rorschach corresponded very closely to the actual change observed by the residential staff *(1953)*.

Such studies demonstrate the validity of the Rorschach. That is, they show that the child reveals, in this test, many of the same personality characteristics which he reveals in life situations. It is an invaluable research tool, also, because it provides a frame of reference within which particular personality characteristics of different children, or of the same child at different times, can be compared. B. Klopfer has said, with regard to the purposes of testing a child in a child guidance clinic:

We are interested to know in any given case which areas of ego functioning are intact, which are impaired, and how much they are impaired. We are concerned with the child's ability to tolerate tensions, to test reality, to differentiate and organize his experience. We want to know the nature of his ego defenses and how rigidly or flexibly he uses them. *(Quoted by Ross, 1959, p. 180.)*

A. O. Ross feels that no instrument fills this large order as adequately as the Rorschach test.

There is a plethora of psychological tests for children, and each has staunch supporters. For example, there are more than a half-dozen sets of pictures for picture-story tests. H. A. Murray's Thematic Apperception Test (TAT) was the first *(1943)*. Modifications for children use animal pictures (Child's Apperception Test *(Bellak and Bellak, 1950)*; pictures of adolescents (Symonds Picture Story Test *1948*); and pictures of school-age children (The Michigan Picture Test, *Hartwell et al., 1951*). Some picture series have been designed with specific meanings, in contrast to the deliberate ambiguity of the TAT series. The Travis Projective Pictures *(1957)* are scenes which are potentially conflictual, such as eating, sleeping, playing with dirt, sibling rivalry, punishment by a parent, jealousy of a parent, and aggression against parents. The Blacky pictures *(Blum, 1950)* are similar, but use a dog hero instead of a child figure. There are similar tests where the child does not tell a story, but does something else with the pictures. In one, he arranges pictures to tell a story (Make a Picture-Story Method, *Shneidman, 1952*). In S. Rosenzweig's Picture-Frustration Test *(1948)*, the child supplies a series of cartoons with his own conclusion. E. Bene and E. J. Anthony devised a technique for assessing the child's family relationships by using mailbox dolls from which the child selects figures to represent himself, the members of his family, and a "Mr. Nobody" *(1957)*. The child then "delivers" to the proper figures "postcards" which contain emotional statements indicating varying degrees of affection and hostility.

There is also an array of psychological instruments which analyze children's drawings such as the Bender-Gestalt *(Bender, 1938)*; Draw-a-Person *(Machover, 1949)*; House-Tree-Person *(Buck, 1948)*; and The Family Drawing Test *(Reznikoff and Reznikoff, 1956)*. There are tests in which the child arranges materials in some way, such as The Mosaic Test *(Diamond, 1944)*; the Twitchell-Allen Three Dimensional Personality Test *(Allen, 1948)*; and the World Test *(Buhler, 1951)*. In Sweden, a special method of administering and evaluating the World Test has been developed *(Danielson, 1962)*. In the "Erica Method," the child is presented with 360 tiny toys arranged according to certain principles, (e.g., animate or inanimate, peaceful or aggressive) and two sandboxes (one with wet and one with dry sand) which he uses to build his "world." He is asked to make three "worlds" at three different sessions. The interpretation is based on his way of handling the materials as well as positioning, number and choice of toys in different categories. The investigators found that analysis of three sessions increased the validity of the results. The first session is often contaminated by transient features reflecting the child's reaction to the strangeness of the situation. This observation highlights a limitation of all tests and indicates the hazard in using supposed short-cuts to reveal "underlying personality."

There are tests which come close to a personality questionnaire, such as the various sentence-completion tests. This listing does not include the many tests for brain injury (See Chapter 7), nor the paper-and-pencil personality inventories which are used for large groups. All the tests listed are commercially available and planned for use in individual diagnosis of emotional disturbances in childhood. There is a scoring manual for each and studies which report significant findings for different groups of children.

One cannot help but be impressed by the ingenuity with which test constructors devise material which will be so interesting to children that they will lose their reserve and provide material for the psychologist to analyze. All because they won't talk!

Clinicians are advised to use a battery of tests:

Ideally, the clinician should, for each patient choose the most appropriate instruments, taking the type of case, the questions to be answered, and his own predilections into consideration. Because of the great number of instruments available, a variety of combinations is possible, but most experienced clinicians eventually arrive at their favorite combination . . . In a sense, the battery becomes a super-test, the Gestalt effect of which has a communicative value which is greater than the data provided by each of the individual tests of which the battery is comprised. *(Ross, 1959, p. 215.)*

This is sound advice, but it should be added that no test battery is better than the person who administers it. The validity of the tests depends almost entirely on the examiner's skill in achieving rapport with a child and his ability to interpret the child's behavior.

The Usefulness of Tests. In assessing the usefulness of the various tests to the child guidance clinic, important questions remain to be answered. First: Does a given test provide unique information? There is no value in confirming the obvious. No studies have been done to determine to what extent the tests yield valid information which is not equally obtainable from other sources. Second: Is the data of value for counseling the parents or in planning therapy? In the author's opinion, psychologists often set themselves the too-ambitous goal of trying to gain a complete understanding of the total personality. The social worker must begin with the incomplete information she obtains from the parents, and no amount of testing will complete the information. It is still necessarily incomplete after the initial diagnostic evaluation.

Interpretation to parents and child

One of the prime objectives of the diagnostic evaluation is to introduce the parents and the child to a psychological way of viewing the child's problems. Pains should be taken to avoid letting the diagnostic procedures become yet another traumatic occurrence in their lives. At the beginning of the study, there must be time to become friends, and, at the conclusion of the tests, there must be time to interpret the results to the child. The interpretation may be brief: "You helped us a great deal and I think I can understand better what has been bothering you. We will try and explain it to your parents so that they can find ways to help you get rid of this problem." The child may have questions. It is possible to explain more specifically, to older children, how feelings influence behavior. The important thing is to maintain empathy with the child and his parents, so that the diagnostic evaluation can be concluded with an interpretation which is meaningful to them.

Other objectives in the evaluation include: (1) determining in what areas and to what extent the child differs from others of his age; (2) assessing the chronicity of his problems; (3) formulating some hypotheses about possible contributing factors, past and present; (4) assessing areas of strength in the child and in the family situation; and (5) deciding on the next step. In addition, an effort is usually made to label the pathology, for the record and for future reference.

References for Chapter 4

Abt, L. E. and L. Bellak, *Projective Psychology*. New York: Alfred A. Knopf, Inc., 1950.

Allen, Doris, *Three Dimensional Apperception Test*. New York: The Psychological Corporation, 1948.

Anthony, E. J. and Eva Bene, "A Technique for the Objective Assessment of the Child's Family Relationships." *Journal of Mental Science*, CIII (1957), 541–55.

Beck, S. J., "The Rorschach Test in Problem Children," *American Journal of Orthopsychiatry*, I (1931), 501–9.

Bellak, L., *The Thematic Apperception Test and the Child's Apperception Test in Clinical Use*. New York: Grune & Stratton, Inc., 1954.

———, and S. S. Bellak, "An Introductory Note on the Child's Apperception Test (CAT)," *Journal of Projective Techniques*, XIV (1950), 173–80.

Beller, E. K., *The Clinical Process*. New York: The Macmillan Company, 1962.

Bender, L., "A Visual Motor Test and its Clinical Use.," *American Journal of Orthopsychiatry Monograph No. 3*, 1938.

Blum, G. S., *The Blacky Pictures: Manual of Instructions*. New York: The Psychological Corporation, 1950.

———, and H. F. Hunt, "The Validity of the Blacky Pictures," *Psychological Bulletin*, XLIX (1952), 238–50.

Buck, J. N., "The H-T-P Technique: A Qualitative and Quantitative Scoring Manual," *Journal of Clinical Psychology*, IV (1948), 317–96.

Buhler, C., "The World Test," *Journal of Child Psychiatry*, II (1951), 69–81.

Buros, Oscar K., ed. *The Fifth Mental Measurements Yearbook*. Highland Park, N.J.: The Gryphon Press, 1959.

Byrd, F., "The Clinical Validity of the Bender-Gestalt Test with Children: A Developmental Comparison of Children in Psychotherapy and Children Judged Well Adjusted," *Journal of Projective Techniques*, XX (1956), 127–36.

Cummings, J. E., "Incidence of Emotional Symptoms in School Children," *British Journal of Educational Psychology*, XIV (1944), 151–61.

Danielson, Allis, "Sandladeobservationer Enligt Ericametoden." *Nordisk Medicin*, LXVIII (1962), 1197–2003.

Despert, J. L. and H. W. Potter, "Technical Approaches Used in the Study and Treatment of Emotional Problems in Children: The Story, a Form of Directed Fantasy," *Psychiatric Quarterly*, X (1936), 619–38.

Diamond, B. L. and H. T. Schmale, "The Mosaic Test: An Evaluation of its Clinical Application," *American Journal of Orthopsychiatry*, XIV (1944), 237.

Dunn, Lloyd M., *Peabody Picture Vocabulary Test Manual*. Minneapolis: American Guidance Service, Inc., 1959.

Freud, Anna, "Assessment of Childhood Disturbances." *Psychoanalytic Study of the Child*, Volume XVII. New York: International Universities Press, Inc., 1962.

———, "Diagnosis and Assessment of Early Childhood Difficulties." Paper presented at Philadelphia Association for Psychoanalysis, Philadelphia, May, 1954.

———, *Normality and Pathology in Childhood*. Assessments of Development. New York: International Universities Press, Inc., 1965.

———, *The Psychoanalytical Treatment of Children*, Part III "Indications for Child Analysis" (1945). London: Imago Publishing Company, 1946.

Goldenberg, H. C., "A Résumé of Some Make a Picture-Story (MAPS) Test Results," *Journal of Projective Techniques*, XV (1951), 79–86.

Goldhamer, H. and A. Marshall, *Psychosis and Civilization*. New York: Free Press of Glencoe, Inc., 1953.

Gorlow, L., C. M. Zimet, and H. J. Fine, "The Validity of Anxiety and Hostility Rorschach Content Scores among Adolescents," *Journal Consulting Psychology*, XVI (1952), 65–73.

Group for the Advancement of Psychiatry, *Basic Concepts in Child Psychiatry Report,* No. 12, April, 1950.

———, *Diagnostic Process in Child Psychiatry Report,* No. 38, August, 1957.

Hartwell, S. W. *et al.,* "The Michigan Picture Test: Diagnostic and Therapeutic Possibilities of a New Projective Test in Child Guidance," *American Journal of Orthopsychiatry,* XXI (1951), 124–37.

Jahoda, Marie, "Toward a Social Psychology of Mental Health," in Ruth Kotinsky and Helen Witmer, *Community Problems for Mental Health.* Cambridge, Mass.: Harvard University Press, 1955.

Jersild, A. T., *Child Psychology* (5th ed.) Englewood Cliffs, N.J.: Prentice-Hall, Inc., 1960, 452–55.

Kanner, L., "Do Behavioral Symptoms Always Indicate Psychopathology?" *Journal of Child Psychology and Psychiatry,* I (1960), 17–25.

———, "Everyday Problems of the Everyday Child." *Current Medical Digest,* September, 1961, 47–53.

Kessler, Jane W. and C. M. Wolfenstein, "A Comparison of Rorschach Retests with Behavior Changes in a Group of Emotionally Disturbed Children," *American Journal of Orthopsychiatry,* XXIII (1953), 740–54.

Klopfer, B., ed., *Fields of Application. Developments in the Rorschach Technique,* Vol. II. New York: Harcourt, Brace & World, Inc., 1956.

Krugman, J. I., "A Clinical Validation of the Rorschach with Problem Children," *Rorschach Research Exchange,* 6 (1942), 61–70.

Lapouse, R. and M. A. Monk, "An Epidemiologic Study of Behavior Characteristics in Children." A paper presented at the Annual Meeting of the American Public Health Association, Cleveland, November, 1957. (Quoted in Kanner, 1960.)

———, "Fears and Worries in a Representative Sample of Children," *American Journal of Orthopsychiatry,* XXIX, (1959), 803–18.

Leiter, R. G., Part I of the manual for the 1948 revision of the Leiter International Performance Scale. Chicago: C. H. Stoelting, 1952.

Levitt, E. E. and W. H. Lyle, "Evidence for the Validity of the Children's Form of the

Picture-Frustration Study," *Journal Consulting Psychology,* XIX (1955), 381–86.

Macfarlane, J., L. Allen, and M. P. Honzik, *A Developmental Study of the Behavior Problems of Normal Children between 21 months and 14 years.* Berkeley, California: University of California Press, 1954.

Machover, K., *Personality Projection in the Drawing of the Human Figure.* Springfield, Ill.: Charles C Thomas, Publisher, 1949.

Murray, H. A., *Thematic Apperception Test.* Cambridge, Mass.: Harvard University Press, 1943.

Nagera, Humberto, "The Developmental Profile: Notes on Some Practical Considerations Regarding its Use," in *The Psychoanalytic Study of the Child,* Vol. XVIII. New York: International Universities Press, Inc., 1962.

Pascal, G. R., "Gestalt Functions: The Bender-Gestalt, Mosaic, and World Test," in D. Brower and L. Aut, *Progress in Clinical Psychology.* New York: Grune & Stratton, Inc., 1953.

Peixotto, H. W., "Reliability of the Despert Fables: A Story Completion Projective Test for Children," *Journal of Clinical Psychology,* XII (1956), 75–78.

Raven, J. C., *Progressive Matrices.* London: H. K. Lewis, 1947.

Reznikoff, M. and H. R. Reznikoff, "The Family Drawing Test: A Comparative Study of Children's Drawings," *Journal of Clinical Psychology,* XII (1956), 167–69.

Ross, A. O., *The Practice of Clinical Child Psychology.* New York: Grune & Stratton, Inc., 1959.

Rosenzweig, S., E. E. Fleming, and L. Rosenzweig, "The Children's Form of the Rosenzweig Picture-Frustration Study," *Journal of Psychology,* XXVI (1948), 141–91.

———, "Aggression in Problem Children and Normals as Evaluated by the Rozenzweig P-F Study," *Journal of Abnormal and Social Psychology,* XLVII (1952), 683–87.

Scherz, Frances H., "Exploring the Use of Family Interviews in Diagnosis." *Social Casework,* XLV, No. 4, April, 1964.

Seigel, Miriam, "The Diagnostic and Prognostic Validity of the Rorschach Test in a Child Guidance Clinic," *American Journal of Orthopsychiatry,* XVIII (1948), 119–33.

Shneidman, E. S., "Manual for the Make a Picture-Story Method," *Journal of Projective Techniques Monograph,* No. 2 (1952).

Starer, E., "An Examination of the Responses of a Group of Young Normal Females and a Group of Female Psychotic Patients on the Three-dimension Apperception Test," *Journal of Clinical Psychology,* IX (1953), 47–50.

Strauss, A. A. and L. E. Lehtinen, *Psychopathology and Education of the Brain-injured Child.* New York: Grune & Stratton, Inc., 1947.

Symonds, P. M., *Symonds Picture Story Test.* New York: Columbia University Press, 1948.

Terman, Lewis M. and Maud A. Merrill. *Stanford-Binet Intelligence Scale.* Manual for the Third Revision Form L-M. Boston: Houghton Mifflin Co., The Riverside Press, 1960.

Travis, L. E., *Travis Projective Pictures.* Glendale, Calif.: Griffin-Patterson, 1957.

Valentine, C. W., *The Normal Child and Some of His Abnormalities.* Baltimore: Penguin Books, Inc., 1956.

Watson, R. I., *The Clinical Method of Psychology.* New York: Harper & Row, Publishers, Inc., 1951.

Wechsler, D., *Manual for the Wechsler Intelligence Scale for Children.* New York: Psychological Corporation, 1949.

5

DIAGNOSTIC NOMENCLATURE IN CHILD PSYCHOPATHOLOGY

Concept of Diagnosis

In the previous chapter, the word "diagnosis" was frequently used, and without formal definition. It is a deceptively simple term. "Diagnosis," derived from the Greek, means "thorough understanding"—which implies an understanding of causation. But what is regarded as a thorough explanation depends on the diagnostician's professional background and theoretical orientation. The pediatrician who is concerned about a child's early morning stomach-ache will feel that it has been diagnosed when the physical findings are negative and he learns that the child is deathly afraid of going to school; the psychiatrist who takes over at this point will seek to explain why and how the child acquired such an extreme fear. The court officer investigating a truancy may find that the boy gave up school in order to gain the approval of an adolescent gang who considered it "chicken" to go to school; the social psychologist will explore the matter more deeply, in order to define the cultural conditions which lead to antisocial gang formation. A teacher who is concerned by a pupil's inability to learn, will feel that it is explained by a low IQ; the psychologist who discovered the low IQ will seek its cause

and refer him to a neurologist. The neurologist, in turn, may find a history and symptoms of organic brain damage, but he will seek to link the specific behavior disturbance and the structural damage. Each practitioner seeks different levels of explanations, depending on the nature of his interest in the specific problem. It is not that one authority is right and the next is wrong; each successive expert is trying to delve more deeply into the nature of the cause-and-effect relationship.

Etiological concepts will vary not only with the level of explanation which is sought, but also with the theoretical orientation of the diagnostician. "Diagnosis" is a term which is most at home in medicine; for it was the doctors who pioneered in the study of emotional problems in childhood, and they used the diagnostic principles with which they were familiar. In medicine, clusters of symptoms are used as the basis of diagnosis until the cause is determined. The beginning of a clinical diagnosis is the labelling of syndromes of symptoms. For example, tuberculosis was first called consumption because of its most conspicuous external feature, the physical wasting, and it was not renamed until Koch isolated the tubercle bacillus and identified it as the specific cause of all the varied external signs. The search for the prime etiological factor has proved to be the most rewarding approach in medicine because it paves the way for treatment and prevention. The medical goal is to treat the cause, not the symptom.

It was hoped that the same approach would be equally fruitful in the understanding, treatment, and prevention of emotional disorders. Description and classification of emotional symptoms would therefore be a first step in the search for cause. But a physician has questioned whether mental illnesses are susceptible to the same kind of analysis as physical illness:

More likely in psychological illness, we deal with multi-factorial causations and the variables are not only the many possible causative factors, but also the variable interactions between them. The search for the one indispensable etiological factor is therefore not likely to be helpful to us in psychiatry. *(Stroh, 1960, p. 240.)*

In other words, all behavior, whether normal or abnormal, is overdetermined; no single act can be explained in terms of one determinant or one variable. Consequently, there is little inclination in child psychiatry to name diseases. Diagnostic formulations are likely to be in paragraph form, rather than in single terms, describing both the strengths and the problems of the child and postulating the major contributing factors, usually several in number.

Principles of Classification of Childhood Personality Diagnosis

The standardization of diagnostic terminology in childhood psychopathology is an unsolved problem. There is no general agreement as to whether the nomenclature should be based on the symptoms, the etiology, the prognosis, or on a combination of these factors. All authors decry the lack of standard classification because, without it, it is impossible to compare data from different sources or to have an accurate interchange of diagnostic information.

The only official diagnostic terminology is the standard nomenclature which the American Psychiatric Association issued through its Mental Hospital Service in 1952. Mental disorders of children and adults are considered together and, of the 62 diagnoses, few are specifically relevant to children. In the major category of "personality disorders," a subcategory of "specific symptom reactions" includes "learning disturbance," "speech disturbance," and "enuresis," among others, and these are problems which are commonly referred to child guidance clinics. In the major category of "transient situational personality disorders," one finds three subcategories of "adjustment reaction," for infancy, childhood, and adolescence. "Adjustment reaction of childhood" includes "habit disturbances," "conduct disturbances," and "neurotic traits." This diagnosis is defined as "transient symptomatic reactions of children to some immediate situation or to an internal emotional conflict." In effect, this definition excludes mental subnormality, organic illness of the brain, and psychotic reactions, but it can be stretched to include almost all the nonpsychotic functional disorders of childhood behavior. In Florida, for example, approximately 40 per cent of the children diagnosed by 17 clinics are reported in the category of "adjustment reaction of children" *(Dreger et al., 1964)*. It is probable that other clinics make even greater use of this diagnostic catchall. A term of such inclusiveness conveys very little information, and is used more as a matter of form than significance.

In desperation, some authors have resorted to a classification in terms of presenting complaints. G. M. Gilbert found that, although most child guidance clinics do not even attempt systematic psychiatric diagnosis, all clinics keep records of the referral problem. A simple catalog of initial complaints is not very helpful. It can be well-nigh endless, and some sort of grouping has to be introduced. For his survey, Gilbert assigned the referral problems to one of the following ten categories: "mental retardation; academic difficulties; aggressive and antisocial behavior; passive, withdrawn, asocial behavior; emotional instability and anxiety symptoms; hyperactivity and motor symptoms; sexual behavior problems; toilet training; speech defects; and miscellaneous" *(1957, p. 38)*. Describing the kinds of patients encountered by a clinical child psychologist, A. O. Ross *(1959)* used four phenotypical categories: "the child manifesting aggressive behavior," "the child manifesting withdrawn behavior and physical symptoms," "the child manifesting bizarre behavior," and "the child manifesting learning difficulties" *(1959 p. 59-70)*. These are examples of categorization of problem behavior without reference to either its etiology or gravity. As a diagnostic scheme, mere paraphrasing of the initial complaint into fancier words seems grossly inadequate. It is like the diagnosis of "mutism" for a child who does not talk. Hopefully, the diagnostic statement goes beyond the initial information provided by the parent and conveys information about cause and kind of emotional disorder.

Examinatoin of other schemes of diagnostic classification reveals certain grouping principles which are based on the four key questions regarding etiology or effect. The differences among various systems of classification lie chiefly in the relative emphasis on one or another of these criteria.

Etiology: Is the behavior organic or functional in origin?

Etiology: Is the disturbance the result of inner conflict or of conflict between the child and reality?

Effect: Does the disturbance result in suffering for the patient or in suffering for other people?

Effect: How much of the individual's functioning is disturbed?

Etiology: Organic or Functional?

All the diagnostic systems in childhood psychopathology include a category of disease entitled "organic disorders." In some schemes this is one of nine or ten diagnostic possibilities *(Chess, 1959; Pearson, 1949)*. In other schemes it is a major subdivision, as in the standard nomenclature of the American Psychiatric Association (used also by *Beller, 1962*), which divides mental disorders into three basic groups: those associated with organic brain disturbances, those occurring in the absence of organic brain disturbance, and mental deficiency in the absence of demonstrable organic brain disease. In each basic group, there are secondary divisions designating the presence of psychotic, neurotic, and behavioral reactions. Similarly, one of the two major divisions offered by M. L. Hutt and R. G. Gibby is entitled "constitutional problems" *(1957)*. This is intended to include all disturbances with a somatogenic basis and includes miscellaneous physical deficiencies and constitutional inadequacies as well as neurological abnormalities. But a review of the number of subdivisions and the space allotted to discussing them reveals that organic disorders are not given a place equal to the other major categories: mental subnormality and functional behavior disorders. Functional disorders comprise the bulk of what are commonly termed "behavior problems in childhood."

In practice, it is not easy either to establish or to rule out an organic basis for a behavior disorder. Children with clear-cut organic conditions (e.g., inflammatory disease of the brain, traumatic brain injury, neurologic degenerative disease) are treated by a pediatrician or neurologist, and seldom find their way to a child psychology facility. Concern for their physical well-being is uppermost, and the associated behavioral disturbances are secondary. The children seen in child guidance clinics, when examined, are rarely found to have neurological damage or if they do, the findings are considered insufficient to explain the child's problem. On the other hand, the significance of minor neurological abnormalities, such as may be revealed by an electroencephalogram, is much disputed (See Chapter 7). Clinicians have their predilections for minimizing or maximizing such findings. In later chapters, when we discuss learning problems and psychotic disturbances, specific examples of the different weighting of organic factors in etiology will be given.

It is unfortunate if the need for labels forces one to take an either-or position. There should be no dichotomy between organic and functional conditions. Mentally retarded children and children with known organic brain damage have feelings and internal conflicts, experience anxiety, and employ defense mechanisms just as do children without organic deficiencies. The emotional problem may be secondary to the organic condition, it may be concurrent, or it may be coincidental. A child with a convulsive disorder may also suffer from shyness and behave asocially because of her dread of exposure; another child might become aggressive and antisocial because of inconsistencies in parental discipline caused by her parents' anxiety about the convulsions. These are indirect results of an organic handicap. It is also possible for a child to develop anxiety for reasons unrelated to convulsive disorder.

Conversely, many conditions which are considered primarily functional may well have an organic component. Not everyone with the same conflicts or experiences will develop the same symptom. Moreover, symptoms tend to run in families, no doubt as a result of identification and learning, but genetic factors probably also play a part. Psychological problems will be expressed in ways determined, in some measure, by an inherited constitution which is organic in the broad sense of the word.

For example, a child who is extremely active may show his problems by "acting out." A child with a sensitive autonomic nervous system may develop psychosomatic complaints as a result of trauma. A child with a predisposition to allergies may develop asthma under stress. A child with mixed cerebral dominance may develop a reading handicap if psychological conflicts also arise. A child with a spastic bladder may develop bed-wetting. Examples could be multiplied indefinitely; they serve only to illustrate the overdetermination of behavior.

Mental Subnormality. In psychiatric nomenclature, mental deficiency in the absence of demonstrable organic brain disease is classified separately. Beller also presents it as a classification intermediate between organic and functional disorders (1962). The determination is based on observation, difficulties in learning, and intelligence testing. In Beller's words

. . . so-called constitutional mental deficiency without discernible physical signs or organic factors is a syndrome which, evidently, can neither be classified as a functional disorder nor as a behavior disorder with an organic basis. It refers to an arrested or delayed development of social and intellectual skills, *the origin of which is as yet unknown,* and one which, to date, has resisted most attempts at modification through physical, educational, or psychological treatment methods.*

It is doubtful whether slow development and a low IQ merit a separate classification. Mental retardation is now viewed as a symptom rather than as a disease, a symptom which may arise from cultural, emotional, organic, or hereditary factors, singly or in combination. Therefore, it should be classified as primarily organic or functional. It is a unique symptom in that it pro-

---

*Quoted from E. K. Beller, *The Clinical Process* (New York: The Macmillan Company, 1962), p. 165. Reprinted by permission.

duces certain complications in the wake of unavoidable frustrations and disappointments for both parents and child, but many of these complications can be ameliorated. Unfortunately, the diagnosis of mental retardation carries with it a morbid connotation of untreatability which suggests that the clinician has no further responsibility beyond establishing its existence. In the author's opinion, mental subnormality should not be the basis of a major diagnostic category, any more than enuresis, convulsive disorder, or giftedness. Retardation is a highly important feature of the child's total personality, but its significance for etiology or prognosis is often overrated.

Etiology: Is the Conflict Inner or Outer?

Reactive versus internalized behavior disorder is an etiological subdivision within the broader category of functional disorders. It is the basis of C. M. Louttit's scheme of classification, in which *direct primary behavior problems* are differentiated from *indirect primary behavior problems (1947)*. The "direct" problems are seen as the "direct outcome of environmental forces operating upon the child" *(p. 20)*. The "indirect" problems cannot be explained in terms of current circumstances. They may be attributable to past circumstances but, by the process of internalization, or learning, they have become an inherent part of the child's personality, not modifiable by simple changes in his environment. Psychoneuroses and psychoses are included in the indirect primary behavior problems.

Louttit states that classification should not be made on the basis of complaints presented at the initial interview.

The true differentials lie in the experiential history preceding the specific act or series of acts. Thus, the allocation of a certain type of problem—e.g., refusal to eat, enuresis, stealing, fears, night terrors, stuttering, temper tantrums, truancy, masturbation, or what not—to one or the other class cannot be done with finality. Rather, children exhibiting these problems are classified. *(1947, p. 20.)*

In view of this statement, it is surprising that Louttit proceeds with a tabular summary of symptoms divided into "direct primary" and "indirect primary" *without* reference to experiential history. Enuresis, for example, is "direct primary." Apparently the necessity of putting some order into the material for purposes of presentation and discussion forced him to make arbitrary classification on the basis of symptoms alone.

This etiological concept (i.e., of direct or indirect reaction) is incorporated in most of the diagnostic systems, although the specific wording varies. Stella Chess uses the term *reactive behavior disorder* to describe behavior disorders which are "reactive to external circumstances, including environmental handling which may be inappropriate to the particular child" *(1959)*. G. H. J. Pearson starts his list of nine psychological illnesses in children with *direct reactions to present environmental stress;* the other eight diagnoses are referable to internalized conditions *(1949)*. Hutt and Gibby propose a category entitled, *transient, adaptive problems*. Problems listed under this heading are associated with deviations in physical growth, with physical illness, or with stresses and conflicts. The characteristic common to this class of disturbances is that "no *fundamental* alterations in the properties of the ego have occurred and that the reaction pattern is likely to be *transient* and *reversible*" *(1957, p. 134)*. They imply that the behavior is justified by the external circumstances and stress the word "adaptive" instead of "reactive." This category is contrasted with other ego disturbances which are considered "non-adaptive" to reality, or internalized.

Beller criticizes the concept of reactivity, or adaptiveness in this sense, as a basis for differential diagnosis, pointing out that if adverse environmental influences persist, some internalization is certain to occur *(1962)*. He is one of the few to discard reactivity as a basis for grouping. In an individual case, it is no more difficult to assess the current environmental factors than to assess the organic factors. In either etiological framework, it is rare to find a case which is 100 per cent one thing or the other. A child may suddenly develop a problem as a consequence of some events, and it may look like a reactive disturbance. But it may be difficult to determine if the reaction is justified by the event. Events have differing impacts on people, depending on their age, sensitization, and interpretation. If reality exists by virtue of someone's perception of it, it cannot be conceived of as totally extrinsic. Almost every case is a mixture of internal and external factors.

There is a rule of thumb which is applied in psychoanalytically oriented child guidance clinics with regard to possible internalization of problems. Under normal circumstances, it is expected that the problems of pre-school children have *not* become internalized and are still quickly responsive to environmental modification. On the other hand, children over five or six are far more complex and more likely to suffer from internal conflicts. This rule does not apply so well to the mentally or physically handicapped child or to the child whose environment includes some gross pathology or deprivation.

The Diagnosis of Psychoneurosis. The concept of internalization is the hub of the diagnosis of neurosis. In the words of Stella Chess: "When the behavioral difficulties in a reactive behavior disorder have become fixated patterns which the child brings even to favorable situations, the term 'neurotic' is appropriately used" *(1959, p. 89)*. She proposes three subdivisions: neurotic behavior disorders, neurotic character disorders, and neurosis. The three are distinguished by the degree of fixation and severity of the disorder.

The greatest elaboration of neurotic disturbances is made by G. H. J. Pearson who distinguishes seven forms of neurosis: acute and chronic anxiety state; anxiety hysteria; conversion hysteria; organ neurosis; compulsion neurosis; perversion; and character neurosis *(1949)*. In this, Pearson follows the psychoanalytically oriented nomenclature for adult patients, in order to establish a continuum between psychopathology in childhood and adult life. Since psychoanalytic therapy has been largely restricted to the neurotic disorders, it is the psychoanalyst who has learned to make the fine psychological distinctions which form the basis of diagnostic groupings within the general category of "psychoneurosis."

Character Neuroses in Children. The classical forms of neurosis in childhood are the subject matter of a later chapter, but the diagnosis of character neuroses illustrates a theoretical principle of classification pertinent to this discussion of nosology. The term sometimes refers to a basic defect in moral character, as in the so-called constitutional psychopath, thought to be totally lacking in conscience because of some inherent fault. The more common meaning of "character disorder" is derived from the psychoanalytic concept of character, which is not tied to morality. Here, character is almost synonymous with personality, in that it refers to the aggregate of the individual's usual patterns of behavior.

In contrast to simple neuroses, character disturbances are more pervasive and are constructed out of habitual behavior without any conscious feeling of anxiety. Beller illustrates the difference well by contrasting an individual with a "compulsive character" and one with a "compulsive neurosis." The individual with a compulsive character is overconcerned with orderliness, meticulously precise, rigid about the proper way of doing things, and so on:

While his attitudes may restrict his life activities, impose hardship on those close to him, and result in much irritation for himself and others, he does not experience his own exaggerated valuation of order as a problem and has no insight into its pathological nature. When his rigid adherence to orderliness gets him into difficulty, he blames external circumstances.[*]

The individual with a neurotic symptom such as a hand-washing compulsion, however, suffers from his disturbance and is aware that his difficulty is largely internal. In the character disorder, the pathological behavior is part of the total personality, ego-syntonic, fitting the patient's idea of what he should be. In a neurotic, the pathological behavior is ego-alien, not accepted by the person as a good part of himself. Considerable effort was made, formerly, to distinguish between character and neurotic difficulties, particularly because the neurotic was thought to be more treatable.

The distinction between character disorders and neurotic illness has been carried over in the field of child psychopathology and is to be found in the diagnostic systems of Beller, Chess, and Pearson. However, the criterion of ego-alien versus ego-syntonic does not apply well to children; the child with the insight to recognize that a symptom is foolish is a rare child. Usually he views his problem, if he thinks of it at all, as externally caused or as the result of some physical peculiarity. A school phobia is rationalized on the basis of the teacher's meanness. Failure at school is attributed to insufficient time. Bed-wetting is considered the result of some vague physical weakness.

In children, the difference between a character disturbance and a neurotic illness is revealed more effectively by the *chronicity* of the disorder. Neurotic illnesses are likely to have a sudden,

acute onset in childhood, whereas the onset of character disorders is more insidious and difficult to date. Another useful criterion is the presence or absence of anxiety. The neurotic child usually has what he would call "scared" or "worried" feelings; the child with the character disorder is less likely to suffer from anxiety. Here again, however, one finds a preponderance of mixed types, containing both neurotic and character problems.

Effect: Who Suffers?

Differentiation on the basis of the effect of the behavior disorder, rather than on its cause, provides the basis for L. Ackerson's classification of behavior problems as either "personality problems" or "conduct problems" *(1931)*. Personality problems result primarily in suffering for the child; conduct problems create suffering for others. There is no other diagnostic system in clinical use which stresses the social effect to this extent. It is included, in a less important way, in Louttit's subdivision of direct primary behavior problems into those with "limited social significance" and those with "serious social significance." Although Ackerson's dichotomy is not widely used, many classification systems take note of the social aspect of the disturbance. Such diagnostic terms as "antisocial behavior" or "psychopathic personality" *(Chess, 1959)* imply that the child vents his emotions with little, if any, inner discomfort.

A Factorial Approach to Diagnostic Classification. One unique research study, employing statistical rather than judgmental methods, suggests this same dichotomy into inner and outer-directed pathology. D. R. Peterson states that, before the etiology and treatment of a child's behavior disorders can be sensibly examined, the disorders themselves must be defined. He studied 427 referral problems and reduced them to a list of 58. Teachers were then asked to rate 831 kindergarten and elemen-

---

[*]Beller, *op cit.*, p. 155.

tary school children on these problems, in three degrees of severity. After a complicated statistical analysis of these ratings, two factors emerged: "The first implied a tendency to express impulses against society and was labelled 'conduct' problem. The second contained a variety of elements suggesting low self-esteem, social withdrawal, and dysphoric mood. It was called 'personality problem'" (1961, p. 208). Peterson refers to previous factorial studies by H. T. Himmelweit (1953) and by L. E. Hewitt and R. L. Jenkins (1946), who used different kinds of data (treatment records and questionnaire results of delinquent boys) and demonstrated the existence of two similar general factors. He makes no reference to Ackerson's identical diagnostic differentiation. Another attempt at factorial analysis of children's behavior problems yielded ten factors and incidentally demonstrated some of the problems in obtaining reliable ratings behavior and choosing items to be rated (Dreger et al., 1964).

Effect: Partial or Total Disability?

In the first edition Child Psychiatry, Kanner divided his textbook material into three main classes: (1) personality disorders forming essential features or sequels of physical illness; (2) personality disorders expressing themselves in the form of involuntary part-dysfunctions; and (3) personality disorders expressing themselves clearly as whole-dysfunctions of the individual (1935). This classification stresses the extent to which the child's functioning is disturbed.

Some notation about the degree of disturbance is usual in diagnostic statements. Excluding severe mental subnormality and organic illnesses, the only behavior disorder in childhood which invariably results in total disability (or nearly so) is psychosis. All psychopathology, by definition, has some disabling effect and, in their most severe forms, neuroses, psychosomatic illnesses, and other psychological conditions can cripple a child as much as psychosis. But psychosis always has a serious effect, as well as a relatively poor prognosis. There is considerable controversy about the etiology of childhood psychosis, and many psychiatrists, like Lauretta Bender (1947), classify it as primarily organic rather than functional. Essentially, the diagnosis of psychosis is based on the absence of normal interpersonal relationships, poor reality testing, the severity of the symptoms, and the malignant effect on every facet of development. Childhood psychosis is a good example of diagnosis which is based on consensus of opinion regarding totality of malfunctioning and prognosis rather than etiology.

Diagnosis, in Learning Theory. Most of the recent diagnostic schemes have followed general medical tradition and, at the same time, have borrowed liberally from psychoanalytic theory. The study of childhood problems has a heritage from a field other than medicine, namely, education. Early in the twentieth century, a group of educators in Austria, Germany, and Switzerland founded the movement of *Heilpadagogik*, or remedial education. This group was concerned with the learning and behavior problems of school children and what they could do to alleviate these problems. The focus was on treatment, on the present and the immediate future of the children, rather than on etiology and past history. Diagnosis was in terms of current events and conscious motivations, which are accessible to educational modification. In the modern version of this approach, childhood emotional disorders are diagnosed as failures in learned behavior, and are not considered analogous to physical illness. Behavioral symptoms are explained in terms of stimulus generalization and reinforcement of the symptom by secondary gains such as anxiety reduction.

One of the few efforts to systematically classify maladjustment in children on the basis of learning theory is T. Pick's. He makes the conventional differentiation between organic and functional by positing three major categories: "(1) organic-structural (e.g., brain injury); (2) biochemical-functional (e.g., endocrine disturbance); and (3) learning-psychological" *(1961, p. 137)*. The third category is further subdivided into those disturbances attributable to : (*a*) lack of learning; (*b*) inappropriate learning; and (*c*) learning of conflict. "Lack of learning" is another way of saying "lack of training," and refers to parental deficiencies in child rearing. "Inappropriate learning" refers to deficiencies in the models the parents provide for identification. Learning of conflict "could best be regarded as a special case of inappropriate learning in which anxiety, including guilt as a special kind of anxiety, was attached to behavior instrumental to need-reduction, in other words, to pleasurable behavior" *(p. 141)*. A simple example of this is furnished by the toddler who learns to climb on a chair to reach the cookies. His behavior (i.e., moving and climbing on the chair) is instrumental to his getting the cookies, which is need-reducing since he is presumably hungry and wants to eat them. But if the child has been forbidden to eat the cookies, the behavior is conflictual and gives rise to guilt and anxiety as well as to gratification. One could say that the child "learned a conflict." His disobedient behavior gets him the cookies, but it also creates the danger of parental disapproval. This simple formulation is easy to follow because the conflict is between immediate gratification and the possibility of disapproval, and both are real. The formulation becomes much more complicated when the troublesome conflicts are compounded of fantasy as well as reality.

Pick contrasts "neurotic conflict" with "sociological conflict." Neurotic conflict is conflict between an instinctual drive, or a primary motive, and a secondary, more socialized motive (e.g., the cookie-stealing toddler). Sociological conflict results when the individual has learned behavior appropriate to one setting but inadequate for another setting. He is not in trouble because of a conflict of motives within himself, but because he cannot quickly enough adapt his behavior to the demands of a different environment. In Pick's opinion, many, perhaps most, cases within the purview of child guidance are of this order. His distinction between neurotic and sociological conflict resembles the differentiation between internalized reactive behavior already discussed.

W. K. Boardman has illustrated learning theory diagnosis and treatment in a report of a "brief behavior disorder" in a 5½-year-old boy. When his mother was hospitalized for nine weeks, Rusty became aggressive, disobedient, enuretic, and ran away from home and school. His problems were understood, or diagnosed, as voluntary attempts to manipulate his parents and achieve his own way. In Pick's words, he exemplified a mixture of "lack of learning" (i.e., learning to behave himself) and "inappropriate learning" (i.e., he knows that misbehavior gets attention). The treatment was whatever punishment was necessary to teach Rusty to avoid the bad behavior. This culminated in the "whipping of his life," and also the turning point in overcoming his misbehavior. "Rusty was learning that rebellion, while exciting, was too costly in terms of creature comforts when he went beyond certain limits" *(Boardman, 1962, p. 296)*.

Of course, this case could be interpreted very differently. A psychoanalytically oriented practitioner would be concerned with the reason for an outbreak of hostility when his mother was seriously ill. Some of the behavior Boardman describes was dangerous to Rusty, some even appearing almost suicidal. This would lead one to suspect a profound guilt (not at all unreasonable in view of a teacher's remark to Rusty that if he did not behave better, his mother would return to the hospital). If this dynamic hypothesis were correct, the severe punishment he received might have cured his symptom, not because he learned, but because it relieved his profound and unconscious sense of guilt. In a diagnostic formulation using psychodynamic principles, there would be concern for all facets of his behavior, including the sudden onset of enuresis, not only the major antisocial symptoms of running away and disobedience to authority.

Psychotherapy is discussed in a later chapter; Rusty is quoted here to contrast diagnosis based on conscious factors and present reality circumstances (i.e., educational, or learning theory approach) with diagnosis based on unconscious factors and defensive efforts to ward off feelings of guilt and anxiety (i.e., dynamic, or psychoanalytically oriented approach). The learning theorist's attention is restricted to the child's relationship to the world; the psychoanalyst also pays attention to his inner feelings. In his critique of the Rusty report, D. R. Miller, commences by discussing the problem of parsimonious explanations (1962). An interpretation viewed by one clinician as superficial and incomplete is satisfactory to another who considers "complex psychodynamic factors" superfluous. The clinical facts, as well as the specific terms, included in a diagnosis depend on two attitudes of the diagnostician: He will be as thorough as he needs to be for his particular stake in the case; also, he will explain abnormal behavior with the same concepts he uses for understanding normal personality development. L. Breger and J. L. McGaugh point out that the "disagreement between the behaviorist and psychodynamic viewpoints seems to rest on a very real difference at the purely descriptive or observational level. The behaviorist looks at a neurotic and sees specific symptoms and anxiety. The psychodynamicist looks at the same individual and sees a complex intra- and interpersonal mode of functioning which may or may not contain certain observable fears or certain behavioral symptoms such as compulsive motor acts" (1965, p. 349). The psychoanalyst may be overly extravagant in searching for all possible relevances in understanding a symptom, but parsimonious explanations are likely to overlook the many forces and trends which working with and upon each other produce neurotic behavior.

Application of Diagnostic Principles

Diagnostic Dilemmas Unique to Childhood

Psychiatric nomenclature also troubles psychiatrists and psychologists who deal with adults, and diagnostic disagreement has been subjected to close scrutiny. In a study by C. H. Ward, et al., (1962) the reasons for diagnostic disagreement were grouped into three categories: inconstancy on the part of the patient (5 per cent); inconstancy on the part of the diagnostician (32.5 per cent); and inadequacy of the nosology (62.5 per cent). It is interesting that the patients were less inconstant than the physicians.

Those who would diagnose children have all the problems of the adult diagnostician, and more. The child is far from constant. He changes unpredictably, depending on circumstances and on his feeling about his interviewer. Since the child seldom comes to an interview on his own, it takes skill, or luck, to elicit significant psychological material, and the results vary with the experience and personality of the examiner.

Even more important, however, is the fact that the child is an immature organism; his constant changing is normal. One cannot be sure about adults, but one can be sure that a child will grow and change. Diagnosis becomes, in part, an answer to the question: "How much will the child grow out of this in the natural course of events?" The diagnostician asks himself, "What is the present problem, conflict, symptom, or whatever, going to do to the expected developmental process?" Still, the child matures and diagnosis is, in the final analysis, a developmental one. To quote Anna Freud:

. . . emphasis is thereby shifted from the purely clinical aspects of a case to the developmental aspect . . . "When diagnosing cases from this point of view, the child analyst or child psychiatrist has to be as intimate with the normal sequence of child development as he is familiar with the neurotic or psychotic disturbances of it. (1946, p. 92.)

A third difference between childhood and adult diagnosis is a corollary of the immaturity of the child. That is, classical forms of neurosis rarely exist in children. The child's personality is not fixed, and the crystallization of a neurosis does not occur. Symptoms do not spell a specific illness, as they typically do in adult mental illness. To quote Anna Freud again:

I recall the case of a little girl who could not go to sleep except when her slippers were placed in a particular way by her bed. This would seem to be part of a bedtime ceremonial which would belong to an obsessional neurosis but on looking further into this, it was a completely disturbed, restless child with uncontrolled motility and disturbed in every other area of her life and with no other obsessional symptoms. Similarly, a boy suffered from the compulsion to count but he had this symptom in the midst of anxiety and hysterical disturbances. Another boy whose main disturbance was an obsessional neurosis had a history of psychosomatic and hysterical symptoms. In the infant neurosis, symptoms may well be isolated or symptoms of one kind stuck in the middle of symptoms of another kind so that one asks is this an obsessional neurosis in the making where hysterical and anxiety

symptoms persist from former times, or is the child retaining this single (obsessional) symptom as a remnant of earlier developmental stages?*

A fourth difference is that the child is still very much under the influence of reality, primarily the reality provided by his parents. He is still being shaped. It is for this reason that the diagnostic process in child psychiatry includes the parents as well as the child. In adult psychiatry, consideration is also given to the pressures of reality, such as unemployment or family responsibilities, but one can arrive at a diagnostic formulation by observing how the person copes with these pressures. We do not expect a total change of personality to be produced by the loss of a job, an unsympathetic boss, a domineering mother-in-law, and the like. External conditions of stress exacerbate the emotional illness of the adult, but they do not determine the kind of illness he suffers.

Effectiveness of Diagnosis in Childhood Psychopathology

To serve any useful purpose, a diagnosis must convey information. This requires a common understanding of the words used and a careful definition of terms. At the least, the diagnosis should describe a symptom or a complex of symptoms in such a way that everyone gets the same picture. But it is not easy to arrive at a consensus of opinion even at this level. For example, the symptomatic diagnosis of enuresis is applied to all bed-wetters over the age of five by some and to those over eight by others. Another example is the diagnosis of reading disability. Most people reserve this term for children who have a specific reading problem, that is, they read poorly in relation to

---

*Quoted from Anna Freud, "Diagnosis and Assessment of Early Childhood Difficulties." Paper presented at the Philadelphia Association for Psychoanalysis, Philadelphia, Pa., May, 1954, p. 3. Reproduced by permission.

their mental age and their achievement in other academic subjects, but a few use the term for any child who is failing in reading.

A diagnosis based on symptoms alone can be very useful if the symptoms are precisely defined in operational terms. A good example is the clinical syndrome of "infantile autism" described by Kanner in 1942. His portrayal of the child's behavior is sufficiently complete and graphic to enable others to compare their patients against his model. One can say that a given child's behavior fits the description of infantile autism, and everyone knows how the child acts. Another clinical syndrome, that of "the brain-injured" child, was well described by A. A. Strauss and L. E. Lehtinen (1947). Clinicians recognize the description as characterizing a certain kind of child patient. But they do not always agree that the underlying cause is brain injury. With a new name, "the Strauss syndrome," the description was stripped of the implication of organic etiology and has remained useful to clinicians.

Symptomatic diagnoses of this kind are useful when they are of a well-described clinical syndrome which is familiar to those employing the diagnostic terms. The label they are given takes on a specific meaning. However, the language of normal and abnormal psychology soon becomes common property and subject to loose usage. For instance, many people know that the dictionary definition of autism is "withdrawal," and they may apply the term "autistic" to any child who seems withdrawn, although he may be only shy and timid. It is unfortunate that psychiatry has not, like medicine, given syndromes the names of their discoverers. This requires that the practitioner be familiar with a particular description and so ensures some degree of professional agreement about terms.

At the next level of utility, a diagnosis should contain some reference to etiology. There may be a positive statement about cause, as in, for instance, "post-traumatic enuresis," which indicates that the enuresis began after a specific traumatic event. Or there may be a negative statement, that is, the diagnosis may automatically rule out certain etiological possibilities. For instance, "reading disability" and "speech disability" exclude reading and speech difficulties resulting from mental retardation. On the other hand, although "infantile autism" was initially thought to rule out mental retardation, further observation has shown that the two conditions may coexist. There are relatively few diagnoses in child psychopathology which automatically exclude the possibility of other behavior disorders.

As we mentioned earlier, there is a dearth of diagnoses which name an etiological agent. Most behavior disorders are multiply determined and do not have a single explanation. The differentiation between organic and functional and, within the functional classification, between reactive and internalized, are attempts to furnish etiological diagnoses.

Finally, a diagnosis should suggest the prognosis and imply the treatment. The American Psychiatric Association's nomenclature emphasized prognosis by classifying "adjustment reaction of childhood" within the broad group of "transient situational personality disorders," since the word "transient" implies a good prognosis.

But there have been few long-range studies of the behavior problems of children, and so there is little information against which to project prognoses. And almost all the follow-up studies that have been made have been studies of the effectiveness of treatment. The factor studied has been treatment versus no treatment, not the different kinds of clinical problems and their natural development.

It is the relationship between diagnosis and therapy which is probably most crucial. Many of the diagnostic terms imply prognosis which may unduly prejudice the therapist. The morbid connotations of mental retardation have already been described. Another diagnosis, equally dire, is "constitutional psychopath." The term implies an inherent lack in the personality, a lack independent of the environment, and to accept this concept of cause is to preclude treatment. We must beware the self-fulfilling prophecy, the diagnosis which so affects the treatment that it becomes half-hearted or modified, and hence does not work, and thereby corroborates the poor prognosis. Kanner spoke eloquently about diagnostic terms:

"Who is a neuropath, a psychopath, a neurotic child, a delinquent? Such terms, though applicable at times, have much too often been used as swear words rather than well-founded diagnoses" *(1944 p. 767)*.

And all too often, we diagnosticians call someone we like and are sorry for a "neurotic delinquent," thereby making him a good candidate for treatment. But someone for whom we do not have a positive feeling we call a "psychopath," thereby expressing our doubts and discouragement.

The foregoing discussion can be summarized in a series of recommendations for clinicians:

1. Every effort should be made to standardize the definition of symptoms and to develop more clinical descriptions which are clearly identifiable and which do not imply causation.
2. It should be understood that an initial diagnosis is inevitably tentative and accepted that diagnosis is a continuing process, subject to change as new information is gathered.
3. Diagnostic formulations should include all approaches already mentioned, i.e., symptomatology, etiology, prognosis, and treatment, rather than be limited to a single approach or system of classification.
4. In recognition of the multiple determination of behavior, diagnoses should show the proportional weight of the contributory factors, rather than be formulated as single entities of disease or phrased in terms of simple yes-or-no dichotomies.
5. One should eschew awe of diagnostic labels. A label does not make a child treatable or untreatable. Moreover, consideration must be given to the meaning of diagnostic terms to others who will come into contact with the case. The diagnostician must be aware of what other people may make out of his terms.
6. Diagnosis should not be a dead end for the family. Reports should be of practical utility to those who will continue to see the child, i.e., the family, teachers, and therapists. W. Wolfensberger warns that diagnosis is an intellectual exercise which gives the professional worker a deceptive feeling of accomplishment. "In diagnosis, the professional can find many rewards and a good deal of security—just the opposite of what the parent typically finds in it" *(1965, p. 30)*. Diagnosticians should have the opportunity and responsibility for following some proportion of their intake cases in order to improve their diagnostic skills and reporting ability.
7. There is need for long-range studies of children with behavior problems, both to improve our predictive judgment and to enable clinicians to select those children whose prognoses show that they are in the most urgent need of treatment.

References for Chapter 5

Ackerson, L., *Children's Behavior Problems.* Chicago: The University of Chicago Press, 1931.

Beller, E. K., *The Clinical Process.* New York: The Macmillan Company, 1962.

Bender, Lauretta, "Childhood Schizophrenia," *American Journal of Orthopsychiatry,* XVII (1947), 40–56.

Boardman, W. K., "Rusty: A Brief Behavior Disorder," *Journal of Consulting Psychology,* XXVI (1962), 293–97.

Breger, Louis and James L. McGaugh, "Critique and Reformation of 'Learning-Theory' Approaches to Psychotherapy and Neurosis," *Psychological Bulletin,* LXIII (1965), 338–58.

Chess, S., *An Introduction to Child Psychiatry.* New York: Grune & Stratton, Inc., 1959.

Diagnostic and Statistical Manual: Mental Disorders. Washington, D.C.: American Psychiatric Association, 1952.

Dreger, R. M., *et al.,* "Behavioral Classification Project," *Journal of Consulting Psychology,* XXVIII (1964), 1–13.

Freud, Anna, "Diagnosis and Assessment of Early Childhood Difficulties." Paper presented at Philadelpiha Association for Psychoanalysis, Philadelphia, May, 1954.

————, *The Psychoanalytical Treatment of Children,* Part III "Indications for Child Analysis" (1945). London: Imago Publishing Co., 1946.

Gilbert, G. M., "A Survey of 'Referral Problems' in Metropolitan Child Guidance Centers," *Journal of Clinical Psychology,* XIII (1957), 37–42.

Hewitt, L. E. and R. L. Jenkins, *Fundamental Patterns of Maladjustment: The Dynamics of their Origin.* Springfield, Ill.: Green, 1946.

Himmelweit, H. T., "A Factorial Study of Children's Behavior Problems," cited in H. J. Eysenck, *The Structure of Human Personality.* London: Methuen & Co., Ltd., 1953.

Hutt, M. L. and R. G. Gibby, *Patterns of Abnormal Behavior.* Boston: Allyn and Bacon, Inc., 1957.

Kanner, L., "Autistic Disturbance in Affective Contact," *Nervous Child,* II (1942–43), 217–50.

————, "Behavior Disorders in Childhood," in J. McV. Hunt, *Personality and the Behavior Disorders,* Vol. 2. New York: The Ronald Press Company, 1944.

————, *Child Psychiatry.* Springfield, Ill.: Charles C Thomas, Publisher, 1935.

Louttit, C. M., *Clinical Psychology of Children's Behavior Problems.* New York: Harper & Row, Publishers, Inc., 1947.

Macfarlane, J., L. Allen, and M. P. Honzik, *A Developmental Study of the Behavior Problems of Normal Children between 21-months and 14 years.* Berkeley, Calif.: University of California Press, 1954.

Miller, D. R., "On the Definition of Problems and the Interpretation of Symptoms," *Journal of Consulting Psychology,* XXVI (1962), 302–5.

Pearson, G. H. J., *Emotional Disorders of Children.* New York: W. W. Norton & Company, Inc., 1949.

Peterson, D. R., "Behavior Problems of Middle Childhood," *Journal of Consulting Psychology,* XXV (1961), 205–9.

Pick, T., "Behavior Theory and Child Guidance," *Journal of Child Psychology and Psychiatry,* II (1961), 136–47.

Ross, A. O., *The Practice of Clinical Child Psychology.* New York: Grune & Stratton, Inc., 1959.

Strauss, A. A. and L. E. Lehtinen, *Psychopathology and Education of the Brain-injured Child.* New York: Grune & Stratton, Inc., 1947.

Stroh, G., "On the Diagnosis of Childhood Psychosis," *Journal of Child Psychology and Psychiatry,* I (1960), 238–43.

Valentine, C. W., *The Normal Child and Some of His Abnormalities.* Baltimore: Penguin Books, Inc., 1956.

Wolfensberger, Wolf, "Embarrassments in the Diagnostic Process," *Mental Retardation,* III (1965), June, pp. 29–31.

Ward, C. H. *et al.,* "The Psychiatric Nomenclature: Reasons for Diagnostic Disagreement," *Archives of General Psychiatry,* VII (1962), 198–205.

6

PROBLEMS IN FEEDING AND TOILET TRAINING

In Chapter 5, we emphasized the importance of trying to understand the meaning of superficial behavior. A symptom is not a diagnosis. It must be interpreted in terms of the objective situation, the developmental · history, and the total personality of the child. The goal of diagnosis is to find the underlying causes of overt behavior, a task made very difficult by the dullness of our fact-finding tools and the multiplicity of the causes. In this chapter, we begin with a discussion of symptomatic behavior, followed by discussion of possible causation. It would perhaps be neater to start with clinical diagnosis, but this approach seldom fits the real situation as we encounter it. The parents bring the child because he does not eat properly, wets his bed, soils his clothes. He does not bear a convenient label identifying him as mentally retarded, psychoneurotic, or hard of hearing. The clinician begins with the complaint and gradually works out the diagnosis.

Disturbances in feeding and toilet training are the first clinical problems we consider, because they usually start in the first two or three years. Even when the symptom appears later, it is partly a regression to this early period. There are other behavior disorders which probably have an equally early origin (e.g., child psychosis and psychosomatic disease), but they are much less common. In E. K. Beller's review of the clinical records of 110 pre-school children referred to the Child Development Center of New York City, feeding disturbances were a presenting problem of 63 of the children (56 per cent) and about three-fourths of these disturbances were said to have started during the first year of life (1962). In her presentation of the symptomatology of 43 children (aged 2 years and 3 months to 4 years and 11 months) referred to a child guidance clinic in Maudsley Hospital, London, England, S. Wolff indicated that 38 children (84 per cent) had one or more "habit symptoms," e.g., eating disturbances, enuresis, soiling, and autoerotic habits (1961). These reports are based on very small samples, but the impression they give, that such disorders are the commonest reasons for referral of the pre-school child is probably correct. The reason for this is obvious: feeding and toilet training are very important in the first three years. It is not coincidental that psychoanalysts place the oral and anal phases of development in this same time span.

Other kinds of psychological difficulties are rarely detected, and even more rarely referred, in the first years. Much psychopathology which occurs in this early period is reconstructed from symptoms which cause concern only in retrospect. This is primarily because so little is expected of the infant. Reluctance to play actively or to feed himself, an absence of social imitation, a deficiency in physical or ego development, or a failure to establish a special relationship with the mother do not cause the concern that they should *in statu nascendi.* Until he walks, not much is expected of the infant.

The devastating effects of early maternal deprivation show up in impaired intellectual and emotional growth when the child is older (see Chapter 15). Children later diagnosed as psychotic have had histories of deviant development which were ignored. S. Brody has made a case for recognizing signs of disturbance in the first year of life *(1958),* but to recognize the symptoms she describes requires a keener eye and greater sophistication than most parents possess. Added to this is the closeness between the mother and the infant. So much behavior which overflows onto the infant is unconsciously determined. For a mother to be able to report her baby's behavior objectively would require her to be able to view herself objectively, a difficult task for any mother with a new infant.

Central Position of Feeding in the First Year of Life

Feeding is generally regarded as the most important single activity in the first year. The infant must be fed if he is to survive. Every new mother feels the weight of this responsibility; some mothers accept it with relish, but most feel some anxiety. The baby's growth is measured by his weight and length, and every visit to the pediatrician results in changes in the baby's diet and modifications of his feeding schedule. Nearly one-quarter of Benjamin Spock's bestselling *Baby and Child Care (1963)* is devoted to feeding. It is no wonder that food intake and amount of crying and sleeping are the sum and substance of the new mother's conversation and questions.

Feeding is also the child's earliest social experience. Interest in food precedes interest in people. The child is fed, and thus learns to associate people with the relief of his hunger pangs. His need for food, coupled with his total helplessness, is the basis of the infant's love for his mother. There are nonnutritive pleasures associated with feeding, also; the baby is held and cuddled. Arnold Gesell and Frances Ilg describe the feeding situation as a "growth matrix out of which other forms of adaptive, language, and social behavior emerge as though they were so many branchings from a main stem" *(1943, p. 311).*

Using experimental techniques, Brody tested the hypothesis that patterns of maternal behavior are more clearly visible in the feeding than in other situations. Her data were selected from a larger project carried out by the Research Department of the Menninger Foundation of Topeka between 1948 and 1951, in which 128 infants were observed by three individuals, at home and in the office, for some six hours each. She used the records of 32 mothers of four groups of 4 male and 4 female infants of 4, 12, 20, and 28 weeks. A five-point rating scale of "maternal response" was applied to six situations: feeding, cleaning, moving, touching, offering objects, and speaking. Other measures included the number of maternal acts and their consistency. On the basis of these maternal responses, the mothers were classified into four main groups: A, "sensitive, consistent, and attentive"; B, "less sensitive, less consistent, and somewhat overactive or overattentive"; C, "insufficiently sensitive, moderately inconsistent, but adequately attentive; and D, "hypersensitive, very inconsistent, and hyperactive." By a meticulous sorting process, she established that feeding provided the clearest indication of which of these four groups the maternal behavior fell into. The mothers displayed a greater variety of attitudes and more individuality of behavior during feeding than during the other five situations observed *(1956)*.

In addition to the statistical analysis, Brody described patterns of maternal behavior in feeding in terms of body contact, tempo, communication, and accessory behavior. She pointed out that the literature which refers to types of feeding, describes breast feeding versus bottle feeding, exact or flexible schedules, and physical positions of the infant during feeding. These criteria, attractively simple as they are, were shown to have little relation to maternal behavior. Breast feeding did not insure gentleness, intimacy, or restfulness. In any case, only 7 of the 32 babies were breast-fed. Feeding the baby when he was hungry, rather than on a schedule, was poorly related to the satisfaction of either the mother or the infant, and holding the baby did not necessarily add to his physical comfort. This may be the most important finding of all. It warns against drawing conclusions about either maternal attitudes or the amount of infantile gratification from single bits of information.

Relationship of Infant Feeding Practices to Later Development

The general idea that oral gratification is an important determinant of personality development is commonly attributed to psychoanalytic theorists, although others have said very much the same thing *(Gesell and Ilg, 1937; Aldrich, 1928)*. In his famous review of research on "Infant Care and Personality," H. Orlansky wrote: "Reasoning from Freudian theory, pediatricians and psychiatrists have advocated systems of infant care which they believe will promote the growth of secure and unneurotic personalities" *(1949, p. 1)*. It was Orlansky's opinion that psychoanalytically based recommendations include prolonged breast feeding, a demand schedule, and gradual and late weaning, and that the importance of unrestricted

infantile gratification is emphasized and all frustration is delayed. In practice, as well as theory, child psychoanalysts are actually as conscious of the dangers of fixation from excessive indulgence as they are of the dangers of deprivation. And, in the 1920's and '30's, there was another influence which encouraged permissiveness, namely, the findings of Gesell and others about the role of maturation. An incomplete understanding of maturational determinants of behavior would also lead one into laissez-faire child rearing. One might simply wait for the child to relinquish one form of gratification for another more mature kind of behavior. But it was the dogmatic pronouncements and mental health promises borrowing psychoanalytic terms which caught the attention of the researchers.

Brody reviewed 14 reports which related breast feeding and the age of weaning to various kinds of personality measures. The measures included emotional symptoms, teachers' ratings, interviews with parents, play with dolls, personality inventories, self-administered rating scales, and projective tests such as the Thematic Apperception Test *(1956)*. One of the few investigations which came close to being longitudinal was that of B. C. F. and C. H. Rogerson *(1939)*. They traced 109 London children who were observed in clinics during infancy and reported significant advantages, particularly in school grades seven years later, for the breast-fed group. However, the 14 reports are inconsistent and contradictory. In addition, the information was usually sketchy and based on the mothers' recollections and the measures of personality were often inadequate.

The 14 studies are open to even more serious theoretical criticism. Mothers do exactly the same thing for entirely different reasons. One mother may breast feed her child because she wishes to be one of the *avant-garde* who subscribe to breast feeding almost as a cult; another may choose breast feeding because of the intimacy which it offers; another mother because she cannot afford the equipment for bottle feeding. W. C. Kvaraceus found that 75 per cent of the delinquents he studied had been breast fed for an extended period, and pointed out that breast feeding might be related to poor planning and economic deprivation, the very same conditions which foster delinquency. It is not so crucial *what* a mother does with respect to specific practices, but rather her reasons, her confidence and pleasure in what she does for the baby, and her ability to adapt her personality to that of the baby. G. H. J. Pearson, a child psychoanalyst, concluded his study of the early histories of 72 problem children with the remark that "parental attitudes exert a more important influence on the formation of the child's personality than the actual events" *(1931, p. 290)*. The merit of this observation became clearer in subsequent research, and gradually attention shifted to the study of parental attitudes and their effect on the child's personality (see Chapter 15).

In retrospect, some of our early concepts of cause and effect seem naïve. Some investigators expected to find a direct relationship between simple facts such as breast feeding or age of weaning, and adult personality characteristics as complex as dependency. Such expectations were, indeed, fostered by early psychoanalytic concepts of character formation. Writing in 1924, Karl Abraham described such characteristics as "generosity" and "imperturbable optimism" as arising from excessive indulgence: "Some people are dominated by the belief that there will always be some kind person—a representative of the mother, of course—to care for them and to give them everything they need. This optimistic belief condemns them to inactivity" *(1924, 1949, p. 399)*. He contrasted these people with other character types who are burdened throughout their life with the after-effects of ungratifying suckling: "In their social behavior, these people always seem to be asking for something, either in the form of a modest request or of an aggressive demand.... One might almost say that they cling like leeches to other people" *(1924, 1949, p. 401)*.

Other character traits were traced back to displacement within the oral sphere:

The longing to experience gratification by way of sucking has changed to a need to give by way of the mouth, so that we find in them, besides a permanent longing to obtain everything, a constant need to communicate themselves orally to other people. This results in an obstinate urge to talk, connected in most cases with a feeling of overflowing. *(Abraham, 1924, 1949, p. 401.)*

These early formulations were narrowly focussed on the possible transformations of the libidinal drives by the nature of reality experience. Freud and Abraham were also impressed by the role of inherited disposition in personality. But their expositions dealt largely with the effect of experience and, reading some of the papers on character types, one might conclude that the individual's fate was sealed as he passed through the psychosexual stages of orality, anality, and genitality. The importance to personality of correction of behavior, or of its reinforcement, as well as of identification with parents, was overlooked.

It would be an equal error, however, to hold that infantile experiences have *no* effect. There is a continuity in child development; a child's responses are modified by his history. His readiness and tolerance for the frustrations of the second year (toilet training, discipline, and so on) are partly determined by his affection for his mother and by the tolerance for frustration which he has developed as he waited for his food.

Emotional symptoms in childhood, to say nothing of personality, can never be traced to any one aspect of infant feeding. From the standpoint of mental health, the goals in this period are: (1) to preserve the physical well-being of the baby; (2) to create an enjoyable experience in which two people participate; (3) to encourage the baby's natural inclinations to give up the bottle or breast (at 7 to 9 months) and to feed himself (at 10 to 14 months); and (4) to allow the baby to retain his pleasure in eating. Different mothers and babies achieve these goals in different ways. Fashions in feeding have changed, but many still do what is natural for them to do. When rigid feeding schedules were in vogue, many mothers adjusted them according to the rhythm of their babies; when demand feeding became fashionable, many mothers tried to work their way toward some regularity in feeding.

Infant Feeding Disorders

Most of the difficulties of the first year are brought to the pediatrician, even when there are major psychological components. Colic is one of the earliest complaints. It has many names and definitions and is not directly a feeding difficulty, but it is closely related. Briefly, colic is sharp intestinal pain, accompanied by abdominal distension, flexion of the legs, and loud crying. Spock distinguishes this syndrome from "irritable crying," which is not associated with pain and is relieved by holding or carrying the baby.

Colic is distressing, and the causes are usually sought in the baby's diet. This leads to a feverish search for a new formula or even a new pediatrician, for pediatricians take a casual attitude toward colic. Colic is never fatal and is outgrown within three to five months, with or without the pediatrician. It is much more common in firstborn infants and is rarely, if ever, observed in a hospital setting. It is therefore thought that colic is somehow a product of maternal behavior, a re-

action to the mother's nervous tension.

Many pediatricians stress the role of inborn constitutional differences in producing colic. H. F. Meyer describes colicky babies as "tense, vigorous, dynamic, stimulated, and lusty" and seems convinced that they are born this way and that they continue to manifest these temperamental qualities throughout life. He gives these babies a good prognosis; they are early in motor development, and they are vigorous and aggressive, qualities which can lead to creativity and leadership *(1960, p. 229)*. Spock remarks that many of these colicky infants are also hypertonic, unusually tense and restless, and easily startled *(1963)*. He infers that these are innate characteristics, although he does not commit himself as to their permanence.

The psychological importance of colic lies less in its cause than in its effect on the relationship between the mother and the infant. It is very fatiguing to both parties. Spock astutely points out that, after a point, the parent feels spurned and even angry. In the wake of the anger comes shame and guilt, and efforts at suppression. He sympathetically advises the anxious mother to get away for relaxation and relief.

In feeding difficulties which do not involve physical allergies or gastrointestinal or nervous defects, the pediatrician stresses the role of parental anxiety. When the baby spits up his milk, does not finish his bottle, refuses new foods, or eats too often and too little at a time, the modern pediatrician tries to give the mother faith in the wisdom of the baby's appetite. "The baby is the one who knows how many calories his body needs and what his digestion can handle."[*]

The experiments of C. M. Davis are frequently quoted to encourage the

---

[*]Quoted from Benjamin Spock, *Baby and Child Care*, ed. Rev. Cardinal Grant (Pocket Books, Inc., 1963), pp. 49–50. Reproduced by permission.

mother. Davis arranged for 15 infants, eight to ten months of age, to be presented with a variety of foods at each meal. Each baby was free to choose what to eat, and how much. In spite of great individual differences in their choices, all the infants gradually selected a well-balanced diet, maintained excellent nutrition, and developed no feeding problems *(1928).* But the advice to "leave it to baby" is hard to follow. It is almost impossible if the mother is anxious, especially if she was herself a problem eater. She may well remember, from her own childhood, that urging and forcing did not work. Nevertheless, she helplessly repeats her mother's pattern, but guiltily, anxiously, and with irritation, at herself, her mother, and her baby. This is but one example of the important general principle that parents have special conflicts in handling problems which are a repetition of their own. Whenever a parent has a blind spot, it is worth exploring for evidence of the same difficulty a generation earlier.

Classification of Feeding Disorders

Feeding disorders can be classified in three ways. The first is symptomatic. A child may eat the wrong things (pica), may eat too little (in its extreme form, anorexia nervosa), or may eat too much (obesity). The second is in terms of the total personality disorder of which the feeding difficulty is a symptom. For instance, L. I. Lesser *et al.* divided their cases of anorexia nervosa into three groups, according to other features of the personality: predominantly hysterical, predominantly obsessive-compulsive, and predominantly schizoid *(1960).* A third basis of classification is the nature of the conflict which disturbs the normal function of eating, described by Anna Freud. On a symptomatic basis, she is concerned mainly with too little or excessive eating.

Anna Freud finds three sources of the conflict *(1946).* The first is organic. "Organic feeding disturbances" are changes or defects in the organism which directly or indirectly affect the drive to survive or his need for nourishment. Infants with severe brain damage, for instance, have difficulty sucking and chewing. But normal children may also have a transient organic difficulty. During illness or convalescence, the need for food is often markedly decreased, and the child may become a poor eater, temporarily. If it is then necessary, for medical reasons, to urge the child to eat or drink more than he wishes, a struggle may ensue. When he has recovered, the mother can withdraw, but if the illness has been prolonged or her anxiety has been great, eating may continue to be an issue.

Anna Freud's second category is "nonorganic disturbance of the instinctive process itself" *(1946, p. 120),* where eating has ceased to be a pleasure. In these situations, meals are tiresome, "forced labor rather than an occasion for wish-fulfillment" *(p. 123).* The child dawdles and fusses, is easily distracted, demands certain foods, snitches food between meals, and so on. The distraught mother coaxes, bribes, threatens, gives in, and may even spoon-feed a grown child. This is probably the most typical feeding disturbance, and it is easily understood in learning theory terms. Eating has become a hated situation because it is associated with struggle. On the other hand, there are certain psychological advantages accruing from the situation. It forces the mother to pay strict attention to the child, and it gives the child a sense of power. He can keep his parents tied up for hours; even if it is an angry sort of attention, it may be better than nothing. Children with such feeding problems eat very well at school or camp where there is no premium on their food intake.

The third category is "neurotic feeding disturbances." These are usually a further development of the second category. The problem has become internalized now, and the child has equal difficulty anywhere or with anyone. Food has become equal to the mother and, even in her absence, the child has disturbed feelings about food. By the mechanism of displacement, ambivalence toward his mother may be expressed in alternation between overeating and undereating; his resentment of her may be displayed in a stubborn dislike of food; his jealous need for her attention may be expressed in greediness, and so on. Anna Freud points out that the association between food and mother is reinforced when the mother offers food as if it were part of herself. Such mothers "are pleased and affectionate when the child accepts the food, and offended when food is rejected as if their love for the child had suffered a rebuff; they beg a badly eating child to eat 'for their sake'" (1946, p. 126).

Other neurotic conflicts, not involving the mother, may also interfere with eating. In discussing aggression, we observed that eating is two-sided. One has to like the food in order to eat it; on the other hand, the result of eating it is to destroy it. The aggressive component may become so laden with anxiety that a child is inhibited in the biting and swallowing of food, a conflict which may become particularly strong about eating something which once was animate. A child may then revolt against eating meat or fish as if he were responsible for the killing. It is possible that the child would not have such an extreme reaction against the very hint of cannibalism unless there were unusually strong aggressive impulses to ward off.

Other kinds of fantasies may intrude themselves. A child may object to certain foods because their consistency or color is reminiscent of feces. Such associations are by no means uncommon to the toddler who has recently discovered his bowel movements and learned to dislike them in the proper fashion of the adult world. In this developmental period, he is much occupied with anal matters and can find them everywhere. A somewhat older child may develop prejudices against foods which are red and thus remind him of blood, or against foods which contain seeds. The careful avoidance of seeds often comes from the mistaken notion that a seed grows in mother's stomach and becomes a baby. Even if he is not told this, he may have observed that a woman gets very fat before she produces a baby, and he may conclude that she ate something to make this baby and that the baby comes out through the anus. The older child, then, may be inhibited from eating by his fantasies about pregnancy. Boys can have this problem because, if reproduction is gastrointestinal, there is no reason why boys cannot have babies. However, such fantasies are more common to girls, who are typically more concerned with the question of making a baby.

To conclude, eating is a function which is usually gratifying and free of conflict, but it can be involved in conflicts at all levels of personality development. The following discussion is in terms of the symptomatology, which may spring from any of the conflicts described by Anna Freud. The first of these, pica, is perhaps the least likely to be a neurotic symptom, and is the most influenced by external conditions.

Pica

Definition and History

The term "pica" refers to the habit of eating clay, plaster, ashes, charcoal, and other substances which are usually considered inedible. It is a Latin word, meaning "magpie," and chosen because of the magpie's reputation for picking up a diversity of things to satisfy either hunger or curiosity. Pica, or strange food preferences, has been reported as a phenomenon of pregnancy, but our interest is in young children.

In the first year of life, infants put everything into their mouth, and almost every child eats some dirt, ashes, sand, or paper. Gradually, the child learns to explore in other ways and begins to discriminate between the edible and the inedible. This discrimination, according to the Vineland Social Maturity Scale, develops between one and two years of age. But children who continue to aimlessly and indiscriminately mouth objects are not usually described as showing pica. The child with pica purposely and persistently searches for plaster, or whatever, to eat; the ingestion is by no means accidental.

Prevalence and Related Factors

The largest study of the prevalence of pica was made by Cooper in 1957. The mothers of 784 children referred for mental hygiene guidance at the Mothers Advisory Service of the John Hopkins School of Hygiene, in Baltimore, were specifically questioned about pica. In only one case did the mother spontaneously complain of pica but, under questioning, 171 reported it. It was reported of more Negro children than white (27 per cent as compared with 17 per cent), and of slightly more boys than girls (55.6 per cent as compared with 44.3 per cent). H. Wortis *et al.* reported that 21 per cent of a group of 272 prematurely born children had it at two and a half years of age *(1962)*. Another recent survey in Washington, D.C., showed the presence of pica in 35 per cent of 380 Negro children aged one to six years *(Gutelius et al., 1962)*. These studies show a surprisingly high prevalence of pica, especially in clinic patients. Characteristically, pica is established in the second year of life and disappears in the fourth or fifth year. However, there are some school children who persist in licking, chewing, or swallowing lead pencils, backs of chairs, and so on.

There has been considerable investigation of the relation of such factors as intelligence, economic status, race, birth history, and nutrition. It was previously thought that pica was much more frequent in retarded children, an opinion bolstered by Leo Kanner's report of 30 pica children, 16 of whom were severely retarded and almost all of whom were of subnormal intelligence *(1957)*. However, except for those cases in which the indiscriminate mouthing is merely another sign of developmental retardation, subsequent studies indicate that the correlation with intelligence is insignificant. There seems to be a higher incidence of pica in the lower economic groups, and among Negroes, even when economic factors are held constant. From her study, Cooper concluded that the only additional differences between children with pica and those without it are that the children who exhibit it have more feeding or nutritional problems and more illnesses and physical defects. She suggests that poor nutrition may be the underlying factor *(1957)*. However, from a carefully controlled experiment with 30 three-year-olds with pica and 28 without it, M. Gutelius *et al.* concluded that "there is no evidence . . . that any nutritional deficiency is etiologically related to pica" *(1962, p. 1022)*. These authors reported lower hemoglobin counts and poorer diets in the pica group, but also found family disorganization and other adverse factors. The children with pica had more behavior problems involving orality (e.g., use of the bottle past two years of age) and presented more disciplinary problems. No differences in their toilet training or in their anxiety was reported. Their average IQ on the Merrill-Palmer test was 94, compared to 98 for the control group.

Causes and Consequences

Attention has been drawn to the problem of pica because of the danger of lead poisoning which, when not fatal, causes permanent damage to the brain. C. F. McKhann discussed pica as the underlying cause of 17 cases of lead poisoning *(1926),* and other reports agree in linking the two conditions. Fifteen per cent of Cooper's group showed some ingestion of paint. Wortis *et al.* suggested that some brain damage, a result of prenatal and neonatal events, exists *before* the onset of pica, and that a brain-injured child reacts more strongly to a noxious environment.

An inadequate physical environment seems to play a causative role in many cases. A child who is bored, restless, cooped up, and unsupervised and who has few toys or little planned activity, may well begin to chew the furniture or window sills. But some children develop pica even when they have good food, interesting and safe toys, and conscientious parents. Such children may be choosing to do this as a way of defying their mothers' edicts. Persistent pica of this type may be an early sign of emotional disturbance, worthy of attention and intervention quite aside from the attendant physical dangers.

Anorexia Nervosa

Definition and History

Literally, "anorexia nervosa" means "nervous loss of appetite." The term was coined by Sir William Gull in 1874. In his study of the disease, he remarked that the patients were usually females of 16 to 23, and he noted the occurrence of amenorrhea, constipation, loss of appetite, slow pulse, slow respiration, and emaciation. He attributed the loss of appetite to a "morbid mental state whose origin is central rather than peripheral." In 1873 Lasèque published an article on hysterical anorexia and described the typical picture as that of a young girl between the ages of 15 and 20 who suffered from an emotion which she disavowed or concealed. Early descriptions concurred in describing the surprising increase in general activity exhibited by the patients and their characteristic lack of concern about getting well.

The definition is variable because there are no clear lines between temporary loss of appetite, diminution of appetite, and true anorexia nervosa. The symptoms may be mild (i.e., chronic underweight and undernourishment) or so severe as to threaten life itself. Excessive loss of weight is essential to the diagnosis, but there is no agreement as to what constitutes an excessive loss. Most patients who find their way into hospitals are probably suffering from the extreme and chronic form of the loss of appetite which many people experience during exceptional stress. When the starvation has advanced far enough, there are concomitant physiological changes which are difficult to reverse and which make even forced feeding difficult. Typically, the anorexic patient eats little and often selects a bizarre diet. One of Charles Lasèque's patients was reported to subsist on *café au lait* garnished with pickled cucumbers *(1873).*

When a doctor attempts to coerce or cajole an anorexic patient into eating, she may ingeniously hide the food, give it away, flush it down the toilet, and so on. When the battle is on, she may increase her apparent weight by adding bulk to her clothes. If all else fails, she induces vomiting or takes laxatives or enemas. The patient is apparently determined not to eat or retain food. E. L. Bliss and C. H. Branch state that the term "anorexia" is somewhat of a misnomer, in that every degree of appetite or distortions of it may be found if a sufficient number of cases are studied *(1960).* But in every case, although the reasons and stratagems to avoid food may vary, the final result is a reduction in the intake of calories, a loss of weight, and semistarvation.

Prevalence and Related Factors

Since the definition is not fixed, the prevalence of anorexia nervosa is hard to determine, and there has been no systematic effort to do so. There is a peak of incidence in adolescence and early adulthood, but it is possible for anorexia nervosa to occur at any age. The youngest patient on record is a four-year-old girl whose psychoanalysis was reported by E. Sylvester. This child was a vomiter, weighed only 23 pounds, and had secondary symptoms of anemia, avitaminosis, and deficiency diarrhea. There was a prior history of excessive finger sucking and pica, for which she had been severely scolded. Considering the rather complicated neurosis involved, it is significant that she was physically and intellectually advanced *(1945)*.

All authors agree that anorexia nervosa is much more common in females. Bliss and Branch, *(1960)* reviewing some 473 published case histories, found that women outnumbered men about nine to one. Indeed, all the oral symptoms discussed in this chapter are more frequent in girls than in boys, although the difference is most marked in anorexia nervosa.

Causation

Anorexia nervosa is considered a symptom of psychopathology, not a disease entity in itself; usually it is a symptom of a *neurotic* feeding disorder. When it is part of a psychosis (e.g., depression or schizophrenia), the diagnosis of psychosis takes precedence.

There seem to be some special factors which predispose a child to choose this, rather than another, neurotic symptom. The common denominators are four in number. First, in almost every case, one or both parents obviously drink or eat too much or have some gastrointestinal symptom. Invariably, food has special importance to the parents of these patients. Second, food intake had been uniquely important to the patient long before the outbreak of the anorexia. Eating or not eating or the offering or denial of food had been the basis of the interchange and power struggle between parent and

child. Often there has been a history of early dietary problems, of relatively little significance except that they helped to establish emotional attitudes towards alimentary functions. Frequently, the anorexic patient had suffered from overweight and compulsive overeating. I. N. Berlin *et al. (1951)* reported the treatment of a 13-year-old girl who alternated between anorexia and obesity. In reviewing the literature, they found close similarities in the family milieux, the developmental histories, and the dynamics of both obese and anorexic patients. Third, most authors describe a special resistance to growing up, particularly to heterosexuality. The adolescent anorexic girl is particularly gratified by the cessation of menstruation and the disappearance of the secondary sex characteristics which would make her attractive to the opposite sex. Fourth and somewhat related to the third, anorexic patients are particularly prone to regression. Their emotional regression is all the more obvious because these children are often highly successful in intellectual pursuits. They may read and search for knowledge voraciously, and maintain considerable intellectual pride and ambition while their bodies degenerate. Anorexia is a good example of an isolated symptom; all the patient's conflicts can be wrapped up in this single symptom.

Treatment and Follow-up

The treatment of anorexia is similar to the treatment of other psychosomatic problems; it necessarily involves medical management as well as psychotherapy. It is difficult to avoid struggling with the patient over her food intake when she is literally starving. Her denial of physical danger and her perverted pleasure in her symptoms are so frustrating and provoking to the therapist that it is easy for him to slip into the role of the anxious, angry mother. Some of the technical aspects of treatment are presented in D. D.

Bond's detailed report of a 16-year-old girl who was successfully treated in about six months. In addition to the special sexual meanings of food and the significance of oral intake in the family, her record clearly shows the role of aggression and guilt in the formation of the symptom. She was particularly angry at her father because of his drinking, his nagging, his jealousy, and his ridicule of her. Her subsequent feelings of guilt forced her to turn her aggression against herself and to starve herself *(1949)*.

The extent and nature of treatment, as well as the prognosis, depend more on the total structure of the personality rather than on the symptom itself. The only follow-up report on a large number of cases was made by Lesser *et al.* on 15 girls who ranged in age from 10 to 16 at the time of onset. The follow-up period varied from one year (for four patients) to more than twelve years (for two patients). The outcome varied, from apparent normalcy (seven cases) to psychosis (two). At the time of the follow-up report all were in good physical health, although two were described as overweight. The authors divided the group according to underlying personality patterns and concluded that those patients with predominantly hysterical personality traits had a better prognosis than those with predominantly schizoid or compulsive traits *(1960)*.

After they mention the common denominators, therapists of anorexics proceed to describe the individual differences and the many possible meanings of food and eating. In the words of E. I. Falstein *et al.*, "Eating may be equated with gratification, impregnation, intercourse, performance, pleasing the mother, growing; or it may represent castrating, destroying, engulfing, killing, cannibalism. Food may symbolize the breast, the genitals, feces, poison, a parent or a sibling" *(1956, p. 765)*. The sexual meanings are usually predominant in hysteria. In compulsive neurosis, the aggressive and anal meanings are more prominent; in such cases, not eating may be a form of ascetic defense, a renunciation of any kind of pleasure of self-gratification. In depression, the chief mechanism is aggression turned against the self. In schizophrenia, the failure to eat may be a symbolic refusal of contact with the world, or it may be specifically related to delusions about poison.

Obesity

Many of the comments which have been made about anorexic patients apply equally well to obese patients and do not need repetition. The role of physiological (i.e., endocrinological) factors has been hotly argued, but H. Bruch, in her extensive work with obese children, found little evidence for disturbed physiology *(1940)*. The constitutional factors are emphasized by some writers on the basis that obese children usually have overweight parents *(Burchinal and Eppright, 1959)*, and it has been suggested that obesity be divided into two types: the endogenous, or constitutionally caused; and the exogenous, resulting from overeating. Although constitutional predisposition is especially obvious in obesity, it should be kept in mind that there is probably some kind of constitutional predisposition to every symptom. Predisposition does not explain why the person has a problem; it only helps us to understand the specific form in which the problem is expressed. Most authors agree, of course, that overeating is the most important single cause of overweight, but again, there is a problem of definition. The line between blooming health and disfiguring and handicapping obesity is indistinct.

The major psychological contributions regarding obesity have been offered by Bruch. Her original observations were of 225 children who were overweight by 25 to 150 per cent *(1941)*. She described these children as fundamentally unhappy and maladjusted. Timid, retiring, clumsy and slow, they were unable to take their place among other children, but their apathy and fearfulness could usually be traced to a time before they were markedly obese. Their obesity appeared to be a secondary symptom, rather than a prime cause of their social maladjustment.

As a group, these obese children were emotionally immature, depending on their mothers for elementary physical care and for emotional satisfaction. Many older obese children were being dressed or washed by their mothers. Bruch reported on children of ten and over who had never had a bowel movement without being coaxed or accompanied to the bathroom. About 40 per cent of those over six were enuretic. Some children of eight or older were still being spoon-fed. Prolonged bottle feeding and an unwillingness to chew solid foods up to the age of about five was not unusual.

Bruch discusses the mothers' attitudes at some length. Underlying their excessive solicitude and overprotection, she found considerable hostility toward the child and a specific unwillingness to allow the child to grow up. She found that the mothers definitely preferred girls and voiced disappointment about their sons: "Girls are better companions," "They stay closer to you," "You don't lose them when they get married." But in order to oblige the maternal wishes, the child must remain infantile and dependent. Bruch theorized that the large size of the obese child was a kind of compensation for feeling small and weak, a feeling encouraged by the mother who could not bear to lose her baby. The obese child resists treatment, not only because eating is gratifying, but also because he unconsciously likes being big *(1941)*.

Treatment

Extreme obesity seriously impairs physical health, but it rarely creates medical emergencies. Treatment is usually directed by a physician, but psychological factors are very important. One report *(Young, 1957)* gives a straightforward picture of the relationship between emotional adjustment, crudely measured by the Bell Adjustment Inventory, and success in weight reduction with an outpatient clinic regimen. Of 31 patients scoring "above average" in emotional adjustment, only 2 failed to reduce. Of 22 scoring "below average," 14 were unsuccessful.

Group therapy using much the same principles as those used by Alcoholics Anonymous, has been frequently employed. In one such project, public health nurses served as group leaders for some 72 high school girls. A different therapeutic program was designed for each of four groups and, although the final numbers were small, the authors concluded that a therapy program which stressed both physical and emotional factors was most effective *(Harmon, Purkhonen, and Rassmusen, 1958)*. The author is not aware of any follow-up study to evaluate success or failure in maintaining the reduced weight.

Bruch reported that cooperation in individual psychotherapy was poor when being fat was the only complaint. Under his placid, cheerful surface, the obese patient often has a demanding attitude, a craving to be loved just as he is. The therapist is asked to provide ceaseless proofs of love, and inevitably disappoints the patient, because he wants to change him. Bruch describes another resistance, stemming from the "image of specialness and potential greatness" which the fat patient maintains regardless of reality. He expects to have his tremendous potential recognized without expenditure of effort and work *(1957)*. It is inevitable that such a person will suffer one defeat after another and live in an atmosphere of frustration and disappointment. And then he comforts and solaces himself by overeating. Sometimes his grandiose daydreams are linked with the idea of slimness: "If I were thin, I could be a great ballet dancer," or whatever. His obesity then serves the positive function of preventing the psychological hurt that would result if the slimness did *not* bring a great stage career in its wake.

Not all obesity reaches monumental proportions. Bruch offers some words of advice to parents who are trying to assist a child to lose weight:

. . . it is senseless even to suggest a diet unless a youngster really wants to reduce and wants to do it on his own. He needs, of course, the cooperation of his parents who must provide the proper food, but without begrudging it or playing watchdog over every bite he eats. Terrible problems develop when a whole family makes the child's eating the center of their concern. The great question is how to convince parents to leave a fat child alone. If this is not achieved, weight and eating become something with which to defy the parents. *(1957, p. 8.)*

These words apply equally well to many other problems. When parents are too involved in trying to get a child to do something, the activity becomes invested with additional meanings. Bruch's sentiments will be reechoed in our discussion of school learning problems. Some parents watchdog the homework, reading, writing, and mental intake of the failing child like a mother hovering over the food intake of the anorexic or obese child.

Some explanation of the relationship between the somatic symptoms discussed in this chapter and those discussed as psychosomatic disturbances in Chapter 13, is in order. Many authorities, including the editors of the *Psychological Abstracts,* classify anorexia and obesity as psychosomatic illnesses. It is clear that these eating disturbances can result in serious physiological changes. However, these conditions may be differentiated from classical psychosomatic states on the basis of the significance of the somatic factors. The physiological changes in obesity and anorexia are secondary to the psychological problems which disturb the normal function of eating. The symptom is a behavioral one, clearly visible to patient and diagnostician. In the psychosomatic diseases, on the other hand, the psychological symptom is more hidden, and the obvious functional disturbance is physiological rather than behavioral. A stomach ulcer, for example, is produced by hyperacidity, hypermotility, and hyperemia, the products of excessive innervations of the autonomic nervous system. The overactivity of the autonomic nervous system is exacerbated by chronic emotional tensions which are more diffuse than those experienced in obesity or anorexia.

Displacement of Oral Conflicts to Other Areas of Functioning

In the foregoing discussion of oral symptomatology, it has been shown that, although these symptoms are usually initiated by the early feeding experiences, they become more complicated as the child grows older. New meanings are attached to the original situation. If the mother is dominating and pushy in the matter of feeding, this is likely to carry over into the negativistic and independent anal phase and complicate matters there. Eating can be linked up with ambivalence and find expression in the conflict between the wish to incorporate something likeable and its simultaneous destruction. During the Oedipal period, the child with a prior conflict about eating, is likely to have more than the usual number of fantasies about oral impregnation and anxieties surrounding the forbidden wish to have a baby. Thus, all the anxieties of later periods can be fitted into the eating problem, and the analysis of the child's difficulty cannot be reduced to the simple elements of the infantile experience.

Conversely, infantile feeding conflicts are not always manifested solely in oral symptoms; they may be displaced to other functions. Eating is a form of incorporation, a process of taking in from the outside world. The difficulty of oral taking in may spread to visual and auditory taking in. We speak of "drinking in with our eyes," of "devouring the sight," of "digesting information," of "voracious reader," of a "hunger for knowledge." There is psychological truth in this.

The carryover from eating to learning may also reflect the repetition of a specific personal relationship. A child who has been fed against his will, for instance, is likely to have residual feelings about superior, stronger persons who want to cram information into him. Learning requires the gracious acceptance of someone's superiority, and it can be inhibited by unconscious feelings against authority.

A brief excerpt from Joe's case history illustrates the mechanisms of displacement:

Joe was an eight-year-old Negro boy of average intelligence when he was first referred for psychiatric evaluation. The referring problem was a reading failure. Despite remedial reading and repeating first grade, Joe was a poorer reader than ever. He was also a poor eater, which caused his mother much anxiety, particularly because he had been a premature baby. She felt that only by dint of her force-feeding had she kept him alive in his early years. Although he was perfectly healthy and well-nourished at eight, she continued to struggle over it. She was impressed by the importance of nutrition and was exceptionally conscientious about it.

Joe was accepted for a kind of mixed therapy, a combined educational and psychological approach. The psychologist was soon frustrated by Joe's apathy and lack of ambition. He performed only when urged and, between appointments, appeared to forget everything learned in the preceding session. His appointments were after school, and the psychologist thoughtfully provided a snack, which Joe invariably refused. On one occasion the snack was potato chips. Joe said he did not like them, but the very next week, he sat in the waiting room contentedly munching potato chips and perusing a magazine which would not be considered "suitable" for his age. Gently, the psychologist confronted him with his statement of the previous week, and lamely he explained that he did not care for "her brand" of chips. This led directly into a discussion of his fights with his mother over having a "clean plate" or eating "just a bit" of every food, and so on. Many times he capitulated in order to win his freedom to go out and play, but it was easy to show him (and his mother) that he carried his resistance over into school, another area in which his mother was very interested and eager for him to perform. The displacement of his feelings to his teacher and therapist was evident. He did not want to accept anything from anyone, and there was no way to force him to learn. He could go through the motions and thereby avoid an open battle, but underneath it all, he did not involve himself and had the unconscious satisfaction of the "last word." The subsequent modifications which were instituted at home, his insight into what he was doing, and putting him on his own for the responsibility of learning relieved the total impasse of his initial condition.

Sucking Habits

Although sucking begins with feeding, the infant's pleasure in sucking soon becomes independent of his need for food. That babies derive comfort from sucking their thumb, fingers, blanket, or whatever, is readily apparent in their body relaxation and facial expression of peaceful contentment. Like so many other signs of emotional difficulty, thumb sucking becomes a symptom only when it persists beyond the appropriate age. Before considering the reasons for its pathological persistence, a brief review of the reasons for normal sucking is in order.

Normal Thumb Sucking

For some time, the origin of thumb sucking was the subject of considerable controversy. The theoretical issue was whether sucking is innate or whether its pleasurable nature is learned by association with feeding. Margaret Ribble and David Levy, both physicians, were major exponents of the theory that it is innate. Ribble observed no "marked" thumbsucking in infants who were allowed unrestricted sucking, which incidentally amounted to only about two and a half hours a day after the first month (1944). Her implication was that thumb sucking occurred as the result of privation. Levy's work is more widely quoted and more emphatic in its conclusions. He questioned mothers and found that the frequency of thumb sucking in infancy was higher among infants who took less time at breast or bottle (1928). Then he checked these clinical observations with animals. He gave puppies the same amount of food in "long time feeders" versus "short time feeders," and found that the puppies getting their food in a short time tended to suck all kinds of objects between meals (1934). These findings were interpreted to mean that thumb sucking could be prevented by allowing sufficient time for the sucking instinct to be satiated.

Later studies, by R. R. Sears and others, necessitated some revision of this thesis. Studying 80 children attended by a pediatrician who favored early cup feeding, Sears and G. W. Wise found that thumb sucking at two and a half was more pronounced in a group of 52 children who had been weaned late than it was in a group who had been weaned early. "Late weaning" was defined as after three months, and 45 of the 52 were weaned between four and seven months. (Most pediatricians would view this weaning as moderately early.) Some of the children had been fed from cups from birth, and still did not suck their thumbs at all. The authors concluded that the more the infant sucks, the stronger his oral drive becomes (1950).

In this argument about the innate versus the learned nature of sucking for pleasure, the absence of thumb sucking is used almost as a criterion of successful infant feeding. There is a subtle suggestion that all thumb sucking is bad and that anything which prevents it is good. But it is dangerous to study isolated bits of behavior rather than the total personality. From the Sears and Wise investigation, for instance, it would seem that to allow no sucking would prevent thumb sucking. However, one might ask about the possible consequences of depriving an infant of such a pleasurable activity. Conceivably, such an early restriction might create an adult who is unable to enjoy himself, or perhaps one who is sexually inhibited. The adult personality would depend on subsequent experiences, but if the parents maintained a puritanical policy of eliminating all the child's pleasure in his body, there would surely be some distortion of the adult.

Despite the heat, the argument over the origin of thumb sucking is empty. We can agree that the urge to suck is innate and that it acquires psychological meaning. If sucking movements were never reinforced by the relief of hunger, they would fade. Sigmund Freud acknowledged the role of learning in his remark:

Furthermore, it is clear that the behavior of a child who indulges in thumb-sucking is determined by a search for some pleasure which has already been experienced and is now remembered.[*]

---

[*]Quoted from Sigmund Freud, *Three Essays on the Theory of Sexuality* (1905). Standard Edition, ed. and trans. by J. Strachey, VII, p. 181 (London: The Hogarth Press, Ltd., 1953). © in U.S.A. by Basic Books, Inc. Reproduced by permission.

Little mystery surrounds the extra sucking in the first year of life. It is an important source of self-gratification, affording relief and relaxation to the baby. In this sense, it is auto-erotic and akin to masturbation. Ordinarily there is a steady decline in the interest in sucking, whether it be for food or for pleasure. The mystery is more why this fails to occur in some children (i.e., fixation) or why some children return to it (i.e., regression).

Thumb Sucking as a Symptom

It is hard to say at what age thumb sucking becomes pathological, because it also depends on the amount of the sucking. Rarely is anyone concerned about it before the child is two-and-a-half or three years old. In a prevalence study carried out in a child health center in Stockholm and reported in 1949, G. Klackenberg found that 14 per cent of the four-year-olds were intensive thumb suckers. There is some evidence that thumb sucking is more common in girls than in boys *(Honzik, 1959)*. Beller remarks a curious sex difference in the age of onset. The majority of the girls in his limited sample of nursery school children began thumb sucking in early infancy, whereas the majority of the boys began after 18 months *(1962)*. In R. Lapouse and M. A. Monk's study of the behavior of 482 school children, aged 6 to 12 and not previously identified as "disturbed", 2 per cent were found to be sucking their thumb or fingers "almost all the time" *(1959)*.

A sucking habit is distressing to the onlooker and usually an embarrassment to the older child, but it is not the kind of symptom which forces professional attention. A child with this problem can get by. However, it is easily detected, it can be objectively defined, and it is clearly functional.

To ascertain the cause of thumb sucking in a particular child, one must look at the total personality of that child. There are two major possibilities: The thumb sucking may be one of a number of infantile habits in an immature child or it may be an isolated infantile habit in a child who otherwise seems average. Because of its frequency in the immature child, it is appropriate to discuss the syndrome of emotional immaturity.

Emotional Immaturity

"Emotional immaturity" is a term used to describe a child who acts younger than his peers. Some indication of the term's popularity with educators is given in a report of a diagnostic and consultant project carried out in the public schools of Cecil County, Maryland *(Bentzen, 1963)*. Of a total school population of 6,026 children, 919, or 15 per cent, were referred for individual study. The highest incidence of referrals was at the first grade level, and the most frequent reason for referral was "immaturity." This was the sole reason for referring 36 of the 120 first-graders. For the other 84, immaturity was associated with other symptoms, such as shyness, fatigability, short attention span, infantile speech patterns and language development, inability to follow directions, and frequent absences from school. This list is very similar to one provided by a group of first-grade teachers in a suburban school system of Cuyahoga County, Ohio:

1. He does a poor job in coloring and cutting.
2. He does not finish tasks.
3. He does not complete directions.
4. He cannot work alone at his seat.
5. He is constantly on the move.
6. He is easily distracted by the other children.
7. He cries and gives up easily.
8. He is easily scared and sticks close to the teacher.
9. He is always eating something or chewing at something.

This syndrome is a conglomerate of emotional, motor, and mental behavior. On the emotional side, it is characterized by low tolerance for frustration, great dependency, and an absence of self-control or self-direction. The child is not oriented to assigned tasks and does not feel responsible for doing his "work." He complains that school is hard and no fun, and he vaguely feels that the teacher does not like him. To the teacher's despair, he demonstrates that he is capable of doing the required work when she gives him her undivided attention. He responds delightedly to praise and compliments, but he cannot function in the group. Without an immediate reward, he takes little pride in accomplishment. In this respect, he is lacking in conscience. In psychoanalytic terms, one would say that there has been no sublimation of instinctual drives into higher-level activities. He still requires the gratifications needed by the younger child to help him tolerate the inevitable frustrations of structured learning.

When teachers describe a child as "immature," it is both a behavioral description and an explanation of the problem behavior. They imply that the child will outgrow this behavior. "Immaturity" has a benign connotation; it is a less opprobrious classification than "emotionally disturbed."

The vast majority of children who fit this description are boys. Frances Bentzen attributed this difference to the physiological retardation of boys and urged that our social system take more cognizance of the developmental differential between the sexes. The implication is that the boys will straighten out if they are given more time to grow up. This suggests that behavioral change at this age level is chiefly the result of passage of time which permits neuromuscular and other forms of maturation to take place on an automatic basis. Little is said about the role of parents and teachers in facilitating the growing-up process.

Although the term is widely used in the schools, it is rarely heard in the clinic. One of the few clinical articles on the subject is Irene Josselyn's description of the treatment of immature children in an institution. She names four possible causes of immaturity:

1. Failure of the child to gain an adequate sense of security in his relationships to his primary love objects, namely, his parents;
2. Situations that imply that danger exists if a more mature status is obtained;
3. Experience upon a more mature level which has created unbearable anxiety, relief from which is sought in regression to a more dependent relationship to parent figures; and
4. Overindulgence of the child during the infancy period so that he feels no impulse to relinquish dependency gratification for more mature satisfactions. *(1950, p. 399).*

Her last point deserves special attention. Overindulgence may result from a genuine misunderstanding about normal development but, other things being equal, parents are rarely so influenced by theoretical dogma as to abdicate their own judgment. Josselyn points out that overindulgent child rearing is usually also grossly inconsistent. Frequently, the overindulgence stems from an identification with the child, rather than from some intellectual bias. Frustration imposed upon the child is felt doubly by the parent. But a parent who identifies so strongly with her child is herself easily hurt and has many personal needs to gratify. The failure of the child to gratify the emotional needs of the parent produces impulsive or unpredictable parental reactions. In Josselyn's words, "whatever the parent gave to the child was a caricature of the child's real need. The child continued to seek gratification in quantity that he did not gain in quality and thus remained immature in his relationship to immature parents" *(1950, p. 399).*

At other times, the overindulgence masks a feeling of ambivalence. The parents have to hide their hostility and prove their love for the child. This pattern is often seen in families with handicapped children. The parent resents the heavy demands, but feels guilty because it is not the child's fault, and then tries to make up for his resentment by being especially nice. This is a never-ending cycle. The child learns to exploit the situation, and he increases his demands. He knows that after a blow-up his parents will feel remorseful and he will get his way. His insatiable demands add to the resentment of his parents, which further increases their feelings of guilt, and so on.

In chapter 15, we discuss in more detail the relationship between child rearing and childhood pathology. Our comments at this point are designed only to caution the reader against accepting the simple explanation that immature children are spoiled children. The spoiling may be a complicated process, not alterable by a little authoritative advice.

Thumb Sucking as a Neurotic Symptom

An isolated infantile habit in an otherwise mature child is likely to be a neurotic symptom. The following brief report of a case of persistent finger sucking illustrates the complexities of symptom formation:

Sally, a highly intelligent, attractive girl, was 11 when she was first seen in a child psychiatry clinic. From infancy, she had had a persistent habit of sucking her two middle fingers, which the parents had tried to ignore. They were distressed because she was wearing the enamel off her teeth, her fingers were markedly calloused, and Sally herself suffered from embarrassment. The parents were more concerned by Sally's lack of friends and her negativistic behavior toward her mother particularly. Although Sally was definitely gifted and evoked a lot of admiration, she used her intelligence aggressively and was cruelly sharp in tongue and wit. She could not keep any friends. According to Sally, she did not feel lonely, but she admitted her discomfort about the finger sucking. She was particularly bothered by the fact that all the strenuous efforts she had made to stop had proved useless; it was to her a great failure of her will power.

In psychotherapy, Sally hoped for some magic solution. The particular magic she had in mind was of an oral nature, some kind of pill which would kill her urge to suck. We soon learned that the sucking was in part an aggressive act against her mother, an unspoken reproach to her that her mother had not given her enough. This meaning was reinforced by the mother's belief (which she had exposed to the child) that sucking represented some basic insecurity and lack of love. It was partly because of their guilt feelings that the parents had scrupulously avoided any interference with the sucking.

It became more and more clear that the sucking was like an addiction and afforded relief for any strong emotion. Whether she was sick, fatigued, excited, sad, lonely, frightened, or angry, Sally took refuge in finger sucking. It was of some help when she began to differentiate these various feelings and to express them in words rather than in automatic, unconscious sucking. Particularly strong were feelings of sadness and loneliness, which she denied and tried to hide with an air of insouciance. She attempted to be very independent and not care about anybody, and so turned to a form of comfort which she could give herself. The symptom might have served her well except that she was chagrined by her inability to control it and by her realization that she was dependent on it.

Gradually we came to the reasons for her perpetual anger and irritability which alienated everyone and left her so alone. Underneath her veneer of success and independence, Sally felt very dissatisfied with herself, particularly with her role as a girl. She was painfully envious of her younger brother and dismayed by her femininity. The prospect of marriage and children held no appeal. Sadly she reported on how much she had hated to "play house" as a younger child, and recalled an incident when an older boy offered her a dime to "play doctor" (which was planned to involve undressing and minute physical examination). With very real tears, she said she would not play: "He would just be throwing his dime away; there is nothing down there worth seeing. I looked." In some way, she blamed her disappointment about being a girl on her mother, and this had increased her aggressive feelings. In all this welter of feelings, many times the only thing which she really liked about herself were her fingers, which tasted "good."

A case of this sort makes one aware of the circular effect of a symptom. More and more, Sally relied on sucking as a substitute for other pleasure, social and physical. She could retreat both from her own feelings and from difficult situations by sucking away in a trance. The sucking served many purposes so efficiently that it would be impossible to account for it with any one reason. To the best of everyone's memory, her oral period was a happy one which involved minimum frustration. The oral symptom, then, was her solution to problems which arose later. Only recently had she begun to feel shame or guilt about the symptom. Until then, it had been a permissible outlet for her many conflicts.

Other common symptoms which involve the oral apparatus are nail biting and grinding of teeth. These cause even less concern than thumb sucking, and it is doubtful that a child would be brought to a clinic solely because of these symptoms. Usually they are reported as subsidiary symptoms, noteworthy only because a more serious problem exists. When Lapouse and Monk studied the incidence of various kinds of behavior in normal school children, they found both symptoms frequently. Severe nail biting was reported of 17 per cent of the children, and teeth grinding of 14 per cent.

Although sucking, biting, and grinding all involve the mouth area, they are very different. Biting is aggressive, and very different from sucking, which is soothing and mesmerizing. In this author's opinion, thumb suckers are rarely nail biters; a child who finds relief in one does not find relief in the other. In her study of the incidence of problems in normal children, J. MacFarlane found nail biting to be the only problem the incidence of which *increases* with chronological age. It is most common in 12 to 14-year-olds (1954).

There appears to be little regression in nail biting. The child is usually on the *qui vive* as he bites his nails, say at a scary movie or during a school test, whereas the child who is energetically sucking his thumb is usually withdrawn and dreamy. This difference justifies the general opinion that sucking is more serious. However, it is possible for any habit to become an all-consuming passion, even something as common as nail biting. All the child's spare energy may then pour into the habit, either to indulge in it or to fight it. Any habit which assumes compulsive proportions has become invested with special meaning. In such cases, one can always find other signs of emotional conflict in the child's life at school, home, or with his friends.

Like many other problems, oral habits may be developmental in origin, and simply outgrown; they may result from poor training and require parental change; or they may be a defense against the anxieties of inner conflicts (i.e., a neurotic symptom). The assessment of the relative contribution of these three factors requires historical data and close observation over a period of time. Although oral habits have their genesis in infancy, it is a mistake to look only to this period for their explanation. The answer often lies in a failure to master conflicts which arose after the oral period, and the oral habits are then a regression to happier times.

Enuresis and Encopresis

Wetting and soiling are clear failures to develop. The symptoms will be discussed separately because their dynamics are quite different.

Enuresis: Prevalence

Authors disagree about the exact age after which enuresis becomes pathological, but no one sets an age younger than three (Kanner's standard) or older than eight. Some writers regard relatively infrequent wetting, say once a month, as enuresis; others include only weekly or greater frequencies. Here again, the lack of agreement makes it difficult to determine prevalence. It should also be noted that, although authors do not always say so, enuresis is usually nocturnal. Daytime wetting is rarer and more serious.

Prevalence figures also vary with the setting of the reporting clinic. Psychiatric clinics in hospitals report the highest rate; because the enuretic children are referred for psychiatric treatment when organic causes are not found. Kanner reported that 26 per cent of the children referred to the Children's Psychiatry Clinic at the Johns Hopkins Hospital were enuretic *(1957)*. In two community clinics canvassed by G. M. Gilbert, enuresis was a referral problem in 12 per cent of the cases, whereas in two mental health clinics located in schools, enuresis was a referral problem in only 1 per cent *(1957)*.

Bed-wetting is so common in school children that it has been argued that enuresis is "an ubiquitous happenstance" *(Tapia, Jekel, and Domke, 1960)*. Lapouse and Monk reported that 8 per cent of the school children they studied wet their beds once a month or more *(1959)*. However, F. Tapia's argument that enuresis is normal was not based only on its frequency, but also on the fact that it often occurs in the absence of other emotional symptoms. He and his co-authors felt that enuresis, in an otherwise well-adjusted child, has no psychopathological meaning. The fallacy of this line of reasoning was discussed in Chapter 4. This author believes that regularly occurring enuresis in school children inevitably has psychological consequences and that it is therefore worthy of attention.

Related Factors

The age of the enuretic child is a somewhat artificial consideration, because the symptom has usually persisted from early childhood. Rarely is it a regression after a period of dryness. Kanner reported that the greatest percentages were found in the 8 to 11-year-olds, but this means only that the adults sought consultation when the children reached these ages. Seventy-eight per cent of Kanner's cases had been lifelong; in the experience of this author, the figure should be closer to 90 per cent.

There is no indication that intelligence is a related factor. Sex is, however. Most reports indicate that enuresis is about twice as frequent in boys as in girls. Cultural factors have been little studied, but it is probable that it is more accepted, and therefore less frequently reported, in the lower classes. This would be an easy fact to verify or refute in a survey of school children of differing backgrounds.

There is considerable disagreement as to what, if any, emotional symptoms or personality characteristics are associated with enuresis. In the opinion of most investigators, it is rarely an isolated symptom. J. J. Michaels and S. E. Goodman found that enuresis was frequently associated with thumb sucking, speech impediments, and temper tantrums, all examples of "immature" behavior *(1934)*. J. L. Despert, reporting on 14 enuretic children stated that "while they ate well and slept quietly, thumb-sucking was present in all these children . . . in varying degrees of intensity and frequency; several also showed other infantile habits—nose picking, biting, teeth grinding, ear rubbing, rocking, genital handling—for periods longer than usually noted in young children" *(1944, p. 298)*. Kanner rarely found enuresis as an isolated symptom. Thirty-two per cent of his cases had eating problems; 26 per cent had temper tantrums; 24 per cent bit their nails; 12 per cent were fearful; 10 per cent soiled. Six per cent were thumb suckers and stutterers, less than other reports would lead us to expect.

Kanner makes the special point that most of the children were generally immature. The incidence of personality characteristics was described as follows:*

Aggressive, fighting, mischievous, cruel
                       8 per cent

Whining, complaining, moody, irritable
                      32 per cent

Restless, overactive, fidgety, excitable
                      21 per cent

Disobedient, impudent, spiteful, stubborn
                      14 per cent

Oversensitive, touchy, self-conscious
                      9 per cent

Timid, shy, bashful, seclusive, unusually quiet   8 per cent

Listless, indifferent, apathetic   5 per cent

Overconscientious, serious-minded
                      3 per cent

These characteristics might be regrouped according to the way the child handles aggressive impulses. The first four descriptions are of aggressive children (75 per cent). The second four descriptions are of children who have turned their aggression against themselves (25 per cent). This regrouping is suggested because it is sometimes thought that enuretic children have difficulty in handling their aggressive feelings.

One negative fact is worth mentioning. Enuretic children do not wet their beds because they sleep more soundly. M. M. Boyd has compared the time needed to awaken 100 nocturnal enuretics and 100 control subjects. There was no significant difference in the time required to wake the two groups. (The same study reported that they also did not differ in electroencephalographic patterns.) Enuretic children sleep through the feelings of bladder tension, but otherwise they wake as easily. Another physical theory is that enuretics have smaller bladders, but there is little evidence for this explanation.

The family history of enuretics usually includes a significant number of relatives with a history of the same problem. Kanner reported that, in 52 per cent of his cases, one or more members of the family were, or had been, enuretic. It would be interesting to know if the family history is more positive in the case of enuresis than in other emotional problems, but no other symptom is so easily identified. However, the fact that enuresis runs in families may have little to do with constitutional inheritance *per se*. A predisposition may determine the choice of symptom, and the choice may be fostered by the fact that the parent who has had that symptom is less able to deal with it effectively in the child.

Secondary Consequences

Enuresis.usually has psychological consequences which create additional conflicts. To understand the psychology of an enuretic child, it is very important to know what diagnostic tests have been undertaken and what treatment measures employed. Some medical tests are traumatic and have the psychological meaning of a surgical procedure on a particularly vulnerable organ. Catheterization and dilation may have been tried. Methods of treatment usually involve shaming, restriction of fluids, alarm clocks, and other devices. And when all this has failed, the child is left to conclude that he is somehow different, damaged, or deficient. Anny Katan has stated that it is a universal fantasy among enuretic children that the genitals are damaged and that, like a broken water-tap, they cannot retain urine. Until the child achieves some success, it is impossible to convince him that this is not so. In his anxiety, he tries to blot out that part of his body and ignore the sensations which originate there, and so the symptom per-

---

*Quoted from Leo Kanner, *Child Psychiatry*, 3rd. Ed. (Springfield, Illinois, Charles C Thomas, Publisher, 1957), p. 448. Reproduced by permission.

petuates itself. Despite his efforts to repress it, the feeling of being different remains and affects the child in other areas. Enuresis is often accompanied by learning problems:

In such cases the child often has the unconscious idea that someone who has not achieved so simple a task as bladder control cannot possibly master a task as difficult as learning. The idea of having an insufficient or damaged genital becomes displaced to the head, the seat of intelligence. The same idea has an entirely different result with other children. Many years ago Freud and Jones drew attention to the ambition of enuretics; they have to prove that they are able to do everything else particularly well, because they are unable to master something as simple as bladder control. *(Katan, 1946, p. 245.)*

The effect of enuresis on the child's view of himself is overlooked by tolerant parents who try to ignore the problem. The parents feel that the child will not be ashamed if they have done nothing to shame him, but any school child is capable of finding out the facts for himself. He soon learns that most children do not wet; in fact, he usually thinks he is the only one who still wets his bed. If the subject is not talked about at home, he may conclude that his parents feel sorry for him and believe that he cannot be cured. Effective treatment of enuresis must begin with a frank recognition of it, and discussion between the parents and the child.

Causes and Treatment

The first case to consider is the simplest form. Has the child been encouraged to stop? The youngster who sleeps in diapers is receiving tacit permission to wet. The first step is to remove the diapers. If the parents are taking him to the toilet during the night, he should be thoroughly wakened and fully conscious of what he is doing and why. Sometimes the bathroom is far away or poorly heated, and the child cannot force himself to leave his bed. Perhaps he fears the darkness. A night light, a bathroom heater, and the firm encouragement of the parents may be all that is needed. Another way to encourage the child is to have him change his own bed linens, which at least makes him face the fact of the wet bed in a realistic way.

Once enuresis is firmly established, however, such simple procedures rarely suffice. Because enuresis is a habit, it is often treated by conditioned response therapy. Such retraining concentrates on the cessation of the symptom. In clinical circles, symptomatic treatment is often scorned, however, because the problem will then be expressed in another form. Still, enuresis is a rather special kind of symptom, containing within it the potentiality of further emotional conflicts. A psychologically harmless cure would therefore be welcomed by many doctors.

O. H. Mowrer and W. Mowrer were perhaps the first to offer a treatment of nocturnal enuresis with a logical rationale in learning theory *(1938)*. All kinds of appliances have been sold, but they all involve the same principle—waking the child with a buzzer, alarm clock, slight shock, or whatever at the very touch of urine. The child usually sleeps on an apparatus consisting of wire mesh foil pads which are separated by a piece of cloth. Moisture completes an electrical circuit which sets off the waking device. In terms of conditioning theory, bladder tension is the conditioned stimulus, the buzzer is the unconditioned stimulus, and waking is the response to be associated with bladder tension.

Follow-ups have been usually made by questionnaire. B. Martin and D. Kubby sent questionnaires to the 220 parents who had bought a commercial appliance. Slightly over half the questionnaires were returned, and three-fourths of these reported improvement which had been sustained for an average of 14 months. The average treatment time reported for girls was less (four instead of six), and their rate of recovery was better (1955). A similar study, reported by W. Baller and H. Schalock included 43 males and 12 females. All the questionnaires were returned, and treatment was reported as successful in 70 per cent of the cases. These investigators specifically asked about the formation of substitute symptoms but found no evidence of it. They also report personal and social improvements in the children following the successful treatment by the conditioned response method (1956). It is, of course, entirely possible that their evaluation methods (a questionnaire and a single interview) were too crude and hasty to discover possible adverse consequences of the treatment, but there is little doubt about the general relief and self-satisfaction which most children experience when bed-wetting is finally brought under control.

When the conditioned response method works, it generally does so in fairly short order, a matter of weeks or, at most, months. A significant number of children do not respond; for these children, bed-wetting may be serving a special purpose which is not easily relinquished. To discover the purpose and alter the behavior then requires individual psychotherapy. Experience has revealed some common dynamic patterns which operate singly or in combination in any given child with this symptom:

1. Enuresis may appear as a regression if there has been a separation from a loved person who was responsible for the initial training. It may appear as a regression after the birth of a sibling who has carte blanche to wet and soil at will. In such instances, enuresis expresses the wish to be a baby again, to return to happier days.

2. Enuresis may appear as a sign of confusion or ambivalence over sex identity. It has already been mentioned that enuretics believe they have damaged genitals, but this fantasy may mask a wish to be feminine. Tony's history illustrates this type of case:

Tony was the younger of two boys, both of whom had been enuretic. Tony had many other problems, including general immaturity, learning difficulty, low tolerance for frustration, and fearfulness. He soiled until he was five, and enuresis persisted into his tenth year. His mother was a dominating person; his father was weak and passive. This mother scorned her husband, and the parents lived a chronic cold war, with no affection and little cooperation.

At the age of four, Tony was accepted for intensive psychotherapy. He soon expressed his fear that wild animals might bite off his penis during the night. Much later, it became clear that these persistent nightmares and terrifying images were kept alive by his halfhearted wish that they might come true. In his view, there were definite advantages to losing his penis: He would not wet his bed, and besides his mother would like him better if he were a girl. Moreover, the prospect of growing up to be like his father was not appealing. He believed he would have to lose his penis, anyhow, because he thought that the penis makes babies by some magical transformation within the woman's body. All of this made his penis a definite handicap, something to put out of his mind as much as possible. In his case, bed-wetting was an expression of his wish to be a girl. Until he accepted a boy's role, he had little motivation to fight the symptom.

3. Pearson (1949) coined the term "revenge enuresis" to describe bed-wetting which serves an aggressive purpose by expressing a child's resentment of his parents. Some children know that they are wetting their beds to spite their parents, but are afraid or unable to express their anger in other ways. More often, the child is unconscious of his resentment and has no insight into the reason for his enuresis.

In the three syndromes described above, the enuresis expresses an unconscious wish, one which is repressed because of the anxiety or guilt associated with it. There is no way of establishing the fact, but it seems logical to assume that when the unconscious wish is strong, a learning approach will fail. When the conditioned response method works it seems logical to assume that the enuresis was the result of faulty training or that the precipitating psychological conflict wore itself out, leaving only the habit. Enuresis may have a simple beginning, as in jealousy of a new baby, but it is a symptom which often picks up new meanings as the child grows. The more remote the onset, the more complicated the treatment process.

Encopresis: Soiling and Withholding

The term "encopresis" (i.e., soiling) was coined in 1926. One of the first reports in the American literature was made by Hale Shirley in 1938. He reported that almost 3 per cent of the children refererd to the psychiatric clinic of the Harriet Lane Home, in Baltimore, had encopresis, and that boys outnumbered girls five to one. There have been few subsequent reports, and these are mostly treatment reports of single cases. Virtually nothing is known about prevalence, epidemiology, or the history of untreated cases.

Charles Burns (1941) divided encopretic children into three groups: (1) feebleminded or untrained children; (2) neurotic children; and (3) children who had dysrhythmic or vasovagal conditions. Fecal soiling may result from impairment of the nervous system or from anatomical defect. Julius Richmond, Evelyn Eddy, and Sterling Garrard described criteria for distinguishing such cases by their history and physical examination and X rays (1954). The following discussion is limited to neurotic soiling, or soiling which is associated with a psychogenic megacolon.

Although encopresis is related to enuresis in that both involve toilet training, the differences are many. First, encopresis is rarer and more serious. No one considers chronic soiling to be an "everyday problem of an everyday child," if the child is over three or four. Second, soiling rarely occurs during sleep. Third, soiling is associated with characteristic accompaniments in total personality. Fourth, soiling almost always has two sides to it: Soilers alternate between loss of control and long periods of withholding. Since withholding can eventuate in a megacolon or in a fecal impaction which requires surgical intervention, soiling often becomes the lesser of two evils. The embarrassment and nuisance of the soiling is actually preferable to the physical dangers of the retention.

More often than not, such withholding has its origin in the training situation. The child retains the feces as his property, in defiance of his parents' wish to take it away. Suppositories and enemas, to which parents sometimes resort, will produce immediate results, but the long-range effect may be that the child will redouble his resistance and give in only when forced to do so. Defecation, like so many other activities, can become the focus of a struggle for power. It is readily linked with unconscious aggressive wishes toward the parent, and can become a weapon for the child.

Constipation can occur in another way. If the parents' disgust is extreme, or their punishment for accidents severe, the child may get the idea that defecation is bad. If he does not understand what his parents desire, and if his feces are disgusting and dirty, he may try to hide them or hold them back. The reaction may become so great that the child cannot acknowledge his physiological needs. His feces escape against his will. The training process has taught him the wrong thing.

There is another kind of withholding which is associated with sexual, rather than aggressive, wishes. We mentioned the notion of oral impregnation in connection with anorexia nervosa. The digestive tract theory of reproduction includes the idea that babies are made and excreted like feces. Prolonged fecal retention may cause abdominal distension which looks like pregnancy, and the young child may get the happy thought that this is the first step to making a real, live baby. This fantasy may be reinforced if the child observes a pregnancy during the anal period, between from 1½ to 3 years of age. He is unlikely to verbalize his questions and his wishes because of the egocentrism which is characteristic of this age. So naïvely confident of his omnipotence, the child may set out to have a baby; with mother none the wiser. Unfortunately, this may look like plain stubbornness and incite the righteous indignation of the exasperated parents.

We have talked about withholding first because it invariably culminates in fecal incontinence when the physiological pressure outweighs the child's psychological resistance. The converse is not necessarily true; soiling can occur without withholding. Like enuresis, it may result from a simple failure in training, or from a simple regression out of jealousy of a baby sibling, or as a regressive reaction to a separation from a loved person or place. In its more complicated neurotic forms, it may reflect a total rejection and denial of the private parts, including both the anal and genital organs. In such cases, soiling and wetting occur together.

Treatment

The personalities of children with anal symptoms usually reflect the displacement of attitudes from anal functions to other activities. The character problem becomes as much a matter of treatment as the symptom itself. Sigmund Freud called attention to the so-called anal character when he described the famous triad of obstinacy, parsimony, and orderliness (*1908, 1955*).

Richmond, Eddy, and Garrard described encopretic children as:

. . . unusually obedient and conforming, often neat in all spheres except the gastrointestinal. School-age children usually performed well and were often favorites of their teachers. The majority seemed to control manifestations of hostility and aggressiveness, except for their soiling, and favorably impressed adults. They usually related poorly to their own age group, and their attitudes were often stoic with infrequent displays of overt emotion. (*1954, p. 398.*)

Such children are often stoical about their symptom, treating it as an unfortunate handicap and hiding their anxiety and depression about it with the same intensity as they hide other emotional reactions. As one boy of eight said, "I push the feelings back inside," which is exactly what he tried to do with his excretory products. If the symptom persists into school age, psychotherapy is invariably lengthy and intensive, encountering all the stubbornness ascribed to "anal characters."

The following partial case report is offered to illustrate the personality dynamics involved:

Sarah was the younger of two children, age seven when she was referred for psychological treatment. She had never achieved dryness and had been subjected to numerous medical examinations and treatments, all unsuccessful. At four, when she started nursery school, she started to soil as well. Her parents were earnest, sincere people with obvious problems of their own which they tried to hide from the children. Because the mother was ill at the time, the father had taken the initiative in training the daughter. At seven, she was bright, articulate, imaginative, and a model of deportment at school. She was favored by her teachers, who felt sorry for her because of her problem, but she was heartily disliked by the other children. Sarah hated school and complained of stomach aches and headaches almost daily. On the surface, however, she was determinedly cheerful, and constantly made up jokes and riddles to make people laugh. Her attitude toward her symptom was one of regret but acceptance; it was a handicap with which she had to live. When she grew up, she planned to have plastic furniture that could not be damaged by her wetting. For a long time, she convinced herself that no one would know of her problem if she herself ignored it. Thus, she could carry on a sprightly conversation without any change of expression, while urinating or defecating. She was quite far along in treatment before she could admit that it was not a well-kept secret. Later, she admitted that she had little control over her urination or defecation. Her wishes to be a boy were exceptionally strong, and she entirely disassociated herself from that part of her body which reminded her that she was only a girl.

The following anecdote illustrates the relationship between her character and her symptom. Sarah was mercilessly picked on by the other children, who were jealous of her favored position with the teacher and also dismayed by her babyish behavior (i.e., the soiling and wetting). She was helpless to defend herself although she seethed with rage inside. She felt she had to be extra nice because she was such a "mess." She always turned the other cheek, which got slapped in turn. One day, a classmate passed out treats to everyone except Sarah. She was incensed, but when it was suggested that she retaliate in kind, she could not bring herself to spend the money! She could not buy candy to give away. This led into a discussion of her stinginess. She held back gifts in the same way that she held back urine and feces and feelings. This was yet another reason for her lack of popularity.

Sarah came to appreciate the extent of her obstinacy and the fact that it often led her to act against her own better judgment. She explained that once she had started something, she didn't know how to stop, even though she had a bad conscience about it. "Once I start, I just can't stop like that. I just have to go on anyhow." Treatment was long and arduous, weaving through attitudes and feelings which finally led, via a circuitous route, to the soiling symptom itself.

The symptoms which have been the subject matter of this chapter form a spectrum which ranges from simple, transient arrests in development all the way to complex neuroses. The diagnostician must be ingenious if he is to sort out the underlying causes of symptoms which look so alike and thus decide on the appropriate treatment. Simple suggestions may sometimes work; complex family adjustments are sometimes required; and direct treatment of the child is sometimes in order.

The clinician must remember the importance of this early period in shaping the child's personality in ways not immediately apparent. The child's toilet training prepares him, more or less well, for later frustrations. It is also important to understand the possible mental elaborations of primitive body functions which occur by way of the fantasy life of the young child. Even when the child's symptom may not seem to have anything to do with eating or with elimination, it may have its genesis in these early experiences. The sophisticated clinician, aware of the continuity of child development, explores the history of every emotionally disturbed child in order to establish the connections between past and present.

References for Chapter 6

Abraham, Karl, "The Influence of Oral Erotism on Character Formation" (1924), *Selected Papers of Karl Abraham, M.D.*, The International Psycho-Analytic Library, XIII, ed. E. Jones, trans. D. Bryan and A. Strachey. London: The Hogarth Press, Ltd., 1949.

Aldrich, C., *Cultivating the Child's Appetite.* New York: The Macmillan Company, 1928.

Baller, W. and H. Schalock, "Conditioned Response Treatment of Enuresis," *Exceptional Children*, XXII (1956), 233–48.

Beller, E. K., *The Clinical Process.* New York: Free Press of Glencoe, Inc., 1962.

Bentzen, Frances, "Sex Ratios in Learning and Behavior Disorders," *American Journal of Orthopsychiatry*, XXXIII (1963), 92–98.

Berlin, I. N. *et al.*, "Adolescent Alterations of

Anorexia and Obesity," *American Journal of Orthopsychiatry*, XXI (1951), 387–420.

Bliss, E. L. and C. Hardin Branch, *Anorexia Nervosa*. New York: Paul B. Hoeber, Inc., 1960.

Bond, D. D., "Anorexia Nervosa," *Rocky Mountain Medical Journal*, XLVI (1949), 1012.

Boyd, M. M., "The Depth of Sleep in Enuretic Children and in Non-Enuretic Controls," *Journal of Psychosomatic Research*, IV (1960), 274–81.

Brody, S., *Patterns of Mothering*. New York: International Universities Press, Inc., 1956.

———, "Signs of Disturbance in the First Year of Life," *American Journal of Orthopsychiatry*, XXVIII (1958), 362–67.

Bruch, H., "Conceptual Confusion in Eating Disorders," *Journal of Nervous and Mental Diseases*, CXXXIII (1961), 46–54.

———, "Obesity in Childhood and Personality Development," *American Journal of Orthopsychiatry*, XI (1941), 467–74.

———, "Obesity in Children: III, Physiological and Psychologic Aspects of the Food Intake of Obese Children," *American Journal of Diseases of Children*, LIX (1940), 739–81.

———, *The Importance of Overweight*. New York: W. W. Norton & Company, Inc., 1957.

Burchinal, L. G. and E. S. Eppright, "Test of the Psychogenic Theory of Obesity for a Sample of Rural Girls," *American Journal of Clinical Nutrition*, VII (1959), 288–94.

Burns, Charles, "Encopresis (Incontinence of Feces) in Children," *British Medical Journal*, II (1941), 767–69.

Childers, A. T. and B. M. Hamil, "Emotional Problems in Children as Related to the Duration of Breast Feeding in Infancy," *American Journal of Orthopsychiatry*, II (1932), 134–42.

Cooper, M., *Pica*. Springfield, Ill.: Charles C Thomas, Publisher, 1957.

Davis, C. M., "Self-Selection of Diet by Newly-Weaned Infants," *American Journal of Diseases of Children*, XXXVI (1928), 651–79.

Despert, J. L., "Urinary Control and Enuresis," *Psychosomatic Medicine*, VI (1944), 294–307.

Falstein, E. I., Sherman Feinstein, and I., Judas, "Anorexia Nervosa in the Male Child," *American Journal of Orthopsychiatry*, XXVI (1956), 751–73.

Freud, Anna, "The Psychoanalytic Study of Infantile Feeding Disturbances," in *The Psychoanalytic Study of the Child*, Vol. II. New York: International Universities Press, Inc., 1946.

Freud, Sigmund, *Character and Anal Erotism* (1908). Standard Edition, Vol. X, ed. J. Strachey. London: The Hogarth Press, Ltd., 1955.

———, *Three Essays on the Theory of Sexuality* (1905), Standard Edition, Vol. VII, ed. J. Strachey. London: The Hogarth Press, Ltd., 1953.

Gesell, A. and F. L. Ilg, *Infant and Child in the Culture of Today*. New York: Harper & Row, Publishers, Inc., 1943.

———, *The Feeding Behavior of Infants: A Pediatric Approach to the Mental Hygiene of Early Life*. Philadelphia: J. B. Lippincott, Co., 1937.

Gilbert, G. M., "A Survey of 'Referral Problems' in Metropolitan Child Guidance Centers," *Journal of Clinical Psychology*, XIII (1957), 37–42.

Glicklich, L. B., "Historical Account of Enuresis," *Pediatrics*, VIII (1951), 859–76.

Goldman, F., "Breastfeeding and Character Formation: Part I," *Journal of Personality*, XVII (1948), 83–103.

———, "Breastfeeding and Character Formation: Part II, The Etiology of the Oral Character in Psychoanalytic Theory," *Journal of Personality*, XIX (1950), 189–96.

Gull, William, "Anorexia Nervosa," *Transactions of the Clinical Society of London*, VII (1874), 22.

Gutelius, M. *et al.*, "Nutritional Studies of Children with Pica: Part I, Controlled Study Evaluating Nutritional Status," *Pediatrics*, XXIX (1962), 1012–17.

———, "Nutritional Studies of Children with Pica: Part II, Treatment of Pica with Iron Given Intramuscularly," *Pediatrics*, XXIX (1962), 1018–23.

Harmon, A. R., R. A. Purkhonen, and L. S. Rassmusen, "Obesity: A Physical and Emotional Problem," *Nursing Outlook*, VI (1958), 452–56.

Hill, J., "Infant Feeding and Personality Disorders," *Psychiatric Quarterly*, XI (1937), 33–58.

Hoefer, C. and M. C. Hardy, "Later Development of Breast Fed and Artificially Fed Infants," *Journal of the American Medical Association*, XCII (1929), 615–19.

Holway, A. R., "Early Self-regulation of Infants and Later Behavior in Play Interviews," *American Journal of Orthopsychiatry* XIX (1949), 612–23.

Honzik, M. P. and J. P. McKee, "Social Behavior Traits in Relation to Certain Physical and Functional Characteristics in Young Children." Paper delivered at the Twenty-fifth Anniversary Meeting, Society for Research in Child Development, National Institutes of Health, Bethesda, Md., March, 1959.

Josselyn, Irene M., "Treatment of the Emotionally Immature Child in an Institution Framework," *American Journal of Orthopsychiatry*, XX (1950), 397–410.

Kanner, Leo, *Child Psychiatry*, (3rd ed.) Springfield, Ill.: Charles C Thomas, Publisher, 1957.

Katan, Anny, "Experiences with Enuretics," in *The Psychoanalytic Study of the Child*, Vol. II. New York: International Universities Press, Inc., 1946.

Klackenberg, G., "Thumbsucking: Frequency and Etiology," *Pediatrics*, IV (1949), 418–24.

Kvaraceus, W. C., "Prenatal and Early Developmental History of 136 Delinquents," *Journal of Genetic Psychology*, LXVI (1945), 267–71.

Lapouse, R. and M. A. Monk, "Fears and Worries in a Representative Sample of Children," *American Journal of Orthopsychiatry*, XXIX (1959), 803–18.

Laseque, Charles, "On Hysterical Anorexia," *Medical Times and Gazette*, II (1873), 265–367.

Lesser, L. I. *et al.*, "Anorexia Nervosa in Children," *American Journal of Orthopsychiatry*, XXX (1960), 578–81.

Levy, D. M., "Experiment of the Sucking Reflex and Social Behavior of Dogs," *American Journal of Orthopsychiatry*, IV (1934), 203–24.

———, "Fingersucking and Accessory Movements in Early Infancy: An Etiological Study," *American Journal of Psychiatry*, VII (1928), 881–918.

MacFarlane, J., L. Allen, and M. P. Honzik, *A Developmental Study of the Behavior Problems of Normal Children between 21 Months and 14 Years.* Berkeley, Calif.: University of California Press, 1954.

McKhann, C. F., "Lead Poisoning in Children," *American Journal of Diseases of Children*, XXXII (1926), 386–92.

Martin, B. and D. Kubby, "Results of Treatment of Enuresis by a Conditioned Response Method," *Journal of Consulting Psychology*, XIX (1955), 71–73.

Maslow, A. H. and I. Szilagyi-Kessler, "Security and Breast Feeding," *Journal of Abnormal and Social Psychology*, XLI (1946), 83–85.

Meyer, H. F., *Infant Foods and Feeding Practice.* Springfield, Ill.: Charles C Thomas, Publisher, 1960.

Michaels, J. J. and S. E. Goodman, "Incidence and Intercorrelations of Enuresis and Other Neuropathic Traits in So-called Normal Children," *American Journal of Orthopsychiatry*, IV (1934), 79–106.

Mowrer, O. H. and W. Mowrer, "Enuresis: A Method for its Study and Treatment," *American Journal of Orthopsychiatry*, VIII (1938), 436–59.

Newton, N. R., "The Relationship Between Infant Feeding Experience and Later Behavior," *Journal of Pediatrics*, XXXVIII (1951), 28–40.

Orlansky, H., "General Review and Summary: Infant Care and Personality," *Psychological Bulletin*, XLIV (1949), 1–48.

Pearson, Gerald H. J., *Emotional Disorders of Children.* New York: W. W. Norton & Company, Inc., 1949.

———, "Some Early Factors in the Formation of Personality," *American Journal of Orthopsychiatry*, I (1931), 284–91.

Peterson, C. H. and F. L. Spano, "Breast Feeding, Maternal Rejection, and Child Personality," *Character and Personality*, X (1941), 62–66.

Ribble, M., "Infantile Experience in Relation to Personality Development," in J. McV. Hunt, *Personality and Behavior Disorders.* New York: The Ronald Press Company, 1944, 621–51.

Richmond, Julius B., Evelyn F. Eddy, and Sterling D. Garrard, "The Syndrome of Fecal Soiling and Megacolon," *American Journal of Orthopsychiatry*, XXIV (1954), 391–402.

Rogerson, B. C. F. and C. H. Rogerson, "Feeding in Infancy and Subsequent Psychological Difficulties," *Journal of Mental Science*, LXXXV (1939), 1163–82.

Ross, S., A. E. Fisher, and D. King, "Sucking Behavior: A Review of the Literature," *Journal of Genetic Psychology*, XCI (1957), 63–81.

Sears, R. R. and G. W. Wise, "Relation of Cup Feeding in Infancy to Thumb Sucking and the Oral Drive," *American Journal of Orthopsychiatry*, XX (1950), 123–39.

Segall, Aliza, "Report of a Constipated Child with Fecal Withholding," *American Journal of Orthopsychiatry*, XXVII (1957), 823–30.

Seqell, W. H. and P. H. Mussen, "The Effects of Feeding, Weaning, and Scheduling Procedures on Childhood Adjustment and the Formation of Oral Symptoms," *Child Development*, XXIII (1952), 185–91.

Shirley, H. F., "Encopresis in Children," *Journal of Pediatrics*, XII (1938), 367–80.

Spock, B., *Baby and Child Care*, Revised Cardinal Giant Edition. New York: Pocket Books, Inc., 1963.

Stendler, C. B., "Possible Causes of Overdependency in Young Children," *Child Development*, XXV (1954), 125–46.

Sylvester, E., "Analysis of Psychogenic Anorexia in a Four-year-old," in *The Psychoanalytic Study of the Child*, Vol. I. New York: International Universities Press, Inc., 1945.

Tapia, F., J. Jekel, and Herbert R. Domke, "Enuresis: An Emotional Symptom?" *Journal of Nervous and Mental Disease*, CXXX (1960), 61–66.

Thurston, J. R. and P. H. Mussen, "Infant Feeding Gratification and Adult Personality," *Journal of Personality*, XIX (1951), 449–58.

Young, C., K. Berrestford, and N. S. Moore, "Psychological Factors in Weight Control," *American Journal of Clinical Nutrition*, V (1957), 188–91.

Wolff, S., "Symptomatology and Outcome of Pre-school Children with Behavior Disorders Attending a Child Guidance Clinic," *Journal of Child Psychology and Psychiatry*, II (1961), 269–76.

Wortis, H. *et al.*, "Children Who Eat Noxious Substances," *Journal of the American Academy of Child Psychiatry*, I (1962), 536–47.

7

DEVELOPMENTAL PROBLEMS IN
SPEECH AND LANGUAGE

This chapter, like the previous one, is oriented toward symptoms rather than diseases. Speech disorders follow problems in feeding and toilet training chronologically, but we will consider some verbal problems out of order because they fit into the context of our theoretical discussion. In this chapter, we will pay some attention to reading disabilities, because they are often preceded by speech difficulties. And, because speech and language problems are frequently associated with organic brain damage, we will discuss the value of psychological tests in differentiating between functional and organic disorders.

It is unusual to find any problem in child psychopathology which is the exclusive interest of any one profession. The medical profession is deeply interested in the problems of feeding and elimination which we discussed in Chapter 6; the problems we are about to consider are of prime interest to yet another group. Speech pathology is a profession in and of itself, with a national organization (the American Speech and Hearing Association) which had 9,218 members in 1962, and with three professional journals—*The Journal of Speech and Hearing Disorders, The Journal of Speech and Hearing Research,* and *ASHA.* However,

difficulties with speech are so frequent a reason for the referral of children for psychological study or psychotherapy that they cannot be overlooked or dismissed as belonging to another field. G. M. Gilbert's survey showed that speech defects accounted for 6 per cent of the referrals to child guidance centers *(1957).*

Functional speech disorders may be grouped into four major categories: (1) voice disorders; (2) articulation disorders; (3) delayed speech; and (4) stuttering. Voice disorders, in many ways the least serious of the four, include marked deviations in loudness, pitch, quality, or flexibility of voice and intonation. The second category, disorders of articulation—the omission, substitution, or distortion of speech sounds—are part and parcel of learning to speak. The most immature articulation error, and the most difficult for the listener, is the omission of sounds *(Templin, 1953).* The vowels are most easily mastered, the consonants next, and the blends least. The consonants themselves are of unequal difficulty; "l" and "r" are usually correctly articulated later than others. Their position in the word also makes a difference. Pre-school children most often correctly enunciate sounds in the initial position, next those in the medial position, and least those in the final position *(Templin and Steer, 1939)*. Normally, all speech sounds are mastered by the age of seven or eight; *(Poole, 1934; Templin, 1953)*. There is a rapid decrease in misarticulation from kindergarten to grade four, but there is very little spontaneous improvement of those articulation disorders still present at grade four.

Articulatory problems are considered the most prevalent of all speech difficulties. Their reported prevalence figures in school populations range from 4.7 per cent *(Power, 1953)* to 10 per cent *(Midcentury White House Conference, 1951)*. L. D. Goodstein has explained such disorders as a failure in learning because of "inadequate speech models, a lack of stimulation in and motivation for adequate speech, or some other more basic emotional disturbance" *(1962, p. 401)*. After a review of the literature, he concluded that the "relationship between personality factors and articulation disorders has not been clearly demonstrated" *(p. 404)*. Wherever possible, it is common professional practice for articulation disorders to be treated by speech therapists alone. For this reason, plus the fact that articulation disorders usually do not have an overwhelming effect on the total personality, only the third and fourth categories—problems of delayed speech and stuttering—are considered here.

Delayed Speech

The normal timetable of speech development, as well as the importance of language in ego development, was discussed in Chapter 2. Without speech, the child is mentally and emotionally handicapped. It is a truism that children do not develop at the same rate and that there is a wide variation around the norm, but if the two-year-old has *no* words with which to com-

municate his wants, professional consultation is in order. This outside limit is the author's definition of "delayed speech."

Traditionally, delayed speech is viewed as organic (i.e., physiogenic) or functional (i.e., psychogenic). This distinction was useful because it made clear that there is more than one possible cause for the same symptom and that emotional factors can produce the same kind of symptom as organic factors. However, there is no clear-cut dichotomy, even in theory. There are some obscure clinical conditions—such as infantile autism, a major symptom of which is lack of speech—which probably result from organic and functional causes. Even organic conditions give rise to secondary psychological effects which increase the handicap.

Organic Causes

Deafness. The possibility of deafness must be considered first. In her account of the history of the deaf and their education, Lauretta Bender pointed out that improved scientific techniques, as well as increased professional and public awareness, bring hearing losses to the attention of doctors and educators at constantly earlier ages *(1960)*. As early teaching and nursery classes have proved their value, the age level for beginning training has gradually been lowered. Some institutions (The Cleveland Hearing and Speech Center, for one) accept one-year-olds. Also, improved test instruments have revealed that deafness is often less total than it was formerly thought to be. The electronic amplification of sound can make this residual hearing valuable. According to Bender, even ten-month-old babies can wear modern hearing aids. A congenital hearing loss can, and should be, detected even earlier than two years of age.

Mental Retardation. Delayed speaking may indicate retardation. But one does not explain the speech delay by attributing it to mental retardation, which is in itself a symptom rather than disease. And mental retardation can result from either organic or functional disturbances (see Chapter 8). Here we shall discuss only the relationship between the age at which a child begins to talk and his intelligence.

Terman *(1925)* found that gifted children (i.e., with IQ's over 140) began to talk at about eleven months, although a few did not talk until they were three. One of the most reliable early signs of mental retardation is delayed speech, as the figures in Table I show.* These are mean figures; the many exceptions are indicated by the ranges.

Although the sample is skewed in the direction of mental retardation, Table I provides convincing evidence of the

relationship between early development and later-measured intelligence. A child should not be expected to talk before he reaches a mental age of 18 to 24 months. A youngster whose IQ is less than 50 (and who is therefore mentally developing at half speed) will therefore be twice as old as the normal child when he talks. Severely mentally retarded children may never reach this level and so never speak. On the other hand, speech can be delayed in relation to mental age. If a six-year-old child has a mental age of four years but does not speak, his delayed speech is not explained by his retardation.

Aphasia. "Aphasia" is a term which has been borrowed from adult neurology and applied to those children who have a congenital language defect, either in understanding or expressing speech. H. R. Myklebust defined it as follows:

TABLE 1

IQ vs. Age of Walking and Talking

STANFORD-BINET INTELLIGENCE QUOTIENTS

Months	Less than 50 (101 cases)	50-84 (246 cases)	85-115 (126 cases)	Above 115 (26 cases)
Walking:				
Mean Age	27.8	18.5	16.4	11.9
Range	9 to 66	9 to 72	7 to 56	8 to 20
Talking:*				
Mean Age	36.7	28.5	21.8	14.4
Range	11 to 77	7 to 48	9 to 48	8 to 24

The differences between the means was significant at the .01 level using Fisher's test, with the exception of the t-test between mean age walking of the 50-84 and 85-115 I.Q. groups which was significant at the .05 level.

*"Talking" was defined as the use of any single words other than simple syllabic combinations such as "mama," "gaga," and "dada."

*These figures were obtained from the histories and tests of young children seen at the Mental Development Center and the Society for Crippled Children in Cleveland. The data were calculated and analyzed by Miss Kirsten Werrenrath.

Aphasia is a language disorder which results from damage to the brain. Aphasia literally means lack of speech but this definition is inadequate because aphasia is not basically a speech disorder. It is a disorder in symbolic functioning. It is an inability to comprehend the spoken language of others, an inability to speak, or an inability to use language internally for purposes of thinking to oneself *(1954, p. 144.)*

Although organic causation is generally postulated, there are often no supporting neurological signs or history of organic truama. The organic cause is presumed on the basis of exclusion of other possibilities rather than positive evidence for organicity. Some clinicians question this assumption and propose a symptomatic rather than an etiologic classification. F. R. Kleffner, for example, has stated:

If I were to rewrite today the definition of aphasia . . . , I would want to exclude the necessity for establishing any defect in the child's nervous system, although this leaves us wide open to significant question in terms of classical meanings of the word "aphasia." In everyday clinical life, the practical application of the term "aphasia" is not based upon observations of the nervous system. So, in defining aphasia abstractly for academic purposes, perhaps we should do as we do in practical clinical communication with our colleagues: simply omit the neurological facet. Operationally, the child we classify as aphasic presents a greater deficiency in speech and language development than we would expect on the basis of our observations of his hearing, intelligence, social behavior, and (if he has had any) his schooling. *(Quoted by Rappaport, 1964, pp. 10–11.)*

Aphasic disorders in young children may be predominantly expressive, predominantly receptive, mixed receptive-expressive, or central. The last, called "global aphasia" by J. Wepman *(1951)*, refers to those children in whom *no* expressive, receptive, or inner language function can be ascertained. When the aphasia is selective, the child may comprehend, but not speak. (Adult patients who have suffered brain injury may retain speech but lose their ability to comprehend it, but this is unlikely on a developmental basis.) A few children even learn to read and write without speaking. Roger is a case in point:

Roger was the only child of anxious, thoughtful, intelligent parents who left no stone unturned in their attempts to get help for him. He was born prematurely, though of normal weight. There was difficulty in getting the baby to breathe, and he was placed in an incubator. In infancy his difficulties in sucking and swallowing were so severe that he had to be fed by tube. At five months, there was abnormal action and marked incoordination of the tongue. No true sucking reflex was obtained in the cheeks. It was felt that the major difficulty was a disturbance of the hypoglossal nerve. He was hospitalized at the age of twelve months and again at 13 months. A pneumoencephalogram indicated mild cortical atrophy. Because of club feet, he wore braces for a while. At two and a half, he had poliomyelitis, but no residual paralysis. At four, he began to have seizures in his sleep. These were controlled with medication.

His hearing was normal, his comprehension of language was good. At nine, his IQ was 69 on the Arthur Performance Scale and 76 on the Peabody Picture Vocabulary Test.

At ten, Roger was placed in a class for severely retarded youngsters. Speech therapy had not been successful. His only sounds were uninflected guttural noises. Therapists commented on the limited movement and poor coordination. He was active and easily excited, particularly when his pantomime and gestures were not understood. He demanded a lot of attention and was sometimes a disciplinary problem. He had some understanding of numbers and was able to do crude printing. He read very well and enjoyed it. Since there was little else for him to do, he read constantly, thereby increasing his reading ability to an exceptionally high level.

Roger's difficulty seemed to be essentially neurological, dating from birth. There was definite but mild retardation of conceptual thinking and motor performance, but his greatest handicap was the absence of speech.

Such a case requires more than the educational programs designed for slow learners or hard-of-hearing children. Kleffner emphasized the pragmatic significance of the diagnosis of aphasia in his remark that the classification of a child as aphasic means only that "we are going to set about teaching him in a particular manner" (quoted in *Rappaport, 1964, p. 11*). In the opinion of some experts in the field, the specialized educational training is best embodied in the "Elements-Association Method" *(McGinnis, 1963)*.

This method was evolved from three basic premises about the aphasic child: (1) that there is no general deficiency in integrating sensory experience, particularly *visual* perception; (2) that the deficiency is primarily restricted to learning "symbolic handles" for naming experiences; and (3) that a deficiency in *auditory memory* prevents the usual association of sound (e.g., the spoken word) with an appropriate object or action.

Accordingly, the McGinnis method starts with written language, broken down into elements of sound, or orthographs, which the child learns to say with the help of all kinds of visual clues, such as different colors, exaggerated mouth movements, and hand gestures. After he memorizes the sounds that go with letters, they are blended into combinations and words. These words, in turn, are associated with pictures of real objects. Thus, the child learns to talk by first learning to read and then learns to attach meaning to the written words by means of pictures. The sequence is the exact reverse of the usual acquisition of language, in which reading and writing follow speech. The method is also unlike the whole-word approach which is used to teach speech to retarded children or to those whose speech has been delayed by lack of stimulation.

These differences in speech instruction have their parallel in remedial reading techniques. G. Fernald teaches the whole word by reinforcing its appearance in several ways: by touch, as the child traces it with his finger tip; kinesthetically, as he traces over the large written word with his fingers and pronounces it; and auditorally, as he hears himself say the word aloud *(1943)*. A. Gillingham starts with single letters, and only later goes to words *(1936)*. This is obviously a much slower process and is usually restricted to children with more serious forms of reading disability—the so-called word-blind, or alexic, child. It is used when other methods fail.

The highly specialized McGinnis treatment is rarely available except in large speech centers and in special schools, such as The Central Institute for the Deaf in St. Louis and The Pathway School in Pennsylvania. There is a film entitled "Teaching Speech and Language: The McGinnis Association Method" which depicts the progress of three aphasic children at The Central Institute for the Deaf during eight months of treatment by the association method.*

Although there are many treatment reports, there is little information about the percentage of success, partly because cure is relative. Some of the children learn to speak well enough to attend conventional schools. Others learn only stereotyped phrases and need to be told what to say; these remain handicapped and require a modified environment. The results are similar to those achieved with emotionally disturbed children, in that there are varying degrees of cure.

Although the term "aphasia" should be used only when speech is retarded in relation to mental age, aphasia can

---

*58 minutes, 16mm, sound, color. Directed by Frank R. Kleffner and George Shames. Produced by The Central Institute for the Deaf (Amadee J. Taussig Trust). For information write to Frank R. Kleffner, Ph.D., Director, Division of Speech Pathology, The Central Institute for the Deaf, 818 South Euclid, St. Louis 10, Mo.

be distinguished from mental retardation. Aphasic children resemble mentally retarded children more than they do deaf children. One can test their intelligence only on the basis of performance tasks (e.g., dexterity tests, puzzles, form boards, copying of forms, matching of forms). Such tests do not tap the symbolic processes which become increasingly important as the child grows older. Many aphasic children require the special curriculum used for slow learners after they acquire some language.

Perhaps because the category is a new one, aphasia is diagnosed frequently. We need a clearer definition of the clinical or educational entity of aphasia. In the author's opinion clinical experience will show that aphasia, in its pure form, is relatively rare and that it is usually associated with other forms of psychopathology.

Mixed Organic and Functional Causes

Infantile Autism. The childhood psychosis known as infantile autism is discussed in detail in Chapter 11. It is mentioned here because one of its features is the failure to use language for the purpose of communication. L. Kanner and L. Eisenberg state:

In three of the eleven cases speech failed to develop altogether. The remaining eight developed a precocity of articulation which, coupled with unusual facility in rote memory, resulted in the ability to repeat endless numbers of rhymes, catechisms, lists of names and other semantically useless exercises. *(1957, p. 57.)*

It is difficult to distinguish between autism and aphasia. The determination rests mainly on the fact that aphasic children relate well to people. The aphasic looks at people, enjoys being with people, likes to play with others, and is capable of genuine affection. Autistic children are withdrawn; and their failure to speak is a secondary result of this primary defect. It is also difficult to distinguish autism from mental retardation, and the two often occur together. Their relationship is discussed further in the chapter on mental subnormality.

Functional Causes

Environmental Deficiency. It has been established that the children of the poor speak later. The parents are likely to consider their children's verbal development as less important than their growing ability to take care of themselves and so leave their mothers freer to care for the younger children or earn some extra money. Middle-class parents are more likely to talk to and listen to their children. O. C. Irwin demonstrated that talking to children of one year increases their vocabulary *(1960)*. In terms of learning theory, their speaking is rewarded by their mother's attention. In terms of psychoanalytic theory, since the child normally identifies with his mother, he talks if she talks.

Any individual, however, may suffer a delay in speaking because of an insufficiency in the environment—if, for example the mother is suffering from depression and is therefore silent. And in any economic group, there are neglectful or handicapped mothers who do not communicate with their children.

Infantilism. Infantilism may occur when the relationship between the mother and the child is such that both resist the infant's growing up and consequent separation from his mother. There may be a combination of constitutional and maternal factors. The baby may be passive and clinging, and fearful of innovations, and these constitutional characteristics may be reinforced by a mother who is herself fearful, overprotective, and more responsive to a helpless infant than to an active child. Z. S. Wolpe points out that speech is associated with other consequences of maturation and can create conflict between mother and child:

Instead of the anticipated understanding resultant from the acquisition of speech, there is heightened anxiety and frustration, for the individual finds a widened rather than a narrowed gap in the area of communication. This is actually what frequently occurs. When the infant is in the babbling stage, the parent is able to coo with him and delight in his dependency. But as the infant moves on to a higher stage in his maturational process, the parent is less and less accepting of his behavior, more and more critical of it, and determined to train the child by imposing demands upon him. The acquisition of speech, equated as it is with maturation, now becomes a symbol of the danger of further maturation, and the child holds tenaciously to infantile speech patterns as symbolic of the period when demands were minimal and when understanding (or acceptance) was heightened. *(1957, pp. 992–93.)*

In lay terms "The child doesn't talk because he doesn't need to." The child is being given everything and is so indulged that words are unnecessary to him. The oft-suggested remedy, to withhold what the child wants and thus force him to ask for it, rarely works. The child feels he is being teased and his indignation, rather than his speech, is aroused. The mother who is fostering an infantile child does so in many ways, and needs to change her general attitude rather than any specific bit of behavior. Tom's mother is a good example:

Tom was the second of four children. Pregnancy and delivery were reported as normal. Tom was an active infant, but a poor sleeper and a fussy eater. He sat up at seven months, crawled at eight months, and walked at twelve months. At the age of one, he said "mama" and "dada." During his first two years, he was treated for a severe eczema, which got worse when he was frustrated or upset. For this reason, his mother tried to always give in to him.

When Tom was first seen, at the age of two, he said four words, but only if he was prompted. Otherwise, he succeeded with all other intellectual tasks expected of a two-year-old. His parents described him as stubborn. He dawdled so much over meals that his mother ended up feeding him. Toilet training was difficult. He was beaten for accidents. His father was irritated by his stubbornness and was determined to break him. The mother made a particular point of the fact that Tom had never been away from his mother or from her mother, who lived with them. His mother disapproved of baby sitters. The focus of parental concern was Tom's speech. It was talked about a great deal, often in Tom's presence. Tom knew that his mother was disturbed, almost hysterical, about it. It was hard for her to stop babying him because of his eczema. Moreover, since he didn't talk, he seemed like a baby.

In sporadic interviews with the mother over a period of a year the counsellor was made aware of the parents' inconsistent expectations of Tom. At the age of almost three, Tom had only a dozen single words, and his parents again were desperate. At this time, nursery school was recommended, in order to get him into a more neutral and consistent environment. A school which had a parent counsellor on the staff was suggested, in order to ensure more regular contacts with the mother. Characteristically, she wavered about the school. She felt that the teachers were too young, that the supervision was insufficient, that Tom would be unable to protect himself, and that he would be upset by the separation from her and that the eczema would become worse. She discussed the pros and cons with everyone in her family, often within Tom's hearing. At long last, she decided to let him go, on the condition that his older sister also attend. This sister, 11 months older, was very quick and verbal.

Here we see that Tom's failure to speak was in part a reflection of his anal stubbornness, aggravated by the father; in part an expression of his wish; shared and reinforced by his mother, to remain a baby; and in part a way of forcing everyone to pay attention to him. In this family of four children under four years of age, competition for parental attention was particularly keen. It was futile to treat the delayed speech as an isolated symptom. It was necessary that the parents change their handling of him in a great number of ways and they found this especially difficult because of Tom's medical history and their own temperaments.

Displacement from Anal Functions. In Wolpe's quotation, reference is made to the increasing demands made on a child which usually coincide with the beginning of speech. One of these demands is toilet training, which can easily become a battle. Once the child gets the notion that his mother is out to take something from him—his freedom, his independence, his pleasure, or his feces—he may gird himself for a long, hard fight. It is very easy for such resistance to overflow or be displaced on to speaking. Toilet training and speech development have many elements in common. First, they both normally occur in the second year. Second, both have to be taught. Third, the child must want to do as his mother does or as she directs. And fourth, both involve production. Occasionally, adult patients retain traces of this early association; sufferers from psychogenic constipation often complain of a difficulty in "getting their words out," and may describe this difficulty in the same terms as they describe their constipation. Children who are delayed in speech because of anal displacement are often unusually acute in their comprehension. When the anal conflict is resolved, they suddenly start talking in a rush, skipping the usual preliminaries of single-word speech.

Post-traumatic Reactions. Ordinarily, post-traumatic reactions show up as a loss of speech in a toddler who is just beginning to talk; they are otherwise hard to detect. The mechanism involved is usually regression. Initially, the child's speech is private communication with his mother, and only she understands what he is saying. If he becomes angry with her and won't talk to her, he has no one to talk to.

Separations, the birth of a new baby, and hospitalizations are typical occurrences. They affect a child's speech in either, or both, of two ways. He may be so overwhelmed that ideas and words cannot come to his rescue. He may be able to react to the shock only in a feeling, preverbal way, without thinking, as if he had had a blow which knocked the wind out of him. The toddler has had the power of words only a short time, and he easily loses it in moments of stress.

Trauma can also make the child afraid of what he might say. He is apt to be very angry at the person who has left him and if he spoke, he might express his anger. He wants to do this, but he does not want to risk driving his mother away again. If he says nothing, angry words can't slip out. Verbal regression following the birth of a new baby may be a way both to hide anger and to identify with the speechless baby, as enuresis sometimes is.

It is not so difficult to help children who spoke a little and then retreated into silence after a trauma. One knows the precipitating incident, and one can imagine what the child is fearing or feeling. The situation is much more complicated when the child has never talked, because there is no change to show which event if any, has been traumatic. In the author's experience, however, the loss of speech following a trauma is rarer than is commonly believed. Parents will volunteer the information that the child spoke, and that he stopped after a sibling was born, but closer scrutiny often shows that the so-called words were only meaningless syllabic combinations or simple imitations. In taking the history, it is important to ascertain that the words were used spontaneously by the child for the purpose of communication. But once the child has reached this level, he rarely loses it altogether, although he may become relatively silent, he may be slow to progress further, or he may start to stutter.

Stuttering

Definition, Incidence, and Related Factors

Stuttering, or stammering, is a disturbance in the smooth flow of speech due to tonic and clonic spasms involving respiration, phonation, and articulation. It is estimated that stutterers of whom half are children, comprise about 1 per cent of the population. The age of onset, in 9 per cent of the cases, is before ten. The greatest number of onsets occur between the ages of two and five, and the peak occurs between four and five. Males outnumber females, although the reported differences range from eight-to-one to four-to-one. There is a strong tendency for stuttering to run in families. D. Barbara reported that 45 per cent of the stutterers he studied had a family history of stuttering (1956). W. Johnson reported that 33 per cent of the stutterers he studied, but only 9 per cent of the nonstutterers, had a family history of stuttering (1955).

It is customary to make a distinction between primary and secondary stuttering (Van Riper, 1953). In the primary stage, there is no awareness of disability or self-consciousness. Many feel that primary stuttering is a developmental phenomenon which will have no special significance if it is let alone. In the secondary stage, there is painful awareness, and bizarre symptoms attend the effort to reduce the tension which the stuttering creates. The stutterer may go to great lengths to fight the symptom, using stereotyped body movements, slapping himself, repeating magical words, and substituting synonyms and circuitous phrases to bypass the most difficult words. He becomes painful both to watch and listen to, and his speech problem becomes a serious social handicap.

There has been considerable research into the personality of the child stutterer. In Goodstein's opinion, there is little evidence that the stuttering child has a special personality or is severely maladjusted (1962). J. G. Sheehan agreed that projective techniques have failed to disclose a consistent personality pattern, and suggested that "perhaps the search for basic personality difference between stutterers and non-stutterers has gone far enough, sapped enough creative potential, and should end" (1962, p. 428).

No significant differences in intelligence have been reported. Stutterers are only slightly retarded in school (approximately six months), a finding which Goodstein feels bolsters his view that they are not neurotic. This line of argument is as fallacious here as it is elsewhere; it fails to recognize that a neurotic conflict may be solved by a single symptom.

Theory and Treatment

The literature on stuttering contains a fascinating number of theories. There probably is no other symptom which has been subjected to such varied explanations. And, since treatment is based on our understanding of causation, therapies have been equally varied. All the theorists agree, however, that conflict is displayed in the interruption of speech, that there is a holding back in a situation which calls for going ahead. Their differences concern the origin and nature of this conflict. The important theories are discussed in this section.

The Mixed Cerebral Dominance Theory. According to this theory, the conflict is basically physiological, a rivalry between the two cortical hemispheres. Its authors, S. Orton (1928) and L. E. Travis (1931), have reasoned that if one hemisphere was not sufficiently dominant, the two would tend to function independently, the two halves of the speech musculature would be poorly synchronized, and a predisposition to verbal difficulty would exist. But Oliver Bloodstein, in his review of stuttering theories, cites findings to the contrary. Stutterers are not especially left-handed or ambidextrous. Moreover, the vast majority of children whose handedness is changed by parents or teachers do not stutter. And therapy designed to strengthen unilaterality (by having the patient use *only* the dominant hand) has not been effective *(1959)*.

Other constitutional predispositions have been proposed. R. M. West regards stuttering as a kind of miniature epileptic seizure, and believes that stutterers and nonstutterers differ in their metabolic organization *(1957)*. J. Eisenson suggests that stuttering is based on a constitutional tendency toward motor and sensory perseveration *(1958)*. Neither of these theories gained the support which the cerebral dominance theory had in the twenties and thirties.

In 1946, Travis modified his view:

In terms of all the clinical and laboratory evidence we now possess, it is very doubtful that the somatic variant alone would operate to produce stuttering . . . My present concept is that our western culture, in demanding an early, harsh, complete and uncushioned renunciation of infantile and childish behavior, works in conjunction with the somatic variant possessed by a few infants and children to produce stuttering. *(Quoted in Van Riper, 1953, p. 56.)*

This probably reflects the current consensus, namely, that there may be some sort of constitutional predisposition toward stuttering but that it is insufficient to explain the symptom. In more recent writings, Travis makes no reference to a somatic variant and considers stuttering a learned response *(1957)*.

The Semantogenic theory. Perhaps the most ingenuous of the theories is Johnson's. He feels that the conflict expressed in stuttering has been induced by undue parental criticism. Almost all pre-school children hesitate and repeat. If nothing is said, the problem is outgrown, but, if attention is called to it, it becomes fixated. The secondary stage occurs when the parents press the child to master the art of talking *(1953)*. Johnson compared the case histories of 46 children referred to a clinic for stuttering with the histories of a control group, and concluded that the only significant difference between the groups lay in the acceptance or criticism with which they were heard *(1955)*. He suggests that the very diagnosis of stuttering, originally made by the anxious parents, is a cause. "Once the parents have persuaded themselves that the child's speech is disordered, that he is a stutterer, they do not react with calm indifference. Their concern, vague and mild before perhaps, now has a disturbing name, 'stuttering' (or any equivalent), upon which to feed" *(1948, p. 198)*.

C. Van Riper shares Johnson's view somewhat. He first counsels the parent, attempting to identify and eliminate fluency disruptors. In other words, the treatment is directed to the environment, not to the child's speech *(1953)*. This approach is well illustrated in the pamphlet "Stuttering is a Family Affair," *(1964)* written for parents of young children who are beginning to stutter, by Dean C. Engel, a speech pathologist, and Isadore Helfand, a clinical psychologist. It is quoted in its entirety, not only because it is such a good statement of the treatment of primary stuttering, but also because it is such a good example of parent education (which is discussed, but not illustrated, in Chapter 15). The principles set forth in this pamphlet are applicable to many behavior problems of young children.

"Stuttering Is a Family Affair"*

What causes stuttering?
   "Experts" answer this question with

---

*Quoted from Dean Engel and Isidore Helfand, *Stuttering is a Family Affair*. Reproduced by permission.

theories, but in all honesty a theory is not a sure fact. We assume that stuttering is not a physical problem. It seems to occur more often in boys than girls, and twins seem to stutter more often than singletons. It starts most often in the young child, although older children can develop this speech habit. Facts such as these can be explained in different ways. As was indicated, most children go through a period, usually between the ages of 2 and 5, when some people might feel they were stuttering.

Children who stutter seem to have personality differences. They are not like one another, and we cannot say that one child stutters for the same personal or emotional reasons that another child does. However, there is a tendency for children who stutter to be more sensitive to disapproval and criticism. They are less sure that what they are or what they say is acceptable to teachers or friends. If he could put into words what is on his mind, the child who stutters might say, "I worry about what other people will say and think of me. I want them to like me and to think well of me."

Usually the child who stutters works hard to win praise and approval. Sometimes, if the pressures are too great, he will fight back. The way we teach this child to get along with the rest of the world seems harder on him than on his brothers or sisters, or the neighbor children. This does not mean that there is something "wrong" with the child, but it does mean that he may need some special handling if we wish to prevent a problem.

Psychologists disagree as to whether the child who stutters is more or less nervous or more or less upset than most other children. However, any increase in tension, nervousness or worry will probably increase the tendency to stutter. For some reason, the child who stutters seems to show his worries in his speech. Other children might have other ways of responding such as difficulty sleeping, fears, anger. In most children, these "symptoms" or signs of nervousness pass away and the child "outgrows them." Sometimes suggestions as to how to handle these problems seem to make them pass away more quickly. Sometimes suggestions serve only as a goal, or guide to what we want, and more attention is necessary.

What have you done?

Perhaps you have tried practically everything that is suggested to you in this booklet, but you have not had much confidence in it; you have shifted from one thing to another and grown more worried and nervous, more anxious and focused more on the problem. Parents often "try" to ignore it, and then become exasperated and start with, "well slow down" or other suggestions. You may have become more worried about how he talks than what he said, and suggest to him "think before you talk." Sometimes this is exactly what the child is doing and he spends so much time mulling, thinking, trying and holding back that the word doesn't come out. When the youngster or oldster is not "inhibited" or doesn't hold back as much, his speech improves.

What can be done?

What follows is a list of suggestions that have been found to be most helpful in the reduction and/or the elimination of stuttering problems. Any single one of these may not apply to your child. However, these suggestions are designed to reduce some of the tension about talking and about the home in general, with the expectation that with this change in the situation, the speech pattern will alter itself and improve.

Should we tell him not to stutter?

No!

With many of us, once bitten, twice shy. If we've been upset or frightened about something before, the chances are, when we are placed in somewhat the same situation, we will be upset or frightened again. This is the same with the child who, once he becomes impressed or aware of his troubles with speech, begins to worry about how he talks and begins to become more nervous and thus has more trouble. We would like to keep him as unaware and as unconcerned about his speech as possible. The parent who feels that his child "stutters on purpose," or because he lacks will power, and has to make an "effort to speak well" may make matters worse because the child tries too hard. So does the parent who tells the child, "take it easy and relax, think before you talk, don't get excited." They all call attention to this child's speech problem and point out that "the way you talk bothers me, so talk better." Changing the situation is much more helpful than asking the child to change the way he talks.

When does he stutter?

If we can discover some of the things which seem to bother the child and make him stutter more, perhaps we can change some of these factors.

A child may stutter more:
  When over-stimulated (excited)
  When competition to speak is high and he has to speak quickly to get his contribution in
  When he expects to be interrupted by another child or adult
  When what he says is being disapproved
  When he thinks he is disbelieved
  When he is confessing a wrongdoing
  When he can't see his listener
  When his listener is reading or doing something else distracting
  When his listener is angry
  When he is tired
  When he expects to be punished
  When discipline is inconsistent
  When his listener is impatient
  When he is asked to "recite" in front of strangers
  When he is afraid
  When he tries to speak in too adult a manner
  When he is trying to use words he is unsure of
  When he isn't sure he is right
  When his parents quarrel
  When competing with an older child
  When "older" behavior is demanded of him
  When he tells a lie
  When compared with another child unfavorably, etc., etc., etc.

Some of these examples would make most children more hesitant in their speech whether they had a stuttering problem or not. Others would affect the speech of only a few children.

Being realistic, you know that you are not going to discover all the factors that bother your child. Some of the things you do find cannot be changed. However, you can probably change some things around so that your child has an easier world in which to speak.

What can we change?

We should try to remember that what the child is saying is more important than how it is being said. Wait patiently for him to manage what he has to say If looking at him seems to make it easier for him to talk, look at him. If not, don't make any issue of it. If a loss of sleep seems to make stuttering worse, try to arrange for a better sleeping pattern. If you have to punish him, and he knows it, talking at that time may be even more difficult for him. You might find that your telling him why he is being punished would be better than having him "confess" his wrongdoing. Give the child more approval and acceptance. Reduce your demands on him. Accept him as someone who is not perfect. Accept him as a child who will make mistakes and is not the worse for it. Ignoring his speech trouble is not enough, we must change some of the things that affect his speech.

Don't make him any more aware of his stuttering than he already is. It is not a good idea to help him by saying words for him. Don't discuss his "problem" in his presence or permit others to do so. Don't demand adult pronunciations, adult grammar, or adult answers from him. He shouldn't be teased and you should try to keep others from teasing him. Don't let him develop the idea that we would like him better or that others would like him better if he talked perfectly.

Encourage him to talk, especially when he is having less trouble. Play down the idea that his speech is on display when company comes and also play down comparisons between him and his sisters, brothers, or neighborhood children regarding talking early, talking well, school progress, etc. Tell him and show him often that you like him. Talk to him in a simpler way using fewer words and easier words. Join in activities and games which involve speech, rhymes, and songs, where verbal behavior is pleasant. You can give him support when he needs it, but enough freedom to develop independence when he is ready to try his wings.

If he asks about his stuttering, tell him that you have noticed it, but that it is nothing to be greatly concerned about. Don't make a big issue of it. Let him do most of the talking on this subject. Listen and reassure him.

In general:

Not only are we concerned about changing our attitudes and behavior towards how your child speaks, and what he says, but it is just as important to change the attitudes in the whole family. Reducing the amount of tension in the house, in general, is a great help to the youngster who stutters.

The strictness, even if it really isn't so strict, might be relaxed even more. One way of helping is to cut down on the number of situations in which you as a parent have to argue, criticize, scold, punish, or get angry with your children. You should not just let everything go and not do or say anything at all. This would be even worse.

A way to start to make a house "more permissive" or more easy going, is to take any three things which seem to always involve an argument. They could be anything: brushing teeth after each meal, going to bed at the exact time, cleaning up his room, talking with his mouth full. Just decide that these three things are not going to upset you or your husband or wife in relation to any of the children. Decide that it isn't important if your son eats with his elbows on the table, and you are not going to correct him for that. You are not going to worry if, let's say, he comes home for dinner a little later. You are just going to be more easy going about everything. It is also a good idea to do this with your husband or wife as well. Just generally decide that some of the things you argue about are just not worth while and let them go. Not all, just three.

Discipline

Discipline is important, and you as a parent are the best judge of how and when you should discipline your child. As you know, if you have more than one child, what is good for Susan seems to be bad for Johnny. However, in the case of stuttering or any problem which has a large "nervous" or emotional component, reducing some of the tension and criticism helps a great deal. The child who stutters may be worried about what he says because it will show disrespect, anger, hurt someone, or hurt him because he will be punished for what he says. The less you keep inside of you, the less nervous or tense you are. Of course we cannot go around telling everyone what we think, but the child who is stuttering may be especially careful.

It becomes more important, then, to let him be a little more outspoken even if sometimes he rubs the wrong way. A good rule to follow in children's "backtalk" is to watch what they do. If your child complains, argues and gets angry but does what you tell him, that's more important than if he keeps his mouth shut, says only nice things, soft soaps you, but doesn't do what you want. As the child who stutters becomes freer, he will be more cocky and give more backtalk. A little spunkiness and confidence wears off and doesn't get bad. So, if your child begins to give you a little "lip" I would not scold or punish him unless he becomes too rebellious in his actions.

Accept yourself:

The child learns to be the person he is because of three things: he has the inheritance with which he came into this world making him different from you and a little like you; he learns what you teach him; and, possibly the most important, he learns how you think and feel about the things you teach him.

If you are an honest person and try to teach him how to cheat, he will probably grow up to be an honest man who may feel his children should cheat a little. If you feel that since you are a pretty decent person and if your child grows up to be like you it wouldn't be so bad, you might worry less about "teaching him good manners" or the "right thing to do." You might feel that he will kind of learn it, like learning to talk English, or eating with a fork. He will pick up many of these things because they are easy and natural. Good manners are convenient, and he will naturally learn them because you have them, and he notices how easy and comfortable you are, and wants to be like you.

A good rule is to accept yourself and feel that maybe it wouldn't be bad if your children were like you. You will find that you worry less about teaching them things, expecting things, or worrying about respect. Children are showing "respect" for their parents when they turn out to be responsible, moral citizens in the world.

Sometimes we not only want more for our children, but we may expect more from our children before they can give it, and then we are disappointed. Take stock of your family; what you expect; what they can do. *Maybe lower some expectancies.* Accept a C instead of a B in school, one ear that is clean, or one "Oh, why do I have to do everything" that he can get away with.

Teasing

The parents of children who stutter or have any "different" qualities worry that their children will be picked upon by other children, made fun of in school and generally tortured. We are all told how cruel children really are. Children are usually more direct, but this is only true if one quality is there. If your child has trouble making friends, if he is a "loner," or is sensitive about whether he is liked or not and waits for other children to invite him to play, talk to him first, or make him feel wanted, then chances are he will not be left out. If he is, they will then pick on him. If your child doesn't want to make friends because he doesn't like the other children or is a child who is happier by himself and doesn't play in the children's games and activities, they may pick on him. If he didn't stutter they would criticize him for any other reason, like one foot is smaller, or his father has brown eyes, or he is rich or poor or anything.

The important thing is that your youngster not expect to be rejected, and then hold back from the group, but to act and feel, as he has a right to, that children will play with anybody who wants to play with them and get along. It wouldn't matter if he had a horn growing out of the side of his head, if he is a member of the group. It becomes important to encourage your child to join and play with other children. If he avoids talking, he is in for trouble.

Fighting

One word about fighting among brothers and sisters. Some of this anger is useful because the kids blow off steam about parents, school, and the world in general in some of their "battles." Often, it is more noise than action and nature seems to protect children so that when they have no control and can do the most harm, they have no strength to do anything. When they can harm, they don't. Generally, if

you turn a deaf ear to some of the wrangling and decide if they are really not hurting each other, tell them to get outside, or just cut it out for the time being. Excitement, anger and punishment merely make the situation worse.

How far to let them go? Well, "if they don't bleed I let them" is a good natured way of saying that if they really are not hurting each other but making noise, don't punish them for it, although you can break it up. If it gets serious, however, separate them and send them away, or discipline them in the way you feel you should.

Stuttering is really a family affair and in a family one cannot separate one member of the family and say he is "IT," and try to change him without doing something to the rest. You can't heat water on one side of a pot without affecting the temperature of the water in the rest of the pot.

Some husbands and wives quarrel openly and intensely in front of the children, or use the children to work off some of the steam that they feel to one another, ("It's cheaper to yell at my children than to see a psychologist.") They might sit down and take stock and just decide that they might compromise, or they might have been letting things get out of hand. Sometimes parents don't realize how intense things are till a "symptom" such as stuttering occurs in the family. Then they have to sit down and realize maybe there has been too much bickering and too many worries about who is getting away with things and accusing each other of a lack of consideration. Often realizing what they have been arguing about and going back a few weeks or a few months to the way things were, can straighten things out and ease things off.

Fears:

At times, there will be some expression of fear or anxiety on the part of your child. Often, the child between the ages of 5 and 9 will have an occasional nightmare or bad night and express a desire to be comforted or reassured, such as sleeping in your bed and the like. At times a child will express fears or shame about doing a variety of things. A way to handle anxiety is to encourage, reassure the child with as much confidence as you have. To force a child to engage in feared activities to the point where the child becomes even more frightened, aggravates the situation. The best thing is to encourage, and maybe coax a little. If the child is still afraid and you see him become more upset, ease off and postpone it to some other time. Often, a child who can feel that he can try something at his own rate will be more comfortable than a child who is pushed into doing something.

What has been said applies to the usual run of children's fears, sometimes as a result of a bad movie, family pressures of a temporary nature, an accident and the like. If the fear persists, and your attempts to manage don't help, it might be well to talk to a professional person about it.

All children need some love and affection, as do their adult parents. Often parents feel worried that their eight year old boy cuddles up like a baby sometimes, or their daughter talks some baby talk. In the child, these are usual, normal, and desirable. One might just as well enjoy having their children babies again and not worry that they will be like this forever. Children become babyish at various times, when they are hurt, frightened, uncertain, when a new baby or competitor enters, when they are ill. Going along with it, and reassuring then often results in its going away. Again, if it persists for an unreasonable period, then it may be a sign of something else. Children have a great need to be grown up and older. Although we worry about their being babies and immature and dependent, the adult with problems is often one who was ashamed or afraid to be a baby when the time was right, and now feels too ashamed to even be able to accept affection when it is right.

What has been suggested is to ease the tension in the home generally and to the children specifically. The fewer times you and your children or husband or wife come to argument or criticism with one another, the easier things are for all in general and the child who is stuttering in particular.

In conclusion:

As has been noted, perhaps as many as 40 per cent of all children who stutter "outgrow it." Many, perhaps almost all, stuttering children can be helped by just changing the circumstances in the home— "environmental manipulation." The prac-

tical parent tries suggestions such as have been outlined here. Three weeks to a month is a reasonable time to try. If you can't change things or if changing things doesn't help his speech pattern, then a more professional approach is indicated. This may involve further parent counseling, therapy for the child only indirectly related to his speech or direct speech therapy with the child. If you need more help you should not feel guilt or blame, as so often we parents can feel. This happens. We really don't know why it happens specifically to some. The mature parent doesn't blame himself or his wife, but feels that if the changes they have made haven't solved the problem, they will try a more individual approach. They will then seek further professional help.

Often parents ask, "how can I know if there is any measurable improvement?" A speech clinician would be glad to work with you to evaluate what has been gained and what might be done.

When the stuttering has advanced to the secondary state (presumably because the child became aware of and anxious about his stuttering and began to struggle with it), Johnson and Van Riper agree that he needs direct help. In this stage, the conflict is between the wish to talk and the fear of stuttering. Therapy is designed to reduce the self-consciousness and anxiety about the symptom itself. Ignoring the symptom will not reduce the child's anxiety at this point; on the contrary, it is now a symptom to be discussed frankly. Among the therapeutic suggestions is one interesting one which seems silly at first, namely, to train the child to stutter as easily as possible. He is encouraged to "go ahead and stutter in his usual way, but with the idea in mind of seeing how easily he can do it" *(Johnson, 1948, p. 233)*. Such an attitude reduces the child's anxiety about the symptom and may enable him to simplify his pattern of stuttering.

Stuttering as the Result of a Disturbance in the Mother-Child Relationship. G. L. Wyatt believes that the stuttering child has "experienced a developmental crisis, a disruption of the patterns of complementary behavior between mother and child which are of vital importance for the learning of language in childhood" *(1962 p. 645)*. She feels that stuttering is referable to a disturbance in the mother-child relationship when the child is practicing grammatical speech, between two and four years. Wyatt does not visualize the problem simply in terms of the parents' criticism of the child's speech; she describes conversation in which the parent "talks over the child's head." The child cannot learn to speak by listening, because the words and concepts he hears are beyond his comprehension.

In contrast to Johnson, Wyatt would start treatment early, as soon as possible after the appearance of compulsive repetitions in a child's speech. The aim of her treatment is to establish successful communication between mother and child; procedures vary according to the age of the child and the stage of the stuttering. Wyatt recommends that the pre-school child be seen together with his mother, and that there be additional separate conferences with the mother alone.

In treatment the stuttering is deemphasized, and attention is paid to the disturbances in the relationship between mother and child. In Wyatt's view, once communication has broken down, complications follow. The child:

. . . reacts to this disruption (in communication) with feelings of loss, bewilderment and helplessness which gradually turned into anger against the mother . . . At the same time the child becomes afraid lest his anger may lead to permanent loss of the love object through rejection or abandonment . . . The core problem in the treatment of the stuttering child is therefore his aggression-anxiety; anger against the mother closely connected with the fear of losing her. *(1962, p. 654.)*

In the author's opinion, this theory, though broader than Johnson's is still overly simple. A great deal is made out of the parents' failure to respond to the child on his own verbal level. But very many parents lack the time or capacity for this, and do not cause stuttering. Also, the disruption in relationship should be far more serious when the separation is a physical rather than verbal one. It would be a step toward validation of her hypothesis if stuttering frequently appeared after separations.

Stuttering as an Approach-Avoidance Conflict. Sheehan and G. J. Wischner *(1962)* have considered stuttering within the framework of learning theory. The original cause of the stuttering then becomes relatively unimportant as compared to the mechanism by which it perpetuates itself. In Sheehan's words, "stuttering is a result of approach-avoidance conflict, of opposed urges to speak and to hold back from speaking. The 'holding back' may be due either to learned avoidances or to unconscious motives; the approach-avoidance formulation fits both" *(1958, p. 303)*. The fear of the symptom itself is a "learned avoidance." The fear of expressing anger at the mother (of which Wyatt wrote) would be an "unconscious motive." Stuttering has twin aspects: The stutterer's words are momentarily blocked and then released. Sheehan first asks, "What stops him?" and then, "What enables him to continue?"

One of the most useful parts of Sheehan's presentation is his description of the levels at which conflict may occur. There are five in all: (1) the conflict may be at the *word level,* on the basis of a phonetic sound which has been associated with stuttering in the past; (2) the conflict may be at the *situation level* (e.g., public speaking or reciting in class); (3) the conflict may be at the *emotional content level,* because the words are forbidden or the thought an anxious one (e.g., the stutterer's speech grows worse when he describes a traumatic experience or gives information he is reluctant to divulge); (4) the conflict may involve the *relationship* between the stutterer and his listener (e.g., the stutterer has difficulty with the teacher and not with his friends, with one parent and not the other); and (5) the conflict may be at the *ego protective level*, that is, the stuttering may have become a defense which serves some secondary ends (e.g., the individual can remove himself from certain threatening situations or abandon certain ambitions on the face-saving basis that he stutters).

The second part of Sheehan's hypothesis is that the act of stuttering reduces the fear which prompted the symptom and that following this reduction of his fear, the stutterer is able to continue speaking. He suggests three mechanisms by which this end is achieved. First, the stutterer is afraid of stuttering. But once it has happened, the worst is over and he can go on. Second, the apprehension is changed to something concrete; it is no longer a vague expectancy, it is a definite fact. Third, if stuttering is an unconsciously aggressive act, it simultaneously punishes the stutterer as well as the listener and thereby relieves any feelings of guilt he may have about his hostility. Then speech can continue. In this formulation Sheehan is looking for the positive value of the stuttering, following Freud's theory that a neurotic symptom is a compromise between conflicting wishes.

In the author's opinion, there is yet another reason why the act of stuttering serves to reduce anxiety sufficiently to allow speech to continue. It is not the spoken word which stimulates anxiety, it is the feeling for which the word stands. The stutterer fears the feeling his words will evoke in himself and the effect the feeling will have on the listener. His words might have some magic power or they might move the listener to retaliation or disapproval. Stuttering is a substitute for the feared feeling, the lesser of two evils. The results are less than the stutterer feared, because what he anticipated is related

to his unconscious feeling, not to reality. When the patient stutters and nothing happens, he is reassured and can go on.

Sheehan makes a strong case for combining speech therapy and psychotherapy:

Treatment may begin at the topmost level of conflict and work downward. Conflicts due to immediate word fear and situation fear are dealt with through that specialized portion of the therapeutic work known as speech therapy. Conflicts at deeper levels are straight problems in psychotherapy, which may be handled concurrently. To the extent that such conflicts express themselves through outward stuttering behavior, they may be reached via the speech therapy. The stutterer's reaction to speech therapy frequently reveals the nature and extent of his resistances. *(1958, p. 319.)*

The importance of the release of feelings and the need to prepare the patient for recovery are emphasized. The therapist and patient must consider the possible consequences of becoming well, because therein may lie many of the resistances to relinquishing the symptom.

Stuttering Representing a Conflict of Gratification of Instincts. In this psychoanalytic view, stuttering is presented as a conversion symptom, the result of an unconscious reason for not wishing to speak *(Fenichel, 1945).* The role of aggression is considered uppermost. In addition, the stutterer retains a faith in the magic power of words, the archaic notion that it is equal to action. "Words can kill," and stutterers are persons who unconsciously think it necessary to use so dangerous a weapon with care.

One of the most readable and complete reports of the psychoanalysis of a child was written by H. Kolansky. The patient was a three-year-old girl. At 29 months of age, Ann woke one morning and greeted her mother with a deeply troubled facial expression as she said,

"D-d-d-daddy, M-m-m-m-Mommy, I can't talk!" Later she began vigorously slapping her thigh and stamping her foot as she attempted to force through the difficult first syllables. Kolansky describes Ann as intellectually and physically precocious, which may help explain why she is an exception to the general rule that secondary stage stuttering does not occur in one so young.

Ann's whole personality changed. She became fussy, cranky, disinterested in play, and developed a marked phobia of insects and of the television character of Zorro. The major traumatic events in her history revolved around the premature birth of twins when she was 27 months old. During her mother's absence at the hospital, which was explained as a "shopping trip," her grandmother toilet-trained her. After a few months, one of the twin sisters suddenly died of pneumonia. For weeks, Ann denied the disappearance of the sister and referred to her sister as if she were still alive.

At the age of three, Ann began in treatment. She saw the psychoanalyst daily, for 36 sessions, and her mother was present at many of the sessions. Kolansky gives a vivid and detailed account of the child's activities and statements, and an equally good account of his part in the treatment. He allowed forbidden feelings to be expressed and explained to Ann the meaning of her symptoms. Kolansky concluded that the stammering had at least two major components:

One was a wish to continue anal soiling, which had to be sharply curtailed at the time of the birth of twin sisters. Later, the conflict over this wish led to the formation of defenses: the anal preoccupation was displaced upward (to the mouth), and concurrently marked reaction formations against soiling developed. The other component of her stammering was a regression to oral sadism, activated by the absence of her mother during hospital confinement when the twins were born, by the severity of the grandmother's final measures to

establish bowel training, and especially by the attention paid to her twin sisters. The desire to bite had to be repressed and then gained access to the speech mechanism with consequent disguised return of the repressed. The child turned much of her aggression against herself, slapping her thighs while speaking, and becoming withdrawn and depressed. The stammering, as neurotic symptoms in general, was thus overdetermined and emphasized wish and punishment components.[*]

The insect phobia was more related to the death of the twin, which Ann understood was caused by a bug. This bug, which had carried out Ann's secret wishes, was waiting to do the same to Ann as she felt she had done to the sister.

This case is interesting not only because of the light it sheds on this young stutterer, but also because it demonstrates the devious ways in which the young child thinks. Kolansky differentiates his treatment from the release therapy described by D. M. Levy (1939). His goal was more than abreaction of traumatic events and permission for the expression of forbidden feelings. He did more than allow the expression of repressed wishes. He verbally interpreted for Ann the meaning of her play and of her fears. He corrected her misunderstandings and explained the reality of previous events. He taught Ann something about herself which she could remember and tell to herself in his absence. With such a young child, it was essential that her mother be an active participant. Her permission for feelings was more meaningful to Ann than the permission of the stranger she was to know so briefly.

This case should be considered in the light of the various theories about stuttering. The fact that Ann's symptom disappeared with psychotherapy argues

[*]Quoted from H. Kolansky, "Treatment of a Three-Year-Old Girl's Severe Infantile Neurosis," *The Psychoanalytic Study of the Child*, XV, 281–82 (New York: International Universities Press, 1960). Reproduced by permission.

against a significant physiological basis. Ann recognized her own stuttering before her parents did, so it was not a result of their concern. There was, indeed, a disruption in the mother-child relationship, but a physical and psychological separation rather than a verbal disruption. However, one of the goals of treatment was to restore friendly and affectionate communication between the harassed mother and the cranky child. The clinical material indicates that the stuttering conflict was at the emotional content and relationship levels, rather than the word or situation level. This may explain why speech therapy was not required. The wishes to soil and bite were but thinly disguised in the speech and phobic symptoms. Ann could reveal them in play and in talk with the therapist, and then the stuttering which served to keep the wishes a secret was no longer needed.

Reading Disabilities

When a child is a poor reader, the causes fall into a number of categories. There may be a visual handicap, identifiable by ophthalmological examination. There may have been inadequate instruction, identifiable by its effects on other children in the same class. There may be poor motivation, in which case there will be difficulties in other school subjects. Or the poor reading may be a neurotic solution for unconscious conflicts, in which case it is likely, though not inevitable, that other areas of learning will be blocked as well.

This still leaves a number of children who have a specific reading disability despite adequate instruction, intelligence, and apparent motivation. The diagnosis is variously termed "word blindness," "alexia," "dyslexia," or "reading disability." L. Eisenberg points out that the term "specific dyslexia" implies an idiopathic condition, that is, one whose cause is unknown *(1962)*. However, some organic cause is often assumed again by the process of exclusion.

In recent years, speech pathologists have become interested in the process of reading for several reasons. First, reading is an integral part of language. In the words of Myklebust and D. Johnson:

It is a symbol system, a means whereby man internalizes, integrates and organizes experience. It is related to the other principal verbal system which he uses, the spoken word. These two verbal systems, the read and the spoken, constitute man's language and each can be understood only in relation to the other. *(1962, p. 14.)*

Second, reading difficulties are frequently associated with speech difficulties. Some children of about six use infantile speech patterns (although they *can* talk), are socially and emotionally immature, and are slow to read although their intelligence is adequate. W. G. Hardy suggests that these children have failed to develop a "critical auditory self-monitoring system," in that they do not listen to others and try to correct their speech to match what they hear *(1962)*. The basic remedial procedure used is auditory training. Here, the slowness in reading reflects the interaction of auditory and visual processes. Although this association between reading and speech problems has been observed, it has not as yet been fully documented. To do so would require a longitudinal prospective study, tracing the later educational progress of *all* children showing a specific type of speech disorder.

Finally, many of the principles of diagnosis and treatment of childhood aphasia are pertinent to the diagnosis and treatment of dyslexia. Reading, as well as spoken speech, can be destroyed by brain lesion *(Geshwind, 1962)*. J. Money draws the following conclusions: "Paralleling receptive aphasias having to do with the spoken word, these post-traumatic reading cases logically suggest a parallel inference, namely, that dyslexia may exist also as a developmental syndrome for which no brain lesion has, as yet, been demonstrated" *(1962, p. 13).* Aphasia and dyslexia have proved to be fertile fields for research into auditory and visual perception, respectively, and the research problems have brought speech pathologists, neurologists, psychologists, and educators into close working alliances.

Organic cerebral factors, which were formerly considered only in cases of cerebral palsy, epilepsy, mental retardation, and psychosis, are now being considered in connection with almost all the learning and behavior disorders of childhood. The reasons for this shift away from the psychodynamic approach are not entirely clear. It may reflect a disappointment with the results of psychotherapy in severe learning disorders. The organicists have suggestions to offer in the way of specific remediation, but more time is needed to evaluate the success of treatment based on psychoneurological premises. The psychodynamic approach to functional reading difficulties is presented in Chapter 10. The discussion which follows here is restricted to the view of reading difficulties as "psychoneurological learning disorders" *(Myklebust and Johnson, 1962).*

Visual Causes

Surprisingly, ocular and optical defects are of negligible significance in producing alexia *(Money, 1962).* Poor readers have irregular and confused eye movements but, in M. D. Vernon's opinion, this is effect rather than cause *(1958).* It is failure to attend to and to comprehend what is read that causes the irregular eye movements and regressions. The remedy is training in the mechanics and comprehension of reading, rather than mechanical regularization of eye movements.

There has been a good deal of investigation to determine whether the dyslexic child does in fact have an inferior perception of forms other than letters and words. A. L. Benton reviewed three studies which indicated that poor readers have inferior visual perception and three studies showing the opposite, and reconciled the findings in terms of the age of the children studied. Perceptual differences are observed in younger children; the differences tend to disappear when good and poor readers of older ages are compared. Moreover, in some of these studies intelligence was not controlled, and IQ is related positively to both reading and visual perception. Benton's conclusion was as follows:

. . . deficiency in visual form perception is not an important correlate of developmental dyslexia. By this I mean that, while it may be a determinant of the language disability in some cases, it is not a significant factor in the majority of cases. A certain level of visual discriminative capacity is obviously a necessary precondition for learning to read, and there is variation in the rate of development of these visuoperceptive skills in the early years of life. Significant retardation in development which extends into the early school years will then necessarily entail a corresponding retardation in learning to read; hence a relationship between the two sets of skills in younger school children will be discernible. *(1962, p. 94.)*

Mixed Cerebral Dominance

This is one of the oldest of the organic theories of the cause of reading, writing, and speech disorders *(Orton, 1928, 1937).* Orton, a physician, objected to the concept of a specific, localized defect implied in the diagnosis of "congenital word blindness" *(Hinshelwood, 1900),* and attributed reading disabilities to what he called "strephosymbolia," meaning "twisted symbols." His reasoning was as follows: In learning to read, engrams, or traces, of the printed words are formed in both cerebral hemispheres. Those in the minor hemisphere (usually the hemisphere *opposite* the preferred hand) are normally suppressed because of the dominance of the major hemisphere. When dominance is not completely established, there is confusion between the engrams of the major hemisphere and the unsuppressed engrams of the minor hemisphere which are their mirror images. This he took to explain mirror writing and mirror reversal of words and letters in reading.

Vernon *(1958)* and O. L. Zangwill *(1962)* reviewed the literature on the relationship between cerebral dominance and backwardness in reading. The investigations are difficult to summarize because they have been contradictory, but they are generally of two kinds. One set of experimental observations has to do with the kind of errors made by poor readers. Vernon points out that complete mirror reversal is rare, and feels that the common error of transposing letters within a word is not the same thing. Observations of normal learners show that the order of the letters in words is a matter of indifference. They have difficulty in differentiating words which contain the same, or almost the same, letters in a different order. Children can easily read upside-down words and do not notice transpositions like "nettims" for "mittens." Reversals are common in the young reader, and that they persist in the poor reader does not prove the case for mixed dominance.

The second set of experimental observations consists of studies of the prevalence of mixed handedness, or mixed laterality (i.e., left-handedness and right-eyedness, or vice versa). Unfortunately, there is no agreement about what constitutes adequate testing for handedness and eyedness. The reports also vary according to the age of the children, the degree of their retardation in reading and their intelligence. The importance of intelligence was shown in M. Monroe's study. She found mixed laterality in 27 per cent of 101 normal children; in 38 per cent of 155 children with specific reading disability; and in 50 per cent of 45 mentally retarded children with associated reading problems *(1932)*. More recently S. Naidoo investigated the handedness of 418 supposedly normal children between the ages of four and six. On the basis of ten tests, they were divided into three groups: right-handed (360); left-handed (38); and ambiguously-handed (20). The last group tended to have a history of slow speech development, a higher incidence of complications at birth, and was significantly inferior in verbal intelligence *(1961)*. Thus, mixed laterality appeared to be linked with lower intelligence, which may well cause poor reading.

In a study of children aged 8 to 14 roughly 40 per cent showed mixed laterality. There was no significant difference in laterality between the normal readers and the poor readers. However, these poor readers were only slightly retarded in reading, an average of about one year *(Witty and Kopel, 1936)*. A. I. Gates and G. L. Bond studied a younger group (mean age of eight and a half) with slightly more serious reading problems (mean retardation of one and a half years) and also found approximately the same number of cross-laterals among the normal and the poor readers *(1936)*. Many other large-scale school surveys have shown that there is no excess of cross-laterality in the poor readers. However, A. J. Harris found three times the normal amount of cross-laterality among the *severely* retarded readers *(1947)*.

In her conclusions, Vernon suggests that there may be a "congenital disposition" toward the occurrence of certain related defects: reading disability, speech defects or infantile speech, motor incoordination, and mixed laterality. She sees these difficulties as a kind of a syndrome, a cluster of symptoms resulting from a lack of cortical maturation, but it is her opinion that such cases form a small minority of all the cases of reading disability. The most important points are, first, that this diagnosis cannot be assumed on the basis of reversal tendencies which reflect only the general confusion of the poor or the beginning reader and, second, that a significant number of good readers also exhibit mixed laterality.

In all probability, the lack of a definite hand preference makes it more difficult for the child to acquire directional consistency but, if all else is equal, he is able to overcome his difficulty. On the other hand, if this constitutional difficulty is associated with other problems (e.g., poor instruction, emotional conflicts, or lack of motivation), a serious reading disability may eventuate. Most workers in this field (e.g., *Money, 1962*) are doubtful of the validity of therapy based solely on cerebral dominance, and yet such methods (e.g., *Delacato, 1959*) continue to be popular because of their apparent simplicity.

Brain Damage

In the 1930's and '40's, the term "brain-injured" was first used to differentiate kinds of mental deficiency. The nature of the early research which distinguished between the exogenous, or brain-injured, and the endogenous, or familial retarded, is described in detail in the chapter on mental subnormality. Late in the 1940's and '50's, the diagnosis of brain injury was extended to children of normal intelligence who displayed the same behavioral characteristics and, usually, failure to learn.

H. R. Myklebust and B. Boshes, among others, have objected to the terms "brain-damaged" or "brain-injured" on the basis that these terms imply that an accident has occurred to a normal brain. They recommend the term "psychoneurological" as a more inclusive diagnosis for all aberrations of behavior which have a neurological component, whether they result from in-

jury or maldevelopment. They emphasize that such disorders may occur in children of average or superior intelligence who seem to be intact neurologically. As for prevalence, they estimate that it would be something in excess of 5 per cent of the school population. In this category, they include the congenital apraxias, aphasias, agnosias, dyscalculias, and dyslexias of classical neurology. In addition, they include disturbances in orientation, such as confusion of right and left, and time disorders, such as difficulty in learning to read time *(1960)*.

The diagnostic criteria are not entirely clear. To some extent, the symptom itself is used as the diagnosis. For instance, "dyscalculia" means difficulty with arithmetic. One way of establishing the diagnosis is by the process of exclusion. E. Daryn *(1961)* states that the suspicion of brain damage comes from the psychiatric-clinical evaluation. If psychodynamic explanations fail to account for particular symptomatology which has been found in other cases where there was cerebral damage, it is assumed that the symptoms are organically caused. Daryn lists the following symptoms as typically organic: "hyperactivity, impulsivity, poor capacity to concentrate, short attention span, low frustration tolerance, destructiveness, infantile characteristics, reading difficulties, anxiety arising out of dependency caused by the sense of physiological incapacity" *(1961, p. 300)*. S. Rappaport's list is even longer. He adds "perceptual and conceptual difficulties" and other personality problems related to "defective self concept and narcissistic hypersensitivity," such as "flight from challenge, overcompensation, control and manipulation of others, and negativism or power struggle" *(1964, p. 42)*. The over-all clinical impression is that of a poorly controlled, poorly functioning ego.

Some authorities use these descriptions as presumptive evidence of organic damage, and others turn to history, neurological examinations, and psychological tests for confirmation. (Psychological tests are discussed in the next section.) Daryn gives a list of "soft" or minor neurological signs which are often overlooked (1961), but neurologists are divided about the reliability and meaning of such signs. Myklebust gives the most generous report of the existence of neurological findings. He states that in 100 consecutive cases of dyslexia, 75 per cent had abnormal electroencephalograms and other neurological abnormalities (*Myklebust and Johnson, 1962*). However, EEG abnormalities depend on the definition of normal. They have been found in 15 to 40 per cent of normal children (*Kennedy and Ramirez, 1964*). Most writers report that "it is usually the case that developmental dyslexia appears without demonstrable early brain injury" (*Money, 1962, p. 14*).

Validation of the organic hypothesis is often sought in the child's early history. A. A. Kawi and B. Pasamanick (1959) found a statistical relationship between reading difficulties and abnormal pregnancies and births, especially toxemia and bleeding during pregnancy. Pasamanick and his co-workers found a similar relationship between complications of pregnancy and stillbirths, cerebral palsy, epilepsy, and behavior disorders. The large-scale studies, in which a group of children with problems have been compared with a normal group have showed considerable overlap, even when there were statistically significant differences. For example, M. E. Rogers, A. M. Lilienfeld, and Pasamanick compared the histories of 1151 children referred for problems with the histories of a control group of 902 children from the same general backgrounds. Sixty-one per cent of the patient group and 69 per cent of the control group had *no* abnormal prenatal and perinatal history. Although this was a statistically significant difference, 21 per cent of the control group had a history of the same

early difficulties suspected of causing organic damage in the patient population (*1955*).

This study points up the importance of distinguishing between risk and damage. C. Kennedy and L. S. Ramirez (1964) reported on monkeys who had been subjected to the same objective condition of risk (i.e., asphyxia early in life). Pathological examinations of the brain revealed differing amounts of damage, including some cases where there was none. When the animals were permitted to develop, their behavior was as varied as the anatomical findings, ranging from normal to massively disturbed learning and motor functioning. The effect of organic trauma, even on nervous tissue, is no more predictable than the effect of psychological trauma.

Treatment is usually remedial education planned according to the specific type of "psychoneurological" problem. Emphasis is placed on eliminating distractions and structuring the external environment. A. A. Strauss and L. Lehtinen first described educational techniques specifically designed for brain-injured retardates (*1947*), and these were later extended and elaborated by Strauss and N. C. Kephart (*1955*).

Plasticity and its Relation to Learning Disorders

The concept of plasticity was introduced by Bender; it is in essence the same as "maturational lag," a concept which she earlier introduced in her theoretical discussions of childhood schizophrenia. (This is discussed in more detail in Chapter 11.) Bender defines plasticity as a "primitive level of organization of physiological (homeostasis), neurological (motility), and psychic and behavioral functioning (including self concept, body image, and language skills) in children who have problems in maturation" (*1963, p. 305*). Plasticity is a tricky concept because too much and too little are equally pathological. Bender is concerned with too much fluidity or plasticity; Strauss and Kephart are concerned with rigidity, or lack of plasticity. They discuss perseveration, rigidity, and stimulus-boundedness as characteristics of the brain-injured which stem from too *little* plasticity of the nervous system *(1955)*.

Other writers have used Bender's concept of plasticity to explain language disorders and learning difficulties. Children with too much plasticity develop unevenly. They lag in some intellectual areas and perform normally, or even well, in others. Cautiously, Bender and others suggest that plasticity may be a symptom of diffuse brain injury, but basically it is used as a descriptive diagnosis. The primary cause of the child's problems is in the "congenitally determined" immaturity of his nervous system functioning, which may give rise to diffuse anxiety. In order to protect himself from this organically determined anxiety, the child may develop neurotic symptoms. Again, treatment is essentially remedial education and specific training.

Psychological Methods for Assessing Organic Brain Damage

Before discussing specific tests and signs, it is important to take a close look at the methodological problems involved in their validation. Although practitioners are often impatient with the slow pace of research, they are, in the final analysis, dependent on research to prove that their tools are good ones.

Definition of Organic Brain Damage

In any discussion of the validity of tests, the first question which arises is: What are we trying to measure? It is impossible to measure brain damage directly; we must approach it via changes in behavior. Indications of brain damage rest on some premise regarding the consequences of brain damage. The starting point is usually some observed alteration of behavior in a patient who is known to have had an organic injury or illness.

Unfortunately for the diagnostician, the possible consequences of injury are not unitary. The kind and extent of impairment depend on many factors, including: (1) the locus of the injury *(Anderson, 1961)*; (2) the extent of the injury; (3) the character of the lesion; (4) the person's age at the time of injury *(Belmont and Birch, 1960; Teuber and Rudel, 1962)*; and (5) the time interval between injury and testing *(Fitzhugh, Fitzhugh, and Reitan, 1961)*. The statement of Strauss and Lehtinen that "all brain lesions, wherever localized, are followed by a similar kind of disordered behavior" *(1947, p. 20)* has not been substantiated by subsequent research. The impressive accumulation of evidence attesting to variations in the performance of brain-damaged individuals has led to such statements as, "In point of fact, there is not *a* minimally brain-damaged child but rather many varieties of brain-damaged children" *(Birch, 1964, p. 6)*. This presents a serious problem to those who seek to validate test findings by using a brain-damaged experimental group. In the opinion of J. R. Haynes and S. B. Sells *(1963)*, the indiscriminate acceptance of the theory that brain-damaged subjects are a homogeneous group is largely responsible for the contradictory nature of many of the findings.

The student should be alert to the criteria by which researchers identify the experimental or validation group as "brain-damaged." Many times, brain injury has been diagnosed on the basis of behavior rather than history or physical examination. Although there are many virtues in inter-disciplinary collaboration, it is important that a neurologist who is validating a psychological finding not know the psychological test results. There is a danger that both the medical and the psychological evidence of organic brain damage will rest on the same assumptions, borrowed from one another rather than independently derived. In clinical practice, the pooling of observations and hypotheses is, of course, entirely legitimate.

Scientific Method in Test Construction

Two important procedures used in validating tests are especially significant to the clinician. The first has to do with the choice of a control group to contrast with the experimental patient group. The brain-damaged and the non-brain-damaged groups must be matched, at least roughly, in IQ and age. If one group is younger or less intelligent than the other, there may be differences in the test results which have nothing to do with the variable of brain damage. Moreover, many psychological tests which differentiate reliably between organically damaged patients and normal individuals become unreliable when psychotic or seriously emotionally disturbed subjects are used in the control group (*Haynes and Sells, 1963*). Unfortunately, it is often precisely this kind of distinction, which the tests cannot make, that the clinician is asked to make, namely, to determine the etiology for an obviously severe behavior and/or intellectual problem.

A second important experimental procedure is the setting of a critical score, a cut-off point between positive and negative results. All the test authors agree that there is no single sign which is found only when there has been organic brain damage. For that reason, a certain number of danger signs, or a particular score, must be recorded before the case is considered one of organic damage. But even with the most carefully designed and best-chosen tests, there will be some overlapping of scores between the brain-damaged and the normal groups. This will result in some false positives and false negatives. For instance, in an unusually careful investigation of brain injury of pre-school children, C. B.

Ernhart *et al. (1963)* arrived at a composite index of impairment. Using the best critical score possible, 72.7 per cent of the brain-injured were correctly identified (leaving 27.3 per cent falsely identified as normal) and 10.6 per cent of the normal children were identified as brain-damaged *(1963)*. These are excellent results for research purposes and valuable in providing new insights and suggestions for further investigation into brain-behavior relationships. But the clinician must be aware that any given patient may represent the exception to the general rule. He must realize that his tests are fallible, and that his diagnosis is at best an educated guess.

Kinds of Tests Used

There are four categories of psychological tests or symptoms which have been used for the diagnosis of brain damage: single variable tests, test batteries, scatter patterns, and personality measures. All the techniques were first applied to brain-injured adults and later adapted for children. It is simpler to diagnose adults, because it is easier to spot the loss of an intellectual function which was once there than to identify one which was never developed. For example, Ernhart *et al.* found that the pattern of relatively great impairment in perceptual-motor and conceptual abilities, combined with relatively little impairment in vocabulary, typical of brain-injured adults, did *not* obtain for pre-school brain-injured children. These children showed essentially the same degree of impairment in all three areas *(1963)*.

Another difficulty in the application of tests to children is the necessity for using age norms. A test finding is positive only when the child becomes too old for it to be normal, a decision which can be made only on the basis of norms for different ages.

Single Variable Tests. Frequent attempts have been made to construct tests for brain damage on the basis of one aspect of behavior. Representative examples include the Spiral Aftereffect Test (*Price and Deabler, 1955; Davids, Goldberg, and Laufer, 1957; Scott, Bragg, and Smarr, 1963*); the Memory for Designs Test (*Graham and Kendall, 1960; Howard and Shoemaker, 1954*); and the Bender-Gestalt (*Bender, 1938*). Of these single variable tests, the Bender-Gestalt is by far the most popular with clinicians. The task involved is copying nine geometric designs composed of dots, lines, angles, and curves, combined in a variety of relationships. It is commonly called "a test of visual-motor functioning." It has been extensively used, and age norms from 5 to 11 years are available (*Bender, 1946; Byrd, 1956; Koppitz, 1960*). Children younger than five find the test too difficult, and children over eleven normally score in the same range as adults. Since it is so widely used for detecting organic brain damage in children, some of the reports on it are summarized in Table 2.

E. M. Koppitz has made the most extensive use of the Bender-Gestalt with children. In her view, the diagnosis of organic brain damage should not, and cannot, be made on the basis of this test alone. Few brain-damaged subjects do well on the Bender test, but not all who do poorly are brain-damaged. Poor vision, young age, negative emotional attitudes, and low intelligence may all result in low scores. Koppitz found that the test correlates highly with school achievement, and so she has suggested that if a child has normal intelligence, does poorly in school, and performs poorly on the Bender test, one should investigate the possibility of neurological impairment. It should also be noted that the diagnostic validity of the Bender test increases when the mental age of the subject is over seven years.

The recent trend in psychology has been away from test-dominated research toward the development of meaningful hypotheses which can lead to more intensive investigation of the mechanisms underlying the organic defects. For instance, granting that many organically damaged children have special difficulty in copying forms, one should ask whether this is a problem in perceiving, a problem in motor execution, or a problem in synthesizing perception and motor performance. M. Bortner and H. G. Birch (*1960, 1961*) found that perceptual recognition was superior to motor execution in a group of adult hemiplegics and children with cerebral palsy. Birch and his co-workers are continuing to make developmental studies of perceptual recognition, of synthesis of perceptions coming in from simultaneous, double sensory sources, and so on (*1964*). At the moment, these studies have provided few answers to the clinician's question: "*What* is wrong?" but they promise to answer the more important question: "*Why* is it wrong?"

Test Batteries. Diagnostic procedures which involve the administration and interpretation of a battery of special tests have usually been investigated in a research setting. The first battery was a group of tests devised by W. C. Halstead (*1947*). R. Reitan modified this battery and has written extensively on its use with adult patients (*1955, 1959*).

The best example of the multiple variable approach to children is that of F. K. Graham et al. (*1963*). These workers standardized a number of test items, chosen either because they had successfully identified brain-injured adults or because they measured functions relevant to theoretical questions concerning the brain-injured child. The items included: (1) the Vocabulary Scale of the Stanford-Binet; (2) Concepts or Block-Sort Test similar to one used with adult patients by K. Goldstein and M. C. Sheerer (*1941*); (3) the Copy-Forms Test previously developed by Graham and B. S. Kendall (*1960*); (4) a Figure-Ground Test adapted from a test developed by Strauss and Lehtinen for older brain-injured children (*1947*); (5) a Tactual-Localization test involving simultaneous stimulation of various

TABLE 2

Representative Studies of the Use of Bender-Gestalt in Diagnosis of Organic Brain Damage in Children

Author	Sample	Number of Cases	Criterion of Organic Brain Damage	Bender-Gestalt Signs	Results
Hanvik (1953)	Child psychiatric patients	20	Abnormal EEG	1 or more 30° rotations on the Bender-Gestalt	16 of 20 with Bender-Gestalt rotations had abnormal EEGs
Chorost, Spivack and Levine (1959)	Adolescents at residential school	68	Abnormal EEG	Same as above	69% of 51 with Bender-Gestalt rotations had abnormal EEGs; 47% of 17 without rotations had abnormal EEGs
Halpin (1955)	Institutionalized mentally retarded groups, matched in age (7-13) and IQ (40-72)	15 in each group	Diagnosis of organic brain damage vs. familial retardation	Rotation	Group with organic brain damage inferior on Bender-Gestalt but had no more rotations, perhaps because of low mental age
Shaw and Cruickshank (1956)	Institutionalized epileptics, matched in sex, age (average, 14 years), and IQ (average, 81) with institutionalized non-epileptics	25 in each group	History of convulsions	Pascal and Suttell (1951) scoring	No difference on total score; epileptic group had more difficulty in placing the figures on paper, spacing them, and making them proper size
Quast (1961)	Child psychiatric patients, 10 to 12 years, divided into 2 groups on basis of history and presenting complaints. One, suspected emotionally disturbed, mean IQ of 100; the other, with organic brain damage, mean IQ of 82	50 in each group	Clinical impression	17 Bender-Gestalt signs previously suggested as organic	9 signs (scalloping, dashing, perseveration, rotations, reversal, confabulation, angulation, major distortion, separation) differentiated 2 groups at .01 level with false positive diagnosis of less than 6 of 50 children suspected of being emotionally disturbed
Koppitz (1962)	Children referred to guidance clinic; divided into 2 groups matched for age and sex but not IQ; one group with organic brain damage, IQ range 75-122 (mean, 90); the other group, elementary school children, age 5-10	103 with organic brain damage 281 Controls	Medical examination and developmental history	Poor over-all score relative to age norms.	About 9% of the subjects with organic brain damage had above average scores, compared to 75% of controls; no sign exclusive to those with organic brain damage; the following "almost exclusive": rotation by 45° of figures 1, 4, and 8, straight line for curves, line for series of dots, omission of figure 2, repetition of parts of figures 1, 2, and 6, after age 7

parts of the body, adapted from Bender's "Face-hand" test *(Fink and Bender, 1953);* (6) a Mark-the-Cars test designed to measure the ability to maintain a set in the face of distracting conditions; and (7) a Peripheral-Distraction test with much the same purpose. These tests were standardized on 108 normal children, 18 in each of 6 age groups proceeding by half-year steps from two and one half years to five and one half years. An additional 137 children were examined to provide a cross-validation sample. When sex, socioeconomic status, or age significantly affected performance, weights were calculated so that performance could be measured independently of such effects. All the results were expressed in standard scores so that one function could be compared to another, and several types of reliability were considered.

The second step was the application of the battery to 70 pre-school children about whom independent evidence of brain injury existed. These cases were located through medical sources (the criteria for inclusion are described by Ernhart *et al., 1963).* The IQ's of all 70 were above 50, and 55 of the 70 had IQ's above 69. Briefly, the performance of brain-injured children was significantly inferior to that of the control subjects on all the tests except the Peripheral-Distraction Test. The differences were less marked, but remained significant when the control group was compared to the brain-injured whose IQ's were above 69. Perhaps the most unexpected finding was that the impairment in vocabulary was as great as the impairment of the other conceptual functions and of the perceptual-motor functions. This contrasts with the differential impairment commonly found after injury to the adult brain *(Graham et al., 1963).*

These findings also contrast with the results of an earlier study in which the same test battery was used on a group of 3-year-olds who had suffered peri-

natal anoxia. The possibly injured anoxic group showed less impairment of all functions than the group known to be brain-injured. There was also a significant difference in the pattern of impairment. The anoxic children, presumably injured during or before birth, suffered significant impairment of vocabulary but not of perceptual-motor ability—the direct opposite of the adult pattern. Impairment of vocabulary seems to be inversely related to the age at which brain injury occurs, and impairment of perceptual and motor functioning seems directly related to age. This provides good evidence that brain damage does not have a unitary effect *(Graham et al., 1962).*

Scatter Patterns. Although the references already cited indicate the fallacy of expecting a single pattern of intellectual performance in organically damaged patients, this approach has been employed in many studies. The idea of comparing results on different concurrent tests for the purpose of determining the extent of mental deterioration was first suggested by H. Babcock *(1930);* the same principle was used in the Shipley-Hartford Retreat Scale *(1940)* and in the Hunt-Minnesota Test for Organic Brain Damage *(1943).* However, it did not gain widespread acceptance until D. Wechsler *(1944)* proposed that certain subtests of the Bellevue Adult Intelligence Scale could be compared with other subtests, and that a Deterioration Index could be calculated on the basis of the discrepancies. Subsequent studies of the diagnostic efficiency of his scatter analysis yielded contradictory results *(Yates, 1954).* It seemed to be most valuable in identifying cases of diffuse brain damage (caused, e.g., by arteriosclerosis) or degenerative diseases (e.g., Pick's disease). Although clinicians stopped using Wechsler's Index, the search for a similar diagnostic technique continued. Six of these efforts at scatter analysis are summarized in Table 3.

TABLE 3

Representative Studies of Scatter Analysis in the Diagnosis of Children with Organic Brain Damage

Author	Sample	Number of Cases	Criterion of Organic Brain Damage	Test Used	Results
Haines (1954)	Children with organic brain damage; children with behavior problems; foster-home children; 3-8 years old; IQ over 45 (group means 89-93)	100 in each group	Developmental history and neurological examination showing definite organic brain damage	Merrill-Palmer	Children with organic brain damage did not show decreased efficiency on subtests presumably measuring conceptual thinking, visual-motor skill, and perceptual judgment
Klatskin (1964)	125 3-year-olds, IQ 90-119; 68 3-year-olds, IQ 120 and over; 70 5-year-olds, IQ 90-119; 48 5-year-olds, IQ 120 and over	311	Medical record of stress before birth; minimal organic brain damage	Merrill-Palmer at age 3 years; Stanford-Binet Form L at 5 years	Average and superior children divided into 3 groups according to stress in perinatal period: Performance of superior children did not vary with prenatal history; average children differed significantly on subtests involving complex visual stimulus (Mare and Foal Puzzle) and on reproduction of complex forms (copying circle at 3 years and copying square at 5 years)
Berko (1955)	Mentally retarded children, average age 9 years and 3 months, average mental age 4 years and 5 months, IQ 48; matched control group	46 in each group	Diagnosis of aphasia by speech pathologist and psychologist	Stanford-Binet	Exogenously mentally-retarded children had wider scatter on Stanford-Binet than endogenously mentally retarded, without reference to kinds of tests passed and failed
Arthur (1958)	Children with mental age 5-6; control group	30 in each group	History of organic brain damage and positive evidence of damage to central nervous system	Stanford-Binet	Performance on perception and motor tests significantly different for the two groups
Beck and Lam (1955)	Children in special classes, IQ below 80, aged 10-11	104	27 with known history of organic brain damage and positive findings on examination;	Wechsler Intelligence Scale for Children (WISC)	Children with organic brain damage had lower IQs (58 vs. 74); only in those with no organic brain damage was Performance IQ higher than Verbal IQ, but some children with no organic

TABLE 3 (continued)

Author	Sample	Number of Cases	Criterion of Organic Brain Damage	Test Used	Results
			48 suspected of organic brain damage from psychological findings; 29 with no evidence of organic brain damage		brain damage had lower Performance IQ than Verbal IQ; no characteristic pattern found in performance on subtests
Fisher (1960)	Institutionalized mentally retarded people, average age of 26, range 16-69; all WAIS scores on norms table	122 with organic brain damage; 386 other	Grouped by state hospital etiology classification	Wechsler Adult Intelligence Scale	Subjects with infections of central nervous system and definite organic nervous diseases had significantly higher Verbal IQ than Performance IQ; no other differences
Rowley (1961)	Children with organic brain damage, in pediatric clinic, aged 6-10; matched by sex, age, and full-scale IQ with an emotionally disturbed group in psychiatric clinic, aged 5-10; IQ over 83 in both groups	30 in each group	Definite evidence of organic brain damage	WISC	No differences in intelligence test pattern between children with organic brain damage and emotionally disturbed children

From the results of these studies, and others of a similar nature, one can draw few conclusions. It is clear that the more positive the evidence of organic brain disease, the more general impairment will be found on intelligence tests. The results are equivocal in regard to the diagnostic significance of specific test patterns. The contradictions could probably be resolved by analysis of the kind of injury, the age at which it occurred, and the age of the patient at the time he was tested. However, it is unlikely any single investigator will ever be able to investigate a sufficient number of cases of every possible permutation to systematically check out each of these variables. This would require collaboration of many researchers, not an easy thing to get. Indeed, it is surprising how many researchers continue to publish their own findings with a given test and particular population without reference to other reports.

The general idea that organically damaged patients are variable and uneven in their performance persists, and more research like that of M. J. Berko (1955) would be useful. Especially needed are comparisons between children with organic brain damage and emotionally disturbed children (matched for age and intelligence), because many of the test items to which brain-damaged children respond differentially are related to psychopathology as well, such as the Block Design and Digit Symbol on the Wechsler Intelligence Scale for Children, or WISC *(Caputo et al., 1963)*. The busy clinician in the position of screening sizeable numbers of children with problems should be alert to isolated deficits in intelligence test performance and should consider the *possibility* of organic brain damage, particularly in a child who appears comfortable and cooperative. It is unsafe to rely on any specific test signs; "there is no substitute for experience and observation of the qualitative aspects of the subject's test performance regardless of the existence or non-existence of quantitative test characteristics" *(Beck and Lam, 1955, p. 157)*.

Personality Measures. Although some analysis of the Rorschach records of children with known organic disease, such as epileptics *(Shaw and Cruickshank, 1957; Zehrer, 1951)* and those with cerebral palsy *(Richards and Hooper, 1956)* has been done, there have been few reports of its use in diagnosing questionable organic disorders in childhood. A clinical instrument becomes useful only when it helps to uncover a disorder which is not otherwise easily discerned. It is unlikely that the Rorschach, for which a mental age of nine or ten is desirable, will ever become the test of choice for detecting possible brain injury in young children.

One important characteristic which has been linked with the diagnosis of brain injury in children is *hyperactivity,* or hyperkinesis. Innumerable authors have described the hyperkinetic syndrome, which includes a short attention span, impulsiveness and distractability, explosiveness, and unpredictability *(Laufer, Denhoff, and Solomons, 1957)*. The organic basis of this behavior was derived from the observations made by E. Kahn and L. H. Cohen of what they called "organic drivenness" caused by brain stem disease *(1934)*. Hyperactivity is considered a cardinal sign of brain injury by Strauss and his followers, and many authorities regard it as presumptive evidence of organic brain damage. Because of the unique place this symptom has had in clinical diagnosis, Ernhart, Graham, *et al. (1963)* included it as part of their psychological study of brain injury in the pre-school child previously cited pp. 154–56. They used two kinds of measures—a questionnaire consisting of 209 items, administered to the parents, and ratings by examiners of eight personality traits. There were significant differences between the brain-injured and the normal children in *all* the examiner ratings, *except* in "fearfulness," which did not differentiate the two groups. The questionnaire results were surprising. The subscales describing characteristics thought to be typical of brain-injured children did *not* differentiate them, except for "unpredictability," but the subscales labeled "maladjustment" (e.g., inactivity, infantilism, negativism, compulsiveness, and inwardness) showed significant differences. The authors arrived at the following conclusion:

The present results suggest that the hyperkinetic personality syndrome is not a typical picture, at least in a heterogeneous group of brain-injured children. Hyperactivity, impulsivity, and distractibility were more common in our brain injured group than in normal children. However, the difference was significant only for Examiner Ratings and not for Parent measures, it was no greater than the impairment in other personality characteristics, and it was less than the impairment in nonpersonality areas of functioning. *(Ernhart et al. 1963, p. 30.)*

It should be noted that in the earlier study *(Graham, et al. 1963)* the reported reliability, of most of the examiners' ratings of personality, after a six-month interval, was so low as to raise serious questions. The reliability of measures not involving personality and of all of the parents' responses was reported to be satisfactory.

It is clear that the child described as "brain-damaged" (*Strauss and Werner, 1941*) or as hyperkinetic displays but one of the possible behavioral consequences of damage to the central nervous system. Not all brain-damaged children have these symptoms, and there is no information to show how many children who are not brain-damaged, but emotionally disturbed, have the same symptoms. Diagnosis is further complicated by the fact that hyperkinesis seems to disappear with maturation:

There has been widespread belief flowing from clinical experience that this behavior pattern, reported so frequently in young children with brain damage, often begins to decline at the age of eight or nine years and may frequently disappear altogether in adolescence. The published literature contains an inadequate body of information on the longitudinal course of hyperkinesis and, in the absence of such information, it is most difficult to assess the value of a variety of methods of treatment and management for hyperkinetic children. It could well be that many of the so-called effective measures for the management of the syndrome of behavioral disturbance owe their reported effectiveness to the time of life at which they are introduced. (*Birch, 1964, p. 24.*)

Present Status

It is important to recognize the limitations of what is known, not only by one's own profession, but also by cooperating professions. In this particular field, the psychologist needs to have some elementary knowledge of the educator's situation, the nature of neurological examinations, and the contributions of speech pathologists. These other professionals should also have some understanding of the usefulness and limitations of psychological methods. Effective interdisciplinary collaboration, in research or practice, requires

the time and tolerance to understand one another.

One should be wary of drawing conclusions from the single case or study. All reports need to be replicated and cross-validated. Too often in our zeal to cure, we accept new research findings as definitive. The clinician should be cautious. Tests which show significant group differences may not be fine enough instruments for individual diagnosis. What looks like a successful treatment technique may reflect only the natural history of the problem or the benefits of taking a positive interest in the child and his family. But one can expect that there will be major developments in this field, and the clinician has a responsibility to keep himself informed.

The researcher can afford, may even be required, to narrow his interest to the exploration of single hypotheses logically derived from a particular theoretical position, but the clinician must not be totally committed to one point of view. Unfortunately, clinical reports often give the impression that the diagnosis was made more on the basis of predilections of the diagnostician than on the characteristics of the individual case. The organically oriented clinicians say little about family relationships, early training, emotional trauma, the management of sexual or aggressive expressions, and other features of the child's life which are routinely covered in a psychodynamically oriented report; the psychoanalytically oriented therapist rarely discusses the child's prenatal history, reports intelligence tests, or requests neurological consultations.

Parental mismanagement is by no means the only alternative to an organic causation. One frequent defense of the hypothesis of an organic cause is the presence of normal children in the family who exonerate the parents. The organicist views the child as the primary source of the problem; the parents are at fault only to the extent that they do not recognize or understand the child's special needs. However, psychodynamic explanations do not rest solely on the psychopathology of the parents. The child's constitution contributes to even the most psychological of problems. And fortuitous circumstances entirely beyond the parents' control often play a part. Moreover, the child's unexpressed fantasies are important. The child himself can arrive at some personal conclusion which is fraught with anxiety for him. It is not only what the parents do or say in reality, but also what other people do or say and how this combines with the child's unconscious wishes which contribute to a psychological problem. Unfortunately, unconscious conflicts are just as hidden as the organic functioning of the brain, so that results of initial examination, both psychological and neurological, can be equally inconclusive.

In the clinical situation, we want a diagnosis so we can formulate an effective plan of treatment. But often the diagnosis does not become clear until *after* a period of treatment. As a practical matter, treatment is often determined by the present weaknesses and strengths of the patient rather than by the original cause. During the diagnostic process, one must keep in mind how the results can be interpreted to the parents and to the child and, above all, how the results of the diagnostic tests will affect the management of the case. It is not particularly helpful, and it may even be hurtful, to tell the parents that their child's reading disability is probably organic, if there are no practical steps for them to take. Sometimes the clinician must put aside his intellectual curiosity or deliberately minimize certain possibilities, and concentrate on only those aspects of the case for which he has some partial solution.

Even when a definite organic factor has been established, psychological factors cannot be ignored. Family relationships are still important, and they are probably being distorted by the child's defect. In a number of studies, the parents of brain-damaged children with associated behavioral disturbances appeared to have serious personality disorders. A vicious cycle is created when the child's difficulties result in part from parental mishandling and environmental trauma and the child's difficulties then affect his parents, creating tension, uncertainty, and inconsistency in them. In the clinical situation, emotional and organic factors must be synthesized into a single treatment plan—which may be incomplete but which must be reasonable in terms of the reality circumstances of the child and his family.

References for Chapter 7

Anderson, L., "The Effect of Laterality Localization of Focal Brain Lesions on the Wechsler-Bellevue Subtests," *Journal of Clinical Psychology,* VII (1951), 149–54.

Arthur, B., "Comparison of the Psychological Test Performance of Brain Damaged and Normal Children in the Mental Age Range of Five to Six," University of Michigan, *Dissertation Abstracts,* XIX (1958), 6.

Babcock, H., "An Experiment in the Measurement of Mental Deterioration," *Archives of Psychology,* CXVII (1930).

Barbara, D., "Understanding Stuttering," *New York State Medical Journal,* LV (1956), 1798.

Beck, H. S. and A. L. Lam, "Use of the WISC in Predicting Organicity," *Journal of Clinical Psychology,* XI (1955), 154–58.

Belmont, L. and H. G. Birch, "The Relation of Time of Life to Behavioral Consequences in Brain Damage: I, The Performance of Brain Injured Adults on the Marble Board Test," *Journal of Nervous and Mental Diseases,* CXXXI, (1960), 91–97.

Bender, L., "A Visual-Motor Test and Its Clinical Use," *American Journal of Orthopsychiatry Monograph,* No. 3 (1938).

———, *Instruction for the Use of the Visual Motor Gestalt Test.* New York: American Orthopsychiatry Association, Inc., 1946.

———, et al., "Symposium: The Concept of Plasticity and its Relationship to Learning Disorders," *American Journal of Orthopsychiatry,* XXXIII (1963), 305–7. (Digest.)

Bender, R., *The Conquest of Deafness.* Cleveland: The Press of Western Reserve University, 1960.

Benton, A. L., "Dyslexia in Relation to Form Perception and Directional Sense," in J. Money, *Reading Disability.* Baltimore: The Johns Hopkins Press, 1962.

Berko, M. J., "A Note on Psychometric Scatter 'As a Factor in the Differentiation' of Exogenous and Endogenous Mental Deficiency," *Cerebral Palsy Review,* XVI (1955), 20.

Birch, H. G., *Brain Damage in Children: The Biological and Social Aspects.* Baltimore: The Williams & Wilkins Company, 1964.

———, and A. Leffold, "Psychological Evaluation of Children with Cerebral Damage," in H. G. Birch, *Brain Damage in Children: The Biological and Social Aspects.* Baltimore: The Williams & Wilkins Company, 1964.

Bloodstein, Oliver, *A Handbook on Stuttering for Professional Workers.* Chicago: National Society for Crippled Children and Adults, 1959.

Bortner, M. and H. G. Birch, "Perceptual and Perceptual-Motor Dissociations in Cerebral Palsied Children." Paper presented at American Psychological Association meeting, New York, 1961.

———, "Perceptual and Perceptual-Motor Dissociations in Brain Damaged Patients," *Journal of Nervous and Mental Diseases,* CXXX (1960), 49–53.

Byrd, E., "The Clinical Validity of the Bender-Gestalt Test with Children: A Developmental Comparison of Children in Need of Psychotherapy and Children Judged Well-Adjusted," *Journal of Projective Techniques,* XX (1956), 127–36.

Caputo, D. V. *et al.,* "Type of Brain Damage and Intellectual Functioning in Children," *Journal of Consulting Psychology,* XXVII (1963), 184.

Chorost, S. B., G. Spivack, and M. Levine, "Bender-Gestalt Rotations and EEG Abnormalities in Children," *Journal of Consulting Psychology,* XXIII (1959), 559.

Daryn, E., "Problem of Children with 'Diffuse Brain Damage,'" *Archives of General Psychology,* IV (March, 1961), 299–307.

Davids, A., L. Goldberg, and M. Laufer, "The Relation of Archimedes Spiral Aftereffect and the Trail Marking Test to Brain Damage in Children," *Journal of Consulting Psychology,* XXI (1957), 429–33.

Delacato, C. H., *The Treatment and Prevention of Reading Problems.* Springfield, Ill.: Charles C Thomas, Publisher, 1959.

Eisenberg, L., "Introduction," in J. Money, *Reading Disability.* Baltimore: The Johns Hopkins Press, 1962.

Eisenson, J., "A Perseverative Theory of Stuttering," in J. Eisenson, *Stuttering: A Symposium.* New York: Harper & Row, Publishers, 1958.

Engel, Dean and Isidore Helfand, "Stuttering Is a Family Affair," unpublished manuscript, 1964. Available from Cleveland Hearing and Speech Center, Cleveland, Ohio 44106.

Ernhart, C. B. *et al.,* "Brain Injury in the Pre-school Child: Some Developmental Considerations: Part II, Comparison of Brain Injured and Normal Children," *Psychological Monographs,* 77 (1963), Nos. 10, 11 (Whole Nos. 573, 574).

Fenichel, O., *The Psychoanalytic Theory of Neurosis.* New York: W. W. Norton & Company, Inc., 1945, 311–17.

Fernald, G., *Remedial Techniques in Basic School Subjects.* New York: McGraw-Hill Book Company, 1943.

Fink, M. and M. B. Bender, "Perception of Simultaneous Tactile Stimuli in Normal Children," *Neurology,* III (1953), 27–34.

Fisher, G. M., "Differences in WAIS Verbal and Performance IQ's in Various Diagnostic Groups of Mental Retardates," *American Journal of Mental Deficiency,* LXV (1960), 256–60.

Fitzhugh, K., L. Fitzhugh, and R. Reitan, "Psychological Deficits in Relation to Acuteness of Brain Dysfunction," *Journal of Consulting Psychology,* XXV (1961), 61–66.

Gates, A. I. and G. L. Bond, "Relation of Handedness, Eyesighting, and Acuity Dominance to Reading," *Journal of Educational Psychology,* XXVII (1936), 450–56.

Geshwind, N., "The Anatomy of Acquired Disorders of Reading," in J. Money, *Reading Disability.* Baltimore: The Johns Hopkins Press, 1962.

Gilbert, G. M., "A Survey of 'Referral Problems' in Metropolitan Child Guidance Centers," *Journal of Clinical Psychology,* XIII (1957), No. 1, 37–42.

Gillingham, A. and B. Stillman, *Remedial Training for Children with Specific Disability in Reading, Spelling, and Penmanship.* New York: Sackett & Wilhelms, 1940.

Goldstein, K. and M. Scheerer, "Abstract and Concrete Behavior: An Experimental Study with Special Tests," *Psychological Monographs*, 53 (1941), No. 2 (Whole No. 239).

Goodstein, L. D., "Functional Speech Disorders and Personality: a Survey of the Literature," in P. Trapp and P. Himelstein, *Readings on the Exceptional Child*. New York: Appleton-Century-Crofts, 1962.

Graham, F. K. and B. S. Kendall, "Memory-for-Designs Test: Revised General Manual," *Perceptual and Motor Skills*, Monograph Supplement No. 2, 11 (1960), 147–88.

——, F. K. et al., "Brain Injury in the Pre-school Child: Some Developmental Considerations. Part I, The Performance of Normal Children," *Psychological Monographs*, 77 (1963), Nos. 10, 11 (Whole Nos. 573, 574).

——, "Development Three Years after Perinatal Anoxia and Other Potentially Damaging Newborn Experiences," *Psychological Monographs*, 72 (1962), No. 3 (Whole No. 522).

Haines, M., "Test Performance of Pre-school Children with and without Organic Brain Pathology," *Journal of Consulting Psychology*, XVIII (1954), 371–74.

Halpin, V., "Rotation Errors Made by Brain Injured and Familial Children on Two Visual Motor Tests," *American Journal of Mental Deficiency*, LIX (1955), 485–89.

Halstead, W. C., *Brain and Intelligence: A Quantitative Study of the Frontal Lobes*. Chicago: The University of Chicago Press, 1947.

Hanvik, L. J., "A Note on Rotations in the Bender-Gestalt Test as Predictors of EEG Abnormalities in Children," *Journal of Clinical Psychology*, IX (1953), 399.

Hardy, W. G., "Dyslexia in Relation to Diagnostic Methodology in Hearing and Speech Disorders," in J. Money, *Reading Disability*. Baltimore: The Johns Hopkins Press, 1962.

Harris, A. J., *How to Increase Reading Ability*. New York: David McKay Co., Inc., 1947.

Haynes, J. R. and S. B. Sells, "Assessment of Organic Brain Damage by Psychological Tests," *Psychological Bulletin*, LX (1963), 316–25.

Hinshelwood, J., "Congenital Word Blindness," *Lancet*, I (1900), 1506–8.

Howard, A. and D. Shoemaker, "An Evaluation of the Memory-for-Designs Test," *Journal of Consulting Psychology*, XVIII (1954), 266.

Hunt, H. F., "A Practical Clinical Test for Organic Brain Damage," *Journal of Applied Psychology*, XXVII (1943), 375–86.

Irwin, O. C., "Infant Speech: Effect of Systematic Reading of Stories," *Journal of Speech and Hearing Research*, III (1960), 187–90.

Johnson, W., *Stuttering in Children and Adults*, Chapter 3. Minneapolis: The University of Minnesota Press, 1955.

——, "Diagnosis as a Cause of Stuttering," in C. Van Riper, *Speech Therapy: A Book of Readings*. Englewood Cliffs, N.J.: Prentice-Hall, Inc., 1953.

——, *Speech Handicapped School Children*. New York: Harper & Row, Publishers, 1948.

Kahn, E. and L. H. Cohen, "Organic Driveness: A Brain-stem Syndrome and an Experience," *New England Journal of Medicine*, CCX (1934), 748–56.

Kanner, L. and L. Eisenberg, "Early Infantile Autism, 1943-1955," in *Psychiatric Research Reports*, American Psychiatric Association (April, 1957), 55–65.

Kawi, A. A. and B. Pasamanick, "Prenatal and Paranatal Factors in the Development of Childhood Reading Disorders," *Monographs of the Society for Research in Child Development*, XXIV, No. 4 (1959).

Kennedy, C. and L. S. Ramirez, "Brain Damage as a Cause of Behavior Disturbance in Children," in H. G. Birch, *Brain Damage in Children: The Biological and Social Aspects*. Baltimore: The Williams & Wilkins Company, 1964.

Klatskin, E. H., "Relationship of Deficits in Intelligence Test Performance of Pre-school Children to Perinatal Experience," *Journal of Consulting Psychology*, XXVIII (1964), 228–33.

Kolansky, H., "Treatment of a Three-Year-Old Girl's Severe Infantile Neurosis," *Psychoanalytic Study of the Child*, Vol. XV. New York: International Universities Press, Inc., 1960.

Koppitz, E. M., "The Bender-Gestalt Test for Children: A Normative Study," *Journal of Clinical Psychology*, XVI (1960), 432–35.

Laufer, M. W., E. Denhoff, and G. Solomons, "Hyperkinetic Impulse Disorder in Children's Behavior Problems," *Psychosomatic Medicine*, XIX (1957), 38–49.

Levy, D. M., "Trends in Therapy: Release Therapy," *American Journal of Orthopsychiatry*, IX (1939), 713–36.

McGinnis, M. A., *Aphasic Children*. Washington, D.C.: Alexander Graham Bell Association for the Deaf, 1963.

Midcentury White House Conference on Children and Youth. Washington, D.C., December, 1950. *Proceedings;* A report of conference sessions, Edward A. Richards (general ed.). Raleigh, N.C.: Health Publications Institute, 1951.

Money, J., "Dyslexia: A Post-Conference Review," in J. Money, *Reading Disability.* Baltimore: The Johns Hopkins Press, 1962.

Monroe, M., *Children Who Cannot Read.* Chicago: The University of Chicago Press, 1932.

Myklebust, H. R., *Auditory Disorders in Children.* New York: Grune & Stratton, Inc., 1954.

———, and B. Boshes, "Psychoneurological Learning Disorders in Children," *Archives of Pediatrics,* LXXVII (1960), 247–56.

———, and D. Johnson, "Dyslexia in Children," *Exceptional Children,* XXIX, No. 1 (September, 1962), 14–25.

Naidoo, S., "An Investigation into Some Aspects of Ambiguous Handedness." Unpublished M.A. thesis, University of London, 1961.

Orton, S., "Specific Reading Disability: Strephosymbolia," *Journal of the American Medical Association,* XC (1928), 1095–99.

———, *Reading, Writing and Speech Disorders in Children.* New York: W. W. Norton & Company, Inc., 1937.

Pascal, Gerald R., and Barbara J. Suttel, *The Bender-Gestalt Test; Quantification and Validity for Adults.* New York: Grune & Stratton, Inc., 1951.

Poole, I., "Genetic Development in Articulation of Consonant Sounds in Speech," *Elementary English,* XI (1954), 159–61.

Power, M. H., "Speech Correction in the Chicago Public Schools," in *Special Education in the Chicago Public Schools* (Rev. Ed.). Chicago: Chicago Board of Education, 1953.

Price, A. C. and H. Deabler, "Diagnosis of Organicity by Means of the Spiral Aftereffect," *Journal of Consulting Psychology,* XX (1955), 299–302.

Quast, W., "The Bender-Gestalt: A Clinical Study of Children's Records," *Journal of Consulting Psychology,* XXV (1961), 405–8.

Rappaport, S., *Childhood Aphasia and Brain Damage: A Definition.* Narberth, Pa.: Livingston Publishing Company, 1964.

Reitan, R., "The Comparative Effects of Brain Damage on the Halstead Impairment Index and the Wechsler-Bellevue Scale," *Journal of Clinical Psychology,* XV (1959), 281–85.

———, "An Investigation of the Validity of Halstead's Measures of Biological Intelligence," *Archives of Neurology and Psychiatry,* LXXIII (1955), 28–35.

Richards, T. W. and S. Hooper, "Brain Injury at Birth (Cerebral Palsy) and Perceptual Responses during Childhood and Adolescence," *Journal of Nervous and Mental Diseases,* CXXIII (1956), 117–24.

Rogers, M. E., A. M. Lilienfeld, and B. Pasamanick, "Prenatal and Perinatal Factors in the Development of Childhood Behavior Disorders," *Acta Psychiatrica et Neurologica Scandinavica* (Suppl.), CII (1955), 1–158.

Rowley, V. N., "An Analysis of the WISC Performance of Brain Damaged and Disturbed Children," *Journal of Consulting Psychology,* XXV (1961), 553.

Scott, T. R., R. A. Bragg, and R. G. Smarr, "Brain Damage Diagnosis with the MMG," *Journal of Consulting Psychology,* XXVII (1963), 45–53.

Shaw, M. C. and W. M. Cruickshank, "The Rorschach Performance of Epileptic Children," *Journal of Consulting Psychology,* XXI (1957), 422–24.

———, "The Use of the Bender-Gestalt Test with Epileptic Children," *Journal of Consulting Psychology,* XXI (1956), 192–93.

Sheehan, J. G., "Projective Studies of Stuttering," in P. Trapp and P. Himelstein, *Readings on the Exceptional Child.* New York: Appleton-Century-Crofts, 1962.

———, "Theory and Treatment of Stuttering as an Approach-Avoidance Conflict," in C. F. Reed, I. E. Alexander, and S. S. Tomkins, *Psychopathology: A Source Book.* Cambridge, Mass.: Harvard University Press, 1958.

Shipley, W. C., "A Self Administering Scale for Measuring Intellectual Impairment and Deterioration," *Journal of Psychology,* IX (1940), 371–77.

Strauss, A. A. and N. C. Kephart, *Psychopathology and Education of the Brain-Injured Child,* Vol. II, "Progress in Theory and Clinic." New York: Grune & Stratton, Inc., 1955.

———, and L. Lehtinen, *Psychopathology and Education of the Brain-Injured Child.* New York: Grune & Stratton, Inc., 1947.

———, and H. Werner, "The Mental Organization of the Brain-Injured Mentally Defective Child," *American Journal of Psychiatry,* XCV (1941), 1194–1202.

Templin, M., "Norms on a Screening Test of Articulation for Ages Three through Eight,"

Journal of Hearing and Speech Disorders, XVIII (1953), 323–31.

———, et al., "Genetic Studies of Genius," *Mental and Physical Traits of a Thousand Gifted Children,* Vol. I. Stanford, Calif.: Stanford University Press, 1925.

———, and M. D. Steer, "Studies of Growth of Speech of Pre-school Children," *Journal of Hearing and Speech Disorders,* IV (1939), 71–77.

Terman, Lewis M., *Mental and Physical Traits of a Thousand Gifted Children.* Stanford: Stanford University Press, 1925.

Teuber, H. L. and R. G. Rudel, "Behavior after Cerebral Lesions in Children and Adults," *Developmental Medicine and Child Neurology,* IV (1962), 3–20.

Travis, L. E., *Handbook of Speech Pathology.* New York: Appleton-Century-Crofts, 1957.

———, "My Present Thinking on Stuttering," *Western Speech,* X (1946), 3–5. Reprinted in C. Van Riper, *Speech Therapy: A Book of Readings.* Englewood Cliffs, N.J.: Prentice-Hall, Inc., (1953), 50–53.

———, *Speech Pathology.* New York: Appleton-Century-Crofts, 1931.

Van Riper, C., *Speech Therapy: A Book of Readings.* Englewood Cliffs, N.J.: Prentice-Hall, Inc., 1953.

Vernon, M. D., *Backwardness in Reading: A Study of its Nature and Origin.* Cambridge, Mass.: Cambridge University Press, 1958.

Wechsler, D., *The Measurement of Adult Intelligence* (3rd Ed.). Baltimore: The Williams & Wilkins Co., 1944.

Wepman, J., *Recovery from Aphasia.* New York: The Ronald Press Company, 1951.

West, R., M. Ansberry, and A. Carr, *The Rehabilitation of Speech.* (3rd Ed.). New York: Harper & Row, Publishers, 1957.

Wischner, G. J., "An Experimental Approach to Expectancy and Anxiety in Stuttering Behavior," in P. Trapp and P. Himelstein, *Readings on the Exceptional Child.* New York: Appleton-Century-Crofts, 1962.

Witty, P. A., and D. Kopel, "Sinestral and Mixed Manual-Ocular Behavior in Reading Disability," *Journal of Educational Psychology,* XXVII (1936), 119–34.

Wolpe, Z. S., "Play Therapy, Psychodrama, and Parent Counseling," in L. E. Travis, *Handbook of Speech Pathology.* New York: Appleton-Century-Crofts, 1957.

Wyatt, G. L. and H. M. Herzan, "Therapy with Stuttering Children and Their Mothers," *American Journal of Orthopsychiatry,* XXXII (1962), 645–60.

Yates, A., "The Validity of Some Psychological Tests of Brain Damage," *Psychological Bulletin,* LI (1954), 359–80.

Zangwill, O. L., "Dyslexia in Relation to Cerebral Dominance," in J. Money, *Reading Disability.* Baltimore: The Johns Hopkins Press, 1962.

Zehrer, F. A., "Investigation of Rorschach Factors in Children Who Have Convulsive Disorders and Those Who Present Problems of Adjustment," *American Journal of Orthopsychiatry,* XXI (1951), 292–302.

8

MENTAL SUBNORMALITY

Texts concerned with emotional disorders of children frequently omit the subject of mental retardation, viewing it as a separate entity. In practice, there is no sharp distinction between emotional and mental development (see Chapter 2). Emotional conflicts of a certain kind and environmental deprivations at crucial periods can produce mental retardation; conversely, mental retardation often produces emotional conflict.

The term "mentally retarded" embraces a range of patients, from the totally helpless child in the crib to the child whose handicap is apparent only in school. In addition to this variation in the degree of handicap, the causes of the retardation vary, and so do physical and personality characteristics associated with it. A great many stereotyped notions exist: that the retarded child is easily spotted by his vacant look, or personifies the "happy moron" idea; that the retarded child is impulse-ridden and potentially dangerous; that the retarded child is automatically good with his hands or has a wonderful sense of rhythm; and so on. But there is almost no valid generalization one can make. Mentally retarded children are as different from one another as are children of normal or superior intelli-

gence. The common denominator is their slowness to learn. This takes them out of the mainstream of educational methods or goals. It also restricts them vocationally, and many cannot compete in the open labor market without special assistance. The retarded all feel the social impact of being different (i.e., defective), and before the realization comes to the retarded individual himself, his parents have experienced the disappointment, bewilderment, and frustration which follow in the wake of the diagnosis.

It is difficult to estimate the prevalence of mental retardation because the definition varies. The most frequently quoted prevalence figure is 3 per cent of the school-age population. The President's Panel on Mental Retardation *(Hormuth, 1963)* estimated that some 5.4 million children and adults are mentally retarded. Twice as many people are retarded as are afflicted by blindness, polio, cerebral palsy, and rheumatic heart disease combined. Only four significant disabling conditions—mental illness, cardiac disease, arthritis, and cancer—have a higher prevalence. The figures alone indicate that mental retardation is a national health, social, and economic problem of major dimensions.

Classification
Diagnosis: Definition and

Terminology

It has been difficult to agree on a term to encompass the whole range of "incomplete development of mind" or "subaverage intellectual functioning." The fashions of the past century are shown in the changes of name of the professional organization first organized in 1877 as the Association of Medical Officers of American Institutions for Idiotic and Feebleminded Persons. It was known as the American Association for the Study of the Feebleminded from 1918 to 1940, at which time it adopted the present name, The American Association on Mental Deficiency. Some experts *(Sarason and Gladwin, 1958)* make a strong case for differentiating between mental deficiency and mental retardation, restricting the term "mental deficiency" to those with demonstrable neurological pathology and the term "mental retardation" to those with no detectable organic damage. In the Soviet Union, only those with demonstrable neurological pathology are considered special cases; the preferred term is "oligophrenia," restricted to children who can be presumed to have suffered an actual brain injury in intrauterine, perinatal, or early infant life, and its study is termed "defectology" *(Wortis, 1960)*. In theory, this is a logical distinction, but the problems in establishing or ruling out an organic etiology in practice were reviewed in Chapter 7.

In 1954, the World Health Organization proposed the term "mental subnormality" as a generic term, which would include both the mentally deficient and the mentally retarded. This suggestion did not take hold, however. "Mental retardation" is still the commonly accepted generic term, but it will probably change again. The impetus for the switch from "mental deficiency" to "mental retardation" came mainly from parents' associations (e.g., the National Association for Retarded Children, established in 1950) which found the older term distasteful. "Mental retardation" may one day come to have the same unhappy connotation. Any term which indicates that a child is stupid or slow is insulting and inevitably becomes undesirable; euphemisms cannot hide the bitter facts. This is not really a question of terminology, but one of changing attitudes.

Criteria of Mental Retardation

It is not difficult to define mental retardation in general terms. A classical definition is that contained in the Mental Deficiency Act of 1927 (still operable in England): ". . . a condition of arrested or incomplete development of mind, existing before the age of eighteen years, whether arising from inherent causes or induced by disease or injury." The recent definition proposed by the American Association on Mental Deficiency adds the concept of social incompetence: "Mental retardation refers to subaverage intellectual functioning which originates during the developmental period and is associated with impairment of adaptive behavior" *(Heber, 1961, p. 499)*.

The criterion for mental retardation which originates during the developmental period is simply the age when the disability was first recognized. More controversial are the criteria for intellectual malfunctioning and social impairment—what they mean, how they can be measured, and their relation to one another. Some definitions and classification systems rely almost entirely on the measurement of intellectual functioning; others stress the social disability.

Dependence on the IQ as the sole criterion of mental deficiency is largely an American practice. The suggested top IQ varies, however. Wechsler suggests a top limit, on both the Wechsler-Bellevue Adult examination (1937) and the Wechsler Intelligence Scale for Children (1949), of 65. The more common is IQ 70, in accordance with Terman's classifications for the Stanford-Binet examinations in 1916, 1937, and 1960. In public schools, children with IQ's as high as 75 are placed in special classes for the educable retarded. The most recent recommendation (Heber, 1959) sets the limit even higher yet: more than one standard deviation below the mean intelligence (i.e., 84 on the Stanford-Binet and 85 on the WISC). By definition, this includes 16 per cent of the population. Since even the lowest 3 per cent are inadequately provided for, this recommendation has not gained much acceptance, but it indicates a trend. As society becomes more complex, the demands on the individual become greater; the intellectual equipment required for "social competence" becomes correspondingly greater.

Although a low IQ is the *sine qua non* of mental deficiency, it is not sufficient to establish the diagnosis, for two reasons. The first is concerned with errors of measurement which produce a normal fluctuation in IQ score. The use of an arbitrary dividing line between the mentally retarded and the "subnormal normal" highlights this problem. There is no significant difference in the intelligence of a youngster with an IQ of 68 and one with an IQ of 72, or between a youngster with an IQ of 73 and one with an IQ of 77. In recognition of this fact, most practitioners allow a five-point margin in each direction when IQ's are used for administrative purposes. The second reason is that there is no perfect relationship between IQ and social behavior. It is safe to assume that individuals whose IQ's measure consistently below 50 are seriously handicapped and retarded in the social and legal senses, but some retarded individuals with

higher IQ's are quite capable of managing themselves and their own affairs. The IQ gives only a limited amount of information, and an individual should not be adjudged retarded unless there is a concomitant behavior problem.

Appreciation of the limitations of the IQ has led many authorities to advocate social criteria as the best means of separating the mentally retarded from the normal population. One of the most prominent exponents of this view is A. F. Tredgold. He proposed a biological and social criterion based on the assumption that the essential purpose of mind is to enable the individual "so to adapt himself to his environment as to maintain an independent existence" (1947, p. 4). He asserts that "to constitute abnormality and defect, the failure must be due to psychological and not to economic and social causes; and there is usually little difficulty in distinguishing between the two" (p. 5). In England, particularly, his arguments had a profound influence. Ann M. and A. D. B. Clarke quote many official documents which suggest the certification of patients as "mentally defective" on the grounds of "anti-social characteristics," despite normal psychometric intelligence. They point out that to adopt social competence as the sole criterion of mental defect leads to the inclusion of many neurotics, psychopaths, and criminals and, furthermore, that criteria of satisfactory social adjustment are quite arbitrary and differ widely in different societies at different times (1958).

In America, Edgar Doll's definition of mental deficiency probably was the most widely used until recently. He suggested six criteria: (1) social incompetence, which is (2) due to mental subnormality, which (3) has been developmentally arrested, which (4) obtains at maturity, (5) is of constitutional origin, and which (6) is essentially incurable (1941). To make the evaluation of social incompetence more precise, objective, and valid, Doll developed the Vineland Social Maturity Scale, for comparing the behavior of a particular patient of any given age with that of the normal person (1953). It was Doll's opinion that the Social Maturity Scale measures the abilities essential for social adequacy and occupational success.

The first three of Doll's criteria have met with general acceptance. The second three have been hotly contested, particularly the criterion of social incompetence which *obtains at maturity*. Follow-up studies have shown that a fair number of individuals who were classified as mentally retarded in their school years are *not* socially incompetent in their adult life. This would mean that the diagnosis of mental retardation could only be made in retrospect; the clinician would have to withhold judgment until the child became an adult.

The current definition does not include Doll's sixth criterion, incurability. This view is best expressed in the AAMD manual:

Within the framework of the present definition, mental retardation is a term descriptive of the current status of the individual with respect to intellectual functioning and adaptive behavior. Consequently, an individual may meet the criteria of mental retardation at one time and not at another. A person may change status as a result of changes in social standards or conditions or as a result of changes in efficiency of intellectual functioning, with level of efficiency always being determined in relation to the behavioral standards and norms for the individual's chronological age group. *(Heber, 1959, p. 4.)*

Mental retardation is thus considered to be symptomatized in mental and social inadequacy for the demands of the present, that is, the individual cannot compete with his age mates in terms of what is expected at this period of his life. As one would expect, the school situation is crucial, and the greatest number of retarded become apparent through educational failure. This is shown in the figures of the Onondaga County survey *(New York State Department of Mental Hygiene, 1955)*. Prevalence reached a peak at 14 years (77.6 per 1,000 population) and then fell off sharply. The sudden drop was not due to wholesale cures; many of the retarded children dropped out of school at this point and simply disappeared from view. In the summary of this survey, it was stated that "the data suggest strongly that behavior leading to the social suspicion of 'mental retardation' is not necessarily a fixed characteristic of the individual children but is rather a complex set of manifestations of some children's relationship to their immediate environment" *(1955)*.

The second part of the current view that mental retardation is a symptom rather than a diagnostic entity is that there is no implication as to etiology. This is in contrast to Doll's criterion of "constitutional origin," which would exclude those children whose mental development is retarded because of environmental deprivation or profound emotional conflict. A major category of the AAMD manual *(Heber, 1959)* is concerned with "mental retardation due to uncertain (or presumed psychologic) cause with the functional reaction alone manifest" (Category VIII). There are five subdivisions: retardation associated with "cultural-familial" factors; retardation associated with environmental deprivation; "psychogenic" retardation associated with emotional disturbance; "retardation associated with psychotic or major personality disorder"; and a wastebasket category, for retardation due to unknown causes. "Psychogenic" retardation is virtually the same as "pseudo-retardation."

Classification of the Mentally Retarded

Classification schemes are based on two systems: one, degree of handicap; and two, cause of retardation. Table 4 shows different classificatory systems based on the degree of handicap.

Table 4 reveals a difference in point of view between the American Psychiatric Association and the American Association on Mental Deficiency as to what should be termed "mild," "moderate," and "severe" mental retardation. Those who work closely with the retarded observe significant differences among those with IQ's below 50, and therefore feel the need of further subdivision. To the clinician who is concerned only with establishing an initial diagnosis, these individuals are more alike than they are different, so a single category suffices.

It is also important to indicate the relative proportion of retarded to be found in these degree categories. Three per cent, usually given as the over-all prevalence of mental retardation is divided as follows: 2.5 per cent are mildly retarded, or educable (IQ's of 50 to 75); .4 per cent are moderately retarded, or trainable (IQ's of 25 to 50); and .1 per cent are in the severely or profoundly retarded, the total care group (IQ's below 25). This is expected from the normal distribution curve; the further from the mean, the fewer the

individuals. However, it is an important point because many people think of the retarded population in terms of the trainable level without appreciating the fact that the greater number are in the higher category.

Classification schemes based on cause of retardation are not as directly comparable as those based on degree. The terms used in Table 5, are not identically defined, but they are similar in that they are meant to differentiate organic from functional pathology.

The subdivisions in Table 5 are roughly related to severity. That is, the majority of the educable individuals (IQ's above 50) will be of the "subcultural" variety and the majority of those with IQ's below 50 will have various manifestations of organic pathology. Furthermore, epidemiological studies have shown that individuals with cerebral damage are fairly randomly distributed through all social classes, but that the "familial" or "nonorganic" individuals are concentrated in the lower classes (*Gardner and Nisonger, 1962*). There is a great deal of overlapping, however.

Within the pathological group, there is a great variety of organic determi-

TABLE 4

Terms Used to Describe Mental Retardation in Relation to Measured Intelligence

Range in IQ Scores on Tests with Standard Deviation of 15	Terms Used in AAMD Manual (1961 Revision)*	APA Nomenclature (1952)**	Former Terms	Educational Classification
70-84	Borderline	Mild	Borderline	Slow learner (sometimes included in educable range)
55-69	Mild	Moderate	Moron	Educable retarded
40-54	Moderate	Severe	Imbecile	Trainable retarded
25-39	Severe	Severe	Imbecile	Trainable retarded
Below 25	Profound	Severe	Idiot	Total-care group

*Heber, 1961, p. 500.
**American Psychiatric Association, 1952.

TABLE 5

Classifications of Retardation by General Etiology

Lewis (1933)	Strauss (1939)	Kanner (1949)	Sarason and Gladwin (1959)	Synonymous Terms
Pathological mental deficiency	Exogenous mental deficiency	Absolute feeblemindedness	Mental deficiency	Brain-injured
Subcultural mental deficiency	Endogenous mental deficiency	Relative feeblemindedness	Mental retardation	Garden variety; familial; retardation due to uncertain causes.

nants or causal agents. H. Yannet indicated that well over a hundred etiologies, diseases, and medical syndromes in which mental retardation represents a more or less important symptom have been described *(1956)*. For example, retarded mental development may result from deficiencies of, or damage to, the central nervous system from any one of the following:

1. Chromosomal abnormalities (Mongolism or Down's Syndrome)
2. Prenatal infections (rubella in pregnancy, maternal syphilis)
3. Iso-immunization (blood type incompatibility resulting in kernicterus)
4. Prematurity of birth (birth weight the important factor)
5. Birth trauma
6. Cranial anomalies (e.g., microcephaly, hydrocephalus)
7. Defects of metabolism (phenylketonuria, cretinism, galactosemia)
8. Childhood accidents (head injuries)
9. Childhood diseases (e.g., post-measles encephalitis, lead poisoning)
10. Heredo-degenerative cerebral diseases

Disorders caused by any one of these ten organic agents include more than mental retardation. There are usually other physical findings which the neurologist or pediatrician uses to corroborate an etiological diagnosis. Except for Mongolism (which afflicts 10 per cent of the institutionalized retarded), clear organic etiology is rare. The majority of the cases elude specific

physical diagnosis. With reference to an *outpatient* population, Kirman concluded that:

A definite cause of mental defect is not found in a majority of cases. Thus, in a series of 154 low-grade defectives . . . the cause was reasonably certain in seventeen. Since most of these patients had been re-examined repeatedly at some of the leading London hospitals, the standard of investigation was probably as high as anywhere else. The uncertainty is even greater in regard to higher-grade patients. *(Hilliard and Kirman, 1957, p. 8.)*

Yannet's findings concerning classification of an *institutionalized* population (Southbury Training School, Connecticut) differ from Kirman's. He found that only 30 per cent of the 2,000 institutionalized patients were classified as undifferentiated and 70 per cent had definite, recognizable clinical syndromes *(1952)*.

Differential Diagnosis

Given the symptom of mental retardation, there is the further task of establishing cause. Excluding medical syndromes, there are two differentiations which particularly involve psychological assessment: exogenous versus endogenous retardation; and psychogenic versus innate retardation. In the author's opinion, it is often impossible to make these differentiations, but clinicians should understand the distinctions and be able to recognize the clear-cut cases.

Exogenous versus Endogenous Retardation

This distinction was first proposed by H. Werner and A. A. Strauss (the later ramifications of their work were presented in Chapter 7). Their early experimentation was done with retarded subjects, and was inspired by Kurt Goldstein's reports on the after-effects of brain injuries of veterans of World War I *(1939, 1942)*. Some of his observations were: (1) that there was a blurring of the sharp boundaries between figure and ground; (2) that there was attention to extraneous, external factors (i.e., forced responsiveness); (3) that there was impairment of the abstract attitude; (4) that there was a catastrophic reaction to failure or frustration; and (5) that defensive measures (e.g., excessive orderliness and withdrawal) were taken to avoid catastrophic anxiety. Goldstein described the patients' sensitivity to any change or surprise, and their rigidity, in a way reminiscent of obsessive-compulsive character disorders. It was his judgment that the patients' need for sameness and repetition arose from an avoidance of the anxiety which would be aroused in them if a readjustment was required.

The logic of A. A. Strauss, Werner, and others was that children who suffered brain damage might show these same behavior patterns. The general experimental design of their early studies was to compare two groups of retarded children institutionalized at Wayne County Training School (IQ's generally ranged from 60 to 80). The groups were relatively small, around twenty children in each. The endogenous group was composed of children whose developmental histories and neurological examination gave no evidence of a "lesion in the central nervous system"; the exogenous group consisted of children "who showed evidence of

brain lesion." In some studies, the two groups were selected on the basis of differences in performance on intelligence tests rather than neurologic criteria. In the exogenous group, the mental ages scored on performance tests were one year or more *below* the Stanford-Binet mental age; in the endogenous group, the mental ages scored on performance tests were three or more years *above* the Stanford-Binet mental age. It is difficult to ascertain if the same children were used in repeated studies.

The experimental methods were ingenious and explored many facets of behavior. Perception was studied most thoroughly, and many differences between the brain-injured children and the endogenously retarded of the same mental age were described. Werner and B. D. Thuma reported differences in ability to see apparent motion *(1942-b)* and in the critical flicker fusion frequency *(1942-a)*. The brain-injured child had more difficulty recognizing figures imbedded in a homogenous background on tachistoscopic exposure because he was more distracted by the ground *(Werner and Strauss, 1941)*. The Marble Board Test *(Werner and Strauss, 1939)* involved a visual-motor task, the reproduction of a model figure on another marble board. The pattern of the exogenous group was incoherent and characterized by unrelated, discontinuous lines and moves.

A number of studies of concept formation were made. Strauss and Werner, using a sorting test procedure, demonstrated that the exogenously retarded child is especially apt to group objects in uncommon, far-fetched, and peculiar ways. He often selected objects for grouping on the basis of some unusual or apparently insignificant detail *(1942)*. Werner and D. Carrison found more animistic thinking in brain-injured mentally retarded children; these children identified with objects and events in nature as much as with people. The theoretical explanation which the authors offered for this is interesting in that it reflects the line of reasoning which relates everything about the child's behavior to the organic defect.

1. In an organism which is driven hither and yon by outside stimulation, the essential difference between oneself as a person, who masters the external world by planful action, as opposed to objects without this ability is less obvious.

2. The pathological condition of fixation, perseveration, rigidity could also obstruct the child's understanding of purposeful activity as a characteristic of a person in contradistinction to a thing.

3. The behavior characteristics of lack of emotional control and motor disinhibition (organic drivenness) also reduces the self-directed behavior of the individual and reduces his awareness of the difference between spontaneous, personal activity and external occurrences in the world of things. *(Werner and Carrison, 1944, p. 60.)*

Two other studies illustrate the interests of the researchers. Werner studied the tendency toward perseveration as a particular aspect of rigidity defined as "lack of variability and adaptability" of response *(1946)*. By means of a behavior rating scale, Strauss and N. C. Kephart *(1940)* had institutional teachers and cottage parents rate a group of retarded children "blind," that is, without knowing the psychological diagnosis. The exogenous group was reliably differentiated from the others in such ways as being "erratic, uncoordinated, uncontrolled, uninhibited, and socially unaccepted" *(1940)*.

Strauss proposed four criteria for the diagnosis of minimal brain injury: (1) a history of trauma or inflammatory processes before, during, or shortly after birth; (2) slight neurological signs; (3) the existence of immediate family with normal intelligence; (4) the presence of psychological disturbances in perception and conceptual thinking of the order described in the

research. According to Strauss, it would be legitimate to base the diagnosis on the fourth criterion alone. The main reason that Strauss's work attracted so many people was that he offered extensive educational recommendations, including special materials and teaching techniques which reduced distractions *(Strauss and Lehtinen, 1947)*.

Strauss's work has been criticized on three main grounds. First, there is a logical fallacy involved in the circular reasoning *re* diagnosis. The diagnosis of minimal brain damage may be established on the basis of behavior alone, but this does not prove that such behavior is characteristic only of brain-damaged children. Second, several attempts to replicate the original experiments have yielded contradictory results *(Keller, 1962; Cruse, 1962; Weatherwax and Benoit, 1962)*. Third, J. J. Gallagher's study of matched groups of brain-injured and familial mentally retarded children raised serious question as to whether the differences between the brain-injured and the otherwise retarded were sufficiently great or consistent to warrant using drastically modified educational and training programs for the brain-injured as a separate group. He also described the individual differences within the group of brain-injured and the role of personality disturbances in preventing them from reaching their full efficiency *(1957)*.

In a critique of Strauss's work, however, it is important not to lose sight of his positive contributions. The studies showed how much retarded children vary one from another, even when they were matched in mental age. Undoubtedly, there are more than two clinical groups. But before Strauss and others made their studies, the retarded were classified only by the severity of the retardation or the medical diagnosis, with no attention to psychological differences. Moreover, his educational proposals were challenging and he offered remedial techniques for circumventing specific weaknesses. Controversy is a good thing when it stimulates thought and research, and this was certainly one result of the endeavor to differentiate between the exogenously and the endogenously retarded child.

One does encounter children who closely fit the Strauss syndrome, and Strauss's descriptions help us to identify and understand them. However, the author personally decries the tendency to think of the organically damaged child as a child of a totally different kind with his own special laws of psychology. Some feeling of the extent of supposed difference is given in the following quotation from Strauss and Kephart:

Everything which we do as normal individuals we do in terms of patterns. These patterns become so instilled in us, and patterned behavior becomes so ingrained, that we cannot get it out. For this reason we cannot appreciate the problem of the brain-injured fully because we cannot truly experience it. We cannot reproduce in ourselves unpatterned behavior and therefore we cannot empathize with the individual who has few patterns. Because our patterns group and regroup themselves constantly and are always in a state of flux, meeting new demands of new situations, we find it impossible to imagine the plight of the individual in whom it is not so. We cannot see what he sees, we cannot feel what he feels, and we cannot follow the processes which bring him to a certain end result. To us his performance seems only bizarre. *(1955, p. 214.)*

In effect it is being said that the organically damaged child perceives and reacts to things in a unique way. The organically damaged child has one way of perceiving and defending himself; other children have another. This is, of course, theoretically questionable. There is an organic substructure to all behavior; in the final analysis, all behavior is determined by the physical activity of the central nervous system. The disruption of ego functioning resulting from severe anxiety or temporary conditions of extreme deprivation

can distort perception and reactivate primitive thought processes and look like organic disease. This means that a diagnosis should not be made on the basis of isolated observations of disordered perception, hyperactivity, perseveration, or any other symptom—that no specific behavior can be considered pathognomic of organic brain disease.

On a less theoretical basis, there is a danger that overstressing the differences between the brain-injured child and the non-brain-injured child may expose the brain-injured child to a new set of psychological difficulties If one thinks this child is so different that it is impossible to empathize with him, then one does not provide the ordinary preparations, explanations, and reassurances. Children with known organic brain disease have the same developmental crises as those without. They are even more susceptible to trauma and need more understanding and support. The following case illustrates how an organic symptom may be exacerbated by situations which normally arouse anxiety:

Christine was the older of two children. Her motor and language development were consistently slow, but normal. She started to use single words at two and, by three, was speaking in sentences. The major presenting problem was in her behavior. She was restless, always on the go, and unable to adjust to nursery school at the age of four. Psychological examination indicated a mild mental retardation (IQ was 72) and considerable unevenness of mental development. Her speech was good, but she had difficulty in fine motor coordination (e.g., buttoning, cutting with scissors, and copying simple forms). She was described by her mother and nursery school teacher as extremely restless and in perpetual motion. She never stayed with one activity for more than a few moments.

A year later, at five, she was hospitalized for a few days of observation. No specific etiology could be determined, but it was the consensus that there was diffuse brain damage. Medication was prescribed to reduce the hyperactivity.

About six months after this, Christine

returned to the clinic for retesting. The hyperactivity, which had decreased considerably, was perhaps even greater than it had been two years earlier. She jumped around, and it was impossible to keep her focussed on anything long enough to get a reasonable idea of her intellectual functioning. She could not bear to be separated from her mother, although she had been attending nursery school without apparent anxiety.

The mother, an unusually perceptive and intuitive person, was surprised by Christine's behavior in the office. She suggested that Christine might be worried about going back to the hospital after the clinic visit, as it had happened before and that she might be worried about doing well in kindergarten, which she was going to start attending in a few days. This seemed plausible and accordingly, both the mother and the examiner assured Christine that she would not be staying in the hospital. Another appointment was made, sufficiently in the future so that the newness of kindergarten would have worn off, and there was some conversation about her worries on this score.

Two months later, Christine returned. She was still anxious about leaving her mother, and reluctant to enter the testing room, even with her mother. It was decided to carry out the examination in the waiting room. In this situation, where Christine felt at ease, she concentrated well. She never left her chair, she followed instructions, and she finished the assigned tasks. Her IQ was six points higher than the original one of 72. The increase in her attention span and the decrease in her hyperactivity was remarkable, considering that telephones were ringing and people were coming and going. Apparently, Christine's hyperactivity was increased more by worry and anxiety than by external events in her environment as long as they did not directly threaten her.

There was little doubt that Christine's problems were organic. On the other hand, she worried about separations (the hospitalization) and about doing well (in kindergarten), much in the fashion of any child of her age. The expression of her anxiety took a particular form because of the nature of her deficit, but its content was expectable in any child who had experienced hospitalization and failure in school.

Psychogenic versus Innate Retardation

As we mentioned earlier, a major change in attitudes is reflected in the use of the term "mental retardation" in Category VIII of the AAMD Manual (*Heber, 1959*), which considers "psychogenic retardation" as a form of retardation no less real than retardation due to organic or constitutional causes. We know that an intelligence test score may be adversely affected by illness, lack of cooperation, unrecognized physical defect, or special circumstances surrounding the test administration which arouse acute anxiety in the child. But it is not this type of psychometric error with which we are here concerned. A sensitive clinician, armed with good information about the child's functioning outside the test situation, is able to recognize the low IQ which is the result of purely transitory conditions. Psychogenic retardation refers to the child who *consistently* tests and functions below his chronological age expectancy in a variety of circumstances.

Before giving the present view of psychogenic retardation, a brief account of its predecessor, "pseudofeeble-mindedness," is in order. In 1942, Margaret S. Mahler published an oft-quoted paper, "Pseudo-imbecility: A Magic Cap of Invisibility," in which she described an 18-year-old boy whose behavior was seriously retarded. He walked with a shuffling gait and sat with his arms hanging listlessly at his sides. His mother and siblings treated him as if he were a child, exchanging kisses and caresses with him—a form of behavior in which they could not have indulged had the patient been a normal 18-year-old boy. Mahler suggested that the desire to retain such infantile gratifications was one of the etiological factors of the boy's neurosis. Moreover, by virtue of his apparent stupidity, he gained access to situations which would normally be forbidden and was able to satisfy his sexual curiosity in a very direct way. (Many normal children feign stupidity or naivete in order to pass unnoticed in the company of adults, and thereby learn their secrets.)

In 1948, L. Kanner proposed a formal classification of feeblemindedness as "absolute," "relative," or "pseudo-feeblemindedness." The prefix "pseudo" indicated that the child had not been born retarded and need not necessarily remain retarded. Kanner also included psychometric errors: "Pseudo-feeblemindedness may be nothing more than the result of a tester's clumsiness" *(1948, p. 375)*. Clinicians who had observed the damaging effect of deprivation, neurotic conflict, or psychosis on the child's capacity to learn, and hence on his measured intelligence, welcomed the dynamic view that intelligence is a function of personality rather than a fixed, inborn quantity. A number of clinical papers and case histories reported instances in which pseudo-retardation served the same defensive purposes as a neurotic symptom. In other words, the child remained stupid and did not learn, in order to obtain some surreptitious instinctual gratification (as in Mahler's original case) or to ward off some anxiety which would arise if he allowed himself to be more knowing.

A good example of a clinical report of pseudo-retardation is that of Nancy Staver who described 17 children of less than average intelligence (i.e., with IQ's below 90), "for whom there is some evidence that retarded intellectual development is an expression of deep-seated personality problems" *(1953, p. 131)*. The families she included were intact families of middle-class status, with no gross social pathology. The parents and siblings appeared to be of at least average intelligence. The retarded children not only had low IQ's; they also were performing scholastically below their mental ages. Staver described the children as follows:

The children show considerable variation in personality; they range from schizophrenic or preschizophrenic children to those showing ego restriction or an obsessional organization as the outstanding characteristic. Infantile adaptations and preoccupations with somewhat bizarre fantasies characterize the majority, and all of them have in common a great fear of separation and death and the use of helpless ignorance as a method of protection. Most of the children at point of referral gave the impression of considerable inadequacy or peculiarity, while most of the mothers appeared superficially to be fairly adequate people, functioning within normal limits in the community. In about half of the cases, neither history nor physical examination of the child gives any indication of possible organic damage. With the remainder of the group there is some possibility of organic impairment, as yet undiscovered. *(1953, pp. 131–32.)*

This paper deals almost exclusively with the mother's involvement with the child's problem. The mothers are described as themselves using intellectual inhibition as a defense in certain critical situations, and encouraging intellectual inhibition as a generalized defense in their children, with whom they identified. The stupidity and consequent helplessness of the retarded children provided the mothers with vicarious gratification of their own dependent needs, and the child's dependent state prevented separation from the mother, a separation much dreaded by her. Discussing the paper, Anne Benjamin remarks that "it has been my experience that emotionally retarded children who function at a feebleminded level with IQ's below 60 could not be decidedly affected even though they were placed in good psychiatric residence schools and were treated psychotherapeutically for long periods of time" *(see Staver, (1953, p. 141)*. She makes a special point of the need for reporting the results of therapy in such cases, in order to determine the reversibility of low IQ's of nonorganic origin.

In a separate article, B. Sperry, Staver and Harold Mann *(1952)* described the dynamics of two of the children included in the above study. Ten-year-old Janet's IQ rose from 69 to 81; seven-year-old Patrick, though not retested, was able to do satisfactory academic work in his regular grade, despite a recorded IQ of 75 to 80. This case material illustrates the associative connections between the destructive fantasies of children and their learning. Certain children need to not learn, in order to defend themselves against fantasies of destroying or being destroyed. In the productions of many of these children, fear of being destroyed or of destroying others through oral incorporation are predominant. The authors suggest that the presence of an oral aggressive fantasy in itself need not inhibit learning, but when the fear of retaliation for such fantasies is great and is attached to the learning material or learning processes, the learning situation becomes the symbolic recapitulation of both the oral aggressive impulse and the fear of retaliation. The authors raise an interesting question: Why is the conflict expressed in the learning situation, rather than in the more obviously related situation of feeding?

The term "pseudo-retardation" has also been applied to a psychological situation in which the failure to learn results from a deprivation, a lack of stimulation at a crucial period. John Bowlby's monograph on "Maternal Care and Mental Health" *(1951)* called attention to the permanent mental and emotional impairment attributable to deprivation, separation, or distortion of the parent-child relationship in infancy. (This is discussed further in Chapter 15.) Particularly in the field of child welfare, the term "pseudo-retardation" is used to describe retarded children with a history of neglect in the first year, as we can see from the following case report:

At the age of three months, Susan came to the attention of the local county child-welfare board, which took custody because of the mother's negligence. The mother was more than willing to relinquish her. At that time Susan's nutritional state was poor and her behavior lethargic and unresponsive. She was placed in a foster home at four months of age and then, because of circumstances beyond anyone's control, she was placed in three successive foster homes between the ages of four and twelve months. The case worker was very concerned over this chain of events, and also because the little girl appeared to be developing poorly.

Her demonstrated skills were around the level of 6 months. At 13 months, tests confirmed the worker's fear that Susan was "not up to normal" for her age. Even more significant, Susan's behavior was abnormal. She pushed all the test materials away from her, and when something was placed in her hand, she drew back from it. She pulled away from anything that was offered her. She refused to play, showed no curiosity, and seemed unable to handle objects.

It seemed reasonable to postulate that Susan's difficulties were the result of her early neglect and the many changes she had experienced. The agency made an energetic and impassioned search for the best possible foster home, and placed her successfully when she was 21 months old.

The following week, Susan took her first bite and began to learn how to chew. She seemed happy, noticed people, giggled and laughed, and played hide-and-go-seek. The third week, Susan was no longer lying on the floor, lethargically scratching the wall with her third finger. She would sometimes do so while sitting, but most of the time she was busy. She began to show a temper. Her eyes seemed brighter and her responses more normal. She said one word—"Daddy." She walked all over the house, holding onto furniture. The sixth week after placement, she was bowel trained. She seemed to understand everything that was said to her. Two months after placement, Susan had passed the strained and junior food level and was feeding herself with a spoon and drinking out of a glass. She finished her meal with a clapping gesture and said "All gone." She took her first steps alone at the age of two.

At 27 months, Susan knew the parts of her body. She liked to tease, and enjoyed emptying the cupboard of pots and pans and placing them in the sink. She carted things all over the house. She could climb up and downstairs and onto furniture. She could do a somersault. She jabbered and sang. She said simple words, associating them with a definite person or thing. She repeated sentences and followed verbal commands. She looked at books and pointed out simple objects when asked to do so.

Susan was retested at 29 months and found to have an IQ of 80. A comparison of her mental age of the two tests indicated an average rate of mental development and the prediction was made that she would "catch up." She was tested again at a little over five years of age, at which time she had an IQ of exactly 100. She was then adopted into this same foster home.

This vivid report of a child living at home, learning to do things and enjoying herself is far more interesting than the changes in IQ. In this case, thanks to the enterprise of the social agency and the excellence of the foster home, the deleterious effects of the early deprivation were reversed. It was not possible to predict this result—Susan might have had some form of retardation which the best environment in the world could not change. However, one must proceed on the most hopeful basis, trying to undo the trauma of the early deprivation by supplying what has been lacking, namely, the stability and affection of a mother. The diagnosis follows the therapy. Retardation because of "cultural deprivation" is a similar concept, although the noxious effects of the deprivation take place at a later age. Pseudo-retardation resulting from deprivation differs from the neurotic retardation described in the clinical reports. In both, the retardation is considered "pseudo" because it was not organically foreordained at birth, but occurred as the result of environmental experience.

The earlier concept of pseudo-feeblemindedness was invaluable in demonstrating the multiple causes of retardation. However, there has been heated discussion about the alleged dichotomy between pseudo-retardation and "real" retardation. In his critique of the concept of pseudo-feeblemindedness, Arthur Benton states:

Since we deal with symptom pictures of multiple etiology, no one specific etiology has any claim to precedence over any other as being the primary antecedent condition of so-called "true" mental deficiency. All cases are examples of "true" defect, by behavioral criteria. Conditions of pseudo-feeblemindedness can be conceived of as being "true" defect states with certain types of etiologic background. *(1956, 1962, p. 95.)*

In essence, this destroys the diagnosis of "pseudo-feeblemindedness." Mental retardation is not considered a disease with a particular cause, course, and outcome, but a symptom which may or may not be permanent, depending on its cause and on its treatment. This point of view was officially adopted in the Diagnostic Manual published by the American Association on Mental Deficiency in 1959 *(Heber, 1959)*.

In part, the controversy which followed this innovation *(Heber, 1961; Garfield and Wittson, 1960; Cantor, 1960; Cantor, 1961)* is one of semantics: What is meant by "real" retardation? This can be settled only by common agreement on an operational definition. The more important argument has to do with treatability.

Clinicians often think of retardation as "hopeless" and of emotional problems as "curable." The difference between pseudo-retardation and true retardation was overemphasized. If a child were diagnosed as pseudo-retarded, the intellectual deficiencies were sometimes unrealistically ignored. The child was treated as if he were intellectually normal, as if his intelligence were in full working order, but covered by a removable mask. Experience showed that the situation was not so simple. It takes a severe, pervasive, and chronic emotional problem to produce mental retardation, and the retardation itself produces problems in relationships, in learning, and in psychotherapy. Even if the intellectual arrest was originally caused by conflict or deprivation, remediation of the cause does not thereby catapult the child into a more advanced intellectual state. Remediation can do no more than permit resumption of the normal learning process, starting from the point where the child was arrested. Hopefully, treatment will accelerate mental growth, but there is no magic way of skipping the intermediate steps. An eight-year-old who is mentally at the six-year level (i.e., IQ of 75), proceeding at an average rate of 12 months' gain in mental age in 12 actual months, will not achieve an average IQ in the average range until he is approximately 14. Intelligence takes time to develop.

Conversely, any retarded child showing emotional symptoms, or one living in poor family circumstances, needs more than educational attention. The crucial question is whether the treatment should be different if the retardation originated as a secondary symptom. On the basis of general theoretical principles, S. L. Garfield and C. Wittson argue that treatment is different for secondary retardation *(1960)*; Cantor argues to the contrary *(1960)*. To date, there is too little clinical evidence to prove the point empirically. Unfortunately, many therapists exclude the organically retarded child even if he also has definite emotional problems. If retardation is diagnosed as secondary to an emotional problem, the likelihood of the child's receiving therapeutic attention is much greater.

There have been attempts to compare the effects of similar kinds of therapy on retarded and emotionally disturbed children. In the study of preschool children, by F. F. Schachter, L. R. Meyer and E. A. Loomis, "the results after a year of psychotherapy show statistically significant gains for both psychotherapeutically treated groups, the schizophrenics and the retardates. Contrary to expectation, the retardate psychotherapy group seems to have made more substantial gains" *(1962, p. 594)*. On a short-term basis, at least, the diagnosis of retardation (presumed "real") did not augur badly for therapy, whereas the schizophrenics

(presumed "functional") did not respond as quickly.

In the author's judgment, the diagnostic differentiation between primary and secondary, or innate and psychogenic, retardation is not easy to make, nor is it as important as commonly believed, *provided the diagnosis is an ongoing process combined with a remedial program.* A child who exhibits both mental and emotional problems needs treatment of both, no matter which came first. Treatment must be gauged to the present level of functioning, and often the treatment indicates what the prognosis is. Therapy should be based on the total picture presented by the child. There should be environmental manipulation, to modify external pressures or lacks; educational procedures which are adapted to the child's current mental level; social experiences which are designed to foster social participation and improved relationships with others; therapeutic measures which are tailored to the specific inhibited, fearful, resistant, or uncontrolled behavior of the individual patient. If such an ideal prescription could be applied in practice, diagnostic labels, which automatically make a child ineligible for one or another kind of educational or treatment program, would be unnecessary. Economy of professional time should be considered *after* a trial period of treatment, thus giving the clinician a better basis for predicting the modifiability of a child's problems.

Programs of Care for the Retarded

S. P. Davies has reviewed social attitudes toward the retarded as they developed over the centuries *(1959)*. The more extreme degrees of deficiency were recognized early. The Spartans cast obviously defective children into a river or left them to perish on a mountainside, and the laws of Lycurgus permitted the deliberate abandonment of idiots.

During the Middle Ages, the retarded were often regarded as *les enfants du* bon Dieu; on the other hand, Luther and Calvin regarded them as "filled with Satan." That which is conspicuously different, and incomprehensible, is equally subject to superstitious awe or fear. And although society has changed, vestiges of these same feelings arise even today in many people when they first encounter a severely retarded child.

The beginnings of a scientific approach came with the famous educational experiment of J. M. G. Itard on the Wild Boy of Aveyron (1801). Victor was a boy of 11 or 12, discovered living like a wild animal, whom Itard, Chief Medical Officer of the French National Institution for the Deaf and Dumb, treated for more than five years on the assumption that his idiocy had resulted from a lack of social stimulation. In modern terms, Victor's case would be diagnosed as one of pseudo-feeblemindedness or psychogenic retardation, with an etiology arising from maternal and environmental deprivation. Itard's work was of interest to the philosophers of his time, who were arguing two schools of thought. The nativists assumed that the individual comes into the world with innate ideas which gradually unfold; the sensationalists (Locke, Rousseau, de Condillac) conceived of the mind as a *tabula rasa* waiting to receive impressions from the outside and believed that all persons originally have equal ability to learn. The words are different, but the controversy is the one we know as "nature versus nurture." Victor was not cured, perhaps because the critical period where such intervention could be effective had passed. Itard's heroic efforts, however, stimulated a continued interest in the retarded and in their education.

Itard's influence carried over into the nineteenth century, primarily through the work of his pupil Edouard Seguin, who combined the roles of physician, psychologist, and teacher. Seguin's physiological studies dealt mainly with the training of the muscles and the training of the senses. Maria Montessori freely credited Seguin with inspiring her educational system of sensory and motor training. Seguin emigrated to the United States in 1850 and played a major part in the establishment of institutions for the retarded. The first, now the Walter E. Fernald School, opened in south Boston in 1848. New York (1851), Pennsylvania (1854) and Ohio (1857) followed in quick succession; by 1890, 14 states were maintaining separate state institutions for mental defectives. These early schools were organized with the hope that physiological therapy might enable the defectives to return home and make their own living. This goal proved to be unrealistic in the majority of cases, and gradually it was recognized that the state institutions would have to plan to provide lifetime custodial care. For many years after Seguin's death in 1880, the custodial aspect was the most prominent one in state institutions.

In the early twentieth century, the diagnosis of mental retardation carried the implication of total incompetence and the necessity for institutionalization. It was known that many of the retarded remained in the community, but professional people considered this a result of a lack of hospital beds. After 1950, largely because of the efforts of parents, community facilities and programs for retarded children began to appear. It was no longer assumed that state institutions were the answer; they were not practical in terms of dollars and cents nor did parents consider them mandatory. The titles of Davies' books reflect the change in attitudes: he wrote *Social Control of the Mentally Deficient* in 1930 and *The Mentally Retarded in Society* in 1959. The first implies separation; the second implies integration.

Present Philosophy of Residential Placement

Custodial facilities will always be required for totally helpless individuals, but institutions have never been able to care for more than a very small percentage of the retarded. Data from the

National Institute of Mental Health indicated that approximately 2 per cent of the retarded resided in state facilities in 1956; the most frequently quoted figure is that 4 per cent of the retarded are in private and public institutions. In 1963, a total of 174,000 patients, a national rate of about 87 per 100,000, was reported to be in state institutions for the mentally retarded *(United States Bureau of the Census, 1964)*. All the states, except Nevada and Alaska, maintain public institutions for the retarded, and we can assume that they will at least continue the *status quo*. Recent studies of new admissions to state residential institutions for the retarded *(Sabagh and Windle, 1960)* indicate an increase in the rate of admission of the severely and moderately retarded, especially at the younger age levels, and a decrease in the rate of admission rates of the educable or mildly retarded, although mildly retarded patients who have serious emotional disturbances or who come from grossly inadequate homes or from communities without provision for their training and education are still institutionalized.

Resources outside the home, other than the traditional large institution, which provide for socialization and training of the retarded child and respite for his family, are described briefly in the *Manual on Program Development in Mental Retardation (Gardner and Nisonger, 1962)*. These include day-care centers, foster homes, family-care placement, boarding homes, halfway houses, and short-term residential care centers. The institutions should be small, near the child's community, and in or near an urban area. Although the recommendations are sound, most states will continue to use the institutions they already have, for economic reasons.

A word should be said about institutional placement of the young child. Mongolism is the one form of retardation which can be diagnosed at birth, and it has been common practice to send the Mongoloid baby directly to an institution. Doctors feel that in this way the mother does not become attached to the child, but recently, many articles have appeared which are critical of this practice. One argument is that it is not necessarily best for the family, because of inevitable feelings of doubt and guilt, and that the decision might better be postponed until such time as the parents understand the problems involved and can participate in the decision *(Solnit and Stark, 1961)*. A second argument concerns the ultimate welfare of the retarded child. Since the emotional needs of the child are essentially similar to those of other children, the warmth of the early mother-child relationship is important. Institutions cannot possibly provide the child with the most beneficial individual attention. Even a Mongoloid child can be further retarded by early deprivation *(Kugel and Reque, 1961; Centerwall and Centerwall, 1960; Schipper, 1959)*. There are infants who should be placed: the retarded baby who needs round-the-clock nursing care, or one whose mother is physically or emotionally ill, or one whose family is distraught. Professional opinion is only against *automatic* placement.

Educational Facilities

A retarded child certainly cannot remain home indefinitely, without some provision for outside training and education. Education has been concerned with the retarded for a longer period of time and to a greater extent than has any other single profession. Classes for the backward were reported in Cleveland in 1875, and existed in most large cities, but it is difficult to trace the development of the special class as such because the retarded were so often mixed with other children who were failing. The program of special classes grew slowly but, by 1927, 15 states had made them either possible or mandatory *(Doll, 1962)*. An International Conference on Public Education report stated that approximately 200,000 educable retarded children were attending special day classes (1960). (Combined with the 1960 figure of 213,000 known retarded children in institutions, this makes a total of 430,000 receiving special care.)

The report indicated that the number of educable retarded children enrolled in special classes had doubled since 1952, and that the number of trainable retarded children in day classes had more than tripled. Despite this growth, only about one-fifth of the mentally deficient children were receiving special education. This is partly because of the cost, about twice that of educating a normal child, and partly because of the woeful shortage of trained teachers. In 1958, there were 15,000 teachers, and 65,000 were needed.

Although definitions vary, the trainable and the educable children are commonly distinguished. The trainable children are expected to learn few, if any, formal academic skills. Reading is limited to the recognition of words which will help them to get about; arithmetic, to the handling of cash. Emphasis is on self-help skills, safety, social and personal relationships, athletics and crafts, speech and language, and simple work habits and attitudes. These youngsters are expected to learn to take care of themselves, to be able to follow verbal instructions, and to talk in sentences. They can assist in household chores, run errands, learn simple tasks which may make them employable in sheltered workshops, and learn to participate inconspicuously in the social life of the family. The realization of these objectives greatly reduces the amount of time and attention they require, but it does not make them socially or financially independent. Because supervision and guidance are going to be necessary throughout their lives, there has been some debate as to whether the responsibility for their training should be in the hands of public schools or welfare agencies. The consensus has been in favor of public

school management of classes for children during the usual school years (6 through 20). In Ohio, alone, the program for the trainable is administered by the State Department of Mental Hygiene and Correction and by the local county welfare boards.

It is harder to find qualified teachers for the trainable classes than for the educable classes. This is partially because teachers want to work where they feel most valuable, and they consider teaching the trainable classes more like baby sitting. It can be considerably more than that, but there is serious question about whether the traditional training in special education is the best preparation (Horn, 1960). There has been a plethora of curricular or program guides for the trainable in the past decade (Williams, 1961; Rosenzweig, 1960; Baumgartner, 1960; Wood, 1960), but little wide-scale testing of their value. And there are, as yet, no comparative results on which to base specific recommendations about teacher qualifications, criteria for class grouping, or program content.

Special classes for the educable retarded have a much longer history. Academic subject matter is very much a part of the curriculum, and pupils are expected to attain levels as high as fourth or fifth grade with some individuals excelling or falling short of this *average* expectation. A film made by the Mental Development Center shows the educational growth of six educable retarded boys over a three-year period. The boys demonstrate the wide variability in achievement among children classified in this category.* In the beginning, special classes were confined to elementary school, but the trend is now to have them in the junior and senior high schools, with programs modified in

*"Three Years Later: A Developmental Study of Retarded Children," 38 minutes, 16 mm, sound. Directed by Donald K. Freedheim. Filmed by Edward Feil Productions, Cleveland. For information write to Donald K. Freedheim, Mental Development Center, Western Reserve University, Cleveland, Ohio 44106.

line with the children's abilities and needs. Some school systems include part-time school and part-time work programs to help the youngsters make the transition from school to employment *(Goldstein and Heber, 1959)*.

Samuel Kirk and his associates at the University of Illinois carried out a very interesting experiment comparing the progress of four groups of pre-school children in different living and educational circumstances. There were 81 children in all, between the ages of three and six, whose IQ's ranged from 45 to 80. Twenty-eight lived at home and attended a community pre-school; 26 lived at home and did not attend a school; 15 lived in an institution and attended a special pre-school class; and 12 lived in an institution and did not attend special classes. These children were thoroughly examined at the beginning of the experiment, when they were discharged from school, and at regular follow-up intervals. Of the 43 who received pre-school education, 30 showed an acceleration in rate of growth during the pre-school period and retained that level during the follow-up period. These children's IQ's improved from 10 to 30 points.

The growth of the control groups did not accelerate in the pre-school period, but the IQ's and S.Q.'s (social quotients) of the control group which lived at home showed an upward trend after the first year of school. Apparently, school accelerates the mental and social development of mentally retarded children even when they start to attend at six. The institutional control group showed a different trend; their IQ's and S.Q.'s tended to drop during the pre-school period, and they did not show any significant increase after starting to attend the institutional classes. This is further evidence of the limiting effect of the institutional environment on young retarded children.

Kirk concluded that there was a difference between children whose mental retardation was diagnosed as organic and those whose retardation appeared to be functional or environmental. Although half of the 14 children with organic defects showed acceleration of mental growth, this was a much smaller percentage than in the other group and the magnitude of change was less. Kirk also concluded that pre-school programs for young mentally retarded children are beneficial, but not essential, if conditions at home are adequate. Although the numbers involved were small, there was some opportunity to assess the effect of an inadequate home on mental development by comparing the progress of four of the children after placement in a foster home, and also by comparing the progress of one pre-school child with that of a sibling who remained at home. Kirk makes a strong case for the possibility of preventing mental retardation by early detection of neglected children and by making a "total push" to develop them. In his judgment, the problem cannot be solved by working through the parents: "It is necessary for society to consider more intensive changes of environment for children in psycho-socially deprived homes" *(1958, p. 208)*. This belief was reiterated by J. McV. Hunt in his exposition on the effects of experience on intelligence *(1961)*. As a result of these opinions, widespread efforts were made to provide pre-school programs not only for the mentally retarded but also for the "culturally deprived."

Follow-up Studies

There have been a tremendous number of studies of the adult adjustment of mentally retarded individuals. Charles Windle reviewed over a hundred articles dealing with the prognosis for the institutionalized mentally subnormal *(1962)*. Most of the reports of the adult status of retardates who remained in the community have dealt with those in the educable range.

J. Tizard *(1958)* summarized 25 long-range and follow-up studies of the

after-school careers of mentally retarded individuals, concluding that a
large majority can become self-supporting and law-abiding citizens. The percentage actually employed varies. D. C.
Charles *(1953)* continued an earlier
study by W. R. Baller *(1936)*, and found
that during the Depression, 42 per cent
of the mentally subnormal group were
on relief (compared to 16 per cent of
a control group of normal adults); during prosperity *(1941 through 1950)*, less
than 10 per cent were on relief. Working with retarded children within the
school milieu, we are likely to overestimate the importance of their IQ's
and underestimate their social potential.

There is an interesting follow-up
study of 2,640 trainable retarded adults
who had been enrolled in New York
City classes from 1929 to 1955. G.
Saenger found that two-thirds were still
living at home and that one-quarter
had been institutionalized after leaving
school. There was no relationship between institutionalization and parental
income, education, or family size, but
there was a high correlation between
behavior problems and institutionalization. Even in this severely retarded
group, one-quarter had had paying jobs
at one time or another *(1957)*.

Marriage and Child Rearing

The emphasis of the follow-up
studies has been on the employment record of the retarded and on their ability
to sustain themselves economically.
One can assume that an individual
who is literate and self-supporting is
as likely to marry as anyone else, but
relatively little is known about the success of the retarded as parents. Our
discussion of this question deals primarily with the educable retarded; the
trainable retarded are unlikely candidates for parenthood, both biologically
(because of infertility) and socially.

There are few reports of the IQ's of
children born to the retarded. M. W. G.
Brandon *(1957)* examined 109 children

of 73 retarded mothers who had been
previously institutionalized. This particular group of mothers had a mean
IQ of 83, a relatively high level. They
had had 150 children, of whom 41 had
died—an exceptionally high mortality
figure. The average IQ of those who
survived was 91, higher than the mothers' but lower than the national average.
Charles reported that the number of
children per family in families with
retarded mothers was 2.03, somewhat
less than the national average. School
records were available for 73 children,
and the majority of these were making
satisfactory progress. Intelligence test
scores, available for 46 showed a mean
IQ of 95. In all these studies, there is
no way of distinguishing the parent
who is retarded because of organic in-
sult or environmental deprivation. In
these cases, one would expect genetic
endowment to be unaffected and the
distribution of intelligence in the offspring to follow the normal curve. The
familial retarded would tend to produce
children of higher intelligence than
themselves (by virtue of the tendency
to regress toward the mean), but lower
than average.

There was a strong eugenic movement at the beginning of this century
to sterilize the mentally deficient. H. H.
Goddard's study of the Kallikak family
(1912) had a long-lasting influence on
both lay and professional opinion. He
believed that feeblemindedness was determined wholly by heredity and that
the transmission of the defect followed
the Mendelian pattern. The care and
control of the feebleminded thus consisted of education, segregation during
the reproductive period, and sterilization.

Indiana passed the first legislation
permitting sterilization in 1907; by 1926
23 states had enacted such laws. In
1955, 28 states had sterilization laws on
their statute books. These laws apply
almost entirely to residents of state institutions. However, the figures com-
piled by Davies and Katherine Ecob

(1959, p. 52) show that eugenic sterilization has been little more than a gesture. California has had the most sterilizations, almost 25 per cent of the total number.

The objective of the laws was to decrease the number of defectives in the next generation, but two objections have been made on a scientific basis. First, as more and more causes of mental retardation are identified, heredity is being considered less important. What has been learned in recent years, about the impact of environment on intelligence, the role of psychodynamic factors in mental development, and the susceptibility of the child *in utero* to unfavorable metabolic and infectious conditions of the mother, has modified our view. Second, even if transmission

TABLE 6*
Number of Sterilizations of Mentally Subnormal Individuals In 50 Years of Legislation

Years	Number	Average Number per Year
1907-1925	1,374	71 per year
1925-1942	16,581	916 per year
1942-1947	5,207	1,041 per year
1947-1955	6,350	794 per year
1955-1958	1,526	509 per year
TOTAL	31,038	

*Quoted from S. P. Davies and Katherine G. Ecob, *The Mentally Retarded in Society* (New York: Columbia University Press, 1959), p. 52. Reproduced by permission.

were almost completely hereditary, sterilization of the institutionalized would not affect the majority of the retarded, who reside outside of institutions. Tredgold remarked that:

. . . even if every defective in existence were to be sterilized, this would not eliminate mental defect, or even appreciably reduce its amount . . . The chief source of mental deficiency is not defective parents, but parents who come of psychopathic stocks and who are "carriers" of mental defect. *(1947, pp. 493–4.)*

There has been some revival of interest in sterilization, on the grounds that a retarded person is incapable of providing a good home environment. This is certainly true of some retarded mothers. It is also true that there are many others who are equally incapable of raising children. This point of view raises sociological and political issues of a very uncertain character. A great deal more information is needed about the comparative success of nonretarded mothers of the same general background. P. Mickelson, in a study of 90 families in which one or both parents had been committed as retarded, found little correlation between the quality of child care and the mother's IQ. There was, however, a high correlation between the quality of child care and harmonious family relationships *(1947)*. Brandon felt that retarded mothers provided attention and care that were average in their neighborhoods *(1957)*.

Since the majority of the retarded do marry and have children, research can be carried out. Its importance cannot be denied. The results might be reflected in changes in the curriculum, particularly for educable girls, with more emphasis placed on family planning. Also, it is likely that the mentally subnormal mother would make good use of a parental guidance service if it were made freely available. Such measures seem more practical solutions than sterilization of those few educable retardates who are found in public institutions.

Developmental Problems of Retarded Children

Research Reports

Thus far, we have presented material regarding the diagnosis and management of the retarded with little emphasis on special psychological characteristics. What does it mean to be retarded, beyond just being slow in school?

Research into the learning of the retarded deals chiefly with differences between their learning and the learning of normal children of the same mental age. The retarded child is not identical to a younger child of average intelligence, even though their mental ages may be identical. There are qualitative differences in their intellectual processes, but there is little agreement about the exact nature and the extent of these qualitative differences. Five related investigations in this area were reported by G. O. Johnson and Katherine Blake, who concluded that "when compared with their intellectually normal mental age counterparts, intellectually retarded individuals can be expected to perform more adequately, less adequately, or with equivalent adequacy, depending on the type of response required by the situation in question" *(1960, p. 154)*. These studies showed the retarded to be more skillful in situations involving direct sensorimotor learning (puzzle assembly and card-sorting tasks), but the findings about rote learning were contradictory. And, contrary to expectation, there was no significant difference between the mean performance of the two groups on the reasoning tasks. Further, this data would suggest that, given comparable levels of mastery, intellectually retarded children and normal children of similar mental ages do not differ in retention, at least in these experimental

situations. These studies highlighted the similarities rather than the differences between the two groups.

A psychological trait long considered characteristic of the retarded is rigidity. Much of the theoretical thinking on this subject derived from Kurt Lewin, who stated that the major dynamic difference between a feebleminded and a normal child of the same mental age was "a greater stiffness, a smaller capacity for dynamic rearrangement in the physical systems of the former" *(1936, p. 210)*. This problem is too complicated, theoretically and methodologically, for a brief review. E. Zigler *(1962)* summarized the research done on the subject of rigidity, and the original work he and his colleagues did adds interestingly to the concept of rigidity. He found that differences in rigidity as measured by satiation time could be related to differences in the subjects' motivation to comply with instructions, rather than to inherent differences in cognitive rigidity. Institutionalized feebleminded children who tend to be relatively deprived of adult contact have a higher motivation to procure and retain such contact and approval than do normal children living at home. In short, retardates tried harder to please, and to keep up the "game" with the experimenter for the sake of the personal attention received. Normal children became bored and tired more quickly. Other studies show that feebleminded individuals differ in the frequency with which they exhibit persistent or compliant behavior, and that these individual differences can be related to the amount of social deprivation which they have experienced *(Zigler, 1961)*. Similarly, C. G. Green *(1960)* found no significant difference in the rigidity of the performance of noninstitutionalized feebleminded subjects and normal subjects. It was the institutionalized feebleminded who showed the relatively long satiation times, the perseverative behavior considered in the past to evidence the inherent rigidity of all the feebleminded. In conclusion, Zigler states:

... recent studies indicate that the feebleminded person must be viewed as an individual and is not to be understood in terms of some stereotyped view of feeblemindedness. Furthermore, these studies disclose that the feebleminded are shaped by and respond to their environment in much the same way as does the normal individual who possesses the same amount of intellect. *(1960, p. 160.)*

Emotional Development in Young Mildly-Retarded Children

Clinical observations go a long way to confirm Zigler's statement. However, the environment of the retarded child, even at home, is altered by the mere fact of his retardation, and the reciprocal relationship between the child's defect and the parent's response to it is a difficult one to unravel. Psychiatrists have tended to assume that the emotional development of the retarded child follows the same pattern as that of normal children. M. Farrell contends that the retarded child differs from the normal one only in the fact that his personality develops more slowly *(1957, pp. 156–7)*.

It is the author's experience, confirmed by others, that there is more evidence of disturbance in emotional development than is usually conveyed or emphasized in reports on retarded children. This fact is frequently overlooked by social workers, psychologists and psychiatrists who interpret signs of emotional disturbance as the cause, rather than the result, of the retardation. From his examination of the cases of 159 young retarded children, Thomas G. Webster concluded that "efforts to find a child who is simply retarded, one who is developing just like other children except slower, have been in vain. Even those retarded children who showed the best emotional development were not comparable to non-retarded children of the same mental age" *(1962, p. 12)*.

The primary characteristic of the retarded child is, of course, that he learns slowly. However, this does not mean that he simply needs more time, more exposure, or more repetition in order to learn. It depends on the nature of the task. If it is concrete and specific, he can learn it much faster than something which is abstract. If it is a demonstration which he can observe and follow, he will find it easier than something explained only in words. For him to learn does not require just repetition; it also requires concretization and simplification.

Related to this is his difficulty with language. Even after he has mastered words, he does not use them to communicate his feelings or his experiences, or to ask questions, as does the normal child. He talks of what is going on in his immediate external environment, or answers questions which are directly put to him. And often, his difficulties in communicating are increased by his parents' attitude. Assuming that "he wouldn't understand anyhow," parents may neglect to prepare him for coming events or to explain things which might puzzle him. During the summer vacation, one child (with a mental age of four and a half, and a chronological age of six and a half) repeatedly asked his mother when school would start again. Her answer was always, "Next Tuesday," because she was sure he could not understand the meaning of weeks and months. Perhaps he would not have understood, but her answer taught him nothing, whereas a calendar, specially marked for him, might have helped him to comprehend. A retarded child is often discouraged from asking questions for another reason: He soon becomes sensitive to the idea of "not knowing," and is afraid to admit his ignorance because it upsets his parents and arouses laughter in others. Retarded children rarely say, "I don't know" or ask the examiner for the answer when they are given psychological tests. They are much more likely to invent an answer. The gifted child is often quick to confess his ignorance and to demand the information from the examiner.

Adults do not generally encourage the retarded child to ask questions which may reveal his retardation. On the contrary, they ask him questions which are designed to reassure themselves. "What color is your truck?" or "How many blocks are there?" ask the parents, and then they wait nervously for the right answer, which will prove his intelligence. This leads to a pattern of withholding and stubbornness on the part of the child; he is constantly compelled to produce something that will satisfy his parents, rather than himself.

The lack of verbal curiosity, both socially and inherently determined, leads to a prolongation of primitive modes of thinking. The child continues to confuse fantasy and reality and to maintain magical ways of thinking. He does not correct his errors in causal thinking and retains the fears and apprehensions of the two-year-old. In part, this accounts for his rigid and stereotyped behavior. He fears novelty and change, clinging to safe routines. In a normal two-year-old, this conservatism is expected; in the retarded child it continues after his mental age exceeds three, four, or even five years.

Many authors comment on the passivity of retarded children. In their work with a small group of retarded pre-school children, K. F. Woodward, M. G. Siegel, and M. J. Eustin, were impressed by the appearance of schizoid characteristics, particularly withdrawal. They commented that improvement over a two-year period was associated with a great increase in activity and aggressiveness, i.e., a decline in passivity *(1958)*. Webster observed that "They often have to be led into new interests rather than seeking them spontaneously" *(1962, p. 21)*. They tend to have difficulty directing aggression to appropriate sources of frustration, and their libidinal impulses tend to lack speci-

ficity. This is partially caused by a lack of imagination and curiosity, one aspect of the intellectual deficit, but it is greatly increased by the peculiar nature of the relationship with the parents. In simultaneous observations of mothers (in case work) and of retarded children in the pre-school of the Mental Development Center, the author has observed that the retarded child identifies with whatever face the mother turns toward him. When she is depressed about his retardation, he also becomes depressed. One symptom of this is the lethargy and passivity previously described. As she becomes more cheerful and outgoing in her relationship with the child, he brightens up and takes more interest in his surroundings.

A final word should be said about the defenses of the retarded child. How does he cope with anxiety or depression? One of his most malignant defenses is that of withdrawal into autism. A common defense is regression, bewildering because it adds to the variability of the child's behavior. When a normal child regresses because of fatigue, illness, or anxiety, his parents are not unduly alarmed. The retarded child is more prone to regression, and his parents react with depression or anxiety, fearing that he is deteriorating. Identification is another defense upon which retarded children rely. They try to secure approval and love by making themselves as much like the loved person as possible. On a conscious level, when in doubt, they will try to find someone to copy. This defense can be turned to excellent advantage. Some retarded children, responding quickly to the consistent and sympathetic interest of a teacher or therapist, experience so-called transference cures. The retarded child is exceptionally vulnerable to the emotional climate in which he is placed, and this is especially difficult because he is so often in a climate filled with sadness, bewilderment, anxiety, and rejection, both conscious and unconscious.

Emotional Problems of School-age and Adolescent Retarded Children

It is often said that if only parents would provide love and acceptance, the retarded child would himself have no feelings of inadequacy. This may be true for the severely retarded child who remains in a closely protected environment at home, school or work, but it is definitely not true for the educable retarded child as he tries to make his way in the community, neighborhood, school, or work. At some point, he becomes aware that he is different, and that the difference is not a desirable one.

Morton, age 10, with an IQ in the mid-seventies, quoted a classmate as saying "he wished he'd never been born." When the interviewer asked why this might be, he replied that his friend did not like being in a special class. On further questioning, he was very thoughtful and concluded that while he did not wish he had never been born, he did not like the special class either. The interviewer asked why, and Morton replied with the questions, "Were you ever in special class? Did you ever want to be in special class? Well, it is the same with me."

Educable retarded children go through much the same sequence of recognition, anger, depression, and resignation that their parents experienced when they learned the diagnosis. They show their feelings in a number of ways: babyishness, negativism, aggressive outbursts, fearfulness, or depression. Many times they link the idea of being stupid with that of being bad. Besides the frustration and bewilderment which arise from the fact of retardation, they have often had more than their share of traumatic experiences, and these have been poorly assimilated because of their lack of understanding:

Terry, age 11, with an IQ in the mid-sixties, was in danger of being excluded from special classes because of his aggressive and uncooperative behavior. In addition to his retardation, he had a number of other problems: congenital club feet which had been corrected by casting, myopia which had been partially corrected with eyeglasses, and a speech defect. He had had two hernia operations, a year apart, when he was eight and nine. Terry explained his aggressiveness as self-defense. According to him, the other boys picked on him (they did tease him) and attacked his genitals (they did not). In a frenzy of fear and rage, he would use any handy weapon to fight back.

It was explained to him that he was so afraid of an attack on his genitals that he thought it was about to happen; in other words, that his fear distorted his perception of reality. The second step was to relate the fear to his surgical experiences and his tremendous anxiety that the hernia would return. He considered himself fragile, and in real danger of being "broken." Fortunately, his anxieties could be relieved by explanation and reassurance.

From the adolescent, one can expect regression, rebellion, and moodiness. The retarded child, however, may express these problems less subtly than the normal child, and his parents are likely to be more sensitive:

Jane, age 15, with an IQ in the low seventies, was very annoyed at what she viewed as her mother's constant interference in her affairs: "She wants to know where I go and what I am doing all the time. She never leaves me alone or lets me make my own decisions." Her irritability with her mother took a verbal form: "Shut up!" or silly name-calling. There was no difficulty in school, but there was perpetual bickering at home.

Hair-do's were a specific bone of contention. Jane tried some hair-do's which her mother considered messy and inappropriate. She laid down a rule that Jane could not "put up" her own hair, but must allow her mother or a hairdresser to do it. Jane was incensed and very insulting. In the agitation, the mother became hysterical and threatened to send Jane away if she did not cooperate. Later the mother recognized this as an extreme reaction to an ordinary event. She confessed that she was much more fussy about Jane's appearance and deportment than she had been with her other girls, because she felt that "Jane already has one strike against her. She cannot afford anything else."

There are, of course, possibilities for far more serious emotional disturbances than those briefly described here. Particularly in the severely handicapped group, one can see children whose behavior is so bizarre, incomprehensible, out of contact and out of control, that it could be labelled psychotic (see Chapter 11).

Psychotherapy

In a review of published studies on psychotherapy for the retarded, S. Sarason and T. Gladwin explain that the paucity of research is due to the common clinical assumption that the mental defective is incapable of profiting from psychotherapy. In addition to theoretical considerations, the tremendous demand for psychotherapeutic time and the scarcity of trained personnel have forced clinicians to give what little time they have to those cases which promise maximum results for minimum time expended (1958).

Contrary to general opinion, a number of studies reported in the Smith College Studies of Social Work (Cooley, 1945; Glassman, 1942; Wegman, 1943) indicated that there was no particular relationship between IQ and adjustment after psychotherapeutic treatment (the IQ's ranged from 60 up). One of the earliest and most frequently quoted reports is the psychoanalysis of a mentally defective boy over a period of four years (Chidester and Menninger, 1936), whose IQ rose from 62 to 90. Although the psychodynamic material is very interesting, and the behavioral improvement very real, the change in IQ is of questionable significance. In all, the subject took 12 Stanford-Binet tests, and there must have been some practice effect. Sarason gives detailed treatment

reports of two of his own patients, both treated while living in an institution for the retarded. Lottie, a young adult with an IQ in the 50's and 60's, improved greatly in sociability and mood over a ten-month period of treatment. She was still unable to make an extramural adjustment, because of unfortunate external circumstances and her lifelong experience with institutional living. The IQ of the other patient, an adolescent boy, increased from 45 to 76, and his general personality was such that Sarason's final diagnosis was "mental retardation" rather than "mental deficiency" (1958).

In 1962 Stella Chess reported the findings of the first three years of a program of individual psychotherapy for mentally retarded children with behavior problems. The children chosen for treatment showed behavior disorders of three kinds: organic brain damage with behavior disorder, schizophrenia, and mental retardation with secondary behavior disorder. Her goals varied for each child and included a wide range from amelioration of fears to the removal of pseudo-retardation. Of the 19 children who attended six or more sessions, only two showed no improvement in behavior. One of these was a brain damaged child, and the other was schizophrenic. The children who responded best to psychotherapy were those who were mentally retarded with secondary behavior problems. The two schizophrenic children who were pseudo-retarded showed significant improvement in both behavior and IQ. Success was judged exclusively by improvement in behavior except for the pseudo-retardates for whom change in IQ was an additional criterion. From her experience Chess stated, "some success in at least alleviating anxiety and fear might be possible with any child, no matter how limited in intelligence" (p. 868).

The Mental Development Center of Western Reserve University, an outpatient clinic serving young retarded children residing at home, has informally described some experience with individual psychotherapy in its biennial report *(1962)*. The staff commented that one special anxiety which regularly appeared was separation anxiety which took many forms. The mechanisms with which these children coped with anxiety were not unique, although they used regression or withdrawal of affect more, perhaps, than normal children. As would be expected, their thinking processes were primitive and considerably infused with magic. This meant that the therapist also had to play an educational role, interpreting reality in a way the child could understand.

Edward Strecker made these comments about the mental deficient: "Behavior tends to be simple and naïve and may be much more readily understood. Vocabulary is limited and speech is not available to mask thought. Usually the emotions are directly expressive" *(1942, p. 6)*. No refutation of these observations has been published, but experience at the Center seems to belie their validity. The unavailability of speech makes communication far more difficult, and it is hard to put oneself in the place of a retarded child. In some respects it is like working with children who are in the pre-verbal stage, but the nature of the reality which retarded children have experienced complicates matters. Hospitalization, rejection, teasing, criticism, and parental depressions are not the usual lot of the normal young child of two or three, but they are commonplace for the retarded child by the time he reaches five or six.

Reports of individual treatment are still scarce; there are no prescribed "indications for treatment" and little information about what to expect. Psychologically, many retarded children are still in the position of normal children under the age of five, whose problems are determined in large measure by the nature of the parent-child relationship and outside influences. Modification of the parents' attitudes and handling of the child often bring about a corresponding change in the child's behavior, but there are retarded children who have internalized their emotional difficulties. Problems which originated in real experiences may have become part of the child's personality, and immune to ordinary environmental manipulation. It is difficult to determine which children will profit from direct psychotherapy until after one has tried to reach them through guidance of their parents.

Therapists working with such children have usually been gratified by the results because therapy is by no means as difficult or as tedious as they anticipated. However, the goal of therapy is not a change in IQ, but rather an improvement in personal and social adjustment and a reduction of the secondary psychopathology.

Parent Counseling

We have said that retarded children frequently have emotional problems which add to their disability and that many of these problems derive directly from the parent-child relationship, which is affected in a special way by the fact of the child's retardation. The normal parent is naturally bewildered by his different child; it is hard to understand what is wrong and what should be done. The situation is different for parents with poor education and low intelligence, who accept their children uncritically and who may fail to recognize and even actively resist any interpretation of their child's limitations. Unfortunately, social and cultural deprivation is a primary cause of the retardation of a considerable proportion of the educably retarded group, and this group is not reached by ordinary clinical facilities. The observations which follow are mainly applicable to those parents who regard their child as different.

Interpretation of the Diagnosis

A great many articles have appeared in, among others, journals of psychology (e.g., *Rheingold, 1945*), medicine (e.g., *Jensen, 1950*), pediatrics (e.g., *Zwerling, 1954*), and mental deficiency (e.g., *Kanner, 1953*), which describe the steps involved in explaining mental retardation to parents. The first step is to acknowledge the problem.

The timing of the disclosure depends on the degree of retardation. In a study of the medical care of 48 trainable retarded children in the Greater Cleveland area, it was found that two-thirds of the parents had been informed of a diagnosis of mental retardation before the child was three. In the remaining cases, there was abundant evidence of retardation by this age, although the parents were not told the diagnosis. The educable child, on the other hand, usually seems normal for the first two years. Delayed speech, commonly the first sign, does not cause great concern until he is three or older.

Parents usually become aware of the difference between their child and others as soon as, or sooner than, their doctor. Initially, however, they tend to view the difference as a temporary remediable condition. They say, "We know there is a problem here; we came to find out what's wrong so we can do something about it before it's too late." They may be thinking of a thyroid or endocrine deficiency, a nutritional lack, or some kind of "nerve pressure." The parents of the educable retarded child, particularly, may ascribe the difficulty to missed opportunities. They feel they should have taught the child more. Such comments as, "He has been pretty much neglected," or "We have never tried those things with him," or "We have always given in to him and never made him do for himself," are disguised ways of saying that his condition is curable. This is especially frequent when speech is delayed. Parents consider a lack of speech a cause of mental slowness in itself, and feel responsible for not having made the child talk. They hope for some kind of remedial recommendations—speech therapy, special school, techniques of instruction they can use, and so on.

The first step is to give the difference a name (i.e., mental retardation), but this is only the beginning of the interpretation of the diagnosis. It leads immediately to an explanation of the cause. This is relatively easy when a definite medical diagnosis, such as Mongolism, can be established; but in most cases, particularly when the child is educable, the retardation is undifferentiated. Only the end-product can be seen; the underlying causes remain hidden from view. Often parents can only be told what is *not* the cause; for instance, heredity. To relieve the ambiguity and give some definition to the situation, one often has to postulate some vague and indefinable organic brain injury.

The third step is a discussion of the prognosis. Considerable skill is required to explain, simultaneously, that the child will progress and yet will remain permanently handicapped to some degree. Parents are likely to think in black and white terms: The child is retarded and therefore will remain just as he is, or he is slow and will catch up with, or stay at least only a year or two behind, his contemporaries. The diagnosis takes on meaning when education is discussed. The realization that the child cannot attend regular public school classes, even a year or two late, has more meaning to parents than his IQ.

Nearly everyone has a preconceived idea of what a mentally deficient person is like; often they link it with sexual degeneracy, physical unattractiveness, or out-of-control behavior of some kind. It is necessary to explore the parents' idea of what mental deficiency means— what they thought mental defectives were like before they found that they themselves had a child in this category. The nature of their prejudices gives some idea of the impact on them of the diagnosis, and factual information which will correct erroneous impressions can be supplied. Although the term "mental retardation" is highly charged, and will eventually become as unpopular as "imbecile," "idiot" and "moron," the term must be used at some point, in order to work through the parents' feelings.

The emphasis in the literature has been on helping parents to achieve an understanding and acceptance of *severely* retarded, or trainable, children. The problem of interpreting *moderate* retardation has been somewhat neglected, probably because such cases first appear in an academic setting and are usually handled within the school. When children are moderately retarded, or educable, many factors reinforce the parents' emotional need to deny the limitation. Frequently, the child presents a mixture of emotional and intellectual problems. The child who finds that he disappoints his parents and makes them unhappy for reasons he cannot understand, becomes insecure and overanxious for praise and approval. This in turn leads to a passive dependency; he does not try to work things out for himself, but looks for external cues to guide him to safe solutions. Then his parents are correct in saying, "He could be smarter if he tried harder," but the question they cannot answer remains. How much smarter?

The fourth step is to help the parents to make practical plans for the child. It is imperative that the professional person be acquainted with the available and appropriate resources. These should be described carefully to the parents, so that they will realize that they are not the only ones with such a problem and to keep them from going from pillar to post looking for a program which fits their child. It is equally important to review for them what is not appropriate or available, to tell them of the lack of treatment drugs, of surgical cures, of magically effective

education, and so on. Obviously, this cannot be done in one, two, or even three sessions; new questions will occur to them and they will want to come back for answers. The important thing is to make them feel that someone is interested and sufficiently well-informed to have the answers they need.

Parental Reactions

It is impossible for any parent to accept this kind of diagnosis without reacting strongly. The reactions will vary, of course. The natural response is one of denial and disbelief, a desperate hope that the diagnosis is wrong. This may take the form of anger against the diagnostician. Or, the shock may so upset the parents that they distort what has been said to them, as in the following example:

Heidi was first referred for psychological testing when she was four, by the neurologist who was treating her for a convulsive disorder. At this point, Heidi was just beginning to use sentences and her parents were interested in getting speech therapy for her, "in order to prepare her for kindergarten." Her IQ was 71, and the psychologist interpreted her delayed language development as part of a general mental retardation. No therapy was recommended, and it was suggested that she continue to attend nursery school for an extra year.

Many years later another Stanford-Binet was requested by her special class teacher, but the parents refused to return to this psychologist. They explained to the teacher that she had told them, "You have a retarded child. Put her away and forget about her." Their recollections, entirely contrary to fact, can be understood in terms of their own fantasies. On first hearing the word "retardation," they assumed that such children should be "put away," and many years later their remembered fears were confused with the remembered words of the psychologist.

With acceptance of the fact of retardation comes shame, anger, and depression. The shame is related to guilt about having created a defective child. The anger is related to self-pity: Why did this happen to me? The search for a reason leads to blaming others: the obstetrician, the psychologist, or even a remote but questionable relative. After exercising these feelings, a parent is usually left sad or depressed. Simon Olshansky has described this "chronic sorrow" as persisting throughout the parents' lives, regardless of whether the child is kept at home or is "put away." He views chronic sorrow as a natural reaction *(1962)*. A. S. Solnit and Mary Stark describe this parental depression as "mourning" for the perfect child they expected, and as grief over the loss of that baby and the appearance, in its stead, of a feared, threatening and anger-evoking child *(1961)*. This would perhaps be most clearly displayed when the condition of a severely defective child is diagnosed very early.

It is the author's opinion that many of the initial reactions are kept alive by guilt over the parents' continuous rejection of the retarded child. It is guilt not only over having created a defective human being, but also over not loving him enough. The rejection is natural, but the parents nevertheless feel guilty because the retarded child has done nothing to deserve his fate. Some parents lean over backward to show love, to hide any hint of irritability or impatience, to protect the child against danger, and to spare him the slightest frustration. But behind the excessive solicitude, one can see the unconscious aggression:

Linda was the only child of a middle-aged couple. Although her early development was slow, her retardation was not diagnosed until kindergarten, when she was found to have an IQ in the 50's. After a period of bitter disbelief, the parents accepted her retardation so completely that they viewed her as incapable of any kind of self-care. Over the years, her IQ dropped into the 40's, and at the age of 13, she was a severe behavior problem, tyrannizing her family into a state of complete servitude. Her mother tried to care for her as one would care for a very small

child. When the counselor tried to persuade her to allow Linda to bathe herself, the mother protested that she could not take the chance. Linda might turn on the scalding water and burn to death; she might eat the soap and poison herself; she might put her head under water and drown. If Linda were out of her sight, the mother pictured her as dead or dying.

Parents of mildly retarded children experience a double-edged depression. They are sad, disappointed and angry, not only for themselves, but also for the child. They can imagine his bewilderment and his disappointments. They can anticipate his questions and their inability to answer, and they feel they are the agents of his future frustrations. Understandably, they are anxious to spare the child, but the educable child is likely to sense something wrong with himself at about the same time his parents first question his mental capacity. When the diagnosis comes, the child is usually old enough and smart enough to sense his parents' disappointment. He knows he is doing something wrong, but cannot be sure what it is. When a mother cries because her child counts poorly, or cannot button his coat, the child sees the tears as his fault. His stupidity puts him in danger of losing his mother's love, just as his disobedience brings about her disapproval.

When the mildly retarded child reaches school age, he encounters questions and comments which inevitably puzzle him. He wonders why he does not go to the same school as his brother; he becomes aware that a younger sister is catching up with him; he learns that six-year-olds are supposed to be in the first grade. He may begin to deny his age and thus keep himself younger, and his parents may unconsciously foster his pseudostupidity because they fear his reactions and questions. The severely retarded youngster, however, can be protected from awareness through watchful supervision. If he is kept in surroundings where he is accepted and liked, he will not question the nature of the world outside his direct experience. Parents can thus keep the retardation their own problem, their own disappointment, and find comfort in the belief that the child is being spared.

Parents of the educable retarded child are forced to realize that they cannot safeguard him against rebuffs, disappointments, and questions. One difficult aspect of the problem is responding to the child's desire to grow up. Normally, when a child shows some resentment of his lowly childhood status, he is appeased and encouraged with the explanation that, "Someday you will be a daddy, you will have a car to drive to work, and you will have your own wife and children," and his jealousy is assuaged by the idea that his turn will come. But when a mildly retarded child is in this stage of development, the parent temporizes, "You will be a big man *like* Daddy." Probably more important than the words, however, is the look of embarrassment and discomfort which comes over the parent's face when he holds out the picture of a future as vague to him as it is to the child.

Objectives in Counseling Parents of Retarded Children

Briefly, the goal of the counselor is to restore an effective parent-child relationship whenever possible and, when it is not possible because of the pathology of the parent or child or because of family circumstances, to help the parents move toward placement. The counseling process starts with a diagnostic evaluation which may well take some time. The extent and nature of the handicap of the young, moderately retarded child often becomes clear as one works with both child and family. The counselor must be well-informed about theoretical issues in mental development, the terminology of retardation, the usefulness and limitations of medical and psychological tests, and the programs of care available. In addition, she must be empathic and under-

standing of varied parental reactions. But the counselor should not perpetuate the parents' mourning; for the sake of the retarded child and of the other children in the family, it is important to free the parents from the debilitating effects of their depression.

As the parents come to understand the permanent nature of an intellectual handicap and are relieved of their feelings of guilt about its cause, the case worker must be alert to the danger of immobilization, an abdication of the parental role. In part, this is a symptom of depression, but it is also an expression of their misconceptions regarding mental retardation. The mother has no idea of what part she can play in the child's development or what influence she can have, and she may feel inadequate to the task of rearing a "different" child. Some parents hang on to their denial in order to maintain a feeling of usefulness. In giving the diagnosis, it is imperative that the counselor also give the parents something *specific* to do. Suggestions about training, discipline, educational and recreational programs, and the like can be helpful.

Maintaining a balance between the needs of the retarded child and those of his normal siblings is equally important. If parents take out their disappointment on the healthy child or expect him to perform at a very high level in order to make up for the defective child, the sibling may suffer. They may ask him to give in to the retarded child and reprimand him severely for displaying any jealousy or hostility. They put him in the position of caretaker and expect him to show unstinting love. Bernard Farber found that a severely retarded child generally affected a normal sister more than a normal brother, probably because girls are expected to help in terms of baby-sitting and caring for the retarded child. Normal siblings may be deprived because family life is restricted by the presence of the retarded child. These situations are not inevitable, but they are possibilities.

It is obvious that it is difficult for parents to maintain a retarded child at home. It requires ingenunity, self-confidence, emotional security, and cooperativeness. With the support of community facilities, it can be done. And it is usually best for the young child and for those children who can be expected to maintain an independent existence as adults. There may come a point of diminishing returns, however, when the family sacrifice outweighs the benefits to the retarded youngster, and it is important that the counselor be responsive to the changing needs of the child and family.

Perhaps the most difficult task facing the counselor is dealing with his own reactions to the problems of mental retardation. It is easy to over-identify with the parents, or to react to their hostility. In a field where there are no cures and no way to measure the success of one's work, one becomes sensitive. And it is hard for many professionals to imagine a worthwhile life based on nonintellectual skills. It is unreasonable to expect that all professional workers can overcome these reactions sufficiently to work with the retarded, and it is perhaps enough that they have insight into their own preferences. It is hoped, however, that in the future this field will be more fully dealt with by those who educate pediatricians, neurologists, psychiatrists, clinical psychologists, educators, social workers, and nurses, so that eventually all these professionals will have a speaking acquaintance with the problems of mental retardation, and some will be attracted to it as a field of specialization.

References for Chapter 8

American Psychiatric Association, *Diagnostic and Statistical Manual: Mental Disorders.* Washington, D.C.: Mental Hospital Service, 1952.

Baller, W. R., "A Study of the Present Social Status of a Group of Adults Who, When They Were in Elementary Schools, Were Classified as Mentally Deficient," *Genetic Psychology Monograph,* No. 18 (1936), 165–244.

Baumgartner, Bernice B., *Helping the Trainable Mentally Retarded Child.* New York: Bureau of Publications, Teachers College, Columbia University, 1960.

Benton, Arthur, "The Concept of Pseudofeeblemindedness" (1956), in E. P. Trapp and Philip Himelstein, *Readings on the Exceptional Child.* New York: Appleton-Century-Crofts, 1962.

Bowlby, John, *Maternal Care and Mental Health,* World Health Organization Monograph, Series No. 2, 1951.

Brandon, M. W. G., "The Intellectual and Social Status of Children of Mental Defectives," *Journal of Mental Science,* CIII (1957), 710–38.

Cantor, Gordon N., "A Critique of Garfield and Wittson's Reaction to the Revised Manual on Terminology and Classification," *American Journal of Mental Deficiency,* LIV (1960), 954–56.

———, "Some Issues Involved in Category VIII of the AAMD Terminology and Classification Manual," *American Journal of Mental Deficiency,* LXV (1961), 561–66.

Centerwall, S. A. and W. R. A. Centerwall, "A Study of Children with Mongolism Reared in the Home Compared with Those Reared Away from Home," *Pediatrics,* XXV (1960), 678–85.

Charles, D. C., "Ability and Accomplishment of Persons Earlier Judged Mentally Deficient," *Genetic Psychology Monograph,* No. 47 (1953), 3–71.

Chess, Stella, "Psychiatric Treatment of the Mentally Retarded Child with Behavior Problems," *American Journal of Orthopsychiatry,* XXXII (1962), 863–69.

Chidester, L. and Karl Menninger, "The Application of Psychoanalytic Methods to the Study of Mental Retardation," *American Journal of Orthopsychiatry,* VI (1936), 616–25.

Clarke, Ann M. and A. D. B. Clarke, *Mental Deficiency: The Changing Outlook.* New York: The Free Press of Glencoe, Inc., 1958.

Cooley, J. M., "The Relative Amenability of Dull and Bright Children to Child Guidance," *Smith College Studies in Social Work,* XVI (1945–1946), 26–43.

Cruse, Daniel B., "The Effects of Distraction upon the Performance of Brain-Injured and Familial Retarded Children," in E. P.

Trapp and Philip Himelstein, *Readings on the Exceptional Child.* New York: Appleton-Century-Crofts, 1962.

Davies, S. P., *Social Control of the Mentally Deficient.* New York: Crowell-Collier Publishing Co., 1930.

———, and Katherine G. Ecob, *The Mentally Retarded in Society.* New York: Columbia University Press, 1959.

Doll, Edgar A., "A Historical Survey of Research and Management of Mental Retardation in the United States," in E. P. Trapp and Philip Himelstein, *Readings on the Exceptional Child.* New York: Appleton-Century-Crofts, 1962.

———, *Measurement of Social Competence,* Educational Test Bureau, 1953.

———, "The Essentials of an Inclusive Concept of Mental Deficiency," *American Journal of Mental Deficiency,* XLVI (1941), 214–19.

Farrell, M., "Mental Deficiency," in Ewalt, Strecker and Ebaugh, *Practical Clinical Psychiatry* (8th ed.). New York: McGraw-Hill Book Company, 1957.

Farber, Bernard, "Effects of a Severely Mentally Retarded Child on the Family," in E. P. Trapp and Philip Himelstein, *Readings on the Exceptional Child.* New York: Appleton-Century-Crofts, 1962.

Gallagher, J. J., "A Comparison of Brain-Injured and Non-Brain-Injured Mentally Retarded Children on Several Psychological Variables," *Monographs of the Society for Research in Child Development,* XXII, No. 2 (1957).

Gardner, W. I. and Herschel Nisonger, "Manual on Program Development in Mental Retardation," *Monograph Supplement to American Journal of Mental Deficiency,* LXVI, No. 4 (1962).

Garfield, S. L. and C. Wittson, "Some Reactions to the Revised Manual on Terminology and Classification in Mental Retardation," *American Journal of Mental Deficiency,* LXIV (1960), 951–53.

Glassman, L., "Is Dull Normal Intelligence a Contraindication for Psychotherapy?" *Smith College Studies in Social Work,* XIII (1942–1943), 275–98.

Goddard, H. H., *The Kallikak Family.* New York: The MacMillan Company, 1912.

Goldstein, H. and Rick Heber, "Preparation of Mentally Retarded Youth for Gainful Employment" (1959), in J. H. Rothstein, *Mental Retardation, Readings and Resources.* New York: Holt, Rhinehart & Winston, Inc., 1961.

Goldstein, K., *After-effects of Brain Injuries in War.* New York: Grune & Stratton, Inc., 1942.

———, *The Organism.* New York: American Book Co., 1939.

Green, C. G., "Social Interaction in Feebleminded Children." Unpublished master's thesis, University of Missouri, 1960.

Heber, Rick, "A Manual on Terminology and Classification in Mental Retardation," *Monograph Supplements to American Journal of Mental Deficiency,* LXIV, No. 2 (1959).

———, "Modifications in the Manual on Terminology and Classification in Mental Retardation," *American Journal of Mental Deficiency,* LXV (1961), 499–500.

———, "Terminology and the Classification of Mental Retardation," *American Journal of Mental Deficiency,* LXIII, No. 2 (1958), 214–19.

Hilliard, L. T. and B. H. Kirman, *Mental Deficiency.* London: Churchill, 1957.

Hormuth, Rudolf, "A Proposed Program to Combat Mental Retardation," *Children,* X (1963), 29–31.

Horn, Ray, *Report of the Governor's Committee for the Mentally Retarded: A Study of Ohio's Community Program for Severely Retarded Children,* State of Ohio, 1960.

Hunt, J. McV., *Intelligence and Experience.* New York: The Ronald Press, 1961.

International Conference on Public Education, 1960, *Organization of Special Education for Mentally Deficient Children,* Geneva, Switzerland: International Bureau of Education, Publication No. 214.

Itard, J. M. G., *The Wild Boy of Aveyron.* New York: Appleton-Century-Crofts, 1932.

Jensen, Reynold A., "The Clinical Management of the Mentally Retarded Child and the Parents," *American Journal of Psychiatry,* CVI (1950), 830–33.

Johnson, G. O. and Kathryn Blake, *Learning Performance of Retarded and Normal Children.* Syracuse, N. Y.: Syracuse University Press, 1960.

Kanner, L., "Feeblemindedness: Absolute, Relative and Apparent," *The Nervous Child,* VII (1948), 365–97.

———, "Miniature Textbook of Feeblemindedness," *Child Care Monographs,* No. 1, 1949.

———, "Parents' Feelings about Retarded Children," *American Journal of Mental Deficiency,* LVII (1953), 375–83.

Keller, J. E., "The Use of Certain Perceptual Measures of Brain Injury with Mentally

Retarded Children," in E. P. Trapp and Philip Himelstein, *Readings on the Exceptional Child.* New York: Appleton-Century-Crofts, 1962.

Kirk, Samuel, *Early Education of the Mentally Retarded.* Urbana: University of Illinois Press, 1958.

Kugel, R. and D. Reque, "Development of Mongoloid Children Reared at Home," *Journal of the American Medical Association,* CLXXV (1961), 959.

Lewin, Kurt, *A Dynamic Theory of Personality,* trans. by D. K. Adams and K. E. Zener. New York: McGraw-Hill Book Company, 1935.

Lewis, E. D., "Types of Mental Deficiency and Their Social Significance," *Journal of Mental Science,* LXXIX (1933), 298–304.

Mahler, Margaret S., "Pseudo-imbecility: A Magic Cap of Invisibility," *Psychoanalytic Quarterly,* XI (1942), 149–64.

Mental Development Center, unpublished Biennial Report, "Psychological Services." Mental Development Center Library, Western Reserve University, 1962.

Mickelson, P., "The Feebleminded Parent: A Study of Ninety Cases," *American Journal of Mental Deficiency,* LI (1947), 644–53.

New York State Dept. of Mental Hygiene, *Onondaga County Survey: A Special Census of Suspected Referred Mental Retardation.* Technical Report of the Mental Health Research Unit, 1954–1955.

Olshansky, Simon, "Chronic Sorrow: A Response to Having a Mentally Defective Child," *Social Casework,* April, 1962.

Rheingold, H. L., "Interpreting Mental Retardation to Parents," *Journal of Consulting Psychology,* IX (1945), 142–48.

Robinson, H. B. and N. M., *The Mentally Retarded Child.* New York: McGraw-Hill, 1965.

Rosenzweig, Louise E. and Julia Long, *Understanding and Teaching the Dependent Retarded Child.* Darien, Conn.: The Educational Pub. Co., 1960.

Sabagh, George and Charles Windle, "Recent Trends in Institutionalization Rates of Mental Defectives in the U.S.," *American Journal of Mental Deficiency,* LXIV (1960), 618–24.

Saenger, G., *The Adjustment of Severely Retarded Adults in the Community.* Albany, N.Y.: New York State Interdepartmental Health Resources Board, 1957.

Sarason, Seymour, *Psychological Problems in Mental Deficiency* (3rd ed.). New York: Harper & Row, Publishers, 1958.

——, and T. Gladwin, "Psychological and Cultural Problems in Mental Subnormality: A Review of Research," *Genetic Psychology Monograph,* No. 57 (1958), 3–290.

Schachter, F. F., L. R. Meyer, and Earl A. Loomis, "Childhood Schizophrenia and Mental Retardation: Differential Diagnosis Before and After One Year of Psychotherapy," *American Journal of Orthopsychiatry,* XXXII (1962), 584–96.

Schipper, M. T., "The Child with Mongolism in the Home," *Pediatrics,* XXIV (1959), 132–44.

Seguin, Edward, *Idiocy: Its Treatment by the Physiological Method.* New York: Wood, 1866.

Solnit, A. S. and Mary H. Stark, "Mourning and the Birth of a Defective Child," *Psychoanalytic Study of the Child,* Vol. XVI. New York: International Universities Press, Inc., 1961.

Sperry, B., Nancy Staver, and Harold Mann, "Destructive Fantasies in Certain Learning Difficulties," *American Journal of Orthopsychiatry,* XXII (1952), 56–66.

Staver, Nancy, "The Child's Learning Difficulty as Related to the Emotional Problem of the Mother," *American Journal of Orthopsychiatry,* XXIII (1953), 131–42. (Discussant: Anne Benjamin)

Strauss, A. A., "Typology in Mental Deficiency: Its Clinical, Psychological and Educational Implications," *American Journal of Mental Deficiency,* XLIV (1939), 85–90.

——, and N. C. Kephart, *Psychopathology and the Education of the Brain-injured Child,* Vol. 2: "Progress in Theory and Clinic." New York: Grune & Stratton, Inc., 1955.

——, ——, "Behavior Differences in Mentally Retarded Children Measured by a New Behavior Rating Scale," *American Journal of Psychiatry,* XCVI (1940), 1117–23.

——, and L. E. Lehtinen, *Psychopathology and Education of the Brain-Injured Child.* New York: Grune & Stratton, Inc., 1947.

——, and H. Werner, "Disorders of Conceptual Thinking in the Brain-Injured Child," *Journal of Nervous and Mental Diseases,* XCVI (1942), 153–72.

Strecker, Edward, "Mental Defects in Children." Co-editor's introduction to special issue, *The Nervous Child,* II (1942), 6–8.

Terman, Lewis M. and Maud A. Merrill, *Stanford-Binet Intelligence Scale.* Boston: Houghton Mifflin Company, 1960.

Tizard, J., "Longitudinal and Follow-up Studies," in Ann M. Clarke and A. D. B. Clarke, *Mental Deficiency: The Changing Outlook.* New York: The Free Press of Glencoe, 1958.

Tredgold, A. F., *A Textbook of Mental Deficiency* (7th Ed.). Baltimore: The Williams & Wilkins Co., 1947.

United States Bureau of the Census, *Statistical Abstract of the United States,* Table No. 96, Washington, D.C., 1964.

Weatherwax, Joy and E. Paul Benoit, "Concrete and Abstract Thinking in Organic and Non-Organic Mentally Retarded Children," in E. P. Trapp and Philip Himelstein, *Readings on the Exceptional Child.* New York: Appleton-Century-Crofts, 1962.

Webster, Thomas G., "Problems of Emotional Development in Young Retarded Children." (Paper presented before the American Psychiatric Association, Toronto, 1962.) *American Journal of Psychiatry,* CXX (1963), 37–43.

Wechsler, David, *The Measurement of Adult Intelligence* (1st Ed.). Baltimore: The William & Wilkins Co., 1937.

———, *The Wechsler Intelligence Scale for Children.* New York: The Psychological Corporation, Inc., 1949.

Wegman, R. S., "Intelligence as a Factor in the Treatment of Problem Children," *Smith College Studies in Social Work,* XIV (1943–1944), 244–45.

Werner, H., "Abnormal and Subnormal Rigidity," *Journal of Abnormal and Social Psychology,* XLI (1946), 15–24.

———, and Donald Carrison, "Animistic Thinking in Brain-Injured Mentally Retarded Children," *Journal of Abnormal and Social Psychology,* XXXIX (1944), 43–64.

———, and A. A. Strauss, "Pathology of Figure-Background Relation in the Child," *Journal of Abnormal and Social Psychology,* XXXVI (1941), 236–48.

———, "Types of Visuo-Motor Activity in Their Relation to Low and High Performance Ages," *American Journal of Mental Deficiency,* XLIV (1939), 163–68.

———, and B. D. Thuma, "Critical Flicker-Frequency in Children with Brain Injury,"
American Journal of Psychology, LV (1942-*a*), 394–99.

———, "A Deficiency in the Perception of Apparent Motion in Children with Brain Injury," *American Journal of Psychology,* LV (1942-*b*), 58–67.

Williams, Harold, *Education of the Severely Retarded Child: Classroom Program,* Office of Education Bulletin, 1961, No. 2. Washington, D.C.: United States Department of Health, Education, and Welfare.

Windle, Charles, "Prognosis of Mental Subnormals: A Critical Review of Research," *Monograph Supplement of the American Journal of Mental Deficiency,* LXVI, No. 5 (1962).

Wood, Donald W., *A Guide to Curriculum Planning for the Trainable or Severely Retarded.* Mt. Pleasant, Mich.: Central Michigan University Press, 1960.

Woodward, K. F., M. G. Siegel, and M. J. Eustin, "Psychiatric Study of Mentally Retarded Children of Preschool Age: Report on the First and Second Years of a Three-Year Project," *American Journal of Orthopsychiatry,* XXVIII (1958), 376.

World Health Organization, *The Mentally Subnormal Child.* Technical Report Series, No. 74, 1954.

Wortis, Joseph, "Mental Retardation in the Soviet Union," *Children,* VII, No. 6 (1960), 219–22.

Yannet, H., "Classification and Etiological Factors in Mental Retardation" (1956), in J. H. Rothstein, *Mental Retardation, Readings and Resources.* New York: Holt, Rhinehart & Winston, Inc., 1961.

———, "The Problem of Mental Deficiency in Children," *Pediatrics,* X (1952), 223–30.

Zigler, Edward, "Rigidity in the Feebleminded," in E. P. Trapp and Philip Himelstein, *Readings on the Exceptional Child.* New York: Appleton-Century-Crofts, 1962.

———, "Social Deprivation and Rigidity in the Performance of Feebleminded Children," *Journal of Abnormal and Social Psychology,* LXII (1961), 413–21.

Zwerling, Israel, "Initial Counseling of Parents with Mentally Retarded Children," *Journal of Pediatrics,* XLIV (1954), 469–79.

9

LEARNING DISORDERS IN SCHOOL AGE CHILDREN

In contemporary America, education has come to be considered the key to success. Since the appearance of the Russian Sputnik in 1957, intellectual achievement has been the subject of national attention. Educators, parents, and eventually children felt the pressure of educational acceleration, as it became clear that the supply of nuclear physicists was inadequate and the demand for unskilled laborers fast dwindling. Seymour Wolfbein, of the Department of Labor, pointed out that the high unemployment rate (about 16 per cent) of those with the least education and training constituted a growing problem (1959). He described dramatic changes in the industrial picture: (1) there are now more white-collar than blue-collar workers, a result of automation; (2) there is an increasing demand for trained skills; (3) there has been a correlative increase in the median years of schooling in the last generation; from 8 to 12.1 years.

With so many available for so few jobs, educational achievement has become a convenient way of screening. Even a janitorial job in industry requires a high school diploma. Parents and teachers are alarmed, therefore, when a child fails in school or consistently falls short of his educational potential, for his future livelihood is threatened. Parents worry, "Will he go far enough

in school to be able to get a good job?" The educator asks, "Will he be a drop-out, a potential delinquent? Is valuable talent going to waste—talent which could preserve our way of life?"

Difficulties in learning have been a frequent reason for referral. G. M. Gilbert reported that academic difficulty was the most common single referral problem, about 45 per cent of the total, as of 1957. There are no statistics which reliably reflect the changing attitudes since then but, in all likelihood, academic difficulty is now the reason for referral of at least three-fourths of the children between 7 and 14 who are being seen. Current attitudes are reflected in the referral of a nine-year-old boy who daydreamed and pulled out bunches of his hair in class. In making the referral, his teacher and parents commented that he was doing very well in school but "If the daydreaming and hair-pulling keeps up, perhaps his school work will be affected." The possible damage to his scholastic average seemed to be the only reason for concern.

A learning difficulty is an inability to conform to a currently acceptable academic norm. A child may fail in school because of poor health, a sensory deficit, poor teaching, or because the scholastic requirements are too difficult for him. A learning difficulty may also be a sign of emotional impairment. When it is, there is a restriction or inhibition of some ego function; e.g., difficulty in learning something new or in retaining it (i.e., memory), or in synthesizing it (i.e., judgment and comprehension), or in using it (i.e., producing work). Such inhibitions are not mutually exclusive and they may appear in various combinations, but to assert that an academic difficulty is "emotional," one or another of these ego inhibitions must be established.

Most children referred for learning difficulties, particularly the younger ones, are poor readers. If their school work is generally poor, they are not classified as having a specific reading disability, but reading is so important that it tends to overshadow everything else and many cases are incorrectly labelled "reading disabilities" when the disability is a general one. The diagnostic categories of "reading disability," "underachievement," and "learning disorder" overlap, and the psychologist who sees a child who is failing in school has no quick or sure way of ruling out the organic factors discussed in Chapter 7. Ideally, a case should not be referred until remedial techniques have been tried. If these are unsuccessful, it is logical to assume that some sort of internal resistance to learning exists and that an intensive psychological investigation is warranted.

The exploration of emotional factors can be constructive even when an organic basis is suspected. It is important that the diagnostic procedure not be itself traumatic, damaging the child's view of himself further. Telling him there is something wrong with his brain is not helpful, nor is psychological study which labels the child "neurotic" or recommends an unattainable treatment. But close study of the child and his family often provides a basis for sound, practical advice, usually directed to the parents, who are in the best position to help increase the child's interest, motivation, and self-confidence. The best results are achieved by combining psychological guidance with sympathetic and ingenious teaching techniques. These techniques may be based on hypotheses of organic damage that need not be made explicit, just as psychological guidance may be based on inferences about unconscious conflicts which need not be spelled out.

There have been more articles about learning disturbances than about any other aspect of child psychology, (except, perhaps, juvenile delinquency) but only recently have authors attempted to define their terms. Many times, the term "learning disorder" is applied to total inhibition of intellectual functioning, i.e., "pseudo-retardation." Other times, it is used synonymously with "underachievement," a learning problem that is revealed mainly in school performance. Underachievement includes learning difficulties which are associated with gross symptoms such as delinquency, seizures, childhood schizophrenia, and severe obsessional states. Difficulties at school are an inevitable consequence of any personality disorder which has a pervasive effect on the ego or superego. But the term "learning disorder" may also mean a primary neurotic learning inhibition, a situation in which the learning difficulty is the major evidence of psychopathology. And this category can be further subdivided, still on a purely symptomatic basis. For instance, the degree of discrepancy between ability and achievement, and the specificity of learning inhibition to particular academic subjects or particular situations are important symptomatic considerations. The following is a suggested diagnostic scheme for the classification of learning disorders:

I. Generalized intellectual malfunctioning, i.e., Pseudo-retardation, (see Chapter 8)
II. Scholastic learning problems
    A. Learning difficulties as a secondary symptom of personality disorder

1. Psychosis (see Chapter 11)
2. Severe neurosis (see Chapter 10)
3. Psychopathic states (see Chapter 12)
4. Organic or constitutional deficits (see Chapter 7)
B. Primary neurotic learning inhibitions
    1. Restriction to specific academic skills (e.g., writing, reading)
    2. Situational reactions to transitory circumstances or developmental phases (e.g., starting school, beginning puberty)
    3. General inhibition of learning (i.e., not learning)
    4. Chronic difficulty in fulfilling school obligations (i.e., not producing)

This chapter emphasizes scholastic learning problems in which learning inhibition is the major symptom (i.e., II, *B*). The literature on this subject reveals two different methods of understanding learning disorders. The educational profession generally employs what Gordon Allport has called the "nomethetic" approach *(1942),* studying large groups of subjects who have been identified as underachievers. This is in contrast to the case-study, or "idiographic" approach used in clinical settings. Educators use a group approach, since public schools cannot afford to undertake costly individual case-study and treatment methods.

These two approaches lead to different levels of analysis. Large-scale group studies depend on statistical analysis to reveal group differences and are only as good as the experimental and statistical methods used. Clinical reports contain a wealth of data about relatively few individuals, tend to be more subjective, and are only as good as the clinician who is interpreting them. Moreover, clinical reports are usually about extreme cases, and it is questionable whether the findings are representative enough to be applied to the large number of milder problems seen

daily in the classroom. It is difficult to unite these two disparate approaches, but their practitioners should attempt to become familiar with each other's work. It is not legitimate, if we wish to understand the subject, to exclude either the educator's or the clinician's contributions.

Group Studies of Underachievement

Definition

"Underachievement" is a popular term, freely used to describe someone who is not doing as well as he could. A more accurate definition, however, must consider: (1) the measurement of his potential; (2) the measurement of his achievement; and (3) the degree of discrepancy which is considered significant.

The Measurement of Potential

Potential is usually measured by an intelligence test. In our discussion of pseudo-retardation, we noted that personality factors often depress intelligence scores. If the child's intelligence is measured by an oral test, individually administered under favorable circumstances, the experienced clinician can detect unusual emotional interference from his observations and from his knowledge of the child's past history. But more often, the child's intelligence is measured by a written test given in a group situation, and it is impossible to assess the role of personality factors in the final test score.

E. E. Cureton and P. E. Vernon, among others, argue that no sharp distinction can be made between intelligence and attainment. That is, they consider the intelligence test a special kind of achievement test. In Cureton's words:

It is obvious that every test of intelligence, as well as every test of school achievement, is a measure of a set of developed abilities. The difference lies in the choice of abilities to be measured and in the method of devising items to measure them. The general intelligence test, as its name implies, tries to measure general ability. To do this, it must include a wide variety of mental tasks, including samples of all the more important types of mental operations and of symbolic content. The achievement test, on the contrary, limits its range of sampling to a relatively narrow and specific set of abilities. The symbolic content covered is fairly definite, and the range of mental operations called for is well-defined and not extremely extensive. *(1937, p. 315.)*

In a similar vein, Vernon concludes that "there is no essential difference between the acquisition of, say, reading skills and the acquisition of reasoning or other capacities which would be conventionally regarded as part of intelligence" *(1960, p. 39)*. These are brave statements which have some validity. We no longer blindly believe that the IQ is constant and we know that intelligence tests do not measure the individual's innate endowment. The development of intelligence can be facilitated or impeded by experience. The nature-or-nurture controversy is likely to remain very much alive, since it can never be settled in definitive, quantitative terms. With respect to the specific problem of underachievement, a "false positive" is highly unlikely, although it is possible to get a "false negative." That is, if there is a significant discrepancy between measured intelligence and achievement, serious consideration is in order. If, on the other hand, there is no such discrepancy, it may be that both the intelligence and achievement scores are being affected by the same personality factors to a like degree, thereby masking a learning disorder of emotional or environmental origin.

The Measurement of Achievement

Achievement is generally measured with standardized achievement test scores and teachers' grades or reports. A group of students identified as under-achievers by their school grades, however, will not necessarily be the same group designated as underachievers by their achievement test scores *(Fenner, 1965; Cohler, 1940)*. The children who score low on achievement tests, in relation to their IQ's have failed to learn as much as was to be expected of them. This group often includes children with specific disabilities (e.g., reading problems). The children who score well on the achievement tests, but who have received poor grades, have been learning the material. Their grades may indicate an inability or unwillingness to produce the required work, or to cooperate with the teacher, and so on.

It seems plausible to assume that the group which is not learning is in more serious trouble. The group which is learning, but not cooperating, has the requisite skills and information, which can become available if there is a change in their motivation or situation, whereas the nonlearners become increasingly handicapped as time progresses. Their problem may be psychogenic, but if they continue to not learn, it becomes a problem which cannot be overcome by purely psychological means. This assumption that the prognosis is poorer for the nonlearners has yet to be tested, however.

The Degree of Discrepancy

Most people do not do as much or as well as they could, but it is difficult to determine at what point such falling short ceases to be ordinary and becomes a problem. Our discussion of this degree of discrepancy is limited to the problems of evaluating the significance of differences in test scores, specifically, intelligence versus achievement tests.

The simplest procedure is to calculate mental age (MA) from an intelligence test, and compare it with the grade-level placement score on the achievement test. In order to compare "likes," the grade-level score may be translated into educational age (EA), assuming that a first-grader normally has a MA of six to seven, and so on. For example, a ten-year-old with a MA of 10 would be classified as an underachiever if his achievement scores were at the second-grade level, about 7 years in EA. The difference between MA and EA is 3 years, and the educational quotient (i.e., EA ÷ MA), 71.

Common sense tells us that a ten-year-old who is at the second-grade level has a serious problem. But were this same child to perform like an average third-grader (i.e., only two years lower than his expectable performance), then it is more difficult to classify him and the decision is necessarily more arbitrary. The statistical problems inherent in the demarcation of underachievement are more important in a research setting than in a clinical one, where obvious, extreme cases are more frequent.

Because of the great interest in underachievement and the bulky but confusing literature which is based on a diversity of research methods, we will take time here to review the statistical considerations involved in defining underachievement. The author is indebted to Richard Wortman, Ph.D., for his assistance in the presentation of these statistical concepts.

Errors in measurement. The first problem concerns errors in measurement. Even repeated physical measurements are rarely identical; they fluctuate around a mean. Repeated mental measurements fluctuate even more. When one measures the same thing twice with the same instrument, the degree of correspondence between the two sets of measurements is called the "reliability" of the instrument, and is an index of its measuring capacity.

However, any specific intelligence test and any specific achievement test are both unreliable to an appreciable extent. This compounds the unreliability of the discrepancy between the two scores, yet it is this discrepancy which is our measure of underachievement. By definition, the greater the unreliability of the tests, the less likely it is that successive tests will identify the same students as underachievers. It is imperative, therefore, that any comparison between two such tests take into account the probable error of each test—that is, the difference that would result from retesting with the same instrument.

Correlation between achievement and intelligence tests. It is often assumed that the intelligence score should correlate perfectly with the achievement score and that, if it doesn't, the difficulty lies with the student or his teacher. There is, of course, some relationship between the two measures (the coefficients of correlation range from .40 to .70), but there is no more justification for expecting an exact correspondence between academic achievement and scholastic aptitude, or intelligence, than for expecting a perfect correspondence between height and weight (which also tend to vary directly with each other).

If nothing is known about the relation between a predicted variable and a criterion (in this case, achievement is the variable and aptitude the criterion) the most likely guess is that all subjects will be average on the predicted variable. (This assumes a correlation of zero between the two.) If the relationship is perfect, the correlation is 1.00 and exact predictions can be made. But there is another factor, the general principle known as "regression toward the mean." The actual scores on the predicted variable, i.e., achievement, tend to be less extreme than those predicted on the basis of the correlation coefficient. The more extreme the aptitude or intelligence score, the more the achievement score drifts toward the mean. Figure 1 illustrates this phenomenon.

The effect of statistical regression is that more underachievers will be identified in the high ability group and more overachievers in the low ability group.

Allowance for this phenomenon can be made by using a regression equation. One can then predict that Johnny will score closer to the average for his age on the achievement test than he scored on the aptitude test. This measure does not eliminate false results, however, for some children may be identified as overachievers—a meaningless term since no one can do more than he is capable of doing. For example, a youngster with

Figure 1

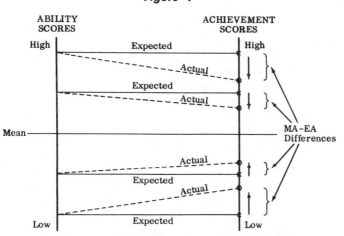

Ability versus Achievement: Regression toward the Mean

a high IQ and an equally high level of achievement will be identified as an overachiever because his measured achievement does not show the expected regression toward the mean.

These statistical problems make the task of defining underachievement a formidable one. There is no "right way" to define underachievement, but it is absolutely essential that the researcher explain his particular operation in detail and recognize the limitations of his tools, at least in terms of their reliability and of their intercorrelation.

Prevalence. The identification of under or overachievers on the basis of test discrepancies is essentially a problem of prediction, and changing the basis on which one makes the prediction will likewise change the number of those who underachieve or over-achieve. R. Thorndike has gone so far as to make the statement that "underachievement is simply underprediction" *(1961).* In careful studies in which a regression equation is used, the underachievers are identified as those whose actual achievement scores fall below the predicted score, but investigators differ about what is a significant difference. If they define it as one standard error of estimate away from predicted scores, about 17 per cent of the group will automatically have lower achievement scores than predicted and about 17 per cent will have achievement scores higher than predicted. If they use the more stringent criterion of two standard errors of estimate, the proportion of both under and overachievers falls from 17 to 2 per cent. By virtue of their definition, researchers will find a predictable percentage of underachievers and a similar percentage of over-achievers.

Age of Detection

The majority of early investigations in this field were conducted at the college or senior high school level (*Altus, 1948; Steinzor, 1944; Winberg, 1949*), but there has been a study trend toward identifying underachievement at earlier ages. M. Shaw and Donald Brown, among others, reported that most underachievers in college had a record of underachievement dating back to high school or even elementary school, and that the origin of the problem seemed to be in the student's home and social setting (*1957*). Edward Frankel reported that underachievement among intelligent high school boys could be predicted from their junior high school records (*1960*). M. Shaw and James Grubb concluded that underachievement was a problem which the high school student brought with him from junior high (*1958*).

Other researchers have found that the pattern of underachievement may be established in elementary school. Henry O. Barrett traced the underachievement of a group of gifted secondary school children back to the fifth grade. He concluded that gifted children with a high level of achievement in elementary school generally maintain it in secondary school and that children with weak performance in elementary school do even more poorly in secondary school (*1957*). Morris Krugman and I. Impellizzeri found that the unsuccessful school performance of a large number of ninth and tenth-graders had begun in the third grade (*1960*). M. Shaw and J. McCuen, who worked with a group of eleventh-grade underachieving boys, found that even in the first grade, these boys were receiving lower grades than achievers, although this difference did not become significant (at the .01 level) until the third grade (*1960*).

Everyone studying underachievement seems to find the beginning to predate the particular age period with which they are directly concerned, and all seem to feel that treatment would have been more effective if started earlier. Despite the importance of early detection, we still do not know at what age, and by what means, we can predict the chronic learning problem. Retrospective studies tell us that underachievers early showed signs of trouble, but we need to know how many children showing the same signs at the same early point did *not* later become underachievers. We also have to be sure of the validity of our identification: Underachievers should be identified by several different techniques or by the same techniques at different times. This would minimize mislabelling due to measurement errors. Some efforts at prediction have already been reported, for instance, Theodore Cohen studied kindergarten children to predict which would underachieve at the first grade level (*1963*). Such studies should be continued over a longer period of time, and long-range research is needed to relate patterns of school performance to post-school adjustment on the job and in the community. In our perfectionistic zeal to have every child perform at the optimum level, we are in danger of identifying every second child as an underachiever in need of special help.

Differentiating Characteristics of Underachievers

There have been many reports comparing underachievers and achievers. The variations in definitions, psychological measurements, and populations make it difficult to summarize the findings, but a few salient points bear consideration:

1. There is one undisputed fact about underachievement—it is predominantly a male problem. All the studies concur in finding a greater number of boys than girls. M. Shaw suggests that approximately half of all the males of above-average ability may be considered underachievers and places the corresponding number of females at about 25 per cent (*1961*). He also finds an age

difference between the sexes; males tend to become chronic underachievers in the early elementary grades, while females generally begin to demonstrate such behavior in late elementary or junior high school *(Shaw and McCuen, 1960)*.

2. Differences in background. As might be expected, underachievers tend to be the children of relatively uneducated parents *(Granzow, 1954; Pearlman, 1952; Ratchick, 1953; Terman and Oden, 1947; Westfall, 1958)*. These studies compared the parents of children from single school districts. A careful epidemological study of underachievement, disregarding school district boundaries, is much needed but would be very complicated. The level of school attainment has been shown to vary with the socioeconomic status of the families, and this difference is partially the result of what we are calling underachievement. But to determine the prevalence and effect of underachievement in different socioeconomic groups, one would have to apply a standard statistical procedure to different school populations and then compare the underachievers so identified in terms of raw scores on the ability and achievement tests. In one study, made in a middle-class, privileged suburban community, a third-grade child of superior mental ability was identified as an underachiever despite achievement scores at the *fourth* grade level *(Birnbaum, 1963)*. None of the third-graders identified as underachievers in this study was below second grade in achievement. One would expect that the underachievers picked out by the same statistical method in another economic area would be far more disabled in terms of the actual level of scholastic achievement although no more numerous.

Independent of the specific variable of socioeconomic status, parents of achievers show a greater inclination to push their children, not only in school but in other areas as well. Parents of under-achievers demand less and demand it later *(Drews, 1957; Winterbottom, 1958)*. Another parental difference which appeared in a group study was greater disagreement about child rearing matters between mother and father of underachieving children when compared with the congruence of opinion between mother and father of achieving children *(Kramer, 1962)*.

3. Differences in intelligence. The relationship between the level of mental ability and the prevalence of underachievement has been much investigated with inconclusive results. If one does not use a regression equation, one finds a greater number of underachievers in the high IQ group and a greater number of overachievers in the low IQ group. Particular attention has been given to the problem of underachievement of children of superior ability. Irene Impellizzeri pointed out that 40 per cent of the high school students who rank in the top third in intellectual ability do not enter college. Of those who do enter, 60 per cent do not finish *(1961)*. In view of the increased need for trained professional workers, such figures indicate a serious waste. Underachievement in children of limited ability also has important consequences *(DiCarlo et al., 1958)*. These children have little margin to spare; if a retarded child fails to utilize what mental ability he has, he becomes helpless and dependent upon society for his support.

In general, underachievers score lower in verbal than nonverbal intelligence tests *(Birnbaum, 1963; Bond and Fay, 1950)*. In C. Birnbaum's study, twenty underachieving third grade boys were matched in group IQ's with twenty achieving boys. The underachievers had a WISC Verbal IQ average 7 points *below* their Performance IQ average. The achievers had a verbal IQ average 6 points *above* their performance IQ mean. Such differences are only a partial explanation of academic difficulty; the next step is further investigation of the factors which give rise to these differences in patterns of intellectual ability.

4. Differences in self-concept. There is fairly consistent agreement that underachievers are generally more negative in their attitudes toward themselves than are achievers *(Shaw, 1961)*.

5. Differences in level of aspiration. A negative self-concept does not mean that ego ideals or ambitions are less. In fact, James V. Mitchell found that at the college level, underachievement was associated with high aspirations and gross overestimation of actual performance *(1959)*. The college achievers set more realistic goals for themselves. Leonard Worell also found that the high achiever characteristically set himself a goal that was close to his previous performance and that he did not believe that he could achieve very much more by exerting himself to the limits of his capacity *(1959)*.

The list of studies of this order is almost endless. Many of the variables investigated have undoubted significance which can be supported by clinical examples. But the research findings are often inconclusive, contradictory, or superficial. Many of the results are descriptive rather than explanatory. This is partly a methodological problem. But it also results from the fact that underachievers are not a homogeneous group. A population selected on the basis of an administrative criterion (i.e., not performing academically as expected) cannot be expected to represent a psychological entity. One would not, after all, expect a population of traffic offenders to be homogeneous! It is important to recognize the varying degrees and kinds of underachievement and their varying etiologies.

Genetic Roots of Learning

In order to set the stage for consideration of individual deviations, the normal genetic roots of learning will be briefly reviewed.

1. Some degree of interest in the world outside the self is basic to all learning. The infant's interest in external reality begins with his dependence and subsequent attachment to his mother. This emotional tie provides the bridge to the rest of external reality and learning about his mother is the prototype for learning about the environment. If the infant suffers prolonged and severe maternal deprivation in his first year, he is susceptible to permanent damage (see Maternal Deprivation and Mental Health, Chapter 15, p. 422–428

2. Toward the end of the first year, the second step in learning—the changeover from passivity to activity through imitation and identification—begins. The toddler wants to do those things for himself that he has experienced his mother doing for him. His ambitions far exceed his ability, and his activity is likely to bring him into conflict with his mother, but his drive to overcome his passivity and to gain active control, to do instead of being done to, gives tremendous impetus to the learning process.

3. From the age of two on, the child's curiosity becomes increasingly intellectual. Again, his ambitions exceed his ability; he will raise questions the answers to which are incomprehensible to him (see Chapter 2). Still, he must be given the opportunity to try to understand the answers. Curiosity must be rewarded if it is to stay alive. During this stage, the child learns that curiosity is useful, that his questions interest his parents, and that their answers help to allay his anxieties and feelings of impotence. At the same time, he is learning to express his thoughts and feelings verbally; he transmutes actions into words with increasing frequency. His facility with language, so important in school, is crucially affected by his early verbal interchange with his parents.

During this same period—approximately two to four years—the child is eager to show off, to exhibit himself physically and to exhibit his achievements. This infantile exhibitionism has to be toned down. He learns to find satisfaction in playing without demanding continual adult attention or praise, but this should be a gradual weaning rather than a sudden rejection or withdrawal of parental interest. If the child should remain dependent on the mother's attention and have no interests of his own, he is ill-prepared for the impersonality of school.

Although the groundwork is laid in the very early years, acceptance of reality and responsibility are the key phases of development in the period between four and six years. The child must master the distinction between make-believe and reality, must relinquish his belief in magic and must shift from primary to secondary thinking processes (see Chapter 2). As long as he thinks anything is possible, or that a wish or thought is tantamount to an act, he has no need for knowledge.

The child's growing ability to distinguish fantasy from reality enables him to begin to understand what he can and cannot do. He must accept his limitations and realize that his dreams of glory are only dreams. Some children, boys in particular, wrestle with this down-grading process. They may resist being shown or taught anything, because they feel that the admission of ignorance is tantamount to an admission of inferiority. Until they accept their status, no one can teach them anything. On the other hand, the child must not degrade himself mentally so much that he gives up. The ideal is a middle course which helps him to understand that although there are many things he cannot do yet, his situation will soon change. (Often, a boy's feelings about himself are sequelae of his defeat in Oedipal rivalry.) In recognizing his limitations, the child must see them as temporary rather than permanent, so that, in spite of the inevitable delays and detours in store for him, he retains his ambition to grow up.

A corollary to the child's acceptance of himself is his increasing sense of identity with other children his age. The realization that they share his problems is a boon, and he gains psychological strength from a friend with whom he can identify and with whom he can share experiences. But then he must also become able to tolerate competition and comparison; his friends are bound to surpass him in one way or another.

To learn to accept responsibility, the child needs a sense of "task orientation." This term refers to his ability to work independently at assigned tasks, even though they may not be inherently enjoyable. The child should be able to carry a task through to the end, without constant supervision or admonition. This reflects his respect for the rules and requests of others. It is easier if his superego is sufficiently developed so that he is proud of doing things correctly, but he may still need praise from his teacher or mother to reinforce his sense of accomplishment.

The important mechanism by which the child comes to enjoy learning for its own sake is called "sublimation" by psychoanalysts. In the dictionary sense, sublimation means "to refine and exalt, to heighten, elevate to a place of dignity or honor." In psychoanalytic theory, sublimation indicates a change in the level on which the child's instinctual drives are gratified, a shift of aim from a primitive level to one that is higher on the cultural scale (e.g., sublimation of sexual curiosity to curiosity about a more impersonal subject such as the planetary system). It is a hybrid concept in that the definition includes both psychological and social criteria. Gratification is delayed and displaced from physical pleasure to socially valued behavior. Through sublimation, the child obtains pleasure from reading and writing and is stimulated by his thirst for knowledge. There is a close connection between sublimation and the superego, but activities directed solely by the superego are dominated by a desire to avoid guilt. Sublimation indicates a more positive satisfaction, a delight in the activity for its own sake. Sublimation is also closely related to the theoretical concept of neutralization of energy and automatization of function. H. Hartmann speaks of a major developmental trend "away from instinctualization of ego functions toward greater (secondary) autonomy, that is, better protection against instinctualization and regression" *(1955, p. 11)*.

In the language of learning theory, the child is motivated by secondary drives which have been superimposed on primary drives through the process of socialization. He has a built-in system of rewards; he reinforces his own behavior by the satisfactions he derives from an ever-increasing mastery of intellectual mysteries. Early identifications with adult persons plays an important part in this gradual process of sublimation.

In the absence of sublimation, or related secondary drives, the school child is handicapped. He does not like school, he is bored, he needs constant prodding or threats, and he can easily forget everything he is taught because he has invested nothing of himself in learning it. Such a child will look at you blankly when you ask, "Don't you want to read like the other children?" He may respond by asking, "Why should I? What's in it for me?" If he has not already discovered the satisfaction of acquiring a new skill through work, no answer you give will have much meaning.

The Parents' Role in the Etiology of Learning Problems

The numerous ways in which normal development can go awry are easy to imagine. A great deal depends on the child's relationship with his parents and the parents' interest in specific aspects of his development. However, the child is developing simultaneously in many ways. His mental development is not an isolated phenomenon. The following is a discussion of some of the specific ways in which parents may hamper the child's ability to use his intelligence. These mechanisms are by no means mutually exclusive; it is entirely possible for parents to contribute in more than one way to a learning inhibition.

Early Childhood Training

A child has many experiences with education and instruction before he enters school. His parents are his first teachers and, if his early training has been coercive, there is likely to be a residue of resentment toward authority. Feelings which have their origin in the parental relationship are easily transferred to the teacher. The teacher then inherits an unwilling pupil, one who resists her authority and her knowledge. There is also the danger, however, of expecting too little, rather than too much. The Fels study shows a positive correlation between maternal concern with the child's development in the first three years and his intellectual growth in the years from six to ten *(Kagan and Moss, 1959)*. M. R. Winterbottom demonstrated that motivation tended to be high in elementary school children whose mothers had demanded and rewarded independent accomplishment in the early years *(1958)*. Such attitudes reflect the mother's willingness to allow the child to grow up; this in turn helps the child to relinquish infantile forms of gratification. E. Buxbaum concluded that particularly children with all-pervasive learning disorders are children tied to their mothers in a partially symbiotic relationship. "They were not physically deprived and left without stimulation. Rather, to the contrary, they were overstimulated and too much taken care of, in so far as their mothers did too much for them in certain areas" *(1964, p. 440)*.

Demanding and rewarding early accomplishment is all-significant, since the training given in the first few years lays the basis for more formal learning later. Toilet training is a good example: If it is done very early, the child is conditioned on a physiological, involuntary basis; he is simply a passive partner. If it is delayed until the child trains himself, then the mother is a passive partner. The child has learned not for the sake of winning another's approval, but because he has elected to be clean. He has learned that dirty, he is socially unwelcome and that clean, he is acceptable in polite society, but the mother's neutrality means that she has not provided the motivation.

A mother who delays a child's training in one area is likely to delay it in other areas—such as teaching him to feed himself, dress himself, and wash himself. All reasonably normal children learn to do these things, but when and why makes a great difference. If a child learns them belatedly, out of sheer necessity, the experience does not particularly contribute to the development of ambition. If these early achievements have been encouraged, recognized, and rewarded, the child incorporates the mother's pride, and is proud of himself for a job well done.

Parental Management of Childhood Curiosity: The Importance of Family Secrets

Parents have ample opportunity not only to teach the child to do things, but also to teach him to wonder. Curiosity is generally thought of as desirable, but only when it is intellectual curiosity about impersonal topics. It is assumed that the child thinks, or feels, only that which he puts into words, but children have thoughts which they do not express verbally; in addition, parents tend to hear only what they choose and to ignore embarrassing questions. Parents commonly ignore early indications of interest in sexual matters—questions about the differences between boys and girls and about where babies come from and how they got there, but there are other kinds of questions which are also discouraged by parents.

For instance, the author has found that a significant number of children with learning difficulties have had seriously ill parents or siblings and that the illness has been kept from the children. Of course, the child is bound to react to the changed emotional atmosphere and to sense the worry and anxiety but, if the subject is taboo, he is afraid to ask questions or share his worries. The case of John demonstrates the extent to which secrecy can affect the child:

John was the youngest of three boys in a moderately well-to-do family. At the age of nine, he was repeating the third grade. His IQ was 110, but his achievement level was second grade, two years short of his mental age and one year short of his chronological age. He shrugged off his failure and explained that he daydreamed and didn't pay enough attention to the teacher. He was a good-looking boy and popular because of his skill in athletics. He had, however, no academic or intellectual interests.

Because a number of appointments were mysteriously cancelled, the case worker inquired. When the mother was asked point-blank, she finally admitted that she had a chronic heart condition. There had been several hospitalizations for this, and she was on a strict regimen. She displayed no anxiety about her physical condition, but was worried about people learning about it. Her heart condition was a closely guarded family secret. Only the oldest boy had any inkling of it. John had been told that his mother went to the hospital (three times) because of a sore throat and that she rested regularly because she was tired. When he heard a rumor that she was ill, he was told that there was nothing to it. In effect, he was asked to believe a preposterous story, and to deny the evidence of his senses. The mother acted as if her problem would go away if no one knew about it, and everyone else became a party to the conspiracy of silence.

John acted like his mother in denying any anxiety about the reality of his school failure. His natural anxiety about his mother's welfare had to be repressed and, with it, all the questions he might have.

He could not afford to think; he could only be constantly active in something which did not require mental concentration.

Ilse Hellman's description of the treatment of three mothers of children with intellectual inhibitions demonstrates the close bond between mother and child and the mothers' lying and secretiveness, which forced the child to appear ignorant and not curious. In these three cases, the mothers were having extramarital affairs and, to avoid feeling guilty, they denied that anyone suspected and would not admit that their lives were entangled with uncertainties, contradictions, and falsifications. Although the learning problems of their children had other determinants, a major factor was the secretiveness of the mothers, which reinforced the impairment of the children's memory, reality testing, and synthesizing (1954). Inhibition of curiosity on any emotionally toned subject—sex, marital conflicts, antisocial escapades, alcoholism, serious illness—can have the same spreading effect. Unconsciously, the child thinks, "If I have to stop thinking about this, which I would really like to understand, the best way to do it is to stop thinking altogether." Curiosity cannot be restricted only to safe subjects.

Parental Management of Childhood Aggression

The importance of ambition and curiosity to school performance is clear, but it is not immediately obvious how aggression is related to learning. Aggression is often thought of only as hostile or antisocial behavior; here, it is used in a broader sense, almost synonymously with activity.

Learning is work which requires the expenditure of energy; the child cannot be an inert, passive recipient of information. In order to learn, he must have the energy to be inquisitive, to penetrate, and to persevere against obstacles. There is much evidence to suggest that the overly aggressive child has a more promising intellectual future than the overly submissive child. In a survey comparing 100 "learners" with an equal number of "nonlearners," all 200 of whom had been referred for psychiatric consultation because of academic difficulties or other problems, Irving Harris found that learning difficulties were associated both with extreme agressiveness and submissiveness. His data indicated that the overly aggressive "nonlearner" (i.e., a youngster referred primarily for school failure) was brighter than the overly submissive "nonlearner" (1961).

This is corroborated by the data which L. S. Sontag, C. T. Baker, and V. P. Nelson drew from individual case studies of children whose IQ's changed markedly over a period of time. According to these studies, the "passive, infantile dependence pattern" led to a decreasing level of performance on the Stanford-Binet, whereas, "aggressive, self-reassuring mastery of tasks, competitive, independent pattern" led to progressively advanced performance (1955). B. Sperry, D. N. Ulrich, and Nancy Staver remark that "the boys whose activity in school annoys the teacher and interferes with their work seem to us to be in a psychologically more favorable position eventually to achieve in school" (1958, p. 646). This is worth noting, because these aggressive, overactive boys are usually the despair of their teachers.

The passive, compliant youngster, on the other hand, quickly elicits adult sympathy and interest. Teachers try to spare him and encourage him, and offer him special help. But there are subtle difficulties involved. The child seems willing, but he can't remember anything. He makes no effort, forgets his assignments, and so on. Sperry *et al.*, give a vivid clinical description of seven boys whose renunciation of success played a major role in their failure to learn. The family patterns required a denial of hostile feelings toward the parents as well as giving in to someone else in order to receive parental approval. In one case, the child was required to give in to a retarded brother, but was not supposed to know that the brother was retarded. Another boy was warned never to argue with his father, but not told that his father had an ulcer. There was a family secret plus the requirement that hostility be repressed. It was important to these boys to be liked, and one way they tried to accomplish this was by not displaying any resentment toward their teacher. Normal childish grumbling was absent (1958).

The author encountered another example of this in Henry, a child taught to be polite and kind at any cost. His parents were themselves models of passivity.

Henry was ten at the time of referral. He had a sister of eleven, who was doing moderately well; his parents were first-generation Americans, of limited education and means. Henry's IQ was 94, and he was placed in the third grade, but his achievement was little better than first-grade level. The parents had only recently become concerned, thinking that he would "grow out of it." Everyone, parents and teachers, was baffled by Henry's learning problem, since he appeared to be eager, and reputedly had no other difficulties of any sort.

Exploration of the living situation indicated some crowding. Henry and his sister shared a small bedroom, and for an extraordinary reason. Some years before, a friend of the mother's had come for a weekend and had never departed. She paid no room or board, had no job, and she constantly criticized and nagged Henry's parents. They didn't like her, but they couldn't get up the courage to ask her to leave. Further inquiry revealed that the father was also passive at work. He had worked at the same place for 12 years, but had had no vacations. The parents recognized the injustice of these situations, but were powerless to do anything.

Henry displayed the same compliance and inhibition of aggression. For example,

his teacher repeatedly mispronounced his last name so that it lent itself to ridicule by his classmates, but he had never been able to correct the teacher and was shocked when the possibility was suggested.

Henry, like the boys studied by Sperry et al., had been taught directly and indirectly to submit to any indignity for the sake of being liked. Even asking a question seemed aggressive to him, and failure seemed less threatening than rejection.

Providing an Ego Ideal which Includes Academic Achievement

The "ego ideal" is a term for the values and aspirations of the child, the person he would like to be. That the specific values of the child are largely those his parents express in word and deed, provides a theoretical basis for the sociological differences which are observed in any study of learning difficulties. The best educational insurance a child has is a family which places a high value on education. Harris found that socioeconomic differences were one of the few general factors which distinguished learners, as a group, from nonlearners (1961). The child of upper middle-class parents with high educational standards has no guarantee of freedom from learning problems, but there is no diagnostic mystery involved when a child from an impoverished family which takes no interest in his school career does poorly in school. The problem is to find an effective treatment. Remedial action has to proceed along a broad sociological front which is beyond the scope of this text.

Values, however, are not homogeneous within any social class. It cannot be assumed from a family's address that it sets great store by intellectual achievement. Considerable stress may be put on possessions and appearances, and intellectual attainment may not be thought the straightest road to riches. A child who is taught at home that "It's not what you know but who you know" naturally looks for short-cuts, and places the possession of helpful contacts above that of knowledge.

Interplay Between Mother and Son

The kind of interplay referred to here is a covert struggle for dominance. For the most part, the cases which demonstrate this to a marked degree are boys of elementary school age, of average or better intelligence, who perform close to expectancy on achievement tests but poorly in the classroom. Their school grades are usually just short of actual failure, and there is often a pattern of erratic ups and downs, with enough high points to prove that the child could get higher marks if he wanted to.

These youngsters usually have a pattern of behavior which involves them with their mothers on a number of issues. They dawdle, mislay things, don't finish projects, don't practice their music, bicker with their siblings, don't brush their teeth or take baths unless they are forced to, eat sloppily, and so on. They rarely get into serious trouble, and are inclined to behave better when they are away from home. Such a child's parents and teachers describe him as irresponsible and immature: "You have to keep after him all the time." The child himself may be happy-go-lucky, even though he complains that he is nagged and hounded constantly.

The clinical question is whether the child really requires such close supervision. There is usually an interaction: The mother feels that her close attention to the child is justified by his indifference and indolence; he, in turn, feels that since he is constantly being taken to task, it might as well be for a good reason. The mother behaves as if she were responsible for the child's successes and failures, and the child reacts to her behavior rather than to her words. One third-grader indignantly told his mother, when she reproached him for having failed spelling; "It's not my fault. You forgot to take the spelling lists out of my pants' pocket!" A third-grader might be forgiven such an attitude, he is still moving toward independence in such matters. But the following illustration, from the case history of an older, under-achieving boy, demonstrates the continuation of the mother's involvement:

Carl was the only child of professional parents, both very eager for him to do well in school. In his pre-school years, his parents were permissive and indulgent, in a conscious effort to keep him happy. He was reported to have toilet trained himself at the age of three. Until he entered school, his mother helped him dress and bathe.

Although Carl never liked school, he had no special fears of it. He daydreamed a good deal, and enjoyed drawing and doodling. He disliked being told anything, and resented lessons. He did not pay attention and never completed his work. He learned to read, but his other work was substandard. He absorbed information, but his output was poor except in oral participation. His IQ was 115, was about average for his group.

Many efforts had been made to motivate Carl. There were punishments and restrictions for poor report cards and money and treats for good ones, he attended summer school; he had been tutored in arithmetic. Every year there was a question of his promotion, but his marks were never so poor that he failed. His parents and teachers worried about him, but he was serene and confident, accepted the punishments graciously, and seemed glad when a bad report was "paid off."

Carl and his mother had been in combined therapy and counseling for almost a year. The boy was 11, and in the sixth grade. For two consecutive report cards he had passed everything but health, because of a special project which he had not completed. When the report cards came out, the mother called the counselor in some agitation. Carl was not going to be allowed out of the house until he finished the project, and she was going to sit over him until it was done. When the counselor remonstrated that this would be a step backward, the mother burst out,

"Well, I'm not going to have another 'F' on *my* report card!" In this slip of the tongue, she betrayed her feeling that she was the one who had been graded and found lacking.

Carl's mother's involvement in her son's success is not atypical. As long as a parent continues to feel that he is responsible for his child's performance, he is accepting the anxiety and motivation that should really belong to the child. To some extent, this is unwittingly fostered by teachers who look to the parents for an explanation of a child's unsatisfactory progress. The parent is afraid to withdraw lest the school consider him lax or disinterested. But the shame of failure or the pride of success are the child's own prerogatives. Parents can be interested and supportive without exerting pressure.

Extreme involvement provides the basis for the acting out of unconscious aggression on both sides. The child may feel that he is loved solely for his performance and that his parents care about nothing else. This gives him a sense of insecurity, but at the same time it gives him a powerful weapon against his parents. A refusal to do well in school can, like revenge enuresis, be a way of getting even without being consciously or overtly aggressive. It is a particularly efficient symptom because the child feels no inner guilt; the symptom itself brings enough external punishment in its wake to make self-punishment unnecessary. Parent-child interplay on the subject of school work is reminiscent of the interplay which may go on with pre-school children regarding eating habits. Parents can provide the invitation, the attractive opportunity, the example in behavior, and some limitations, but they can neither force the child to eat, nor to learn. Both eating and learning arise from the child's inner drives—from physical hunger, in the one case, and from a combination of curiosity, desire to master his environment, and wanting to grow up, in the other.

"Fathers of Sons with Primary Neurotic Learning Inhibitions"

M. G. Grunebaum *et al.,* in an article with this title, brought the role of the father into sharp focus. In most reports on parental contributions to childhood psychopathology, the mother is the central figure and the father a vague one. However, in a boy's learning problems, the father's part seems fully as important as the mother's.

Grunebaum *et al.,* drew their conclusions from the treatment of 18 elementary school boys with normal IQ's. The boys were reported to have no neurological or physical impairment which would account for a learning deficiency and were from homes without gross social pathology. The learning problem was the major complaint in each case (although 9 of the 18 also had enuresis). On standardized achievements tests, the boys scored from one to two years below expectancy. Thus, they were not pseudo-retarded, but were nonlearners.

The 18 fathers, although all of the middle class, regarded their own achievements as below standard. They considered their work unimportant and tedious. The author comments, "The readiness of these men to accept a self-derogatory role with an attitude of helpless resignation was impressive" *(1962, p. 464).* These men often considered their wives superior, and the wives usually agreed.

A family situation of this kind is conducive to the formation of a learning problem since the parents tacitly expect the child to fail also. And the possibility of his actually succeeding, in a way the father could not, may expose the child to paternal jealousy, his own Oedipal guilt, or excessive admiration or resentment from the mother, depending on her neurotic structure. These reactions to a child's superior achievement do *not* occur, however, if a father's failure has been determined by outside events, rather than by his own neurotic inhibitions. An immigrant father, one who had to start work at an early age, or one who never had a chance to attend school can enjoy his son's success and believe that the same success could have been his had he had the proper opportunities. The father who considers himself a failure despite opportunities to succeed has more conflicts about his son's achievements.

In this sort of family, the child's school performance is affected by his identification with his father. The boy's view of achievement, competition, and masculinity is distorted; achievement and competitiveness are equated with feminity. The life of a grown man has no appeal. If the father dislikes his work, there is nothing for the boy to anticipate except more tedium and onerous responsibility. The child is faced with a dilemma: Should he imitate the passive, weak, but so-called masculine role of his father, or should he try to be active, competitive, and successful in the aggressive style of his mother? When there is such a conflict, passivity is the easier alternative.

Learning Inhibition as a Neurotic Solution of the Child's Conflicts

The preceding section was devoted to the influence of the child's relationship with his parents on his learning. We noted that learning involves a teacher and a pupil, requiring the pupil's acceptance of the teacher's authority and, in exchange, her encouragement of his curiosity and ambition to succeed. In this relationship, the child responds in accordance with his pre-school experience. It was also pointed out that the child's reactions to his parents' conscious and unconscious wishes, and his identification with their behavior, are of great importance.

Now the emphasis shifts to the child's internal conflicts and the role that an inhibition of learning may play in warding off anxiety. Here, the child's fantasies and unconscious wishes are of major importance. This does not mean that the parents have had nothing to do with the development of internalized conflict, but that the conflict has become so integral a part of the child's personality that changes at home do not bring about parallel changes in the child. However, there are no sharp lines of demarcation; a severe learning difficulty is the result of combined forces and even if it is the result of internalized conflicts, the battle with the environment continues. We are simply looking at the same symptom from a different viewpoint.

Displacement of Feeling from Oral and Anal Functions to Learning

The first step in learning is taking in. In the child's unconscious, the intake of knowledge and the intake of food may seem identical (see Chapter 6). Difficulty at this primary level has profound effects, even producing pseudo-retardation *(Sperry, Staver, and Mann, 1952)*. Children who have equated eating and learning show poor absorption, appearing not to understand what they are taught, not remembering from one time to the next; they can, however, often retain knowledge acquired on their own, knowledge which has not been "fed" to them through instruction.

Children whose difficulties stem from anal conflicts are more likely to have difficulty with respect to output. Withholding may take the form of refusal to participate orally (e.g., never offering an answer or comment in class), or it may take the form of excessive doubting, a kind of mental stuttering in which the child is never sure, but hems and haws, giving first this possibility and then that.

Displacement of Feelings from Genital Functions to Learning

The child's conflictual attitude toward learning may also be a displacement of his concern with the genital differences between the sexes and about his own genital adequacy. He first learns about sexual differences through his eyes. Vivian Jarvis *(1958)*, in an article on visual problems in reading disabilities, links neurotic conflicts about looking with fantasies in which women have penises. A child warding off the anxiety caused by looking at something avoids looking closely at anything. There are several subjects on the Stanford-Binet which require visual comparison of objects, but occasionally, a child will refuse to look at them, saying flatly, "They're all the same." If a child will not look, for fear of seeing differences, he will have considerable trouble learning to read.

Having observed parental intercourse or having seen a pregnant woman may create a looking inhibition. One six-year-old expressed a dislike for the difference between capitals and small letters, saying that there should be only one size. He said that the small *b* was inside the big *B*, and that this made him nervous. This child had acquired some information about pregnancy. He knew that the penis had something to do with it, and concluded that the penis came off inside the woman to make a baby by transformation. Hence his anxious feeling about pregnancy and his fear of seeing small things inside larger ones. An inhibition of looking can also come from a visual shock of a non-sexual kind; witnessing any terrifying scene or object could have a similar effect on the child.

In discussing the child's feeling of genital adequacy, we have already mentioned that enuresis is frequently associated with learning problems. The boy who considers his genitals defective is likely to assume that his mind is defective as well (see Chapter 6). A girl may consider her femininity to be a defect in itself, as Sally did:

Sally was a girl of superior intelligence, the child of professional parents. A brother was born when she was seven, and she was jealous of him, feeling that he had all kinds of advantages because he was a boy. She came into treatment because of phobias, but she also had school difficulties, particularly in spelling. In one school essay she had spelled "King Arthur" eight different ways. The therapist commented that Sally surely knew that only one spelling could be correct. It then came out that Sally could not tolerate looking at anything she had written; she said it was like looking at herself in a mirror. With the information she had given before, this inhibition which resulted in the terrible spelling could be linked to her feelings about looking at her own genitalia. This was the locus of a feeling of devastating unattractiveness.

The feeling of genital inadequacy can be displaced to aspects of learning other than looking. There is a certain amount of exhibitionism involved in showing what one can do or what one knows and the child may fear that in displaying his knowledge, he is displaying something else at the same time. If he has a deep conviction that his genitals are not right, he may be equally convinced that his knowledge is not right.

An obsession with damaged genitals may come from a confusion about the reason for sexual differences, obvious malfunctioning (e.g., enuresis), or guilt about masturbation. Young children commonly believe that masturbation is injurious to the genitalia and adolescents usually think it is injurious to the mind, an example of the close association between genital and mental functioning in the unconscious. What the child may demonstrate in class is his own idea of himself, derived from his idea of his genitals. His behavior may be foolish and out of control, making him an object of ridicule, and earning him the title of "class clown" *(Tarachow, 1951)*. Such a child is constantly on exhibition, demanding attention from everyone, but in silly ways. Usually he is restless and overactive, with fleeting tics and mannerisms. He resembles the hyperactive organically damaged child, but the basis for his activity is radically different. It keeps him too busy to think about masturbating and, at the same time, is an unconscious confession. Many children think of masturbation as "goofy," not unlike the exhibitionistic clowning in school which usually brings the punishment that the child thinks is deserved by someone who masturbates.

Inhibition of Learning to Avoid Anxieties Incumbent in Growing Up

The beginning of school symbolizes the beginning of growing up. If a child has some reason to fear growing up, he will not be happy about his advancement in status. He may be jealous of a younger sibling who remains at home, he may seek overgratification of infantile pleasure, or he may have fantasies about the prospective dangers of adult life. It may seem far-fetched to think a first-grader could be worried about adulthood, but in his mind the intervening years are telescoped, and entering school seems only a step away from becoming a mother or father. Parents aggravate these unrealistic tendencies when they urge the child to do better, in school as preparation for a future educational career. One second-grader who was doing poorly in school had been repeatedly warned by his parents that he would have to try harder so he could go to college, because without a degree he would not be able to get a good job and support a family. He related this to his therapist and added, with genuine distress, "I don't even know who I'm going to marry yet!" His parents were catapulting him into a state of anxious responsibility more properly part of young adulthood, and he naturally wanted to hold off the day of reckoning as long as possible.

Another side of the wish to be an adult is an ambition so intense that the reality of being still a child is too humiliating to be acceptable. Some children deal with this by denial; they preserve their wishful fantasies of strength and omnipotence and admit to no limitations. The following case shows clearly how wishful thinking can interfere with learning. At the time of the psychological study, Stuart was seven and doing poor work in the second grade, in spite of superior mental ability. During the course of an individually administered intelligence test, some of the reasons for his poor school performance became clear.

Stuart was cocksure of himself and felt that there was nothing he could not do or did not know, remarkable self-confidence in view of his school marks. But his self-confidence was shaky; he had to feed it constantly and bolster himself with reiterations of his mental powers, comparing his mind to a rocket that zoomed all over. When anyone tried to slow him down or pointed out an error, Stuart was enraged, argued, and refused to accept correction or help. To have done so would have been to admit to a major defeat in his own private war. Stuart was happy only when he had convinced himself that he was capable of anything and everything. In sports, he refused to play with children his own age, tried to compete with older boys, and bragged about nonexistent home runs.

At first glance, Stuart was a happy-go-lucky child, but a second look showed that this happiness was spurious. He could not afford to see things as they really were, and his inability to accept help from others made him more prone to errors than other children of similar ability. Part of his mind recognized this fact, but he recoiled against it and resorted to even greater wishful thinking and denial. His friends reacted badly to his bragging, older boys wanted no part of him, and again he was forced to deny these painful humiliations.

The cause of Stuart's fantasies of being grown-up, and of his inability to accept himself as a seven-year-old boy, was not hard to determine. His father had died when he was four and a half, and Stuart had volunteered the idea that "now I am the husband of this family." His mother had been relieved and gratified by his response to the loss of the father, and had encouraged him to act grown-up. Naturally, Stuart was not up to the goal which he had set for himself, and he and his mother needed help in order that he might reestablish himself as what he really was, a boy only seven years old.

Inhibition of Learning to Avoid Anxiety of Competition.

It is inevitable that competition will play an important role in the school situation. It is one of the first opportunities that the child has to compare himself and his achievements on an equal basis with other children. In school, the child will inevitably compare himself with other children of his own age, in terms of height and weight, athletic ability, attractiveness, and eventually, in reading, writing and arithmetic.

One can readily sympathize with the child who is afraid of failure; he responds well to encouragement and praise, and reacts favorably when he has had some successful experience. The educator often sees such children, and they clearly prove that nothing succeeds like success. Other children, however, make it difficult for educators because they won't try. They never do enough to achieve an honest, successful experience, and one failure or near-failure brings on another. In some instances, such children will not exert any effort because they prefer to fail as a result of not trying, rather than risk the disappointment of failure after they have made a genuine effort. It is face-saving to think "it doesn't matter because I didn't really put much into it." By assuming an I-don't-care attitude, one is protected in advance against embarrassment or disappointment.

The underachiever of average ability who is assured that he can do better is in danger of assuming that he has limitless potential. He may, like Philip, comfort himself with the thought that some magic day, after having put forth just a little effort, he will find himself at the top of his class:

Philip, aged 13 and in seventh grade, received a report card with failing grades in all his major subjects. In elementary school, he had consistently received poor grades and had been told he could "do better." His IQ, 112, was average for his group. He had never worried about his school work until he began to fail in seventh grade. The school instituted a strict regimen of supervised study and special help, but it was hard for him to profit from the extra time and attention because he daydreamed. When the counselor asked him about his fears and expectations about school work, Philip replied that he wanted to get all A's on his report card. The fact that this goal was five grades removed from his current level of achievement seemed to mean nothing to him. Anything short of this miraculous perfection held no incentive for him.

It is unrewarding to some children to work diligently only to reach a mediocre level. The injustice of individual differences angers them, and they are frustrated by the fact that some other children can do better with less work. These children may consider anything less than top position to be ignominious and may actually prefer failure to the mediocre grades they would earn if they tried.

Conversely, a child may be anxious in a competitive situation lest he be too successful. This is more rare, and the child is usually an intelligent one with great imagination and complex thought processes. The fear of success was noted in the discussion of fathers whose sons had primary learning inhibitions, and it is also a factor in the total inhibition of aggression in Henry's case. To recapitulate briefly, success may bring the child into active rivalry with the father; even if the parents are encouraging, the child may fear success because of its relationship to the Oedipal situation. It is dangerous to the child because it seduces him into considering himself a real rival to his father, with all the attendant anxieties. These children react negatively to conspicuous success and try to preserve their anonymity. One bright eight-year-old was being given an individual Stanford-Binet which, because of his superior intelligence, was taking a long time. To encourage him, the examiner commented that the test items were for children older than himself. The boy thereupon shook his head emphatically and announced he was through, adding, "Don't ask me any more questions. Only a father knows things like that." He felt he was getting dangerously close to the position held by his father.

Fear of success may also have a more general significance. Edith Weiskopf (1951) points out that the desire to succeed and the desire to be liked by one's fellows are frequently incompatible. The successful person may feel he is the target of envy and aggression. These may or may not actually exist, or he may be exaggerating them or projecting them from his own psychology. The successful person may think, "All the others must be angry with me for beating them, because that's the way I'd feel if the shoe were on the other foot," thus imagining jealousy and envy in proportion to his pleasure in winning. Teen-age girls who suddenly become interested in attracting boys may very consciously avoid success in school. A bright girl may hide her intelligence in the hope that this will make her more appealing to boys. But what begins as a maneuver may develop into an automatic, uncontrollable defense.

The beloved fool of legend and literature is the classic illustration of an intellectual blocking to ward off hostility. He is an innocent, appealing, and harmless figure, protected by all and envied by none. He may know more than he admits, but he makes everyone else feel superior.

Failure as a Result of an Unconscious Need for Punishment

This is closely related to anxiety about success, and also to masturbatory guilt. Some children show a perverse determination to put themselves in the worst possible light, going out of their way to deserve punishment. This may lead to delinquency, but it often takes the simple form of failure. The mechanism may not become obvious until provoked by praise or compliments.

Susie, eight years old, was referred for school failure. She freely described her difficulties, listing one inferiority after another. She was restless and anxious during the test, and did not do well (IQ of 90). She repeatedly declared that she was stupid and did not know anything. At first glance, it seemed that she was worried about her inferiority and defeated by her hopelessness. One might think she needed encouragement and some experience with success.

While Susie waited for her mother, she made a fine drawing about which the examiner complimented her. Susie became incensed, threw the drawing into the waste basket, and exclaimed angrily, "Now you've spoiled it!"

When a child reacts with anger or anxiety to a sincere compliment, he feels a special need to fail. Individual psychotherapy is strongly indicated when the encouragement and reward of achievement has a negative effect. Parents and teachers neither can nor should start saying the opposite of what they mean in order to trick the child. It is important that they remain realistic so that the nature and extent of the child's psychopathology can be clarified.

Diagnostic Guide

The following diagnostic guide will be useful in many clinical situations, but it has specific reference to learning problems because their assessment includes several unique features. First, a complete diagnostic study necessitates educational as well as clinical information and is best undertaken jointly by the school and the clinic. Second, the causes of the learning problems are often quite separated from results, both chronologically and in the minds of the parents and the teacher. Finally, this guide provides an opportunity to summarize the material discussed in this chapter. Specific topics are mentioned only briefly, since it is assumed that their relevance to a learning symptom has been made clear.

I. *From the School*

A. *Definition of the problem*

With the aid of the individually administered intelligence test, standardized achievement test, and the teacher's observations, the extent and nature of the learning difficulty can be defined. Is general intellectual functioning depressed, as in pseudo-retardation, or is it limited to one academic subject? What is the discrepancy between expectation and achievement, and what is the duration of the symptom? Is there a failure to learn or a failure to produce? Is there withholding of both oral and written work?

B. *Child's response to school situations*

Is the child restless and overactive or passive and prone to daydreaming? Does he ignore the other children, pester them, or fight with them? How is he regarded by the others? Does he appear anxious, depressed, preoccupied, defiant, indifferent, lazy, curious, or happy-go-lucky? Does he respond differently to different teachers? Does he ask for help? Does he respond to individual assistance? Does he enjoy himself in free play during recess or in games? Does he have any nervous habits?

II. *From the Parents*

(In interviewing parents, one is concerned with obtaining factual information about the child, but also with assessing, if possible, the parents' attitudes and feelings. The best method is to start with general inquiries and follow up with specific questions.)

A. *General inquiry*

1. "What is the problem which concerns you?" The parents may be specific and well-informed about this, or vague and perplexed, or even so indifferent that they are there only because they were told to come.

2. "When did you first learn of the difficulties? What were you told? Have you done anything about this before?" The parents may seem astonished that a problem exists, and insist that they were never informed of it. If their account of what has been said to them is inaccurate, the distortions they introduce will be helpful in understanding them.

3. "Have you any ideas what the possible causes of the school problem might be?" The parent may blame the school, themselves, or some physical defect, or they may intuitively sense a psychological cause.

4. "Were there any problems before he started school? Did you anticipate his having difficulties?"

5. "What has been said to the child about his school failures? How does he feel about them?" One hopes to get an indication of the parents' closeness to the child and of their ability to communicate with him.

B. *Specific inquiry*

1. *Current behavior*

a. Other symptoms: Enuresis, thumb sucking, lip licking, sleep problems, feeding difficulties, fighting, dawdling, and so on.

b. Peer relationships: Choice of playmates, role usually taken by the child, interest in seeking companionship, close friendships, teasing, being teased, and so on.

c. Physical activity: Degree of interest and form it takes, reaction to instruction in sports, reaction to competitive situations, reaction to sports involving physical contact with other players.

d. Family relationships: Acceptance of parental authority, of criticism, restrictions, requests, and punishment. Responsibility for self-care and for helping in home. Relationship to siblings, patterns of dominance, bickering, jealousy, and so on.

e. Expressed feelings about going to school: History of reluctance to attend, differences in mood during school and vacation periods, comments about work, successes and failures.

2. *Pre-school history*

a. Birth and early development: Abnormalities or special worries during the first years. Age of walking, development of speaking.

b. Feeding: Usual appetite, food preferences, history of force feeding, present attitudes, age of weaning from bottle.

c. Toilet training: Time if recalled, parents' recollection of relative easiness, history of constipation, history of force, participation by the parents.

d. Early discipline: Easy or difficult to control, means used, manner of handling early aggression (e.g., biting and kicking), manner of handling verbal aggression.

e. Mental development: Verbal development, intellectual curiosity (i.e., questions asked), expression of curiosity about sex differences, birth of babies, death, God, and so on. Nursery school.

f. Medical history: Previous illnesses, operations, accidents, present defects (e.g., allergies, visual defects).

3. *Family history*

a. Family illness or crises: When, how explained to the child, his reactions.

b. Chronic tensions in home: Financial, marital difficulties, in-laws, crowding and so on.

c. Separations from parents: When, how long, reasons, how explained, child's reaction.

d. Parent's educational experiences: Schooling. Was it easy, enjoyable, difficult, or what? Their current occupations and attitudes toward them.

e. Parental handling of current school problem: Degree of interest, what has been said and done, degree of accord between parents about handling of the problem, evidences of interplay between parents or parent and child.

f. Indications of identifications: Father-son, mother-daughter, father-daughter.

III. *From the Child*

No attempt is made here to describe the diagnostic usefulness of psychological procedures or to recommend any special battery of tests; this would require extensive presentation and a critique of the voluminous literature available. None is foolproof, and even those tests which differentiate diagnostic groups (e.g., organic versus functional) overlap to an embarrassing extent. In studying an individual child, one must evaluate the tests in the light of his history and behavior.

A. *Attitudes*

1. Child's awareness of the problem: Evaluation of his expressed feelings about the difficulty, particularly in terms of anxiety and involvement.

2. His self-concept: How does he see himself—as a top student, a bad child, or a foreordained failure?

3. Reactions to success and failure: Level of aspiration, realistic understanding of his limitations, pleasure in success, reactions to difficult questions, admission of lack of knowledge, and so on.

B. *General behavior*

1. Patterns of withholding and blocking: Kinds of situations which arouse these reactions.

2. Response to examiner: Degree of openness, readiness to establish a relationship, eagerness to confide, ability to verbalize reactions and experiences, tolerance for work involved in taking tests.

3. Special preoccupations: Aggression, violent ideas, intimations of catastrophe or danger, self-devaluation, intrusion of fantasy into tests.

4. Activity or passivity: Extent to which he is governed by a wish to be liked, to avoid trouble, and so on. What awakens spontaneity? Frequency with which he asks questions. Degree to which he resents being told what to do.

It is impossible to predict how much psychological material will be drawn from one or two sessions with a child. He often shows his reactions in nonverbal ways which require a close eye. A child is usually defensive and guarded, since he has had so little part in the process of referral. He expects the interviewer to be like other adults, remonstrating with him or asking him unanswerable questions. He tends to be cautious about confiding things, either out of loyalty to his family or from fear of retaliation from them (see Chapter 4). Thus, it is usually unwise to ask the child directly about his parents or his feelings toward them. The best way to learn how to relate to children and how to recognize their underlying emotions is to work with them. Clinical experience is the best training ground. It is well to keep in mind that there is no such thing as a typical case of learning inhibition. The varieties of symptoms and causes of learning difficulties are many.

Changing attitudes toward educational attainment have produced many significant benefits. The prevalence of underachievement in underprivileged children from deprived circumstances has received particular attention. Public schools, especially in large metropolitan areas, have joined forces with other community agencies to widen the cultural horizon of these children, and many schools are experimenting with pre-school programs for children as young as three, in order to prepare them for the regular academic curriculum.

On the other hand, the increased pressure for achievement has blinded many people to the fact that children today are in fact doing more and better academic work than their parents did. R. F. Schiefelbusch, J. Dodd, and E. Drews point out that the average fourth-grade child is a year younger and a year more advanced than the fourth-grader of 30 years ago (1963). The norms of achievement tests have had to be revised. The exceptional child with a true learning problem needs the help of the clinician and the educator, but these specialists must take individual differences into account and avoid trying to force every child to adhere to a uniform level of achievement and productivity.

Treatment

Like the diagnostic process, the treatment program usually entails the cooperation of educator, parent counselor, and child therapist. Rarely can one person carry out all three of these functions. Time must be set aside for sharing information from the different sources and for working out techniques of collaboration. N. M. Prentice and Sperry describe three programs for children with psychogenic learning inhibitions: 1. brief tutorial interventions in psychotherapy for the purpose of illuminating the dynamics of the learning inhibition; 2. simultaneous tutoring and therapy, the tutor and therapist each nonetheless functioning separately with different techniques and in different areas, and 3. therapeutic tutoring alone which combines aspects of both the therapeutic and educational function but retains as its primary emphasis the teaching approach (1965, p. 522). Edith Buxbaum describes another form of combined treatment where a special school is housed in the treatment building. This is similar to the day hospital program for adult patients (1964).

Whatever the specific means, it is imperative that the therapy and education of the child be closely related. Some of the notorious difficulty in treating learning problems may stem from failures in this collaboration. Many of these children have very little conscious anxiety and bring nothing about school or learning to their treatment sessions. Since the problem is manifest in school, the parents also contribute relatively little and it is difficult for the therapist to connect the fantasies and feelings which the child demonstrates in the office, or which the parents report from home, with the failure in school. It is an intellectual exercise for the therapist and her interpretations, which are usually tentative and vague, are easily sloughed off by the child. With some current, specific examples of mistakes or omissions in school, the therapist can direct the child's attention and help him to see where he is hurting himself. On the other hand, when a teacher knows that a child is in psychotherapy, she is likely to question her role. She may assume that a child in treatment needs security and acceptance above all else and therefore expect very little from him. This provides an unrealistic situation where there is nothing to make the child anxious and he continues to slide through without learning. Buxbaum described the philosophy of the treatment school as follows: "In the schoolroom minimal standards of behavior and of academic achievement were permissible. The teachers reduced their demands to the point where the child could produce. *From this level on, demands were made vigorously and it was expected that they would be fulfilled.* Failures to produce in any one subject or in general were constantly brought to the awareness of the student and of the therapist, who then could deal with them as he saw fit" *(1964, p. 427).* (Italics are the author's.)

The work with the parents is equally important. It is very rare to cure a learning problem by treating the parents, but it is equally unusual to find a learning problem which has been completely internalized. The techniques of working with parents are described in Chapter 15. A mechanism which is particularly frequent in parents of children with learning problems is isolation, i.e., the sharp separation of school life from home life. Since the problem seems to appear only in school, the parents cannot see how they are affecting the situation. To confront them with "what they are doing wrong" will be taken as an attack and arouse their defensiveness unless a relationship has been established with their counselor. The treatment of a long-standing learning problem is slow and costly in professional time. We do not know much about the prevention of learning problems except that the efforts should be made in the first two or three grades of school. The teachers of these grades should have diagnostic consultation services available to them on short notice. To be effective, these services should include someone especially trained in parent guidance and the dynamics of learning who has the time to work with both teacher and parent of a child with an incipient learning disorder.

References for Chapter 9

Allport, Gordon, *The Use of Personal Documents in Psychological Science.* New York: Social Science Research Council, 1942.

Alpert, Richard, "Anxiety in Academic Achievement Situations: Its Measurement and Relation to Aptitude," *Dissertation Abstracts,* XVIII (1958), 643.

Altus, W. D., "A College Achiever and Nonachiever Scale for the MMPI," *Journal of Applied Psychology,* XXXII (1948), 385–97.

Barrett, Henry O., "An Intensive Study of 32 Gifted Children," *The Personnel and Guidance Journal,* XXXVI (1957), 192–94.

Buxbaum, Edith, "The Parents' Role in the Etiology of Learning Disabilities," *Psychoanalytic Study of the Child,* Vol. XIX. New York: International Universities Press, Inc., 1964.

Birnbaum, C. R., "A Study of Underachievement in Elementary School Children." Unpublished dissertation, Western Reserve University, June, 1963.

Bond, G. L. and L. C. Fay, "A Comparison of the Performance of Good and Poor Readers on the Individual Items of the Stanford-Binet Scale, Forms 'L' and 'M,' *Journal of Educational Research,* XLIII (1950), 475–79.

Cohen, Theodore, "Prediction of Underachievement in Kindergarten Children," *Archives of General Psychiatry,* IX (1963), 444–50.

Cohler, Milton J., "A Comparative Study of

Achievers and Non-achievers of Superior Intelligence," *Summaries of Doctoral Dissertations,* Northwestern University, VIII (1940), 74–79.

Cureton, E. E., "The Accomplishment Quotient Technique," *Journal of Experimental Education,* V (1937), 315–26.

DiCarlo, Louis M. *et al.,* "A Comparative Study of Some Characteristics in Achievers and Non-achievers Among Children with Retarded Mental Development." Mimeographed report, Syracuse Research Institute, 1958.

Drews, Elizabeth M., "What about the Gifted Child?" *College of Education Quarterly,* Michigan State University, III (1957), 3–6.

Fenner, Elmer, "An Investigation of the Concept of Underachievement." Unpublished doctoral dissertation, Western Reserve University, 1965.

Frankel, Edward, "A Comparative Study of Achieving and Underachieving High School Boys of High Intellectual Ability," *Journal of Educational Research,* LIII (1960), 172–80.

Gilbert, G. M., "A Survey of 'Referral Problems' in Metropolitan Child Guidance Centers," *Journal of Clinical Psychology,* XIII (1957), 37–42.

Granzow, Kent R., "A Comparative Study of Underachievers, Normal Achievers, and Overachievers in Reading," *Dissertation Abstracts,* XIV, No. 4 (1954), 631–32.

Grunebaum, M. G. *et al.,* "Fathers of Sons with Primary Neurotic Learning Inhibition," *American Journal of Orthopsychiatry,* XXXII (1962), 462–73.

Gundersen, R. O. and L. S. Feldt, "Relationship of Differences Between Verbal and Non-verbal Intelligence Scores to Achievement," *Journal of Educational Psychology,* LI (1960), 115–21.

Harris, Irving D., *Emotional Blocks to Learning.* New York: Free Press of Glencoe, Inc., 1961.

Hartmann, Heinz, "Notes on the Theory of Sublimation," *Psychoanalytic Study of the Child,* Vol. X. New York: International Universities Press, Inc., 1955.

Hellman, Ilse, "Some Observations on Mothers of Children with Intellectual Inhibitions," *Psychoanalytic Study of the Child,* Vol. IX. New York: International Universities Press, Inc., 1954.

Impellizzeri, Irene, "Nature and Scope of the Problem," in Leonard Miller, *Guidance for the Underachiever with Superior Ability,* Office of Education Bulletin, OE-25021. Washington, D.C.: United States Department of Health, Education and Welfare, 1961.

Jarvis, Vivian, "Clinical Observation on the Visual Problem in Reading Disability," *Psychoanalytic Study of the Child,* Vol. XIII. New York: International Universities Press, Inc., 1958.

Kagan, J. and H. A. Moss, "Parental Correlates of Child's I.Q. and Height: A Cross Validation of the Berkeley Growth Study Results," *Child Development,* LII (1959), 365–98.

Kramer, David P., "Interparental Differences of Opinion as Manifested in Children's Academic Achievement." Unpublished doctoral dissertation, Western Reserve University, January, 1962.

Krugman, Morris and Irene Impellizeri, "Identification and Guidance of Underachieving Gifted Students," *Exceptional Children,* XXVI (1959–1960), 283–86.

Mitchell, James V., "Goal Setting Behavior as a Function of Self-Acceptance, Over- and Underachievement, and Related Personality Variables," *Journal of Educational Psychology,* L (1959), 93–104.

Norman, R. D., B. P. Clark, and D. W. Bessemer, "Age, Sex, I.Q. and Achievement Patterns in Achieving and Non-achieving Children," *Exceptional Children,* XXIX (1962–1963), 116–23.

Pearlman, S., "An Investigation of the Problem of Academic Underachievement Among Intellectually Superior College Students." Unpublished doctoral dissertation, New York University, 1952.

Prentice, Norman M. and Bessie M. Sperry, "Therapeutically Oriented Tutoring of Children with Primary Neurotic Learning Inhibitions," American Journal of Orthopsychiatry, XXXV (1965), 521–31.

Ratchick, Irving, "Achievement and Capacity: A Comparative Study of Pupils with Low Achievement and High Intelligence and Pupils with High Achievement and High Intelligence Quotients in a Selected New York City High School," *Dissertation Abstracts,* XIII (1953), 1049–50.

Schiefelbusch, R. L., J. Dodd, and E. Drews, *Our Underachieving Children,* Bureau of Child Research, Public Information Series, No. 4. Lawrence, Kansas: University of Kansas, 1963.

Shaw, Merville C., "Definition and Identification of Academic Underachievers," in Leonard Miller, *Guidance for the Underachiever with Superior Ability,* Office of Education Bulletin, OE-250021. Washington, D.C.: United States Department of Health, Education, and Welfare, 1961.

———, and Donald Brown, "Scholastic Underachievement of Bright College Students," *Personnel and Guidance Journal,* XXXVI (1957), 195–99.

———, and James Grubb, "Hostility and Able High School Underachievers," *Journal of Counseling Psychology,* V (1958), 263–66.

———, and J. McCuen, "The Onset of Academic Underachievement in Bright Children," *Journal of Educational Psychology,* LI (1960), 103–8.

Sontag, L. S., C. T. Baker, and V. P. Nelson, "Personality as a Determinant of Performance," *American Journal of Orthopsychiatry,* XXV (1955), 555–62.

Sperry, B., D. N. Ulrich, and Nancy Staver, "The Relation of Motility to Boys' Learning Problems," *American Journal of Orthopsychiatry,* XXVIII (1958), 640–46.

———, et al., "Renunciation and Denial in Learning Difficulties," *American Journal of Orthopsychiatry,* XXVIII (1958), 98–111.

———, N. Staver and Harold E. Mann, "Destructive Fantasies in Certain Learning Difficulties," *American Journal of Orthopsychiatry,* XXII (1952), 356–66.

Steinzor, B., "Rorschach Responses of Achieving and Non-achieving College Students of High Ability," *American Journal of Orthopsychiatry,* XIV (1944), 494–504.

Tarachow, Sidney, "Circuses and Clowns," *Psychoanalysis and the Social Sciences,* Vol. III. New York: International Universities Press, Inc., 1951.

Terman, L. and Melita Oden, *The Gifted Child Grows Up.* Stanford, Calif.: Stanford University Press, 1947.

Thorndike, R., "Methodological Issues in Relation to the Definition and Appraisal of Underachievement." Paper given at American Psychological Association Convention, New York, September, 1961.

Vernon, P. E., *Intelligence and Attainment Tests.* New York: Philosophical Library, Inc., 1960.

Weiskopf, Edith A., "Intellectual Malfunctioning and Personality," *Journal of Abnormal and Social Psychology,* XLVI (1951), 410–23.

Westfall, F. W., "Selected Variables in Achievement and Non-Achievement of the Academically Talented High School Student." Unpublished doctoral dissertation, University of Southern California, 1958.

Winberg, Wilma, "Some Personality Traits of College Underachievers," *Proceedings: Iowa Academy of Science* (1949), 267–70.

Winterbottom, M. R., "Relation of Need for Achievement to Learning Experiences in Independence and Mastery," in J. W. Atkinson, *Motives in Fantasy, Action and Society,* pp. 450–78. Princeton, N.J.: D. Van Nostrand, Co., Inc., 1958.

Wolfbein, Seymour, quoted in "Here's a Look at Tomorrow's Workforce," *Nation's Business,* XLVII (June, 1959), 82–85.

Worell, Leonard, "Level of Aspiration and Academic Success," *Journal of Educational Psychology,* L (1959), 47–54.

10

PSYCHONEUROSIS IN CHILDREN

Diagnosis, rather than symptomatology, is the proper starting point for a consideration of psychoneurosis in children. In previous discussions of feeding, training, speech and learning problems, it was pointed out that these symptoms may, or may not, have the structure of a psychoneurosis. Certain of the cases cited might easily have served as examples of psychoneuroses, focussing on the underlying conflicts rather than on outward symptoms. Although diagnosis—understanding the cause—is the goal of the clinical evaluation, a large proportion of clinic patients, children especially, do not receive a formal diagnosis (see Chapter 5). Statistics on child outpatients are usually given in terms of presenting complaints, degree of impairment, and other associated characteristics, without any diagnostic labels.

Although symptoms do not generally tell us the nature or the etiology of a problem, perhaps the one symptom which is typically psychoneurotic in structure is *phobia*. Phobias and irrational anxiety are the major presenting complaints we will consider in this chapter.

"Psychoneurosis" is sometimes synonymous with "emotional disturbance," mainly to differentiate both from "psychosis," which is more serious, and from organic behavior disorders. Prop-

erly, a psychoneurosis is a special form of emotional disturbance, i.e., an *internalized conflict*. "Emotional disturbance" is the generic term. If the symptomatic behavior is directly related to bad environment, or is the result of deficient training, the child should not be diagnosed as having a psychoneurosis. Of course, sufficient exposure to a noxious environment leads eventually to the implantation of habits, feelings, and attitudes which cannot be easily sloughed off when the environment is altered. Still, the disturbance which was initially caused by severe environmental trauma or deprivation, is not necessarily a psychoneurosis. Psychoneurosis implies not only internalization, but also conflict between different parts of the personality. If a child has been deceived and mistreated in his first home, he will be distrustful of affectionate overtures made in a new one; he may continue to be aggressive and conniving without any noticeable change. His disturbed behavior cannot be viewed as only reactive (as witness its continuation in a better environment), but it does not necessarily prove that he is caught up in a tangle of conflicting feelings and desires. The result of prolonged mistreatment or deprivation is more likely to be a defect in personality, a failure to develop the ability to feel genuine affection for others, to tolerate delay, to appreciate reality, or to acquire a conscience. In a psychoneurosis, on the other hand, all the basic elements and functions of a whole personality are present. A history of environmental trauma does not automatically rule out psychoneurosis, but one must get below the surface, the overt behavior, for additional clues as to motivation and cause. Psychoneurosis is one of the most benign of psychiatric diagnoses because it responds most favorably to psychotherapy. For this reason, many clinicians are eager to recognize its existence in a child, regardless of specific presenting problems.

Among the indicators useful in determining the presence of a psychoneurosis is the age of the child. The complicated structure of a psychoneurosis requires a degree of development of the mind and the personality rare in the pre-school child. The exceptions to this general rule, seem to be precocious children (e.g., the three-year-old stutterer previously cited, *H. Kolansky, 1960*). A second indicator is the child's current environment. If the home is filled with tension, bickering, or out-of-control parental behavior, the child's symptoms can be understood as a direct reaction. It is not necessary, in such cases, to evoke the mysterious workings of the unconscious to explain why the child is upset or disturbed; common sense provides the answers. A corollary indicator to this is whether the child responds to efforts to modify his environment. If the child is not reassured by realistic explanations, if his symptoms are not modified by encouragement or special training, if he does not respond to more time, more attention, more consistent discipline, and so on, then it can be assumed that the source of the problem lies within the child.

It would be hard to estimate how many children identified as "emotionally disturbed" actually suffer from a true psychoneurosis. These are the children who baffle their parents, teachers, and pediatricians because no external cause can be found. Often, the neurotic child himself agrees that there is no "reason" for him to act or feel the way he does. He just does, and he can't help himself. Not only is the cause internal, but it is also unconscious. Without some concept of the unconscious it would be impossible to understand a true psychoneurosis. Opinion varies, in accord with different theories of personality, as to what feelings or wishes become unconscious, and why. It is generally agreed, however, that a neurotic symptom is created by memories or feelings of which the patient is not consciously aware and that the neurotic behavior is not voluntary. Briefly, the neurotic child reacts as if imagined or past events are a real and continuing part of the present. The neurosis involves, for the older child, the magical thinking which is normal in the very young, egocentric child (see Chapter 2) although he is capable of logical thinking about issues which are free of conflict. In the area of the neurosis, the child operates as if his thoughts were the equivalent of deeds; only when they are brought out into the open can he recognize them as harmless in and of themselves. Magical thinking is characteristic of all neurotic children, but it is more obvious in some forms of neurosis than others.

In the following material, the basic concepts of anxiety and defense mechanisms are considered. (The theory relevant to these concepts is contained in Chapter 3, where they are considered in the context of personality development.) In pathological deviations, anxiety is excessive or the mechanisms evoked to mitigate it become so crystallized that the child's ability to function is impaired. Neurotic symptoms may assume various disguises.

They appear to be very different on the surface, but closer inspection reveals many similarities.

Formation of a Symptom in Terms of Intrapsychic Conflict

We have said that a psychoneurosis stems from an internalized conflict, at least part of which is unconscious to the child. In learning theory terminology, the conflict is between opposing drives or wishes. The equivalent psychoanalytic term is "intrapsychic conflict" or "structural conflict," indicating that the conflict is between different structures of the mental apparatus. The symptom itself is formed in the ego structure as a result of conflict between the ego and the id, or the ego and the superego (see Chapter 1).

The understanding of the formation of a neurotic symptom was considerably increased by Sigmund Freud's work on the psychology of dreams; his major theoretical contributions are contained in *The Interpretation of Dreams* (Freud, 1900, 1953, Chapter 7). Briefly, he enumerates three sources of dreams: (1) physical sensations impinging upon the sleeper (e.g., full bladder, thirst, heat, and cold); (2) the day residue (i.e., memories and thoughts left over from the day's events or pre-sleep occupations); and (3) instinctual wishes. The id impulses become stronger during sleep, when the vigilance of the ego is less and the potential for regression is greater. Even in sleep, however, the ego maintains some guard and reacts with anxiety if forbidden wishes are crudely expressed. If the anxiety is sufficiently great, the sleeper wakes up apprehensive and, in any case, discontinues the dream. It is assumed that the sleeper is motivated to preserve sleep and that, as long as possible, he seeks to defend himself against waking by disguising forbidden wishes, usually in such a way that the dream seems completely illogical. There is an important distinction between the manifest dream content (i.e., what is consciously remembered) and the latent dream content (i.e., unconscious wishes) which becomes clear only when the individual provides his associations with the dream. Such operations as condensation and distortion, by which the latent dream was transformed into the manifest dream, are called the "dream work."

The importance of Freud's study of dream psychology is twofold. First, dreams provide access to the unconscious mind and are thus useful in psychoanalytic therapy. Second, the interpretation of dreams, using dream symbols and the unique associations of the dreamer, is helpful in understanding the development of neurotic symptoms. Symptoms, like dreams, are a compromise formation between a repressed element and the defenses of the ego. They also have a latent (i.e., unconscious) meaning which has been successfully disguised, at least to the patient, although the forbidden wish may be obvious to the onlooker.

A compulsion in a ten-year-old boy illustrates our last point. The boy was in psychotherapy for a number of chronic problems, or this particular compulsion might not come to our attention, since by itself it was not serious:

Chris repeatedly tucked his shirt into his pants. He said he was afraid his shirt might slip out, his pants slip down, and his underpants might show. However, Chris did in fact exhibit his underpants each time he loosened his belt to adjust his shirt. Although the ostensible purpose of the compulsion was to prevent any immodesty or exhibitionism, it was obvious that he was exhibiting a good deal. Thus, the symptom provided him with a legitimate opportunity to gratify his wish to show off his nether parts, but satisfied his superego at the same time.

Often neurotic symptoms look grossly inconsistent to the observer. Severe obsessive-compulsive neurotics with a great horror of dirt and a fetish about cleanliness, for example, may leave certain areas of their home truly dirty, thereby satisfying both the unconscious wish and the defense against it. Excessive solicitude, or fear for someone's safety, often masks a hidden, opposite wish. It must be remembered that the wish would not be hidden if it were not for conflict. The anxiety may arise from a simple fear of discovery and retaliation, or be a result of conflict between negative and positive feelings for the same person, or stem from guilt about any and all aggressive thoughts.

The similarity of processes involved in the formation of ordinary dreams and in the formation of neurotic symptoms was one of the considerations which led Freud to assert that there was no sharp division between normal and abnormal. Charles Brenner remarked that the "phenomena of human mental functioning and behavior range from the normal to the pathological in much the same way as the spectrum of an incandescent solid ranges from red to violet, with no sharp line separating one color from the next."*

In analyzing a neurotic symptom, one tries to discover what purpose it serves. No matter how much the patient is suffering because of his neurosis, the symptom originated to protect him from something which seemed worse—a greater feeling of anger, sadness, excitement, or a disturbing inner conflict. One looks for the source of the underlying conflict primarily in forbidden sexual or aggressive wishes. Learning theorists would agree with this formulation, in essence. Since all behavior is motivated, the symptom also is motivated, usually by the fact that it reduces anxiety. J. G. Sheehan's presentation of stuttering in approach-avoidance conflict terms is a good example, the main thesis being that the stuttering reduced the tension sufficiently to permit the individual to resume speech *(1953, 1958)*. Otherwise, the patient would not be released from the state of hesitation or repetition. Learning theorists might take exception to the important role accorded the sexual wishes of the child by the psychoanalysts, but the general approach of both theories is otherwise similar.

Anxiety States

"Anxiety," as used here, is a fear which is either not justified by external reality, or which is an extreme reaction to a real threat. (See Chapters 2 and 3.) The younger the child, the more difficult it is to draw the line between inner and outer reality. Some of the common fears of young children already mentioned in Chapter 3 illustrate mechanisms which are involved in the complex structure of the full-blown neurosis. Such childhood phobias are considered normal because they appear so frequently in young children and are outgrown, but they are structurally similar to the fixed phobias of later childhood.

In some forms of neurosis, there is no feeling of anxiety; in others, the patient is aware of a great deal of anxiety. Since one purpose of a neurotic symptom is to defend *against* anxiety, it may seem strange that anxiety can itself be a neurotic symptom. If the patient is very anxious, what is he warding off? The answer is that the symptom disguises the source of the anxiety. The place, person, thing, or activity which the child fears is only a substitute for the real object, manifest fear which disguises a latent fear just as the manifest dream hides the latent dream content. This is why a phobia does not yield to reassurance. In childhood, the most common anxiety states are sleep disturbances and phobias.

---

*Quoted from Charles Brenner, *An Elementary Textbook of Psychoanalysis* (New York: International Universities Press, 1955), p. 197. Reproduced by permission.

Sleep Disturbances

Sleep disturbances fall into two major symptomatic categories: difficulty in going to sleep, and difficulty in maintaining sleep. It is highly improbable that any child gets through his first five years without ever being reluctant to go to sleep or awakening from a nightmare. Arnold Gesell regards waking up at night and reluctance to go to sleep as characteristic of the 15 to 30-month-old child (1943).

The fact that such problems are common in the pre-school years does not mean that they have no psychological meaning but that, within normal limits, they do not require professional attention. They are an expression of developmental anxieties which are part and parcel of growing up, but they are worth studying because they help us to understand the pathological variants of later ages. As Selma Fraiberg points out, "The fact that a particular symptom should be considered typical for an age is of special interest to us since we would then expect that its relationship to developmental problems of that period could be investigated and secure for us some additional knowledge of the early mental process."* In psychoneurotic disturbances, these early mental processes are retained.

Reluctance to Go to Sleep

Young children are characteristically uninterested in going to bed. Devices to postpone bedtime are familiar to every parent, and bedtime rituals can take hours if parents are unwary. Up to a point, the problem may simply be one of parental indulgence. After the parents have set reasonable limits on the child's procrastination, however, it often becomes clear that he is genuinely afraid of being left alone and that he has real difficulty in falling asleep. For the very young child, sleep is like a

---

*Quoted from S. Fraiberg, *The Magic Years* (New York: Charles Scribner's Sons, 1959), p. 285. Reproduced by permission.

separation and sleep disturbances are linked with separation anxiety. The child is afraid to leave his mother; something might happen to her as a result of the mean thoughts he had during the day, or perhaps he might get into trouble in her absence. Asleep, he is in special danger because he has abandoned control. For younger children this loss of control may be dangerous, because of their fear of doing bad things. The two-year-old is anxious over his aggressive wishes and fears losing parental affection. Toilet training is, at best, newly established, and the wish to soil and wet at leisure is close to the surface. Dimly, the child realizes the temptation and fears the event.

At this stage, the child is comforted by the physical presence of his mother or father, which assures him that they are still all right and also protects him from temptation. Unfortunately, if the parent habitually sleeps with the child, new anxieties may develop. Other supportive measures are better, such as leaving the bedroom door open at night so the child feels less alone, or looking for ways during the days to reduce his anxiety about accidents and mistakes. He may find comfort in a bed toy, a stuffed animal, or a favorite object which becomes a magic talisman against danger. It is the author's opinion that parents are well-advised to remain neutral with regard to such comforters. If the child spontaneously elects to give a stuffed animal this value, fine. It is his own idea, and he can give it up later. If the idea comes from his parents, it has the additional weight of adult authority, which may prolong his magical thinking and his reliance on objects and rituals. Ordinarily, a sleep disturbance at this age is transitory, and experience helps the child to overcome it. Mother is always safe, and the danger of soiling or wetting abates.

Another peak in sleep disturbances occurs between four and six years. These are far more complicated than the earlier disturbances of sleep, although the same principles hold. The fear of loss of control is there, but it is now masturbation, rather than wetting, which is feared. The temptation to masturbate is particularly strong when the child is alone, in bed, and it is night. The aggressive wishes which may emerge in sleep, or just before sleep, are aimed at siblings, parents, and friends. At this stage, the child peoples the dark room with imaginary wild animals or supernatural creatures, and repeated proofs that they are not really there do not allay his certainty that they really are. The following case illustrates the connection between the anxieties of the Oedipal complex and the eruption of a night fear:

An intelligent five-year-old boy was having nightly difficulties in falling asleep. He complained miserably of a skeleton in his bedroom. He did not fight against going to bed, but he lay awake for long periods, talking to himself and keeping his mind occupied, actually becoming more wakeful, and finally fleeing from his room. This was the boy's only symptom, and it was decided to help him through his mother rather than to start psychotherapy.

The first step was his explanation that he thought the skeleton was that of his father. There is only one way to become a skeleton, or a ghost, and that is by dying. The second step was that the dead father was going to attack him. The boy was both frightened and sad in relating these facts. At this point, the mother took the initiative. She recalled to the boy a recent suggestion he had made, to the effect that his father should "join the Marines." At the time, this had been treated humorously by the parents, but now the mother remarked that perhaps the boy wished that his father really would go away and stay away. The boy said nothing, did not even appear to hear her. Another night she went one step further, suggesting that the son might be afraid his father knew some of these secret bad wishes. She assured him that nothing would really happen to the father, and also that he would not be angry. At this point, the boy objected—indicating that he

had followed her every step—and rejoined that of course his father would be mad if he knew. Who wouldn't? The mother was able to convince her son that this would not be the case, and that was the end of the skeletons.

In this situation, an Oedipal anxiety was transformed into fear of a skeleton —which could just as easily have been a ghost, robber, Martian, lion, tiger, or, especially for girls, a witch or a snake. The child's aggressive wishes are repressed because he fears retaliation, fears they might come true, or has a sense of guilt. The repression is only partial, however. The aggressive feelings remain extant, although the true source and object are lost from sight and replaced by something dangerous which will do to the child what he wanted to do to someone else. This projection still creates anxiety, but the child finds it more acceptable to be afraid of a skeleton than to acknowledge his confused feelings about his father. The amount of anxiety may be very little less, but it is at least contained and it is restricted to a time and place; thus, there is less sense of inner conflict, confusion, and guilt.

Another sleep disturbance at this age has a different form. The child is not kept awake by scary imaginary objects; he is afraid of sleep itself. You can't tell what might happen while you're sleeping. There might be a terrible fire, or a tornado, or an earthquake. An atom bomb might fall. All these improbable events seem imminent to the child; he almost knows he is going to die as a result of some such catastrophe. How can he be so sure? Barring hysterical parents who have fostered such ideas, we look for the clue in the child's inner mental life. All these dire events are overwhelming and powerful; a person would be helpless to defend himself. It is often possible to trace this kind of fear to similar feelings about their sexual excitement.

The dread of sleep might also spring

from a fear of not waking again, particularly if death has been explained to him this way. Fear of death, i.e., thanatophobia, is a basic fear which is expressed to some degree in all specific phobias. Death, of course, is the ultimate danger, and although one would not expect a child of four or five to be thinking about death, many children this age are quite concerned about it. For one thing, death is a new idea which they must assimilate. Their conception of time is poor, and they are not so reassured by the explanation that it comes only to the old. Then, too, death is the ultimate punishment, perhaps especially appropriate for one who is hiding aggressive thoughts and feelings.

Many parents and educators have been concerned that the amounts of violence on mass media programs might make children more aggressive. E. Maccoby's review of the research indicated that children are quite ready to imitate aggressive behavior, and aggressiveness, at least in play situations, was increased after viewing movies and cartoons depicting fights (1964). Television cannot be considered the source of aggressive feelings. Most television programs exist by virtue of their demonstrated popularity with children. Their appeal is based on the child's psychology as it exists, and they are not deliberately intended to alter it. Fantasies about aggression, and its result, death, are unavoidable for young children. However, if a child becomes an addict of pictorial mass media, this is a danger signal. As Maccoby points out, there is a strong relationship between such addiction and problems of interpersonal adjustment. It is not that television causes the problem but it can serve to reinforce and augment it.

Nightmares

The chief difference between nightmares and the disturbances we have already discussed is one of timing. In the former, the wishes break through the ego defenses with the resultant anxiety coming *after* sleep; in the latter, the process goes on *before* sleep, resulting in a reluctance to go to sleep. Often, children are unclear about whether they are recounting a fantasy, a so-called day dream, or a dream they had while asleep. Their fantasies are so real that they become confused.

It is unusual for two-year-olds to complain of bad dreams, but they may awaken in a state of terror which indicates a nightmare. Nightmares reach a peak between four and six years. R. Lapouse and M. A. Monk reported that 28 per cent of the six to twelve-year-olds they studied were still having nightmares (1959). It would be rare for a parent to seek professional help solely because nightmares, unless they were sufficiently frequent and intense to disrupt the household.

After a nightmare (in contrast to a bad dream) the child awakens feeling helpless and in fear of suffocation. He usually wakes up fully enough to give an account of the disturbing event and to respond to his parents' reassurance. There is also an extreme form of nightmare, night terror, or pavor nocturnus, after which the child has great difficulty reorienting to reality. He is hard to waken, his panic does not abate, and waking does not help him to regain control. In such night terrors, the child is often reliving a traumatic event, possibly the primal scene. Anthony James found that his subjects with sleep disturbances had spent more time in the parents' bedroom after they were two years old than had his control subjects (1959); such a history is strongly suggestive of opportunities for witnessing parental intercourse. It is likely that the child would be awakened by the commotion, which would appear to him like a struggle, and the circumstances lend themselves to the development of a sleep disorder rather than to some other symptom. This possibility is frequently repressed by the guilty parents. Other possibilities include hospitalization, accidents, or any event which has the character of overwhelming shock or surprise.

The personality of children who experience sleep disturbances has been relatively little studied. James suggests that they have a greater capacity for visual imagery. He postulated that sleep disturbance was determined by "psychophysical responsiveness" *(p. 35)*— another acknowledgement of the elusive constitutional predisposition which is always an important determinant of symptomatology.

Normal and pathological sleep disturbances are distinguished by degree, rather than kind. The best diagnostic criteria are severity and chronicity. The normal child's need for sleep eventually outweighs his anxiety; if there are many successive nights of total wakefulness, or almost nightly nightmares, the problem requires professional attention. The other criterion has to do with persistence over a period of time. The child of four or five who still needs someone to stay with him until he falls asleep, the child of eight or nine who still has weekly nightmares, the child of ten or eleven who still requires a night light or who is still afraid to go up to bed alone—need help. This does not mean that only these extremes are noteworthy, but milder problems can often be alleviated by counseling the parents.

Effective treatment requires some appreciation of the psychological mechanisms involved. Logical reassurance counts for little. The child acts as if he had some secret knowledge that he is in danger, the parents notwithstanding. What he knows, and what his parents do not, are his own bad feelings—feelings which are wild, dangerous, and alien to his normal self. These are the very same qualities possessed by the supernatural creatures or the improbable events which he fears or which appear in his nightmares. The fears represent both the projection of his feelings and the deserved punishment.

Leo Rangell reported the case of a seven-year-old boy who was treated by his father on the basis of guidance supplied through an exchange of letters with a psychoanalyst. The child had a history of severe nightmares, was waking at least once every night in a state of anxiety, disliked going to school (despite good marks and good behavior), and had recently developed a "nervous stomach." The sleep problem was but one of a number of signs of anxiety and unhappiness. Rangell prints the exchange in full, and they provide an excellent picture of the history and the therapy. He speaks of the "seemingly monotonous repetition of one theme, the wish to get rid of the father" *(1950, p. 383)*, which became increasingly apparent over a period of about ten months. Toward the end of this period, the boy had two nightmares, both about his father being killed. The father described the child as guilty, apprehensive, and unhappy when he related these dreams. In this instance, the father did *not* interpret the underlying hostile wish, but simply explained that such dreams were not unnatural and that he was not hurt, insulted, or angry about them. This reassurance was very meaningful to the child, since at last the real cause of the anxiety was exposed, and that was the end of the nightmares. The other symptoms were also relieved.

There are relatively few reports of treatment of sleep disturbances in children, and they are mainly found in the psychoanalytic literature. Therapy is usually effective in a fairly short time. One cannot use successful results to validate the treatment without also considering the number that would be expected to show spontaneous remission without treatment, but treatment reports such as Rangell's are extremely helpful in showing the origin of a symptom and its dissolution, and it is quite possible that the same processes occur when there is spontaneous remission. Most of the reports of psychoanalytic treatment describe children who are unusually intelligent, sensitive, imaginative, and articulate, and whose parents have similar characteristics. It would be interesting to have equivalent psychological data about less gifted children suffering from the same anxiety symptom.

Childhood Phobias

The subject of dreams is not far removed from the subject of fears in childhood. A. Jersild, F. V. Markey, and C. L. Jersild concluded that children's dreams are a reflection of their fears, since a large number of dreams contain the same themes that children report when they tell about their fears (1933). Like nightmares, childhood phobias are so common that mild, transient phobic reactions are regarded as a normal part of early development. A *phobia* has been defined as a "morbid fear," and as being "irrational" and "persistent." It is omnipresent, and engenders great anxiety. Only the phobic reactions of school children, five years and older, are considered in our discussion.

Most frequently, childhood phobias are of school, transportation, and animals. It is impossible to obtain a complete list of the incidence of phobias in childhood because casual surveys do not differentiate reported fears from true phobias. A school-age child may express a dislike for dogs and be frankly uneasy if one is nearby; this is a reported fear. If the child is preoccupied with the possibility of encountering a dog and is in a constant state of anticipatory anxiety, he may not want to walk to school, visit freinds, or leave the house at all, to avoid seeing or hearing a dog. This is a phobia. The hallmark of a phobia is the child's preoccupation with the object or situation he fears. Severe phobias can be disabling.

Causes

The determination of the cause of a phobia depends largely on the theoretical position of the clinician. In some cases, it seems easy to explain the initial anxiety: a big dog barked loudly, jumped on the child or bit him, and from then on the child had great fear of dogs. The frightening incident conditioned him to a fear. Often, the parent will try to recondition the fearful child by introducing the feared animal as a pet, usually with no success. The best pets are sometimes mean, dirty, and a general nuisance, and it is particularly unfortunate when a pet that has been introduced to reassure a child is banished after a short stay because of its aggressive or messy habits. A pet may also be dismissed because the child failed to take care of it in the expected fashion. In any case, the child is likely to react to the loss of the pet, and this may surprise the parents since the child feared the animal, or seemed indifferent to it. The child's reaction may arise not from a feeling of loss, but from guilt or anxiety. Children readily identify with animals, seeing themselves in the dog that bites or messes. If such a dog is exiled, the child may feel he will be sent away for the same reasons.

A shade more complicated would be an explanation in terms of a vicarious frightening experience—that is, an incident occurring to someone else, but observed by the child or reported to him, and thereby implanting some fear. But it is extremely doubtful that fears based solely on experiences of this sort would be permanent or that they would fit the clinical criteria of phobia.

The next level of complication involves repression. English Bagby described two childhood phobias which persisted into adulthood. The traumatic episodes involved a forbidden and unconfessed act on the part of the child. According to Bagby, the element of guilt and the unpleasant nature of the experience caused "protective forgetting." When the original event was recalled, many years later, the phobias disappeared *(1951)*. The first explanation, i.e., conditioning, was that a real and frightening experience caused the morbid fear; the second explanation adds the complication of guilt and the necessity for repression. Both explanations accept the premise that a single experience can be the cause of a long-lasting phobia.

S. Rachman and C. G. Costello offer a learning theory explanation, but believe that the conditioning agent is an attack of anxiety which is then associated with a particular object, place, or activity *(1961)*. Freud also noted that a phobia generally sets in after a first attack of anxiety had been experienced in specific circumstances (e.g., in the street, on a moving vehicle, or in solitude), but sought to find the cause of the anxiety *(1909)*. It is this original cause which makes the phobia persist; the phobia persists because it protects the patient against a greater anxiety. The phobia gives him something to fear which is outside of himself, something which can be avoided. This is better than being afraid of something which is inner and seems inescapable.

Animal and Transportation Phobias

The paradigm of animal phobias in childhood is the horse phobia of five-year-old Hans, reported by Freud *(1909, 1953)*. In this study, he showed that the child's phobia was not derived from the frightfulness of the horse, but from the child's own frightening impulses that were first projected, and then displaced. A phobia starts with repression; the original offensive idea or wish is made unconscious. Hans' repressed wish was to attack his father. The next step is projection: It is not he who wishes to attack the father, but the father who will attack him. The third step is displacement: It is not the father who is dangerous; it is the horse. Fearing the horse instead of the father is a way of solving the conflict. The hatred is deplaced onto the horse, and the father, who has been loved and hated simultaneously, can now be loved completely. Freud also points out that a boy associates with his father daily, whereas the threatening horse can be avoided by not going out of doors. The dynamics are identical with the night fears previously described, except that the feared object is real.

Horse phobias are now virtually non-existent; the most common animal phobias involve dogs or insects. Dogs are likely to be feared because they might bite, and this also applies to some insects, although most of these are feared because of their association with dirt. Spiders and snakes are characteristically dreaded because of the fear of physical contact and the anticipation of a crawling sensation, suggesting that unacceptable sexual, rather than aggressive, feelings are being projected onto these innocent animals. It is doubtful that treatment would be recommended for a child who had no problem other than a single animal phobia, however.

Phobias involving transportation (e.g., trains, busses, cars, or airplanes) are more likely to require treatment because they interfere more with the child's life. Again, the specific phobia must be carefully examined in order to establish the nature of the projected impulse. The disturbing factor may be the physical sensation of motion, the close contact with strange people, the fear of not returning, the possibility of accidents caused by wild drivers, and so on. In transportation phobias, special exceptions are usually made. For instance, a nine-year-old girl felt safe with women drivers, but not with men, but only on short trips. On long trips, even with women drivers, they might be held up by highway robbers. Another girl would travel only with some member of her family. She could not take school trips with her class because she foresaw that terrible catastrophes would befall them, but she was quite happy to stay behind and imagine them perishing. The fantasies of these two girls suggest that the first is struggling mainly with sexual wishes; the second, primarily with aggressive feelings.

Such phobias trouble the parents as well as inconvenience them, and help is sought. Psychological study reveals that a child who has a severe phobia avoids many other situations, and that he usually suffers from other, less obvious inhibitions and restrictions. Treatment then is aimed not only at relief of the specific symptom, but also at freeing the total personality.

School Phobia

Without question, the phobia of greatest concern (and one unique to childhood) is school phobia. The extensive material available attests to the professional interest in school phobia. Prolonged absence from school cannot legally be ignored; this symptom demands attention. A child's reluctance to go to school is the result of a morbid dread of some aspect of the school situation—the teacher, other children, the journey, eating in the lunchroom, or any other detail of school life. It is usually accompanied by somatic complaints which disappear once the child knows that he does not have to go to school. H. S. Lippman has given a graphic description of a typical parental reaction to this kind of situation:

They discussed with Anne the happenings of the past few days in school, and asked about the subject matter, her teachers, and her schoolmates. They tried to learn something about her recent social life, especially to discover any unfortunate emotional experience. When they found nothing to explain why Anne should have a dread of school, they suspected that she was withholding facts from them. The next morning when it was time for Anne to leave for school, her parents became anxious. Her father was annoyed by what he termed "nonsense"; there was nothing to fear. Anne admitted as much. He had to go to work, and he became angry as Anne started to cry and he insisted that she put on her wraps and come along with him to school. When the mother acted as though she felt he was doing the wrong thing, he became more annoyed; the mother's behavior increased his doubts about what he was doing. Realizing that this was no time to change his mind, however, since that would only confuse Anne more, he got into the car with her. Anne cried all the way to school, saying she knew she could not make it. Her father assured her she would get along well as soon as she was at her desk with all her friends around her. Anne and her father walked up the school steps, but as they approached the entrance Anne grew pale and vomited.

Realizing that he had made a mistake, her father returned home with her . . . Usually, driven by their anxiety, parents first urge their child to go back to school, beg him, and then try to bribe him with gifts. When these methods fail they often resort to punishment, in the belief that the child is being willful and stubborn. When parents become panicky about the child's not going to school, their anxiety intensifies the child's suffering. By the time they bring the child to a child guidance clinic on the advice of school or school social worker, the child feels ashamed of his helplessness and guilty about the anxiety he has caused his parents. Absence from school has made him feel that he is behind in his school work and will never be able to catch up with his classmates.[*]

Related Factors

In the general population of child guidance clinics, boys outnumber girls, but most authors report that school phobias are more common in girls:

	Girls	Boys
Eisenberg (1958)	10	16
Suttenfield (1954)	4	1
Talbot (1957)	16	8
Waldfogel, Tessman, and Hahn (1957)	25	28
Coolidge et al. (1960)	3	1
Van Houten (1948)	10	2
	68	56

[*]Quoted from H. S. Lippman, *Treatment of the Child in Emotional Conflict* (New York: McGraw-Hill Book Company, 1956), p. 86. Reproduced by permission.

School phobia may occur at any age, but it is more common in the lower elementary grades. When the acute symptoms develop late, there is often evidence that the foundation was laid in the beginning of school. There seems to be a direct relationship between age and the severity of the underlying disturbance (*Coolidge et al., 1960*). Interestingly, although school phobias occur in all mental ability groups, the child in real danger of failing does not develop this symptom. It is one of the paradoxes in the psychopathology of childhood that youngsters with clear-cut learning difficulties do not express a reluctance to go to school; they want to go even though they may have little success.

Parental Pathology and School Phobia

The role of the mother in creating a school phobia is frequently emphasized. Many authors agree with A. M. Johnson's assertion that school phobia is no more or less than a specific form of separation anxiety, a fear of separation shared equally by mother and child (*Johnson et al., 1941*). Leon Eisenberg described the behavioral cues by which mother and child communicate their anxiety about separation to one another (*1958*). From his material, one can see —or surmise—that by frequent, unconscious communication, the parent has taught the child to fear school. The mother herself thinks of school as a cold, impersonal place, and sympathizes excessively with the child's complaints. The child senses that her parent wishes her to remain home and, if this fits her own desires, a school phobia may be in the making.

There have been efforts to probe the origins of this mutual anxiety about separation. What precedes the outbreak of acute anxiety over the school situation? There has been confirmation of Johnson's original observations that mothers of phobic children have a poorly resolved dependency relationship with their own mothers (*1941*).

The typical mother is described as closely identifying with the child, and even subservient to his needs:

She is determined that there shall be no deprivation of either his physical or emotional needs and constantly sacrifices her own comfort and convenience to his . . . She adopts an "antiseptic" attitude toward him and and tries to protect him from pain, shock, and frustration. She goes to considerable trouble and planning to prevent his coming into contact with anything unpleasant, this category usually including the painful factors of life, e.g., sex, childbirth, illness and death. (*Waldfogel, 1957, p. 757.*)

J. C. Coolidge, P. B. Hahn, and Alice Peck commented that these mothers generally succeed in providing adequately for the infant, but that they have difficulty when the child begins to move toward independence (*1957*). Coolidge *et al.* related the necessity of frustrating the children, or disciplining them, to the mothers' neurotic conflicts about the aggression necessarily involved, in such parental behavior (*1962*). Such mothers view even the most ordinary or unavoidable privation as cruel and develop guilt feelings all out of proportion to the actual situation.

The literature on school phobia abounds with statements to the effect that it never exists in isolation, but is always intimately associated with a complementary neurosis in the mother (e.g., *Estes, Haylett, and Johnson, 1956*), leaving one with the impression that the mother is the cause. This explanation must be regarded as a partial one, for several reasons. First, the same dynamic conflicts have been observed in mothers of children with different kinds of problems (e.g., psychosomatic disorders and psychoses), so it is questionable that there is a specific cause-and-effect relationship between the mother's problems and the child's. Second, school phobia does not especially run in families. Why is only one child so affected? Third, investigations of parental psychopathology have not involved the use of control groups, so one cannot know how many mothers with the same conflicts are raising children who are free of phobias. Unfortunately, much of information about parents of disturbed children is gathered only *after* the children's symptoms are reported; and only after intensive study.

However, whatever the origin of the child's school phobia, there is no doubt that the mother's reaction will affect its duration and intensity. An immature mother will have a difficult time coping with her child's anxiety, and may reinforce, rather than alleviate, it. Reading the clinical case material, one wonders what was primary and what secondary —that is, how much of the mother's anxiety was engendered by the child's obvious distress, and to what extent her anxiety created his distress. Even when the separation anxiety starts with the mother, the psychopathology will, after a time, be internalized, becoming an integral part of the child's personality structure. The child learns the psychology of the mother and makes it his own. In most of these cases, one sees only a continuous cycle, with no clear-cut starting point.

It would be worthwhile to investigate patterns of maternal behavior with respect to children's fears. All children are reluctant to go to school at sometime or other, but no effort has been made to see what parents normally do about it. Careful study might define more sharply the unique features of the "phobogenic" mother.

School Phobia and the Child

In the concern for the psychopathology of the parents, it is easy to lose sight of what happens inside the phobic child. Forbidden wishes are repressed, projected, and displaced in classical fashion. The end-result, and clearly one major purpose, of the school phobia is that the child remains home; since his mother is usually also home, he can be

with her. (It would be interesting to know the incidence of reported cases of school phobia in homes of working mothers.) Coolidge *et al.*, describe the psychology of the child as follows:

The central concern in the child is the fear of abandonment by the parents. The child fears that some danger from the outside world will befall the parents, particularly the mother, and that thus abandoned, he will either die of lack of care or because of lack of protection be a victim of violence from the outside world. This underlying fear is considerably intensified at the outbreak of the symptom, bringing with it an increase in the dammed-up aggressive fantasies which stem from murderous wishes toward the parents. These are experienced as too dangerous, and the child defends himself by regressing to increased dependence on the mother while displacing the anger associated with his hostile wishes to the outside world, notably the school. *(1962, p. 330.)*

In the above analysis, the role of aggression is paramount. The child, fearful of aggression, regresses to earlier dependency. And, increasingly dependent upon his mother for protection, he is more than ever in conflict about his feelings of aggression toward her; without her he will be totally defenseless against the violence he imagines in, or projects into, the outside world. Remaining at home reassures him that his hostile wishes against the mother are not coming true, and that he is still well-protected.

The fact that girls are more prone to school phobias than boys might be related to their greater readiness to admit to dependence or anxiety. Girls are also likely to be more ambivalent toward their mothers, and thus less able to express their aggression openly. It would be a mistake to assume (as Coolidge *et al.* appear to) that hostility is the sole agent in the formation of a school phobia. Erotic components undoubtedly play a considerable role in the arousal of the troublesome hostility, as the case of Mary Ann will show a little later.

Treatment

From what has been said, it is obvious that the treatment of school phobia involves the collaboration of the mother, the child, and the school. The school must help the absent child to maintain his academic progress; preferably through individual help in the school building rather than in the home. When the child returns to class, he may need special consideration; his attendance may be irregular at first, but the school must welcome him even if he is absent more than he is present. The teacher may have to seat him close to herself, meet him at the door, modify toilet or lunch rules for him and, above all, accept him on whatever terms are necessary. Fortunately, children with school phobias are seldom overtly aggressive, and it is relatively easy to persuade school staff to accommodate them. All hands should cooperate in the effort to get the child back to school, on any basis short of physical coercion. Counseling of the mother may give her an insight into the child's need for independence and help her to recognize the influence of her own anxiety.

With young children, the results of therapy for school phobias have been encouraging. Samuel Waldfogel, Ellen Tessman, and Pauline Hahn believe in prompt action in the event of an incipient school phobia and suggest that this symptom be considered an emergency in clinical practice (1959). In 25 out of 26 cases in which treatment was initiated promptly, school attendance was resumed after a few weeks. However, when treatment was delayed for a semester or more (5 cases), it persisted for months and even years. In one case, the phobia persisted after four years of therapy.

On the basis of these observations, the authors undertook an exploratory program of identifying cases for early treatment. As a field unit of the Judge Baker Guidance Center, the authors spent some time in the public schools of Newton, Massachusetts, encouraging the referral of children with incipient school phobias. Over a two-year period, 36 such children were referred. Sixteen were seen briefly in the school setting, 4 were referred to the Guidance Center for more intensive therapy, 5 showed spontaneous recovery, and 11 were untreated either because the parents were uncooperative or because treatment time was not available. A follow-up study indicated that the untreated children were not as well off as the others. Only 3 of the 11 were free of symptoms, compared with 22 of the 25 who were treated. The authors point out the probable connection between unwillingness to accept treatment and the severity of the problem, a selective factor which suggests that the treated cases were likely to improve with or without treatment. Nevertheless, they conclude that this pilot program proved the value of early detection and prompt intervention (1959).

Logically, the treatment of school phobia should vary in accordance with the nature and depth of the conflicts involved, but in practice, the form of treatment is more likely to be determined by the therapist's theoretical orientation. A.A. Lazarus, Davison, and Polefka describe the application of classical and operant conditioning procedures in the treatment of a nine-year-old boy with a school phobia (1965). They offer two motivations for the avoidance behavior (i.e., the phobia): intense fear of the school situation and secondary reinforcers (i.e., special attention from parents, siblings, and therapists). The first part was handled by systematic desensitization, taking the boy back to school for short visits accompanied by the therapist. In this stage, the authors speak of allaying the anxiety by means of distraction and humor, a method which does not work with severely phobic children. In the second stage of the treatment program, the operant conditioning phase, the boy was rewarded with various tokens for remaining in school on his own. The authors describe the boy's father as harsh and restrictive and the mother as inconsistent and ambivalent. The authors mention briefly that they gave the parents a "long list of specific 'do's' and 'don't's'" to which the parents responded "in an intelligent and receptive manner" *(1965, p. 229)*. The entire treatment program extended over four and a half months.

The following case illustrates the psychotherapeutic treatment of a five-year-old girl with a severe school phobia. Mary Ann was seen twice a week for almost a year; the treatment was deemed successful in that the school phobia was gone and did not return during the follow-up period of ten years. Although the report focusses on the psychodynamics revealed in the course of psychotherapy, collateral methods were used which might be called desensitization and operant conditioning. During her year of treatment she attended a private kindergarten as often and as long as she could with the aid of any reassurance and encouragement which the mother and teacher could give. Secondary gains were reduced as much as possible by studied indifference to her when she was at home during school hours. It was particularly important that her mother did not help her with schoolwork during these times because Mary Ann was intellectually ambitious and disliked the prospect of her friends getting ahead of her. The dynamics are complex and are presented here in some detail so that the reader can form his own conclusions, independent of the author's (who was also the therapist).

Diagnostic Evaluation. Mary Ann was referred to a child psychiatry clinic when she was five years and nine months old, because she could not attend first grade. She cried, refused to go, and vomited if forced. Since she was so young and so upset, the school recommended that she remain at home for the year. Subsequently, Mary Ann began to show the same reactions whenever her mother left her. She had difficulty getting to sleep, and whined, and cried. Her father often lay down with her to help her get to sleep. There was a history of thumb sucking from the age of six months, for which she had been reprimanded, spanked, shamed, and "painted" with bad-tasting ointment. At the time of study, she sucked her thumb only at night.

Until she was five, the parents lived with the maternal grandparents, and the mother worked as a secretary until they moved into their own home. The maternal grandfather died shortly before the move; shortly after the move, a baby brother was born.

The mother was an attractive and girlish person. Many observers commented on her anxiety and helplessness, her lack of imagination regarding Mary Ann's feelings, and her occasional angry look when discussing her daughter's troubles. She was quick to discuss her own difficulties and gagged and vomited at moments of stress, as Mary Ann did. She was particularly naïve about sexual matters, and reported that her mother-in-law had to tell her everything. She did not recognize her own aggression and tried to maintain an air of constant cheerfulness and sweetness.

Mary Ann was an attractive child, robust and alert, with an IQ of exactly 100. In the first few interviews, she could not be separated from her mother, and sat on her lap much of the time. On the other hand, she was frankly aggressive, stepping on her mother's foot by accident, blowing in her face, and talking about how she liked to tease her mother by putting worms on her. She talked a lot about playing house with a girl friend, and said that she always wanted to be the mother.

Treatment: On the whole, treatment was stormy, with great excitement and outpourings of emotion. In order to maintain a clear view of the separation problem, Mary Ann attended a private kindergarten for the rest of the year.

The first stage of treatment dealt with her feelings about her teacher and mother. She declared that she was afraid of the teacher, but it soon became clear that she was jealous and envious of the teacher. It was easy to show her that it was she who was angry at the teacher—from jealousy—

and that she assumed that the teacher was likewise angry with her (projection). The displacement from the mother to teacher then became obvious. For weeks she was afraid that her mother was angry with her and complained that her mother was not smiling at her. She made elaborate efforts to please her mother and constantly pestered her for praise and approval. Casual indifference was interpreted as punishment.

On the other hand, she said that her mother was not really pretty, that she just had pretty clothes. She suggested that her mother might sleep with someone other than the father, and dreamed that her mother was sleeping with Davy Crockett. Her constant fear that her mother was angry with her was interpreted as a projection of her own anger and expectation of punishment. During this period she was attending kindergarten with fair regularity, but life at home was very difficult.

In about the third month of treatment, Mary Ann made a rash of confessions to her mother. The first crimes confessed were unimportant ones, but they were soon followed by confessions of sexual games with an older boy, a neighbor, which astonished and frightened the mother. The mother kept the therapist informed by letter (in addition to weekly interviews), and wrote the story as follows: "Mary Ann and this friend saw a picture of a nude woman, a skeleton and a man with a knife, which had blood on it. The boy told her he was going to make her into a skeleton. Also, at the same time, the two of them were curious about the sex of each other. They were playing upstairs. I knew nothing until she told me today . . ."

Several days later: "Yesterday I got Mary Ann off to school. When she came home, it started again. She wanted to stick a knife in herself, hurt her privates, cut her ears off, pull out her hair. At supper she wanted to stick a knife in her brother. After supper she wanted to see her father without clothes, then it was me. She screamed and cried all evening about hurting herself. Kept yelling, 'Please help me forget about the picture!' She still wanted to do something bad to herself.

"The next morning she could not go to school. I gave her an eggnog. She told me she thought I'd poisoned it. She talked constantly about the picture. She wants to take a gun and shoot her father. She'd like to duck her brother's head in the toilet. She can't stand cigarettes and small birthday candles; she thinks she should do something to her privates with them. Wants to burn all of us, so she can get a lot of money. She felt better at noon, and ate a little bit. Then she thought she would kick the house down, burn herself with my iron, dump water all over, break my perfume, tear her clothes and all of ours. This is all so unbelievable; it isn't my Mary Ann at all."

For a period of about a month, the excitement continued on and off. Confessions of wanting to steal everything, to disrobe, that her private parts felt "stiff," and wishes to destroy herself and everyone else were repeated constantly.

During this period, the therapist reviewed with Mary Ann the details of her sexual games, which had been stimulated by an older girl as well as by the boy. Her jealousy and rage at almost everyone was discussed. She was angry at her brother because he was a boy and had something she didn't have. She was angry at her mother because she had both a husband and a baby. She was angry at her father because he preferred the mother. (He had discontinued sleeping with Mary Ann by this time.) Everyone had something, or was something, that she was not. To add to her sorrow, she had the sneaking suspicion that she was somehow to blame. She feared that she had damaged herself with her sexual experimentation, and that no one loved her because of her badness. She was tremendously excited sexually, but tried hard not to give in to the temptation to masturbate. She was full of anger and guilt. A better explanation of sex differences was provided for her, and it was also necessary to set her straight on the origin of babies. She had some idea of the father's part, but imagined it as a sadistic attack on the woman.

After the spate of confession and the turmoil of excitement, things settled down. Mary Ann began to take great interest in school, particularly in writing, where she excelled. She was pleased that her copying looked exactly like the printed words of the teacher's. She also wanted to walk like the therapist and suggested that they could both wear the same kind of shoes. Every effort was made to supervise her more closely and reduce the external sources of sexual stimulation. The next fall, she entered first grade and proceeded to do well. Two years later, her mother returned to see the therapist about a problem of her own. When the therapist inquired about Mary Ann, the mother glowed with pride about her success, and seemed to have forgotten the events just described.

In this situation, the concatenation of internal and external events was too much for a five-year-old to handle and little assistance was given by the mother, who fit the description of infantile dependency given by many authors. She shared many of Mary Ann's somatic and anxiety symptoms, and was particularly prone to denial, especially about sexual matters. It would be an oversimplification, however, to say that this mother was the "cause" of Mary Ann's phobias.

The case is also interesting from another point of view. Much childhood fantasy is unbelievably diffuse and violent. Mary Ann's fantasies about her body and about being poisoned are not unlike the ideas expressed by adult schizophrenic patients. However, she did not lose her sense of reality. She *felt* these things but she *did not believe* them. Also, she did not draw away from people but remained open to their influence. The admixture of sexual and aggressive feelings, of simultaneous love and hate, of attraction to and fear of sexual excitement, created inner conflicts for which the school phobia would probably have been only a temporary solution.

Hysteria in Childhood

Although the diagnosis of hysteria is common in adult psychiatry, it is seldom applied to children—not because hysterical symptoms are rare in childhood, but because clinicians hesitate to affix the formal name "hysteria" to be-havior disorders in children. This reluctance is due, for one thing, to the fact that childhood disorders rarely take the crystallized form of a classical neurosis. A child's behavior is relatively fluid, and the diagnosis of hysteria implies fixity and permanence. Hysterical symptoms in children (e.g., tics) make a short-lived appearance to express a transitory conflict. Also, the diagnosis "hysteria" has implications about underlying structure and cause, and such knowledge is not easily obtained in a diagnostic evaluation. It is not, however, unusual to see hysterical outbreaks in adolescents, and one should be familiar with the psychological meaning of this term.

As in all neuroses, repression is the first defense. If the repression were entirely successful, there would be no anxiety or specific neurotic symptom. However, if the conflicts are great, complete repression means a constant drain of energy. Successful repression, which would save the patient from obvious symptoms, would leave his personality weak and impoverished. This might be discernible as a general emotional emptiness or intellectual sterility, with complaints of moods of depression, vague dissatisfactions with the self (and others), and a feeling of failure to get anywhere in life. If these symptoms were understood as the side-effects of massive repression, such persons could be classified as having an "hysterical character," even in the absence of specific neurotic symptoms.

Symptomatic Picture

Hysterical symptoms appear when repression breaks down and the unconscious thoughts emerge in some guise; they can be seen as (1) isolated emotional outbursts; (2) disturbance of sensation or motility; (3) alterations in consciousness; or (4) temporary loss of a sense of reality.

The first of these is commonly recognized as hysterical. In sudden outbursts, all the feelings and ideas which are normally hidden come to the surface; the person weeps, rages, goes into a panic, and loses all control. Later, he is surprised, apologetic, or may even have forgotten what happened. Almost everyone has had such episodes at some time or another, but they occur more frequently, with less provocation, and with less behavioral control in an hysterical neurosis. (More diagnostic tolerance is allowed for adolescents, who have a special propensity for hysterical behavior because of the unique conflicts of adolescence.)

The second category of the classical picture of hysteria involves another mechanism. The source of conflict is not projected, as in phobia, but is *converted* into some disturbance of sensation or motility. The conflict and all the anxiety are repressed, and the patient may even seem quite cheerful. This diagnostic sign has been called *la belle indifference.* Conversion symptoms have almost infinite variety; hysteria has been known as the "great imitator" because hysterics can simulate almost any known organic condition. There can be anaesthesia, i.e., a loss of sensation, or hyperaethesia, increase of sensation. There can be a loss of motility (e.g., hysterical paralysis) or an abnormal increase of motility (e.g., tics).

In the third category of hysterical symptoms there is a loss of consciousness (e.g., fainting, sleep walking), or a splitting of consciousness (as in the famous cases of double personalities or amnesias). These are often called "dissociative reactions." In these states one part of the mind, in an effort to blot out a conflicting wish, represses another part in which free expression of the forbidden impulse is permitted. This is the psychological condition which exists in hypnosis. The hypnotist artificially, and temporarily, produces hysteria. In the execution of a posthypnotic suggestion, the source of the suggestion is repressed; the person performing the acts has no conscious volition or awareness of why he does them. Not everyone is susceptible to this kind of suggestion; subjects who are easily hypnotized usually have hysterical personalities.

In the fourth category—disturbances of the sense of reality—the most common symptom is hallucination, more probably visual than auditory. Hallucinations ordinarily signify the presence of a psychosis rather than an hysterical psychoneurosis in adults, but the reverse is true of children. (Reasons for this are given in a later discussion of the psychodynamics of hysterical hallucinosis.) There are obvious symptomatic differences between the psychotic and the neurotic hallucination. The neurotic hallucinatory experience is an isolated disturbance of sensation (as a tic is an isolated motor act), and it is always the same in character. Despite its vividness, the hysterical patient knows that others do not share it, and he builds no elaborate superstructure on it. The hallucinatory experience remains isolated from the rest of the hysteric's personality, and he knows that it is a symptom. In schizophrenia, however, hallucinations are the beginning of another reality, one constructed by the patient to explain the appearance of the hallucination. One hallucination leads to another; in each is heard a definite voice which seems real. The schizophrenic acts on the basis of his hallucination, unable to distinguish it from reality.

History and Incidence

For centuries, hysteria has interested doctors and others faced with the problem of differentiating between the "real," the "imagined," the "organic," and the "functional." The word itself was originally coined by Hippocrates. It comes from *hysteron*, meaning uterus, since it was originally applied to a convulsive condition said to occur in widows and spinsters, presumably because of migration of the uterus. Medical interest in the subject was revived toward the end of the nineteenth and beginning of the twentieth centuries, when many new theories were advanced. H. Bernheim *(1897)* and J. Babinski *(1908)* suggested that hysteria was psychological rather than an organic process and explained it on the basis of self-suggestion, or autohypnotism. This meant that hysteria need not be restricted to women—an idea first considered ridiculous. Freud studied hysteria in an effort to understand the reason for the specific self-suggestion. Why does the patient develop an hysterical paralysis or blindness? For what purpose does he develop limitations of sensation or motor activity? Freud soon saw that the patient did not create the symptom voluntarily and that the true reason was unconscious. From an analysis of hysterical symptoms, he arrived at a formula for a neurotic symptom: (1) inner conflict; (2) unsuccessful repression; and (3) return of the repressed conflict in the form of the symptom. According to this, hysterical symptoms contain some part of the original conflict, but in a form unrecognizable to the patient. (Illustrative cases may be found in the section on Cause and Treatment.)

Since the beginning of this century, an apparent change in forms of psychoneurosis has made the "grand hysteria" of Charcot's day increasingly rare. Robert Waelder suggests that this shift in symptoms is a result of changes in methods of child rearing. In Victorian times, management of children was strict. There was a rigid routine, a general policy of suppression, little regard for the intensity of a child's emotions, and little awareness of his potential for emotional excitement. In the event of psychological difficulties, repression was the only recourse available to the child. Sometime around World War I, the pendulum swung in the opposite direction, and extreme indulgence became the fashion. This kind of rearing produced children who were poorly equipped to bear anxiety and frustration, and their personalities were molded so as to avoid any situation that might arouse anxiety. The characteristic defense mechanisms of children raised very permissively would be avoidance, acting out, and pleasure-seeking, rather than repression and inhibition which provided the substratum of classical neuroses *(1960)*. Whether Waelder's historical explanation suffices or not, it is an accepted fact that the classical clinical pictures of hysterical and obsessional-compulsive neuroses are becoming more rare, and diffuse character disorders are becoming more frequent.

The literature on psychopathology in childhood contains few references to hysteria. The most complete psychodynamic exposition is provided by G. H. J. Pearson *(1949)*. In 1947, C. F. Walker reported a follow-up study of two girls who had hysterical difficulty in walking at the ages of 11 and 13 years. Both girls had made adequate adjustments, and remained well. In 1953, E. Robins and P. O'Neal found 27 cases of childhood hysteria in 51,311 children admitted to a metropolitan children's hospital during a 15-year period. Also in 1953, L. Dawes reported a single case of grand hysteria in an adolescent girl. In 1962, Irving Kaufman reported a single case of conversion hysteria in an eight-year-old girl with hysterical blindness.

The most extensive report on hysteria in childhood was provided by James T. Proctor. He makes the point that the diagnosis of hysteria is established more frequently in medical than in psychiatric settings and asserts that its incidence varies in different cultural environments. He reported on 191 unselected, consecutively diagnosed cases in the child psychiatric unit of the Department of Psychiatry, University of North Carolina School of Medicine. This group included twenty-five cases, or 13 per cent, which were diagnosed as conversion hysteria or dissociative hysteric reactions. Proctor remarks that:

Our cases are often of a dramatic nature, and, from perusal of the literature, it seems they are more often florid than commonly seen in other areas of the country; for example, tic-like pelvic thrusts associated with a request for circumcision in a ten-year-old Negro boy; paraplegia in an eleven-year-old Negro female.°

The following table shows some comparisons between hysteric patients and other child psychiatry patients in Proctor's sample:

	Age	Sex	Race
Hysterics (25)	40% (under 12)	56% males	33% Negro
	16% (12)	44% females	67% White
	44% (13-16)		
Others (166)	55% (under 12)	63% males	10% Negro
	9% (12)	37% females	90% White
	36% (13-16)		

differences in order to explain the relatively large number of hysterics.

One question concerns the high incidence of childhood hysteria in our geographic area. We get hints from observations of our culture, with its largely rural population distribution, low educational level and generally low economic status . . . Our geographic area has been spoken of as the Bible Belt, and even over the radio in the early morning one can hear sermons about hellfire and damnation, with the firm belief expressed that Christ's return to North Carolina is imminent, with various magical ideas about why he is to return to North Carolina specifically. There is also considerable residual belief in hex doctors, faith healing and other magic . . . Such primitive and repressive attitudes are, of course, important, but there are further factors of early stimulation of the child by discussion of original sin, as well as through disapproval of all pleasure, which hint at, and perhaps emphasize, the desirable nature of these things, while at the same time denying them. Such inconsistencies are often acted out; e.g., it is not uncommon for sex to

Proctor's figures indicate that the diagnosis is at least as common in boys as in girls, that hysterical children tend to be older than the other patients in child psychiatry, and that relatively more Negroes than whites are diagnosed as hysterics. There are other reports to the effect that hallucinations are more common in Negro than in white children (*Bender and Lipkowitz, 1940; Esman, 1962*). Discussing related factors, Proctor emphasizes cultural

be taboo, yet to find repeated exposures to the primal scene, the son sleeping with the mother to an advanced age, or the daughter with the father. This results in great stimulation with denial of even verbal discharge, and we are reminded of Freud's ideas about accumulated tension and its relation to hysteria.°

Proctor thus suggests that extreme inconsistency between action and word is the breeding ground for hysterical reactions. The child's sexual feelings and Oedipal wishes are kept alive by the parents' unconscious seduction while, at the same time, sexuality is decried and linked with horrible punishment on a verbal level. The child is made totally unable to admit or accept his sexual feelings, and prevented by constant stimulation from completely repressing them. The sexual feelings emerge as an hysterical symptom which discharges some of the tension without arousing anxiety, since its nature is not consciously recognized. Proctor, like Waelder, thus attempts to link the patient's culture with his choice of symptom.

°Quoted from James T. Proctor, "Hysteria in Childhood," *American Journal of Orthopsychiatry,* XXVIII (1958), p. 397. Reproduced by permission.

°Proctor, *op. cit.,* p. 398.

Psychodynamics of Specific Hysterical Symptoms

Because they are so commonly observed, tics deserve special mention. Tics usually involve the musculature of the face, neck and head, as in blinking the eye, wrinkling the nose, stretching or twisting the mouth, rolling the tongue around outside of the mouth, clearing the throat, yawning, shrugging the shoulders, shaking the head, and so forth. In diagnosis, a tic must be first be differentiated from neurological conditions (e.g., postencephalitis or infectious chorea). Then, within the category of the functional, a further distinction must be made between transitory and permanent tics. A child with a tic which has persisted for months usually has other demonstrable psychological problems as well.

Many times the tic contains a clue to the underlying conflict. Some facial grimaces, for instance, look suspiciously as if the person is aggressively making a face at somebody. The head-shaker is saying "No" to some unconscious wish. Wrinkling of the nose seems to say, "Something doesn't smell good around here." Blinking the eye suggests an attempt to blot out something which was seen. The child has no awareness either of the tic or of the feelings or memory which prompts it. He can neither stop it nor explain it.

Tics are isolated disturbances of motility, and are usually hysterical. But they are closely related to the fidgeting which plagues schoolteachers and parents. It is almost universal among schoolboys but, in its severe form, it can be as great a problem as any other in child psychopathology. Adults often interpret the restlessness of children as purely voluntary, admonishing them to sit still as if all the child had to do was to want to cooperate. Actually, the fidgeting may be quite beyond his control. In some cases, the restlessness is no more than a sign of diffuse anxiety, a kind of general movement that is an effort to restore a feeling of ease. At other times, it has a more specific meaning; it may be used as a defense against some other motor act which is forbidden, such as masturbation (see Chapter 9), so that the child fidgets in his seat in order to keep himself from doing something even worse. It is very annoying to adults, but few children do it just to annoy.

Margaret S. Mahler points out that children who fidget or have tics have often had many restrictions placed on the use of their muscles. Their parents require perfect behavior, but are not interested in their locomotion, social and athletic ability, or independence. Motor development may have been restricted because the parents feared the child's experimentation with his body might cause him some physical harm; in some cases, early illness may have limited the child's activity. Such restrictions are particularly difficult for youngsters who are what Margaret Fries called the "hyperactive congenital" type *(1944)*. A tic is a compromise between doing and not doing, a compromise which Mahler implies would not be required if the parents had restricted the child's activity less. It is clear that pathological motor activity is only aggravated by constant parental remonstrance, but there are no controlled studies to suggest the degree to which parents are to blame for its beginning.

Hysterical Hallucinations. The problem of hallucinations in children has been discussed by Lauretta Bender and H. Lipkowitz *(1940)*, Louise Despert *(1948)*, and M. F. Weiner *(1961)*. Brenner *(1951)* and Aaron Esman *(1962)* presented clinical material on seven such children, of two to seven years. Only one was described as clinically psychotic. These cases were not formally labelled "hysterical," but were discussed only in terms of the symptom. However, they fit the paradigm of repression, projection, and displacement developed here for hysteria. All their hallucinations were visual. What the children saw, in many instances, were scenes in which a phobia appeared to come true—a biting rat or dog, a butterfly, or crawling bugs, roaches or snakes. Each child hallucinated only one or two of these creatures. The hallucination goes one step further in projection than the phobia.

These hallucinations can be explained in terms of the level of ego development, in terms of internal conflict, and in terms of past experience. Reality-testing is directly related to age, and young children normally have more difficulty distinguishing fact from fantasy than do older children. It is quite possible that hallucinatory experiences in pre-school children are more common than we know, since such an experience might be brushed aside by both parent and child if it were not accompanied by intense anxiety. In the cases described in the literature on hallucinations, the experiences were recurrent and very frightening, indicating that more than a simple error of judgment was involved.

All authors agree that psychological stress prompted the outbreak of the hallucinations. The impact of a psychological conflict overwhelms the child's perception of reality, and the visual hallucinations represent a regression to an earlier stage of ego-functioning in which a thought is equal to a real image (see Wishful Hallucination, Chapter 2). Weiner explains these hallucinatory experiences as "attempts to deal with internal emotional stimuli by translating them into concrete perceptual material that will allow the child to utilize his previously learned stimulus-response patterns" (1961, p. 550). The precise nature of the conflict varies but, in the reported cases, worries about pregnancy and wishes to have a baby were crucial predisposing factors. To Brenner's patient, a little girl of three and

a half, the hallucinated bugs represented male seeds that were flying around in the air and which might enter her vagina. His report makes it clear why she chose this particular fantasy and why it had fearful significance for her (1951).

Past experiences sometimes predispose a child to form hallucinations under psychological stress. Bender and Lipkowitz (1940) suggest that some children may be constitutionally endowed with a more vivid fantasy life and raise the possibility that a constitutional difference of this type might explain the greater incidence of hallucinations in Negro than in white children. Although Esman made the same observation regarding incidence, he thought it more probable that "many Negro children, due to well-defined socio-cultural influences, suffer from significant deviations in ego development, particularly in the area of reality testing and impulse control, so that the pathways to direct discharge and loss of differentiation are more open to them" (1962, p. 340). He presents five cases which corroborates Proctor's thesis that excessive stimulation combined with punitive moralism provides fertile ground for the development of an hysterical symptom. Specifically, Esman suggests that repeated visual exposure to sexual scenes and adult genital organs (in families where sexual attitudes alternate between extreme laxity and extreme puritanism) are characteristic of children suffering from visual hallucinations.

The following case example differs from those described in the literature, in that it occurred in an adolescent girl and was auditory, rather than visual. The experience was rather casually described to the therapist and, had it not been for other problems, it is doubtful anyone would have learned about it.

Daphne was in psychotherapy from the age of nine to eleven because of excessive fearfulness, crying spells, a phobia of death, and difficulties in school and with friends. At 15, she voluntarily returned to her therapist because of a recurrence of some of her old problems. She had no dates with boys and found it very difficult to concentrate at school. Casually, she mentioned that when it was quiet and she was taking an examination or supposed to be doing her homework, she heard a kind of warning signal like a low whistle. Her hallucination was always the same, and she realized that only she could hear it. Nevertheless, it seemed very real. She could not understand its source: "It just comes by itself."

From the previous therapy, a great deal was known about Daphne's early experiences. She was the older of two children in a family of limited means. Daphne slept in her parents' bedroom until the age of four. About then, she was sent to her grandparents for some months because of the sudden hospitalization of her father and her mother's wish to remain near him during his illness. Daphne was told only that it would be "a nice change" to visit with her grandparents. Other traumatic events included a kidney condition when she was six, at which time her brother was born. It was also known that she had engaged in considerable sexual play with other girls her age, usually strip teases and parading around in the nude. Her early ideas about marriage revolved around notions of undressing and exhibiting.

In early adolescence, Daphne became concerned about her masturbation and told her parents about some vaginal irritation. They consulted a close relative, who casually examined her at home and tried to reassure them. As a result of this physical complaint, there was a good deal of "looking" on the part of the mother, Daphne, and the medical relative. Daphne was quite excited by this, but alarmed as well. At 14, she decided to give up masturbation for the sake of her health. She was sure that it irritated the vaginal area and was responsible for her acne.

Shortly after this resolve, Daphne heard the warning signal for the first time. When asked, her first association was to a repeated dream she had had as a younger child. In this dream, a rocket was about to take off into the air, and the hallucinatory signal was like a whistle to warn bystanders of the take-off. Now, when everything was very quiet, her mind wandered to romantic fantasies about herself and boys. The warning whistle stopped the fantasies. It was a warning to stop the mounting sexual excitement engendered by the fantasies (the rocket about to go off), a warning against masturbation, and it sounded like the "wolf" whistle of boys attracted to a girl, a whistle she would have liked to really hear.

Thus, the hallucination expressed both the wish to be sexually attractive and a warning about the dangers of sexuality. It cut short her fantasies, but it also kept her from thinking about the school work at hand.

Daphne's hallucination was midway between the normal person's voice of conscience and the malignant voices heard by the schizophrenic. In her case, no one would have raised the question of psychosis. She had an outgoing personality and a good sense of reality. Her previous history helped in establishing the diagnosis of hysteria.

Diagnostic differentiation is not always so easy; it is particularly difficult to assess the seriousness of symptoms which first appear during adolescence. Adolescents can become very disturbed and still emerge psychologically intact. On the other hand, the adult form of schizophrenia first appears at this time. Projective psychological testing is of some help, but there are still problems peculiar to adolescents (see Chapter 4) which limit their predictive value. In many cases, differential diagnosis is impossible until some time has elapsed.

Treatment of Hysteria

It is relatively easy to cure an hysterical symptom. Hysterics are characteristically friendly, establish a relationship quickly and, because they are usually suggestible, respond quickly to a therapist's contradictions of their symptoms. One would expect this, since they are so suggestible to their own thoughts. But it is easier to cure a specific symptom than to cure the hysterical patient of the tendency to create new ones. These are the patients who undergo miraculous recoveries on the basis of transference. While they are under the influence of the therapist, they do well, but relapses are common. It was largely because of his work with hysterics that Freud became dissatisfied with treating a symptom *per se;* a cure based on hypnosis or suggestion did not last. In place of suggestion, he tried to use insight, to relieve the repression so that the patient could work through the underlying conflict and thus obviate the need to form new symptoms.

Obsessive Compulsive Neurosis

Obsessive compulsive neurosis is the second major category of neurosis; it occurs in combined form, in conditions which are predominantly obsessional, or in those which are predominantly compulsive. In an obsessional state, the patient is plagued with omnipresent, disagreeable thoughts (e.g., he may find himself constantly reminded of dirty words which shock him or be haunted by thoughts of doing something violent). It has been called an ideational disturbance because the symptoms are ever-recurring ideas, rather than actions or bodily sensations. Adolescent or older patients, particularly, generally overevaluate intellect and attach great importance to ideas, words, and reasoning. The obsessional patient's thinking, however, does not serve to help him master his feelings or his environment. The obsessional neurotic is rendered helpless by intrusive and disturbing mental preoccupations.

The compulsive side of the neurosis involves acts. Like the obsessional neurotics, the compulsive neurotics are generally, and obviously, concerned about conflicts between aggressiveness and submissiveness, cruelty and gentleness, dirtiness and cleanliness, order and disorder. Compulsive symptoms vary, but they often have to do with cleanliness (e.g., compulsive handwashing), safety (e.g., checking door locks and gas jets), or superstitious rituals (e.g., doing things in a certain order, counting to a particular number, or touching things a certain number of times). The patient is aware of his behavior, but his recognition that it is foolish is not sufficient to give him control over it. He is compelled to perform the act or else be overwhelmed by anxiety. He is usually in an agony of doubt and can never satisfy himself that he (or perhaps a friend or relative) is *really* clean, *really* safe, or whatever else it is that is so important to him. This leads to a painful repetition of the compulsive act. Obsessive compulsive neurotics are also often depressed as well as anxious. The usual age of onset of a compulsion neurosis is later than the usual age for beginning hysteria, although children of all ages demonstrate short-lived compulsions.

Normal Variants

Diagnosis involves (1) differentiating between simple repetitions and compulsions; (2) differentiating between hysteria and obsessive compulsive neurosis; and (3) differentiating between schizophrenia and obsessive compulsive neurosis. The normal variants will be considered first.

Like almost every aspect of childhood psychopathology, obsessional compulsive symptoms have their prototype in normal development. At about two years of age, for instance, many children behave compulsively. They show a tremendous respect for order, routine, and sameness, and a corresponding anxiety about change or innovation, particularly about bedtime rituals. Such behavior is part of the magical thinking typical of the age (see Chapter 2). Similarly, the toilet-trained two-year-old may show great anxiety over dirt or accidents, and is far more likely to be worried about a spot on his clothes or a broken vase than his parents are. This is part of the reaction formation of the age, a defense which helps him to fight off instinctual wishes which he has recently learned are bad. He leans over backward to stay within the new laws.

The same kind of superstrictness may be observed in the young school child. Benjamin Spock, describing the compulsive behavior of children of eight to ten, attributes it to struggle to gain perfect self-control.

The commonest is stepping over cracks in the sidewalk. There's no sense to it, you just have a superstitious feeling that you ought to. It's what a psychiatrist calls a compulsion. Other examples are touching every third picket in a fence, making numbers come out even in some way, saying certain words before going through a door. If you think you have made a mistake, you must go way back to where you were absolutely sure you were right, and start over again.

The hidden meaning of a compulsion pops out in the thoughtless childhood saying, "Step on a crack, break your grandmother's back." Everyone has hostile feelings at times toward the people who are close to him, but his conscience would be shocked at the idea of really harming them and warns him to keep such thoughts out of his mind. And if a person's conscience becomes excessively stern, it keeps nagging him about such bad thoughts even after he has succeeded in hiding them away in his subconscious mind. He still feels guilty, though he doesn't know what for. It eases his conscience to be extra careful and proper about such a senseless thing as how to navigate a crack in the sidewalk.*

Spock remarks that mild compulsions should not be a cause for concern if the youngster is "happy, out-going, and doing well in school. On the other hand, I'd call a psychiatrist for help if a child has compulsions that occupy a lot of his time (for instance, excessive hand-washing, precautions against germs), or if he is tense, worried and unsociable."* One might also add that compulsions which are common to the child's group are like games, and probably mean relatively little to the individual. In a pathological state, the compulsion is unique to the child and is not shared by his contemporaries.

Psychology of Obsessive Compulsive Neurosis Compared with Hysteria

The problem of distinguishing between neuroses is complicated by the fact that a combination of characteristics may be found in a given individual (e.g., a single compulsive symptom in a basically hysterical personality or vice versa). Superficially, a phobia looks like a morbid preoccupation, but a phobic patient is in a better position than an obsessive compulsive neurotic because he can ward off his anxiety by avoiding certain objects or situations. He feels well as long as he is not in school, on a bus, on a height, in a closed room, or near a dog. The source of the anxiety has been projected outside and therefore can be avoided. But the obsessional neurotic's anxiety is internal; it is a morbid preoccupation from which there is no escape. The obsessional patient recognizes that there is no real danger, but he is ceaselessly tormented by inner fears and thoughts nevertheless. Often, these preoccupations are fears of what he will do to himself or others, rather than of what might be done to him.

The major difference between the compulsive act and the tic is that the compulsive patient is aware of what he is doing. The hysterical throat-clearer for example, does not know when or how often he clears his throat. The compulsive patient knows every time, and may try to stop altogether or do it only a specified number of times. The compulsive also usually has some sort

---

*Quoted from Benjamin Spock, *Baby and Child Care*. Rev. Cardinal Giant Ed., Pocket Books, Inc., 1963, p. 390. Reproduced by permission.

*Spock, *op. cit.*, p. 391.

of rationalization. He clears his throat so he won't choke or he is double-checking to make sure that he is getting rid of a postnasal secretion. The patient himself does not consider the rationalization sufficient to explain the number of times he has to do it, but he feels he has a reason.

Below the surface, there are characteristic differences in the defense mechanisms employed in the two major neuroses, although both involve repression and displacement. Often, the displacement in compulsion neurosis is onto a small detail which is magnified all out of proportion to its real significance. But the two neuroses differ in that the obsessive compulsive neurotic makes less use of projection and conversion, and more of *reaction formation, undoing,* and *isolation.* Reaction formation was described as frequent in the pre-school child, in whom excessive virtue reveals the strength of latent wishes. The obsessive compulsive is likely to set impossible standards for himself and others, and may suffer great guilt from his too-strict conscience (see Chapter 3). "Undoing" mechanisms are magical devices for appeasement, serving penance, or warding off imagined danger. Repetition, often taking the form of undoing, is described by Otto Fenichel:

The idea is that for the purpose of undoing, an activity has to be repeated with a different intention. What was once done with an instinctual intention must be repeated with a super-ego attitude. The warded-off instinct, however, tends to enter the repetition and has to be repeated. Usually, the number of necessary repetition quickly increases. "Favorite numbers," the choice of which may have a separate unconscious meaning, are set up, and determine the number of necessary repetitions; eventually, the repetitions may be replaced by counting. *(1945, p. 288.)*

The mechanism of isolation is very prominent in common compulsions about touching and not touching. The patient tries to put things into tight categories (e.g., dirty or clean, nice or not nice). The slightest suggestion of contact contaminates the object or thoughts belonging to the clean or nice category.

While the obsessive compulsive has a harsh and punitive superego, the obsessional neurotic behaves as if he were divided into both the bad child and the stern parent. He does a bad thing, or thinks a bad thought, and then punishes himself. A vignette from the history of an eleven-year-old girl illustrates this psychological operation, with the help of reaction formation and undoing:

Jane was a constant worrier and a perfectionist, always dissatisfied with herself. Her parents were bewildered because their reassurances had no effect; they felt guilty for somehow causing their daughter to feel insecure. They gave the following as an example of how Jane punished herself totally without cause:

One evening, Jane concocted an elaborate fruitade, for herself. Her father, who had a mild upper respiratory infection, thought she had made it for him, and drank it. When he discovered his error, he offered to help her make another drink. Jane refused, decided to take a piece of chocolate cake to her room instead, but left it untouched. Asked about it, Jane gave the following explanation: Her first reaction to her father's mistake had been one of great resentment and disappointment. Immediately, she felt guilty because, after all, he had been ill and perhaps she should have thought to make him a fresh fruit drink. To atone for her selfishness, she decided to postpone eating the cake. At first, she planned to eat it later, but then she decided she did not deserve to have it at all. So she stared at the cake all evening, and willed herself not to eat it. She found herself getting more and more resentful, and correspondingly more guilty, until, finally, she decided that she should try to give up eating cake *forever.*

In Jane's fierce concentration on this admittedly silly episode, there are hints that the renunciation involved pleasures more profound than eating the cake. One might also suspect that she harbored thoughts against her father which were more aggressive than the simple ones of which she was conscious.

Typically, the minor feeling is substituted for the more unpleasant possibility. By total concentration on the substitute, the obsessive compulsive attempts to reduce the anxiety and guilt which the real thing would undoubtedly arouse. The following illustrates the working out of a specific compulsion in the course of psychotherapy:

Peter, age 10, was in treatment for a number of problems. He developed fleeting compulsions and had many superstitions regarding the magic meaning of numbers. His compulsions were usually to check on something. He reported that he had to check on whether the freezer door was closed. He might do this 20 or 30 times and still feel uneasy. He feared that he might have left it ajar and caused all the frozen foods to melt. In treatment, he confessed that part of him really wanted to leave the door open, as an angry gesture toward his mother. It was the anger that caused the anxiety displayed in the checking compulsion.

The psychological principle used so far to differentiate types of neuroses is the nature of defenses, or how the symptom functions in the personality. Another category for differentiation is the *type of conflict* which engenders the neurosis. In Freud's formulation, both hysteria and obsessive compulsive neurosis have their origin in conflicts evolved from the Oedipus complex, but in the obsessional neurosis there is further regression along both libidinal and ego lines. Whereas the hysteric continues to wrestle with predominantly sexual conflicts, the obsessive compulsive regresses to the anal-sadistic level of libidinal organization, struggling with conflicts of aggression and cleanliness and utilizing many of the psychological defenses common for a normal youngster in the anal-sadistic phase *(1913, 1958)*. One might well ask whether all compulsion neuroses are

actually based on a regression, or whether they could as easily represent a *continuation* of the anal-sadistic phase, without the libidinal advances of the Oedipal conflict or the mental advances accruing with age. Frequently, one sees in mentally retarded children an obsessive need for sameness, (see Chapter 7), ritualistic behavior, and other signs of rigidity which cannot be disrupted without causing anxiety. Such behavior is prolongation rather than regression. The history of the onset of symptoms helps to distinguish between the two. Also, the retarded child with compulsive behavior does not have the harsh superego typical of the neurotic compulsive, nor the same sense of inner conflict. He is genuinely afraid of outside danger, partly because of his limited understanding of why things happen. The neurotic compulsive, however, recognizes the unreal basis of his fear. Finally, the retarded child with compulsive traits is sufficiently infantile in other ways that the compulsive behavior is not out of keeping.

Differentiation of Obsessive Compulsive Neurosis and Schizophrenia

The difference between psychotic and neurotic symptoms was discussed in connection with hysterical hallucinations. Hallucinations so rarely, if ever, have an obsessional basis that this is not a problem in differential diagnosis, but obsessive thoughts or compulsive acts may be so bizarre and intense that they resemble the delusional ideas of schizophrenic patients. Despert cites the case of a thirteen-year-old girl to illustrate the differential diagnosis:

Complaint as formulated by the mother at the time of N. J.'s referral was, "she's incessantly speaking of her 'minds'—it's like a phonograph record. She rushes from play saying, 'I've got more minds,' and becomes frantic if you don't agree that they are silly." These "minds" were later identified as numerous and complex obsessive thoughts associated with compulsive acts. The symptoms were of more than seven years' duration, and had been preceded by night terrors which began at approximately five and a half years . . . As an infant she had a transitory compulsion to rub a blanket on her mouth, and she was five when a persistent ritual began—every piece of clothing and bed clothes had to be put at exactly the same place, at the head or foot of the bed, before she could fall asleep. At six years, the "toad stool" incident took place: she inadvertently stepped on the excreta of a toad. She screamed that she was poisoned, and developed a compulsion to rub the toad stool on her toe, then suck her toe. She had to be forcibly prevented from carrying out the act.

Following this incident she gradually developed a multiplicity of compulsive acts and complained of a variety of obsessive thoughts, which she called having "minds." "The mind tells me that if I touch the table [or other objects], the mind is going to kill me . . . the minds bother me mostly at night . . . they tell me to pinch my finger in the door . . . to kill myself . . . to break my arm . . . poke scissors in my eyes . . . I won't drink water because my mind tells me it would be poisoned . . ." "I go to my mother and beg her to tell me it's silly, tell me!"*

Although this child is extremely disturbed and handicapped, the description is not that of a schizophrenic. The girl recognizes the "minds" as thoughts (not voices) she cannot get rid of and is aware of the abnormal character of her thoughts. However strange the obsessive thoughts or compulsive acts may be, if the patient still knows they are unreal the break with reality has not taken place. Diagnostically, psy-

chosis is not determined by the severity of disturbance or the degree of social handicap, but by the patient's subjective experience, his own insight. Despert's case is an interesting contrast to the previously quoted case of the hysterical girl who heard the warning signal. In both cases, a part of the mental apparatus is split off in such a way that the patients are, in effect, talking to themselves. However, the patient with the "minds" is in perpetual conflict, whereas the symptom of the hysterical girl is much more circumscribed. An obsessional neurosis usually affects the functioning of the patient more totally than hysteria.

Incidence and Treatment

The bibliography dealing specifically with childhood obsessive compulsive states is more limited than that of any other clinical diagnosis. Despert believes the problem is more common than the literature would indicate, and suggests that many of these cases are mistakenly diagnosed as childhood schizophrenia. In a series of 401 consecutive cases from her files, she reported 68 children (52 boys and 16 girls) to be suffering from obsessive compulsive neuroses of varying degrees of severity (1955).

In the author's experience, obsessive compulsive symptoms are frequently observed in children with emotional problems, but they are rarely dignified by the full title of "obsessive compulsive neurosis." Children do not often acquire the total rigidity of the obsessive compulsive; a single obsession is recorded as a "morbid fear" and a single compulsion as a "habit disturbance." Compulsive masturbation is an example of this kind of childhood symptom: The youngster masturbates once, is frightened and remorseful, resolves not to repeat the act; fears that he has damaged himself; repeats the masturbation just once more in order to be

---

*Quoted from Louise Despert, "Differential Diagnosis between Obsessive Compulsive Neurosis and Schizophrenia in Children," in *Psychopathology of Childhood*, Hoch and Zubin, eds. [The Proceedings of the American Psychopathological Association, 44th Annual Meeting, New York, 1954] (New York: Grune and Stratton, 1955) pp. 241–43. Reproduced by permission.

sure that everything is still intact; then fears that this last time was the one time too many; and finally becomes caught up in an endless circle of checking and rechecking. Although the mechanism is that of a typical compulsion, clinical records tend to stress the behavior (i.e., the masturbation), rather than its underlying structure.

Treatment is by individual therapy, and its success depends on the severity of the condition and the patient's ability to tolerate anxiety. Treatment is complicated by the fact that, in many ways, the behavior of the obsessive compulsive is laudable: it is only the extent to which it is carried which makes it pathological. As the therapist tries to relax the strictness of the child's conscience, he is forced to play the part of the devil's advocate, and both parents and child may find it hard. As Fenichel points out, the regression implies that treatment must penetrate one level deeper than in the case of hysteria *(1945)*. Ambivalence interferes with the therapeutic relationship, and the therapist is heir to the stubborness and hostility which characterize the obsessive compulsive's feelings toward anyone significant. On the other hand, once these feelings are worked through in treatment (which is usually lengthy), the improvement is likely to be permanent.

Obsessional Character Neurosis

The distinction between neurosis and character neurosis was considered in the discussion of nomenclature in Chapter 5. The obsessive compulsive patient recognizes the excessiveness of his concern and acknowledges that there is no justification in reality for his compulsive precautions or obsessive thoughts. The therapist may find it difficult to help him relax the vigilance of his superego, but the patient is intellectually willing to cooperate. In a character neurosis, however, defenses of the patient's personality are totally acceptable to the patient's ego, and there is little motivation for change.

Pearson classified character neuroses as being of two types: (1) those in which the ego imposes great restrictions (usually in the nature of reaction formations) on the instinctual drives, in order to appease the severe superego; and (2) those in which the ego imposes insufficient restrictions on the instinctual drives, with resultant conflict between the individual and his environment *(1949)*. Character neuroses of the first type are similar to obsessive compulsive neuroses. The child is a perfectionist, a worrier, and a model of deportment. He obeys the rules and is quick to point out infractions committed by others; he is meticulous about cleanliness, health, and care of property. His inhibitions and restrictions may be so great that he is handicapped socially and intellectually, and other children may regard him as a goodygoody or a selfish prig. He may lack creativity and spontaneity because of his slavish regard for rules.

Because of his conformity and compliance, a child with this character structure is usually much admired by adults. But if he continues to be dependent on detailed directions and regulations, he will probably become a passive adult—never getting into trouble, but also never achieving any outstanding success. The habits of rigid self-control which are extravagantly admired in the child may eventuate in an adult who is cold and emotionless and who has difficulty in social and sexual relationships. Although it is usually the rebellious child who is viewed with alarm and for whom a grim future is predicted, a sharp eye should be kept on the opposite situation. The future of the perfect child contains hazards as well. Abnegation of sexuality or aggressiveness can cripple the personality as much as total inability to delay gratification or tolerate frustration.

Conclusion

The fact that formal diagnoses are avoided in working with emotionally disturbed children accounts for the dearth of literature on the problems considered in this chapter. This is not to say, however, that these conditions are rarely encountered in guidance clinics. On the contrary, "neurosis" may be the appropriate diagnosis for any of the symptoms which have been so thoroughly investigated and reported (e.g., learning problems, delinquency, speech difficulties, and enuresis). In this chapter, we have been concerned with the psychological processes which may underlie any one of these behavior problems, and particularly with the nature of intrapsychic conflict, the kinds of inner conflicts, the mechanisms used to handle these conflicts, and the mechanics of symptom formation.

Many writers have espoused the view that childhood psychopathology is the result of abuse. Granted that pathology does, indeed, result from mistreatment, it is still important to realize that a severe neurotic symptom may result from the child's fear of his own wishes, even though the environment may be neither exciting nor terrifying. Achieving a good balance between one's own selfish wishes, the demands of reality, and the moral demands (real or imagined) of one's parents is a difficult task for any child, one which inevitably involves some anxiety. It is perhaps even more difficult for the imaginative, sensitive child who is devoted to his parents and mentally capable of recognizing the incompatibility of some of his inner feelings.

Neurosis is a disease of civilization and there is no way of inoculating a child against it. The best prevention is sympathetic recognition of what the child is up against, patience with the transitory symptom, and a willingness to accept professional guidance when a child does not outgrow a symptom. Although neurosis has a bad name, it is by no means the greatest danger in bringing up children, and well-timed help is usually quickly effective.

No satisfactory answer has yet been found to the problem of why different people require different neuroses. Freud remarked that "we divide the pathogenic determinants concerned in the neuroses into those which a person brings along with him into his life, and those which life brings to him—the constitutional and the accidental—by whose combined operation alone the pathogenic determinant is, as a rule, established" *(1913, 1958, p. 317)*. He proposed a number of solutions, among them, a theory that passive sexual experiences in early childhood result in a predisposition to hysteria and that active ones result in a predisposition to obsessional neurosis *(1896, 1962)*, but he later repudiated this idea *(1906, 1960)*. His second theory was that the form of a neurosis depended on the period of life at which the traumatic experience occurred, or else on the period at which defensive action was taken against the revival of the traumatic experience (i.e., the timing of the repression). However, with all his hypotheses about the importance of the nature and timing of events in the formation of a neurosis, Freud always gave considerable place to the role of heredity. He felt that there was a constitutional predisposition which, when combined with traumatic events, led to a specific neurotic development.

Where are we to look for the source of these dispositions? We have become aware that the psychical functions concerned—above all, the sexual function, but various ego functions too—have to undergo a long and complicated development before reaching the state characteristic of the normal adult. We can assume that these developments are not always so smoothly carried out that the total function passes through this regular progressive modification. Wherever a portion of it clings to a previous stage, what is known as a 'point of fixation' results, to which the function may regress if the subject falls ill through some external disturbance."[*]

Further elucidation of constitutional predispositions was considered a problem of biological rather than psychological research. There has been little progress in our understanding of this problem since Freud's own time, although there has been a consistent trend toward the investigation of earlier periods of life, to study both constitutional differences and the effect of maternal behavior on infant development. There has even been some observation of neonatal differences, which are presumably innate rather than acquired (see Chapter 13). Although research and treatment are directed toward experimental factors, psychologists are aware that the patient's experiences are often an insufficient explanation of the visible psychopathology.

A final word should be said about the importance of the patient's history and of his own statements to the understanding and the diagnosis of symptoms. There is relatively little information to be gathered from the mere statement of a symptom, but a great deal can be learned from the story of its onset and the patient's explanation of it. The clinician's most important single tool is his ability to listen to the patient and his parents. The information on which to base the diagnosis is contained in the patient, not in the theory.

---

[*]Quoted from Sigmund Freud, *Disposition to Obsessional Neurosis: A Contribution to the Problem of Choice of Neurosis* (1913). Standard Edition. Ed. and trans. by James Strachey, XII (London. The Hogarth Press, Ltd., 1958. © U.S.A., Basic Books, Inc.), p. 317–18. Reproduced by permission.

References for Chapter 10

Babinski, J., "My Conception of Hysteria and Hypnotism (Pithiatism)," *Alienist and Neurologist*, XXIX (1908), 1–20.

Bagby, English, "Two Instances of the Childhood Origin of Phobias," *Journal of Abnormal and Social Psychology*, XVII (1922), 12–18. Reprinted in Wayne Dennis, *Readings in Child Psychology*. Englewood Cliffs, N.J.: Prentice-Hall, Inc., 1951.

Bender, L. and H. Lipkowitz, "Hallucinations in Children," *American Journal of Orthopsychiatry*, X (1940), 471–509.

Bernheim, H., *Suggestive Therapeutics: A Treatise on the Nature and Uses of Hypnotism* (2nd rev. Ed.), trans. C. A. Herter. New York: G. P. Putnam's Sons, 1897.

Brenner, Charles, "A Case of Childhood Hallucinosis," *The Psychoanalytic Study of the Child*, Vol. VI. New York: International Universities Press, Inc., 1951.

———, *An Elementary Textbook of Psychoanalysis*. New York: International Universities Press, Inc., 1955.

Coolidge, J. C. et al., "Patterns of Aggression in School Phobia," *Psychoanalytic Study of the Child*, Vol. XVII. New York: International Universities Press, Inc., 1962.

———, et al., "School Phobia in Adolescence: A Manifestation of Severe Character Disturbance," *American Journal of Orthopsychiatry*, XXX (1960), 599–608.

———, P. B. Hahn, and Alice L. Peck, "School Phobia: Neurotic Crisis or Way of Life?" *American Journal of Orthopsychiatry*, XXVII (1957), 296–306.

Dawes, L., "The Psychoanalysis of a Case of 'Grand Hysteria of Charcot' in a Girl of Fifteen," *The Nervous Child*, X (1953), 272–305.

Despert, Louise, "Delusional and Hallucinatory Experiences in Children," *American Journal of Psychiatry*, CIV (1948), 528F–37F.

———, "Differential Diagnosis between Obsessive Compulsive Neurosis and Schizophrenia in Children," in Hoch and Zubin, *Psychopathology of Childhood*. (Proceedings of the 44th Annual Meeting of the American Psychopathological Association, New York, 1954.) New York: Grune & Stratton, 1955.

Eisenberg, Leon, "School Phobia: A Study of Communication of Anxiety," *American*

Journal of Psychiatry, Vol. CXIV (1958), 712–18.

Esman, Aaron, "Visual Hallucinosis in Young Children," *Psychoanalytic Study of the Child,* Vol. XVII. New York: International Universities Press, Inc., 1962.

Estes, H. R., C. H. Haylett, and E. M. Johnson, "Separation Anxiety," *American Journal of Psychotherapy,* X (1956), 682–95.

Fenichel, Otto, *The Psychoanalytic Study of Neurosis.* New York: W. W. Norton & Company, Inc., 1945.

Fraiberg, Selma, "On the Sleep Disturbances of Early Childhood," *Psychoanalytic Study of the Child,* Vol. V. New York: International Universities Press, Inc., 1950.

———, *The Magic Years.* New York: Charles Scribner's Sons, 1959.

———, *Disposition to Obsessional Neurosis: A Contribution to the Problem of Choice of Neurosis* (1913), Standard Edition, Vol. XII, ed. and trans. by James Strachey. London: The Hogarth Press, Ltd., 1958.

Freud, Sigmund, *Analysis of a Phobia in a Five-Year-Old Boy* (1909), Standard Edition, Vol. X, ed. and trans. by James Strachey. London: The Hogarth Press, Ltd., 1953.

———, *My Views of the Part Played by Sexuality in the Etiology of the Neurosis* (1906), Standard Edition, Vol. VII, ed. and trans. by James Strachey. London: The Hogarth Press, Ltd., 1960.

———, *The Interpretation of Dreams* (1900), Standard Edition, Vols. IV, V, ed. and trans. by James Strachey. London: The Hogarth Press, Ltd., 1953.

———, *Heredity and the Etiology of Neurosis* (1896), Standard Edition, Vol. III, ed. and trans. by James Strachey. London: The Hogarth Press, Ltd., 1962.

Fries, Margaret E., "Psychosomatic Relationships between Mother and Infant," *Psychosomatic Medicine,* VI (1944), 159–62.

Gesell, Arnold and F. Ilg, *Infant and Child in the Culture of Today.* New York: Harper & Row, Publishers, 1943.

James, Anthony, "An Experimental Approach to the Psychopathology of Childhood: Sleep Disturbances," *British Journal of Medical Psychology,* XXXII (1959), 19–37.

Jersild, A., F. V. Markey, and C. L. Jersild, "Children's Fears, Dreams, Wishes, Daydreams, Likes, Dislikes, Pleasant and Unpleasant Memories," *Child Development*

Monographs, No. 12. New York: Columbia University Press, 1933.

Johnson, A. M., "School Phobia: Discussion," *American Journal of Orthopsychiatry,* XXVII (1957), 307–9.

———, et al., "School Phobia," *American Journal of Orthopsychiatry,* XI (1941), 702–11.

Kaufman, Irving, "Conversion Hysteria in Latency," *Journal of Child Psychiatry,* I (1962), 385–96.

Klein, E., "The Reluctance to go to School," *Psychoanalytic Study of the Child,* Vol. I. New York: International Universities Press, Inc., 1945.

Kolansky, H., "Treatment of a 3-year-old Girl's Severe Infantile Neurosis," *Psychoanalytic Study of the Child,* Vol. XV. New York: International Universities Press, Inc., 1960.

Lapouse, R. and M. A. Monk, "Fears and Worries in a Representative Sample of Children," *American Journal of Orthopsychiatry,* XXIX (1959), 803–18.

Lazarus, Arnold A., Gerald C. Davison and David A. Polefka, "Classical and Operant Factors in the Treatment of a School Phobia," *Journal of Abnormal Psychology,* LXX (1965), 225–30.

Lippman, H. S., *Treatment of the Child in Emotional Conflict.* New York: McGraw-Hill Book Company, 1956.

Maccoby, Eleanor E., "Effects of the Mass Media," in Hoffman and Hoffman, *Review of Child Development Research,* Vol. 1, Russell Sage Foundation, New York, 1964.

Mahler, Margaret S., "Tics and Impulsions in Children: A Study in Motility," *Psychoanalytic Quarterly,* XIII (1944), 430–44.

———, Jean A. Luke, and Wilburta Daltroff, "Clinical and Follow-up Study of Tic Syndrome in Children," *American Journal of Orthopsychiatry,* XV (1945), 631–47.

Pearson, Gerald H. J., *Emotional Disorders of Children.* New York: W. W. Norton & Company, Inc., 1949.

Proctor, James T., "Hysteria in Childhood," *American Journal of Orthopsychiatry,* XXVIII (1958), 394–406.

Rachman, S. and C. G. Costello, "The Aetiology and Treatment of Children's Phobias: A Review," *American Journal of Psychiatry,* CXVIII (1961), 97–106.

Rangell, Leo, "Treatment of Nightmares in a Seven-Year-Old Boy," *Psychoanalytic*

Study of the Child, Vol. V. New York: International Universities Press, Inc., 1950.

Robins, E. and P. O'Neal, "Clinical Features of Hysteria in Children, with a Note on Prognosis: A Two to Seventeen Year Follow-up Study of 41 Patients," *The Nervous Child,* X (1953), 246–71.

Sheehan, J. G., "Theory and Treatment of Stuttering as an Approach-Avoidance Conflict" (1953), in *Psychopathology: A Source Book,* ed. C. F. Reed, I. E. Alexander, and S. S. Tomkins. Cambridge, Mass.: Harvard University Press, 1958.

Sperling, Melitta, "Etiology and Treatment of Sleep Disturbances in Children," *Psychoanalytic Quarterly,* XXIV (1955), 358–68.

Spock, Benjamin, *Baby and Child Care* (rev. Cardinal Giant Ed.). New York: Pocket Books, Inc., 1963.

Suttenfield, V., "School Phobia: A Study of Five Cases," *American Journal of Orthopsychiatry,* XXIV (1954), 368–81.

Talbot, M., "Panic in School Phobia," *American Journal of Orthopsychiatry,* XXVII (1957), 286–96.

Van Houten, J., "Mother and Child Relationships in 12 Cases of School Phobia," *Smith College Studies in Social Work,* XVIII (1947–1948), 161–80.

Waelder, Robert, *Basic Theory of Psychoanalysis.* New York: International Universities Press, Inc., 1960.

Waldfogel, Samuel, J. C. Coolidge, and P. B. Hahn, "The Development, Meaning and Management of School Phobia," *American Journal of Orthopsychiatry,* XXVII (1957), 754–80.

——, Ellen Tessman, and Pauline Hahn, "A Program for Early Intervention in School Phobia," *American Journal of Orthopsychiatry* XXIX (1959), 324–33.

Walker, C. F., "Hysteria in Childhood," *American Journal of Orthopsychiatry,* XVII (1947), 468–76.

Weiner, M. F., "Hallucinations in Children," *Archives of General Psychiatry,* V (1961), 544–53.

11

PSYCHOSIS IN EARLY CHILDHOOD

In contrast to psychoneurosis, the literature on psychosis and psychotic-like conditions in childhood would fill several volumes. This is a fairly recent development. Until the publication of Charles Bradley's book on childhood schizophrenia in 1941, the literature was scant. In the ten-year period from 1946 to 1956, however, 542 titles appeared (*Ekstein, Bryant, and Friedman, 1958*). This interest is all the more remarkable because psychosis in any form is rare in childhood. For example, of 6,869 children evaluated in the various outpatient psychiatric clinics and mental hospital community services units of Ohio, only 2.7 per cent were diagnosed as psychotic compared with 8.0 per cent diagnosed as psychoneurotic and 41.6 per cent diagnosed as transient situational personality disorders (*Ohio Department of Mental Hygiene and Correction, Annual Report, 1963*). If the total figures included all the children seen for psychological diagnosis and help in nonmedical settings such as schools, the proportion of psychotic children would be much less.

The interest is best explained by the great amount of controversy surrounding psychosis. Although there is some difference of opinion about the exact diagnosis of psychoneurosis, e.g., the fine line of difference between neurosis and character disorder, and some difference of opinion about the relative importance of external conditions and internal conflicts aroused by instinctual wishes in causing psychoneuroses, these differences are greatly magnified in the variety of opinions on childhood psychosis. The basic issues concern both the what and the why of childhood psychosis. Is it a disease entity with specific symptoms? Or is it a descriptive term applied to miscellaneous conditions with common gross disturbances in human relationships and adjustment to reality? The lack of consensus necessitates a somewhat tedious discussion of the terminology proposed by various authors, but semantic classification is important since the terms used often contain implications as to cause. Definitions vary in degree of inclusiveness and the importance of certain symptoms over others. The less restricted the definition, the greater the opportunity for different causes to be at work. Opinion about cause is divided between psychological and organic explanations, with a majority favoring an organic point of view, or at least giving a great deal of weight to constitutional factors. The nature of the organic hypotheses, however, is varied and admittedly speculative; the paucity of data leaves much room for argument.

William Goldfarb is one of the few who has avoided committing himself to either the organic or the psychodynamic point of view; he integrates the two in a conceptual model in which the primary cause can be either inherent deficiency in the child or psychopathology in the parent *(1961)*. This accords with the author's opinion but it is not the generally accepted view.

"Psychosis" is another word for "insanity" and thus, for a long time, was applied only to adult patients. The American Psychiatric Association Manual defines psychoses as "disorders characterized by a varying degree of personality disintegration and failure to test and evaluate, correctly, external reality. In addition, individuals with such disorders fail in their ability to relate themselves to other people and to their own work."

In adult patients, the most common psychotic condition is schizophrenia; manias, depressions, and organic psychoses constitute the bulk of the remainder. Although a psychotic patient may receive psychotherapy from a non-medical person, it is generally agreed that the patient should be under medical supervision. Because of the degree of their irresponsibility and lack of judgment, such patients often require hospitalization, drugs, or physical forms of treatment such as electroshock. Further, the diagnosis of psychosis has legal significance, in that the patient is no longer considered responsible for his acts. This does not mean that all psychotic patients are dangerous to themselves or to others, but it does mean that they function—in some ways and at some times—according to subjective dictates which they equate with external reality. Thoughts and feelings are projected into the outer world, and then perceived by the psychotic patient as unassailable proof of his own ideas. Like the very young child, he makes no distinction between his own ideas and those of others. Clearcut symptoms

of psychosis (involving the mechanism of projection) are hallucinations, delusions of grandeur, or delusions of persecution. Psychosis is the most serious form of mental illness, although remissions and cures do occur in some 33 per cent of adult cases.

A distinction should be made between two general categories of psychosis in children which the author has labelled "regressive" and "developmental," respectively. In *regressive* psychoses (which include all those mentioned above) there is a history of apparently normal development with a later deterioration in personality and a sharp break with reality at some point. We have some recent evidence indicating that development before the eruption of obvious psychotic signs may not be so normal as it appears. E. Lane and G. Albee found that adult schizophrenics had significantly lower scores on intelligence tests during childhood than their siblings and conclude that this "supports the thesis that schizophrenia has its roots and measurable effects in early childhood many years before the actual recognized onset of the disorder *(1965, p. 752)*." Nevertheless, in the classical form of schizophrenia, there is usually an obvious turn for the worse, many times occurring in late adolescence. It was its relatively early age of onset which prompted E. Kraepelin *(1896)* to call it *dementia praecox* ("early insanity"). Since adult regressive psychoses are well described in the literature, e.g., *Bellak, 1958,* and are similar to those of adolescents, they are not formally presented here. It is appropriate, however, to inject a warning about the difficulties of differential diagnosis in the period of adolescence. Because of the sudden influx of instinctual drives concomitant with greater social demands, there is an increase in anxiety and in defensive ego maneuvers. The adolescent may show disturbed behavior (e.g., withdrawal, depression, rituals, hypochondriacal preoccupations, bizarre fantasies) which look like that of a psychotic patient. In a study of the Rorschach records of 300 supposedly normal adolescent girls, Lawrence Frank *et al.*, commented on the number whose records could have been interpreted as psychotic *if* they had been the reactions of adult subjects *(1953)*. More license is allowed in applying diagnostic criteria to adolescents; it is much better to err on the conservative side and adopt a wait-and-see attitude. Premature diagnosis may lead to unnecessary hospitalization, thereby confirming such an adolescent's greatest fear—that of being crazy.

This chapter deals with developmental psychoses, those which are by definition unique to childhood. These conditions have their beginnings in the first five years of life. It is extremely rare for any psychotic disturbance to make its first appearance between five and ten; there is no well-documented case reported in the literature nor has the author ever observed one. Parents may give a history of normal development until the age of two or three years, but peculiarities in behavior usually become apparent toward the end of the first year, when the child fails to take a normal interest in people and does not play or communicate normally. Such cases are conspicuous even to the casual observer; psychosis is one of the few conditions in childhood psychopathology where there is something to see. A triology of motion pictures, produced by the Institute of Psychiatry of the University of London, shows vividly the strangeness of psychotic symptoms in childhood (*The Psychotic Child*, New York University Film Library). These children look odd. Their mannerisms and postures are peculiar, and their abnormality is even more apparent when one tries to play or talk with them. No one expects such children to outgrow their difficulties, because they do not appear to be like normal children of any age. Very

few ever get into public schools; if they do, there is no question about whether or not they are disturbed.

Diagnostic Criteria

Clinicians have reached the point of agreeing that childhood psychosis exists, but they have not yet agreed on where to draw the boundaries of the term. Some clinics avoid the diagnosis and others find schizophrenia in every severely disturbed child.

The original behavioral criteria proposed by C. Bradley and M. Bowen *(1941)* are the most generous and inclusive:

1. Seclusiveness
2. Irritability when (1) is interrupted
3. Daydreaming
4. Bizarre behavior
5. Diminished number of personal interests
6. Regressive nature of personal interests
7. Physical inactivity
8. Sensitivity to comment and criticism

According to these criteria, the extremely quiet, shy, withdrawn, sensitive child might be called schizophrenic, although shyness and excessive daydreaming are much more likely to be neurotic. This is shown in a follow-up study of 34 individuals who had been referred to a child guidance clinic some 16 to 27 years earlier because of shy, withdrawn, anxious, or fearful behavior. D. P. Morris, E. Soroker, and G. Burruss found only two schizophrenic adults in the group and commented on this low incidence "in a group selected on the basis of personality traits which presumably predispose to this disease" *(1954, p. 753)*. A shy, sensitive child is in contact with his environment, perhaps too much so. His withdrawal from participation in social activities is a defense against the anxiety aroused by interaction with others—anticipation of social failure, criticism, or whatever. One also finds that shyness may be a reaction formation against unconscious aggression, and that anxiety is related to the child's fear that the aggressiveness will somehow become evident. His daydreams are peopled with imaginary characters and feats of honor; the wishes expressed in fantasy are very social in nature.

Although parents and observers may describe the psychotic child as "living in a world of his own" because of his inaccessability, there is no evidence that he is fantasizing. The psychotic child is not pretending anything. He may be entirely preoccupied with visual, auditory, or kinesthetic sensations which have little thought content. A toy car is fun because its wheels spin, not because the child can pretend he is driving it. Psychotic children do not make believe; they exploit their toys for their physical properties. The psychotic child, isolated from social contact, should not be confused with the neurotic (or normal) child who is preoccupied with fantasies.

Delusions and hallucinations, the hallmarks of adult psychosis, are rare in developmental psychoses. When they are present in children, they are also more likely to reflect a neurosis (see Chapter 10). The psychotic child may be confused with severe obsessive compulsive neurotics (*Despert, 1955*), or with severe hysterics (*Harms, 1945*). Differentiation is based on the child's insight, that is, on whether he recognizes his symptoms as being peculiar to himself and knows that he is different from other people.

This leads to the question of the relationship between neuroses and psychoses in general. One theoretical assumption is that psychosis is ranged along a continuum which borders on a neurosis at some point. This suggests that a disease process can move along such a continuum and be called a neurosis at one point, and a psychosis further along. In other words, the difference between psychosis and neurosis would be essentially quantitative. An alternative concept is that there is an inherent or basic defect of such quality or severity that the child never goes through a phase which could be called normal or even neurotic. In the author's opinion, this is a better description of developmental psychoses. Psychotic children are not simply more disturbed: their ego-functioning and object relationships are disturbed in very special ways, and they do not progress through the normal stages with the normal developmental anxieties. Their development proceeds along different lines at different rates, resulting in a combination of extremely primitive, arrested reactions and reactions at or near their age level.

It is far easier to say what childhood psychosis is *not*, than to say what it is. Many of the more recent criteria offered are couched in general theoretical terms which are difficult to translate into observable behavior. For instance, the psychoanalytic view represented by Marion Putnam is that "in spite of the considerable divergence in the clinical picture, depending on the age of onset, severity of the illness, and types of defense used, there is a core problem which manifests itself as a lack of clarity in the child's perception of himself as a person separate from his environment" (*1955, p. 521*). How does a child show this difficulty in behavior? What symptoms might occur as a result of his lack of ego boundary or self-image? The organic view represented by Lauretta Bender gives rise to the same questions, although she provides an elaborate set of diagnostic signs, mainly neurophysiological. Leo Kanner has stated the most specific behavioral criteria, establishing two major symptomatic requirements for the diagnosis of autism: inability to make affective contact with people and an exorbitant need to preserve "sameness" in the environment.

In the author's judgment, the most important single sign is a severely disturbed relationship with people. This may take the form of a lack of interest in, or awareness of, people (i.e., autism) or it may take the form of an inability to separate from another person (i.e., symbiosis). From this distorted relationship with people arise difficulties in communication (a detailed description of language and thought disturbances is given later), inability to imitate or to engage in normal play, extraordinary preoccupations with inanimate objects, and clinging to a mechanical, routinized, compulsively repetitious mode of living. Neurotic children, of course, also have disturbed relationships with people, but not to the same extent and without side-effects which encroach upon every aspect of their functioning. (By selecting this criterion as the *sine qua non* of childhood psychosis, the author admits to a preference for dynamic descriptions of psychotic behavior, rather than descriptions couched in physiological or cognitive terms.)

Terminology

There is continual discussion about the proper, all-inclusive label for developmental psychotic conditions. Choosing a general term depends largely on one's concept of the nature of the disorder. Those who use the term "schizophrenia" feel that it is essentially the same illness which affects adult patients, even though the symp-

toms are very different in children. Adherents of this point of view do not require a history of normal development followed by regression in order to apply the diagnosis "schizophrenia"; they believe that schizophrenia may begin at birth or at any time thereafter. Others feel that infantile psychosis is a very different kind of illness than adult schizophrenia and that the use of the same diagnostic label is misleading. Such theoretical differences make it difficult to consider questions of etiology, associated characteristics, treatment, and prognosis in general. Opinion on these subjects falls into schools of thought which are associated with well-known child psychiatry centers. To confuse the issue further, specific clinical syndromes have been described. These can be considered subdivisions of the general category of developmental psychosis, but there is no general agreement about what to call them, either. Table 7 is an outline of the nomenclature which is commonly used:

Of the subdivisions in Table 7, the category of autism is by far the most important. It is such a common symptom of childhood psychosis that the term "autism" is used interchangeably with "childhood psychosis," although most authors agree that there are other forms of childhood psychosis.

TABLE 7

Nomenclature In Childhood Psychosis

General Terms:

Schizophrenia		(Bradley, Despert, Bender, Goldfarb)
Atypical		(Rank, Putnam, Pavenstedt)
Infantile psychosis		(Reiser)

Specific Categories:

A)* Autism	(Kanner)	
Symbiosis	(Mahler)	
B)** Organic	(Goldfarb)	
Non-organic	(Goldfarb)	

A)°   According to degree and kind of deficit in object relationship.
B)°° According to associated physical findings.

Diagnosis of Infantile Autism

Clinical Picture

In 1943, in "Autistic Disturbance of Affective Contact," Leo Kanner described 11 children whose symptoms appeared to constitute a unique syndrome. This was termed "early infantile autism" *(1944)*. In his clinical description, he emphasized that the autistic child had *not* had a withdrawal from established contact with others (i.e., a regressive defense), but had always been aloof.

Autistic children look normal. In fact, they usually seem bright because of an alert, thoughtful expression. Their motor coordination seems normal; indeed, they usually move quickly and are energetic and skillful with their fingers. Their pathology is soon evidenced, however, by their avoidance of another's eye and by a lack of visual or auditory response to others. They are deaf and blind to people. In retrospect, one can detect the first signs of psychopathology in infancy. There was no social smile, no evidence of pleasure in the mother's company. One mother complained, "He didn't look at me when I fed him in my arms," and other typical complaints include, "He was never cuddly," or "He never noticed when I came into or left his room." There was no physical reaching out: the autistic child did not get set to be lifted into his parents' arms. There was no particular reaction to strangers, either. Usually, these children were regarded as especially good babies, because their demands were few: they were content to be left alone and did not make the normal fuss at bedtime or other moments of separation. Such information regarding early infantile characteristics is admittedly tenuous, because it is always obtained after it is well established that the child's affective relationships are very limited. However, there is no doubt by the end of the first year. There is no imitation of gestures (e.g., waving bye-bye) or sounds, and also the baby remains uninterested in social games like peek-aboo and pattycake.

The failure to imitate, derived from a lack of personal relationships, gives rise to another major symptom—the failure to use speech for purposes of communication. In most autistic children, including 3 of the original 11 studied, speech is totally absent. When they do speak, their language has a strange, parrotlike quality. The child does not appear to be talking to anyone nor to expect any answer; he utters repetitious, stereotyped phrases and engages in no conversational give-and-take. For example, the autistic child seldom answers "Yes," or "No," but is likely to echo the question. Personal pronouns are also repeated as heard; consequently, the child speaks of himself as "you" and of the person addressed as "I". Kanner, discussing the literal nature of these children's comprehension of language, tells of a child who learned to say "Yes" when his father told him that he would put him up on his shoulders if he said the word. The word came to indicate the desire to be put on the father's shoulders. It took many months before it could be detached from this specific situation and and much longer before the child made the generalization of "yes" as indicative of assent *(1957)*. Younger autistic children (or those who remain severely autistic) ignore verbal instructions or suggestions so consistently that deafness is invariably suspected. But their response to sound is normal; in fact, one child of the original group was able to identify some 18 symphonies before the age of two.

The autistic child's facility with objects is in striking contrast to his response to people and language, but his interest in toys is more restricted than that of the normal child. Things that spin, puzzles, reflections of light and shadow, for example have been known to engross an autistic child for months on end. For him, everything is form. If he likes to look at books, it is for the form of the letters and words, not for the accompanying pictures. S. Ritvo and S. Provence, speculating on the autistic child's absorption with playthings, noted that a toy given to a normal child becomes important largely because it comes from the parent or an adult. To autistic children, the plaything is important because it can be manipulated, rolled, spun, fitted together, juggled, clutched, and so on. It makes no difference if a picture is upside down when they assemble a puzzle—the handling of the object is an end in itself (1953).

This leads to a striking observation about the psychometric performance of such children: Kanner states that, although they have been viewed as mentally retarded, their "cognitive potentialities are only masked by the basic disorder" (1957, p. 739). Since it is impossible to engage these children in an orthodox examination situation, an evaluation of performance depends wholly on test materials which are intrinsically appealing to them and which do not require demonstration, instructions, or abstract thinking. This usually means using pegboards, form boards, and puzzles, and their performance on these tests is often normal or superior. Six children, from 22 to 39 months old, were studied by Ritvo and Provence, and their perception of form was, without exception, the area of highest performance (1953). Kanner reports that all the children he observed did well with the Seguin form board.

Related to this intense preoccupation with special objects is what Kanner considers the second cardinal characteristic of such children: their "anxiously obsessive desire for the maintenance of sameness" (1943, p. 245). Changes in routine or furniture arrangement can be extremely disturbing to them. Kanner describes the anxiety of an autistic child about moving into a new house. He remained upset until his furniture was arranged as it had been in the old house (1957).

This dread of change seems to be a major factor in autistic children's repetitious tendencies and in the resulting limitation of the variety of their spontaneous activity. The autistic child's desire to live in a static world makes it difficult to teach him anything new. These children apply their emotional and intellectual energies to things instead of people; people may come and go, but things should stay the same. Nevertheless, changes occur constantly, with the result that these children are always threatened.

Some of the behavior *rarely* associated with autism is worth mentioning here. Bed-wetting, thumb sucking, nail biting, and masturbation are seldom observed. Autistic children may enjoy playing with their bodies, but such play is a repetitious, rhythmic movement (e.g., rocking); they may even play with their fingers as babies do. Although Kanner reported some refusal of food, this has not been mentioned by other clinicians. The author found it a major problem only in two children who presented a mixture of autism and retardation.

These children are few in number. Kanner stated that he had seen fewer than 150 cases in 19 years, although his clinic at Johns Hopkins serves as a sort of national clearinghouse for this disturbance. He had seen an estimated 20,000 children in this period, which puts the occurrence of autism at less than 1 per cent of the clinic population (1958). In 1963, David Reiser, director of the James Jackson Putnam Children's Center, stated that since the establishment of the Center in 1943, more than 240 of the 2,800 children studied there have been given the diagnosis of "atypical development," a term somewhat more inclusive than infantile autism. Bender, in a 20-year (1934–1954) period at Bellevue Medical Center, diagnosed as schizophrenic

850 cases or 8 per cent of the 7,000 children seen. It must be remembered that these figures come from centers which attract a disproportionate number of such cases because of their special interest in these conditions.

Despite their rarity, however, the children are unforgettable. Their pattern of development is so unlike that of other children, and the autism so difficult to penetrate, that the condition remains a mystery of intellectual as well as humanitarian concern to all child therapists. Writing on infantile autism, S. Sarason and T. Gladwin commented that "the importance of these cases to the development of a science of psychology would seem to be vastly beyond what their relatively rare occurrence in the general population would suggest" *(1958, p. 345).*

Differential Diagnosis

Schizophrenia: Some authors feel it necessary to distinguish infantile autism from childhood schizophrenia. David Reiser suggests the term "infantile psychosis" as a substitute for "early infantile autism" and "atypical child," but feels that it should be differentiated from childhood schizophrenia on theoretical as well as clinical grounds. He thinks that the critical factor is the time of onset of symptoms, and the term "childhood schizophrenia" should be reserved for "cases of personality fragmentation in which the apparent signs and pathologic process begin after the age of five."* Rimland also favors considering "infantile autism and childhood schizophrenia as separate and quite unrelated disease entities."** He would

also restrict the diagnosis "childhood schizophrenia" to children whose disordered behavior appeared after an initial period of normal development. Rimland argues that schizophrenic children have more physical and neurological symptoms than autistic children, who are unique in their good health and excellent motor development. He offers a diagnostic checklist of 76 items, with an "autism key" and a "schizophrenia key," but he describes this as an "armchair" instrument, provided to facilitate research. More clinical data are needed to evaluate the usefulness of these keys and to determine whether they actually can be used to sort psychotic children into two distinct groups, as he suggests. In the author's experience, it is not easy to pinpoint the time of onset nor to substantiate the so-called normal period of development. In contrast to Reiser's and Rimland's points of view, Bender *(1947),* and Kanner himself *(1954),* classify autism as one of the possible forms of schizophrenia, thus avoiding the issue of differential diagnosis.

Mental Retardation: The literature exhorts clinicians to be particularly alert to the differences between mental retardation and infantile psychosis. There is general agreement that differentiation is difficult, but it is considered important because "early detection as a step toward earliest possible treatment is of crucial importance among psychotic infants, in contrast to some of the irreversible types of mental retardation, for which a 'wait and see' attitude is not so s⸗rious."* The author, as she stated in Chapter 8, does not agree with this opinion. However, we presuppose a positive approach to the treatment of mental retardation. This is the result of the author's belief than an *a posteriori* diagnosis is safer than an *a priori* one, and that a retarded child is susceptible to the same traumatic factors as one of

---

*Quoted from David E. Reiser, "Psychosis of Infancy and Early Childhood, as manifested by Children with Atypical Development," *New England Journal of Medicine,* CCLXIX (1963), p. 845. Reproduced by permission.

**Quoted from Bernard Rimland, *Infantile Autism* (New York: Appleton-Century-Crofts) p. 76. Copyright © 1964, Meredith Publishing Company. Reprinted by permission.

*Reiser, *op. cit.,* p. 791.

normal intelligence, and therefore the same benefits (though perhaps not equally) from the same therapeutic approach.

Initially, it was thought that autism and mental retardation were mutually exclusive or that, if they coexisted, retardation was a secondary effect of autism. Reiser, in accord with his view of etiology, places great stress on the criterion of a history of profound disturbance in parent-parent and parent-child interaction during the neonatal period. Those with different views of cause would not consider this a significant criterion for differentiation.

In the early symptomatic descriptions of autism, mental retardation was ruled out because of the autistic child's alert expression, his normal motor development, and the fragmentary evidence that he functions at or above his age level. However, the author's extensive experience with mentally retarded children leads her to doubt that these criteria are valid evidence of the absence of mental retardation. L. Eisenberg *(1958)* points out that performance tests, on which these children do so well, are known to correlate poorly with other measures of intelligence. Indeed autistic behavior and mental retardation are frequently seen in combined form in the clinic. In those cases where mental retardation can be ruled out, the children are usually less autistic and demonstrate some signs of meaningful relationships. The more severe the autism, the more it is likely to be associated with mental retardation, and it is extremely difficult—if not impossible—to say which is primary and which is secondary. No doubt, primary autism will lead to intellectual retardation, since only so much can be learned from inanimate objects. Conversely, it is possible for the mentally retarded child to suffer from trauma or parental neglect to such an extent that he develops secondary autism as a defense (see Chapter 8).

Again, the diagnostic problem is complicated by etiology. Several writers have suggested that infantile autism is, first and foremost, a problem of *intellectual* functioning. In a postscript to a case report of an "idiot savant," M. Scheerer, E. Rothman, and K. Goldstein discussed the parallels between the mental and emotional processes of the autistic child and those of an 11-year-old defective boy whom they studied for a period of five years. This boy, whose IQ was 50, had remarkable musical aptitude, was verbally responsive, and could do arithmetic rapidly and calculate dates, but he could not absorb or learn in a normal way and was "lacking in social awareness." Special experiments were devised to study him, he was given standard tests, and his spontaneous behavior in everyday life was observed. The authors concluded that his various deficiencies were the result of a general impairment of abstract capacity. His precocities were interpreted as a result of the channeling of energy and the hypertrophy of special abilities through extraordinary exercise *(1945)*. Having so little outlet for self-expression and for a sense of mastery, this defective child had concentrated all his energies on those limited skills which were relatively intact, and thus they were greatly strengthened and improved.

Today this boy would be diagnosed as autistic in most child psychiatry clinics. Scheerer and his co-authors doubt that the intellectual abnormalities of such children are secondary, and suggest that their lack of ability to think abstractly produces their social deficiency. Bernard Rimland's reasoning is similar:

Baffling and paradoxical though early infantile autism has been considered, it is possible to trace its diversity of symptoms to a single critical disability: *The child with early infantile autism is grossly impaired in a function basic to all cognition: the ability to relate new stimuli to remembered experience.* The vital connections between sensation and memory can be made only with difficulty. New sensation can be related only to sharply limited fragments of memory. The child is thus virtually divested of the means for deriving from his experience. This impairment has two readily observable and interdependent consequences: 1) The child cannot understand relationships nor think in terms of concepts, symbols, analogies or abstractions, and 2) He cannot integrate his sensations into a comprehensible whole —his perception of the world is vague and obscure.°

According to this hypothesis, the basic deficiency is intellectual, and autism is "a rare and unique form of oligophrenia."°° This makes the problem of differentiating between autism and mental retardation irrelevant, because it makes autism a subcategory of mental retardation.

It still does not seem possible, to the author, that social symptoms can be explained on the basis of intellectual deficiencies. Many children with similar cognitive problems (e.g., mental retardation, brain damage) have no difficulty in relating to people, so there must be some additional factor in autism which operates either in addition to the cognitive problems or as a common cause of both the intellectual and social deficiencies.

Language disorders. The behavior of the child with a "language disorder due to brain injury" (see Chapter 7) resembles in many ways that of the autistic child (e.g., language deficiencies, impairment of abstract thinking). Kanner points out that these autistic children see their world as a series of fragments rather than a cohesive whole, an observation similar to H. Werner and A. A. Strauss's description of perceptual difficulties (1941). The stereotyped ritualistic behavior is like that of the brain-injured, and the anxiety about novelty or change is reminis-

cent of the "catastrophic reaction" which Goldstein described in brain-injured war veterans (1942).

In his book on the diagnosis of auditory disorders in childhood, Helmer Myklebust considered autism a form of "psychic deafness": "some children do not use their auditory capacities because they are emotionally disturbed. Such children have psychic deafness" (1954, p. 182). He regards autism as an emotional defense unconsciously employed like an hysterical neurotic symptom by an innately normal child. In his discussion of the differential diagnosis of autism and aphasia, he stresses the emotional and social peculiarities of the autistic child. But he also speaks of the "intact symbolic capacities" of the autistic child, and contrasts him with the aphasic, who is deficient in symbolic behavior in general.

Briefly, autism, schizophrenia, mental retardation, and language disorders (such as aphasia, psychic deafness and the Strauss syndrome of brain-injury) are similar and overlapping conditions. It is possible for any one of them to exist in pure form and to represent a distinct clinical entity. There are, however, a significant number of cases in which differential diagnosis is, at best, very difficult. As his parents make an odyssey though diagnostic services, the same child may receive four or five different diagnoses, as successive clinics diagnose the case in terms of their special area of interest and experience. They may be equally correct in terms of the definitions they are using, but this is of slight consolation to bewildered parents in search of specific answers and—above all—effective treatment.

Degrees of Autism

Is autism a specific disease? Or is it a cluster of associated symptoms which can be manifested in varying degrees? Rimland is a strong exponent of the first position. He finds variation in

———
°Rimland, *op. cit.*, p. 79.
°°Rimland, *op. cit.*, p. 123.

severity, but notes the "absence of blends," or i.e., of continuous gradation from normal to autistic. Rimland uses "the large void between autism and normal behavior"[*] as part of his case for biological causation. He argues that if autism were a reaction to environmental factors, it would be more diverse than it is. In the author's experience, however, variation in severity cannot be dismissed so easily. How autistic must the child be to warrant the diagnosis "autism?"

Despite the multifaceted nature of autistic symptoms, it has been constantly reiterated that the distinguishing feature is deficiency in personal relationships. The child is more retarded in this area than in any other aspect of development. Not all children described as autistic, however, remain totally unaware of other people; in time, there is usually a progression away from autism toward some relationships with people, although of a peculiar character. In the author's opinion, autism is relative rather than absolute; that is, it is relative to what is expected of a child in comparison with other children of his mental or chronological age.

There are scales which can be used to assess development of intelligence, social maturity, and motor performance, but there is no way of evaluating the level of personal relationships. The following normal expectancy scale is offered not as a tried-and-true measuring instrument, but rather as a rough diagnostic guide. The autistic child, when first seen, rarely behaves at a level as low as Level 2 on this scale, and Level 6 seems to represent the ceiling, at least for the autistic children observed by the author over a period of time.

1. The most primitive normal response is the infant's desire for physical contact and his visible relaxation when he is picked up, carried, or rocked.

2. At about three months, the normal infant is perceptually aware and visibly attentive to others. He looks at people, listens to them, and shows that he is entertained by their activities. He smiles at the sight of someone else's face.

3. Sometime during the second six months of life, the normal baby begins to respond selectively to people. He becomes choosy about whom he will allow to do things for him; he is less friendly, or even anxious, with strangers; and he behaves differently even with different people with whom he is familiar.

4. Almost simultaneously with Level 3, the normal baby shows a definite interest in imitation, indicating that he has incorporated what he has seen others do and is turning from passive to active. He enjoys imitation, in the sense that he likes to see his mother and himself doing the same thing or making the same sound. He perceives the identity of action and sound and is pleased by it.

5. The normal toddler shows increasing reliance on his mother and goes to her when he is hurt or frustrated. By this behavior, he shows that he considers her a source of comfort and assistance.

6. Gradually, the normal toddler comes to modify his behavior in order to please his mother. He tries to conform to what she says, he gives her things in a gesture of generosity, and he beams when she praises him. There is a corollary to this in the teasing and negativism by which the child tests his power and independence by nonconformity. Although it is negatively directed, it is definitely part of a relationship, and is born out of the ambivalence of feeling which is normal for the age.

7. The three-year-old starts to view people as a source of information and becomes increasingly anxious to communicate verbally, expressing thoughts, feelings, and experiences. He wants to share his ideas and find out about others.

8. Again, almost simultaneously with Level 7, the normal child begins to demand exclusive attention and admiration, and shows obvious jealousy and resentment at having to share.

9. The demands for attention extend to fantasies and a wish to be everything, including a husband to the mother.

10. In the normal child of six, seven, or eight, one sees the culmination of identifi-

---

[*]Rimland, *op. cit.*, p. 60.

cation with the parent of the same sex, a display of behavior, temperament, and speech based on the remembered example rather than on the immediately presented model of behavior.

11. The normal child becomes interested in children his own age, wants to participate in their activities, wants to act and look like them, and is aware of what they think of him. He is able to share the feelings of others.

Although autistic children outgrow some of their autism, they remain egocentric. They are unable to see themselves as others see them; they lack tact and poise; they cannot join a group; they remain socially isolated. They may learn to travel in company, but not *with* company. One ten-year-old boy was able to attend a regular class, abide by the rules, and learn the lessons, but he never seemed to recognize his classmates when he saw them outside; he knew them only in terms of their position to him in the school room. Another boy, of the same age, was able to function academically at his own age level in a psychiatric treatment residence, but approached complete strangers with the same aplomb with which he might approach an old friend. On a bus, he introduced himself, asked people for their names and birthdates, and chattered about himself. He did not recognize their uneasiness and their attempts to withdraw, nor realize that these strangers neither knew nor cared to know about his personal experiences. This boy also used many made-up words without realizing that they had no meaning for the listener, and he assumed that everyone shared his memories, knew the people he had known, and been to the places he had been. In these ways, he demonstrated the egocentrism normal in a two or three-year-old.

Just as the autistic individual is unable to identify with someone else, so he is unable to empathize with others. He can neither accept their personalities nor put himself in their position. Eisenberg cites the example of a stu-dent, called upon to speak at a football rally, who predicted that the home team was going to lose. His prediction was based on statistical probability, so he could not understand the round of boos which greeted him *(1958)*.

Interestingly, none of the follow-up reports on autistic children contains any information about romances or marriages. (Autistic boys outnumber girls about 4 to 1, according to Kanner [1954], and the author has observed the difference to be even greater.) It seems highly doubtful that even an ex-autistic boy would ever acquire enough social interest or skill to approach matrimony. There is also curiously little known about the sexual development of these youngsters. There is little evidence of masturbation. And there are few signs of specifically sex-oriented interests, which would seem to be a natural corollary of the lack of identification with the parent of the same sex or with peers of the same sex. Their interest in mechanical objects may look masculine, but this impression is counterbalanced by their complete disinterest in sports. Things and activities are interesting only *per se,* not because they are perceived as masculine or feminine.

The case of Bobby illustrates some of the theoretical problems involved in differential diagnosis:

Bobby came to professional attention when he was three and a half years old, because he did not speak at all. Mental retardation was ruled out later, when he demonstrated a comprehension of language and an ability to read. Bobby had the alert appearance and the ability to solve puzzles ascribed to autistic children; he was advanced in motor development; and neurological and electroencephalographic examinations (two criteria proposed by Rimland as differentiating autism from schizophrenia) were negative. The time of onset of his symptoms was hard to establish: Bobby had never talked, and had always seemed different from his younger brother, but his mother was vague about details. There was abundant evidence of what Reiser terms "profound disturbance in parent-parent and parent-child interaction during the neonatal period."[*]

The major problem here was to differentiate between aphasia and autism. Autism was established on the basis of: (1) consistent avoidance of other's peoples eyes; (2) absence of imitative behavior; (3) absence of signs of affection or preference for one particular person; and (4) stereotyped, manipulative play with toys. He did *not* show tremendous anxiety about change although he did like routine.

At the age of 6, Bobby suddenly began to talk, but he was difficult to understand because he never addressed himself to a specific listener. His tone was flat and expressionless, and he used peculiar grammatical constructions, including the reversal of pronouns. His speech seemed to confirm the diagnosis of autism, although there were still some who argued that it resembled that of aphasic children. It should be mentioned that this child was known to many agencies, including the Cleveland Clinic, Parents Volunteer Association for Retarded Children, the Mental Development Center, Cleveland Hearing and Speech Center, and the United Cerebral Palsy Association, all in Cleveland. Accordingly he had many diagnostic labels, although the agencies cooperated in a unified treatment plan.

Family History: Bobby's mother readily admitted that she had been depressed, lonely, and isolated during his early life. She gave the youngster adequate physical care, but was uncommunicative and preferred to read. His father was dependent, irresponsible, and unable to hold a job. A brother was born when Bobby was two years old, and a year later the mother returned to work. A chaotic period followed. For a few weeks, the father tended the children, toilet training Bobby in two weeks by spanking him. After this, there was a succession of baby sitters, none of whom proved satisfactory. The mother then left her husband and moved in with her own parents; she continued to work, and the grandmother took care of the two boys during the day.

[*]Reiser, *op. cit.*, p. 884.

Behavior—Age 4: Bobby's vocalizations were limited to an "mmmmm" or a high-pitched "eeeeeeee." He was hyperactive and sometimes aggressive. It was impossible to assess his comprehension accurately because he was so uncooperative, but his grandmother reported many examples of his understanding of what was said to him. He usually ignored people. He showed no imitation; he never looked at people directly, he appeared deaf to their remarks, and he very rarely changed his facial expression. His only contact with people was mechanical—he would use the psychologist's hand as an agent to do him some good, actually turning her into an impersonal instrument. He was content to be left alone with toys, especially those which could be manipulated, and he indicated discomfort when anyone interfered.

Period of Psychotherapy: The therapist soon learned that Bobby was able to read words; his grandmother reported that he asked about words by pointing at them, and that he never forgot them. When these words appeared in a different context and print, he would point to them if asked to. Since this represented a spontaneous interest and special ability, written words became the vehicle of communication. The therapist printed special word cards, matched this with her own actions, and attempted to get him to respond to her behavior. This was always difficult because of his lack of imitation. One of his first social acts was his pleasure in peekaboo. As time progressed, he indicated the desire to be held and sung to as if he were a very small baby. There were also days when he ran around, teasing and acting negatively, but it appeared that he might be building some sort of relationship.

Psychological Test Results: Bobby's first psychological test was given when he was four, after six previous attempts. On the Merrill-Palmer Scale he achieved a mental age of two years and nine months, and an IQ of 56. His performance with the Seguin Form Board and Picture Puzzles were at the level of performance with the four-year-level. Six months later, he was given the Peabody Picture Vocabulary Test, which involves choosing one out of four pictures which fits the word said by the examiner. On this test, he obtained an IQ of 87.

At the age of 5 years and 7 months, on the Leiter International Performance Scale, a test involving matching blocks with pictures of both concrete and abstract nature, Bobby's mental age was 5 years and 3 months, and his IQ was 94. His test performances indicated an ability to perform tasks requiring concrete, specific functions, but no ability in abstract areas. Bobby's test behavior was a combination of negativism, teasing, and withdrawal from the examiner, either by crawling under the table or blocking out the examiner's presence by shutting his eyes and holding his hands over his ears. When he did comply with the psychologist's requests, he performed in an automatic manner, without looking at her.

Educational Program: At five, after one year of therapy, Bobby was enrolled in a nearby nursery school for the retarded. There, he played alone and read. He made no friends and, although he was cooperative with the teacher, it was apparent that he had little, if any, relationship with her. The therapist visited occasionally, and Bobby never appeared to recognize her.

At six, Bobby was enrolled in an academic readiness program designed for brain-damaged children. Simultaneously, a plan was made to restrain the use of his right arm because of a lack of hand preference. Within weeks Bobby began to talk, using short sentences and phrases. He answered direct questions and communited specific desires. He remained isolated in the group, giving little heed to the other children and pursuing his own line of interests.

Bobby's story demonstrates not only the difficulty of diagnosis, but also the difficulty of evaluating treatment factors. The mechanical restraint of his right arm preceded the onset of speech, but this does not necessarily mean that this was the crucial factor; the improvement was probably the result of a combination of factors, including the patient efforts of his mother, grandmother, and the therapist to engage him in a relationship, and the consistent interest of all the dedicated teachers with whom he came in contact.

Diagnosis of Other Forms of Childhood Psychosis

Most people consider autism only one form, although the most common, of childhood psychosis. The following discussion deals with another subcategory, symbiosis, and also with the criteria proposed for a general diagnosis of childhood psychosis.

Symbiosis

The literature on symbiosis is only one-tenth as large as that on infantile autism. The person most often associated with descriptions of the clinical syndrome is Margaret Mahler, a child psychoanalyst. Less has been written about symbiosis than autism, partly because it was defined only in 1952 (as compared to 1943, for autism) and partly because there seem to be fewer cases. Further, symbiotic children are less strange than autistic ones. They are often diagnosed as "borderline"; that is, on the border between psychosis and neurosis.

The symbiotic child has too close a relationship with his mother, a relationship which brooks no separation, however brief. While the autistic child is content to be left alone, the symbiotic child is overwhelmed by panic unless he is with his mother. According to Mahler *(1952)*, these children are rarely conspicuously disturbed in the first year of life except, perhaps, in their sleeping. They may be described by their mother as "cry-babies" or as "oversensitive" infants. Their disturbance becomes apparent gradually or manifests itself abruptly at critical developmental points at which normal children become increasingly independent. Symbiotic psychotics can tolerate abnormally little frustration. Clinical symptoms are manifested between the ages of two and a half to five, with a peak of onset in the fourth year. The child cannot move out of the stage of total dependency; his ego is borrowed from his mother, and he cannot attain even the independence of the normal three or four-year-old. Many pre-school children suffer from separation anxiety, but the symbiotic child differs in the degree of his anxiety and in the extent to which his ego is affected.

Jim first came to the author's attention when he was enrolled in a pre-school for mildly retarded youngsters. He participated very little, only watching the others and sometimes following suit if required to do so. At times, he seemed entirely out of contact, completely silent and unresponsive except for violent headshaking. He was skillful in hand work, but unfortunately inclined to use this skill destructively—cutting things up, breaking toys, and so on. Toward the end of the school year, his mother stopped coming with him in the morning and staying in the building during school. Apparently, Jim could not tolerate this, although for a long time she had been in another part of the building, out of his sight and hearing, and he stopped talking to anyone at the school.

As an infant, Jim had been inactive, apathetic, and extraordinarily sensitive to change. He was content in a crib or highchair, but he screamed uncontrollably for hours when he was put on the floor or in the playpen. New people and new places upset him so much that the parents avoided them. By the time he was a year old, the mother felt that he was different from other children because of his lack of responsiveness and normal playing. He never crawled or got into things. He walked at 17 months. Some of his hysteria in new places stopped when he was two years old. When he was four, the parents went to a speech center because his speech was mainly echolalic, with no conversation, and they were referred to child psychiatry. At that time, the parents described his unusual destructive behavior. He hit people, "going for their eyes"; he lay in bed, giggling and ripping up the sheets; he tore up flowers, wallpaper, his sister's school papers, and even grabbed papers from total strangers. After doing something wrong, he would often call it to his mother's attention: "I tore the light." He showed marked separation anxiety. His mental age was then of two years and eight months; his IQ was 67. His age equivalent on the Vineland Social Maturity Scale was also two years and eight months. X-ray examinations, EEG's, and neurological consultations were essentially negative.

Observation of Jim began at six years and nine months. He was seen 26 times, at first weekly and then more often. His behavior was about the same as it had been when he was four. His speech was less echoing, but one had the feeling that he was repeating something which had been said to him on some previous occasion. He talked about his behavior and events at home in a monotonous way which brooked no discussion or questioning. When he was alone with the therapist, he talked about himself in much the same complaining way that his mother talked about him.

He could not be engaged in give-and-take conversation on any subject. Neither could one play with him; for a few moments he would look at pictures or toy objects, but he soon attacked and destroyed them. He also drew simple geometric forms, over and over.

Initially, Jim's problem seemed to be simple anxiety over separation, but gradually it became clear that underneath his fear lay a great wish to make things "go away." One day, when he was visiting at the pre-school with his mother and the therapist, the other children left for a field trip. Jim insisted that they would never come back, and would not be reassured. When it was suggested that he wished they would stay away forever, he tacitly agreed, but he appeared to be angry when he was told that he did not have the power to achieve this end. Jim had proved to himself that he had great power to make things disappear. He repeatedly broke the television set, thereby making the picture go away. For hours he played with a little mechanical calendar, trying to make the windows free of numbers and letters, blank like the television screen. Obvious pleasure came when he was successful, but with this proof of power came increased anxiety—if he could make so many things vanish, he could not really rely on any kind of permanence; even his mother could be "wiped out."

The nature of the child's relationship with his mother was a curious one. He was able to substitute another person (his father, his therapist, or even his sister), and would then show the same clinging attachment to that person—but if, for one moment, he could not see the substitute, he was frenzied. His relationship with his mother did not seem to be a distinctive one since it could easily be transferred to another person.

Although some of the dynamics of Jim's behavior became more understandable, little change was effected. He could accept the therapist as a substitute for his mother, but he remained incapable of any kind of adaptation to a group. His play continued to be restricted to the acting out of aggression, and his parents were unable to control him sufficiently to prevent his doing serious material damage. The devastating results of his destructive behavior gave him both pleasure and anxiety, and it was almost impossible to shake his belief in the omnipotence of his aggressive wishes.

In many respects, Jim corresponds to the clinical description given by Mahler for symbiotic psychosis, specifically: (1) "anxiety reactions so intense and so diffuse that they are reminiscent of the organic distress of early infancy"; (2) "from the third year onward growing discrepancy between the rate of maturation of partial ego function versus lag of developmental individuation"; (3) "stereotyped speech productions"; (4) conflict between a craving for body contact and a shrinking from it; and (5) "agitated catatonic-like temper tantrums and panic-stricken behavior" *(1952, p. 292, 298)*. In Jim, these took the form of peculiar shaking and hissing spells. There are also some characteristics (e.g., the echolalic speech) which are usually ascribed to the autistic child, but his pathologically

close tie to his mother is a contraindication of autism.

Infantile Psychosis

Most people, impressed with the significant similarities between autism and symbiosis, conclude that they are different manifestations of the same illness (i.e., psychosis). Others feel that "there remains, nevertheless, a large group of active psychotic young children who are not characterized by a symbiotic tie with a parent, and whose psychosocial state is not 'autistic.'"[*] But if the definition is to be widened beyond those conditions already described, the question arises as to what criteria will be used for this more general definition?

It is worthwhile to note the clinical contributions made by the staff of the James Jackson Putnam Center (Reiser, Rank, Putnam, Pavenstadt, and Brown). This center, started in Boston in 1943, chose to concentrate on the study of infants, pre-school children, and their mothers. The research groups fell into two categories: (1) children showing "atypical development" (the older generic term for "infantile psychosis," introduced in a case study of an atypical two and a half-year-old child by Putnam *et al.*, 1948); and (2) children whose parents had suffered psychotic episodes. From the outset, the staff was interested in the effects of clear-cut maternal psychopathology on the child's development; this is one reason for their stress on the role of the mother's personality in the genesis of infantile psychosis.

Reiser gives the following description of infantile psychosis:

Infantile psychosis is characterized, first, by absence or impairment of contact with reality; second, by absence or impairment of meaningful verbal communication;

[*]Reiser, *op. cit.*, p. 846.

third, by autistic withdrawal from social interaction; fourth, by striving for sameness and constancy; fifth, by unevenness and lack of integration among components of mental and emotional functioning; and, finally, by general disparity among motor, verbal, social and adaptive achievements appropriate for their age.*

Although the individual clinical picture varies, common features include a lack of contact with reality, little or no communication, and a lack of integration and uniformity of ego development. Reiser explains the variations in form in terms of the depth of regression, the level of development before personality arrest occurred (sometimes in the first five years), and the child's specific experiences.

The following table (Janet Brown's) gives some idea of the possible variety of symptoms. They are ranked in the order of their frequency of occurrence in a group of 40 atypical children. The children, aged 1.4 to 5.6 years with a mean age of 3.6, were selected from a group of 73 closed cases diagnosed as atypical development (or infantile psychosis) *without* organic complications, physical handicaps, or a psychotic parent. They included the 20 cases judged "best" and the 20 judged "worst" on the basis of a follow-up study. Speech characteristics could be rated only in 21 of the 40 cases, as the others did not speak at all.

Childhood Schizophrenia

The clinical picture that Lauretta Bender gives of the schizophrenic child includes children in the categories already mentioned, and more:

The youngest schizophrenic children, those in the first two or three years of life, show disturbances in the vegetative rhythms and habit patterns, in motility and object relationship. Mothers are most distressed by the inability of the child to relate to herself, to siblings, to play materials, or food or clothes. Language has no

*Reiser, *op. cit.*, p. 790.

objective use for sign value, communication or interpersonal relations.*

Her description of those with a later age of onset resembles Mahler's description of the symbiotic child:

There is generally a searching, penetrating, even aggressive, clinging dependence. They are attractive, intriguing, and appear gifted. They attempt to solve their problems by an excessive identification or interpenetrating relationship.**

Bender comments on the rarity of hallucinations, and suggests that they are neurotically determined and represent the voice of conscience. She considers withdrawal a specific symptom only in those cases with a very early age of onset. Her diagnostic signs are expressed in physiological terms, in accordance with her interpretation of cause:

1. Disturbance in vaso-vegetative functioning.
2. Disturbance in normal rhythmic patterns (sleeping, eating, elimination).
3. Unevenness in somatic growth and non-specific endocrine dyscrasias.
4. Dysrhythmia in electroencephalographic examinations.
5. Motor awkwardness (history of anxiety about walking alone, climbing stairs, etc.).
6. Continuation of early reflex patterned activities such as coreoathetosis.
7. Postural reflex responses.
8. Bodily dependence, leaning on others.
9. "Soft" neurological signs, grimacing, expressionless voice, etc.
10. Lack of concern about body secretions.
11. Perceptual problems.
12. Language disturbances.

In a later paper, she states that 60 to 85 per cent of the cases diagnosed

*Quoted from L. Bender, "Childhood Schizophrenia," *American Journal of Orthopsychiatry*, XVII (1947), p. 49. Reproduced by permission.

**Bender, *op. cit.*, p. 53.

TABLE 8

Incident of Symtoms in Forty Cases

Rank	Symptom	Number of Cases
1	If speaks, odd quality to voice	18*
2	Low tolerance to frustration	36
3	Preoccupations present	32
4	Ignores other children	29
5	Attention: preoccupied or distractible	29
6	If speaks, echolalia present	14*
7	Stimuli excluded (pain, visual, acoustic)	27
8	Strong or unusual fears	26
9	Excessive mouth activity	26
10	Aggression self-bound	25
11	Understanding of speech uncertain	25
12	Bladder training incomplete	23
13	Bizarre movements present	23
14	Negativism high	23
15	Aggression absent	22
16	Bowel training incomplete	21
17	Object manipulation primitive	20
18	Aggression diffuse	20
19	No speech	19
20	Mother ignored	18
21	Separation problem	18
22	Affect intense	17
23	High anxiety	17
24	Afraid of other children	16
25	Avoids adults	16
26	If speaks, pronouns reversed	8*
27	Hyperactive	15
28	Aggression incomplete	15
29	Ignores adults	14
30	Selective food intake	11
31	Heedless of physical danger	11
32	Fleeting attention span	11
33	No social smile	11
34	Affect flat	10
35	Sleep disturbance	9
36	Biting inhibition	9
37	Identification with animals	8
38	Inhibition in amount of motor activity	7
39	Inhibition of skills in motor activity	7
40	Identification with inanimate objects	7
41	Excessive food or liquid intake	6
42	Ostentatious soiling	5
43	Avoids mother	5
44	Low food intake	5
45	Sex identification unclear or confused	4
46	Withholding of stools	2

*Of a total of 21.

Source: Quoted from Janet L. Brown, Ph.D., "Prognosis from Presenting Symptoms of Preschool Children with Atypical Development," *American Journal of Orthopsychiatry*, XXX, No. 2 (April, 1960), p. 386. Reprinted by permission.

as schizophrenic have abnormal EEG patterns *(Kennard and Levy, 1952, cited by Bender, 1961).* The nature of the abnormality—a predominance of low voltage slow waves—has been considered evidence of immaturity *(Hill, 1952).*

To test the diagnostic validity of these signs, Bender and W. Helme compared two groups of 30 children each. One group was hospitalized for psychosis and the other was hospitalized for nonpsychotic emotional conditions. The original diagnosis was confirmed by a follow-up study of both groups eight years later; a review of the original clinical symptoms indicated that certain signs differentiated better than others. The following table lists the differentiating factors in the "vaso-vegetative and motor areas" which seem most significant.

TABLE 9

Abnormalities	Schizophrenics	Controls	Chi Square	Probability
Vascular or homeostatic	13	0	14.14	.001
In eating or sleeping patterns	11	3	4.56	.04
In posture or balance	22	7	13.07	.001
Whirling/cohesiveness	20	3	25.48	.001
In voice or speech	22	8	11.33	.001

SOURCE: Quoted from L. Bender, M.D., and W. H. Helme, M.A., "A Quantitative Test of Theory and Diagnostic Indicators of Childhood Schizophrenia," *Archives of Neurology and Psychiatry,* LXX (October, 1953), Table 4, p. 421. Reproduced by permission.

It is interesting to note that enuresis, motor hyperactivity, grimacing, and "some abnormality in coordination" did not help to distinguish between the two groups. The "whirling" test is a "soft" neurological sign: the examiner rotates the child's head, and he responds by turning his body accordingly. This response is normal in children up to six or seven but, after that age, the normal child stands firm. The schizophrenic child, however, continues to respond by rotating his whole body, and whirls with delight. Bender compares this with the retention of "tonic neck-reflex attitudes" in schizophrenic patients, which is evidence that foetal characteristics are being carried into maturity.

In the 1953 study, the greatest number of significantly differentiating signs were reported in the areas of "body-image, self-world perceptions and reality-testing." These were evaluated on the basis of free and figure drawings. The Bender Gestalt Test shows "characteristic immaturities, fluid gestalten, fragmentation, and distortions in fore-ground-background relations, including rotation of figures on the background. Human figure drawings depict the body-image difficulties with unclear body boundaries, transparencies for internal organs and some representation of the retained tonic neck-reflex attitudes, and isolation of figures from the earth or any object" *(1961, p. 545).*

There are reports of the results of psychological tests given to child schizophrenics *(Des Lauriers and Halpern, 1947; Mehr, 1952).* L. Des Lauriers and F. Halpern indicated that IQ's vary widely, from retarded to highly gifted, and they felt that there was no scatter of test results which could be considered diagnostic of childhood schizophrenia. They classified the Rorschach records into two major categories; many resembled protocols given by children with organic brain disorders (e.g., they were short and showed poor form, perseveration, and intellectual and emotional impoverishment). Unlike the organically damaged patients, however, the schizophrenics did not involve themselves in the task; they often responded without even looking at the card and were unable to relocate their responses. The other group produced records similar to those of neurotic compulsives, but the authors noted some differentiating signs. As a result of their interpretations of the Rorschach responses, Des Lauriers and Halpern offer the following comments about the disease process:

These children are struggling with problems of outer and inner reality and are unable to find anything fixed to which they can hold, nothing they can accept, nothing to give them security or reassurance. They are overwhelmed with anxiety, not in the usual neurotic sense, as a result of inner conflicts, but because the whole world appears to be a menacing, ever-changing force. *(1941, p. 64.)*

Bender's paper indicated a third group of diagnostic signs—"anxiety and neurotic symptoms." The only significant difference between the groups was "diffuse anxiety," which she considers the nucleus of the schizophrenic problem, and reactive rather than causal; i.e., a reaction necessitated by the disruptive effects of the schizophrenic process. The way in which an individual deals with anxiety largely determines his symptoms; defenses against anxiety will vary with age, sex, and specific experiences. She also suggests that extreme anxiety is, in itself, suggestive of schizophrenia *(1953)*.

Bender also remarks that, when the onset is early, it is difficult to differentiate schizophrenia from organic deficiencies. But apparently this would involve differentiating among organic brain diseases and would actually be unnecessary, since Bender includes so many organic diseases under the rubric of childhood schizophrenia. When the onset occurs before puberty, the differentiation to be made is between schizophrenia and neuroses *(1947)*, but according to her later comments this, too, is an academic question, since "neu-

rotic disorders in children severe enough to require professional help are defense reactions to a disorganizing brain pathology or schizophrenia" *(1961, p. 535)*. Now we can understand her statement that schizophrenia is more frequent than is commonly recognized; she subsumes a great many diverse conditions under this heading, their only common denominator being the severity of disturbance.

Etiological Concepts

Organic Hypotheses

Infantile Autism. Rimland, who restricts definition of infantile autism to a "cognitive dysfunction," offers a specific cause:

We have suggested that the symptoms of autism could be the consequence of an impairment in the function of the reticular formation of the brain stem, and presented data from the neurophysiology laboratory and elsewhere in support of the hypothesis of reticular formation . . . A number of case studies were reported which led to the hypothesis that, at least in some instances, early infantile autism could be caused, or very accurately simulated, by an excess of oxygen given in early infancy. In view of known vast differences in infant reactivity to oxygen, it was suggested that even atmospheric oxygen might exceed the tolerance threshold for a small fraction of genetically-predisposed infants, as it appears to do in some cases of retrolental fibroplasia.[*]

R. R. Koegler and E. Colbert also suggest the reticular core as a possible site of the origin of the neurophysiological disturbances "since this area of the brain influences both upstream and downstream conduction and in general is the only area which has an influence on every other area; disease or abnormality here could account for the widespread neurophysiological changes noticed in childhood schizophrenia *(1959, p. 1048)*."

---

[*]Rimland, *op. cit.*, p. 119.

Childhood Schizophrenia. Bender regards schizophrenia as a basically organic abnormality in the central nervous system, a complex and subtle form of neurological disorder with diffuse rather than focal pathology. Bender's clinical contributions over the years reveal her consistent interest in the organic factors which determine child behavior; her early publications were concerned with the psychological consequences of organic diseases such as encephalitis. In a paper entitled "The Brain and Child Behavior" *(1961)*, she gives an account of her professional training, and those who have influenced her thinking most. Psychologists might be interested in the special mention she makes of G. Coghill, H. Kluever, S. Orton, and A. Gesell. In the field of neurophysiology, she speaks of Percival Bailey and his work on encephalitis, and she studied psychiatry with Adolph Meyer. One of the most influential figures has been her husband, Paul Schilder, best known for his work on body-image perception *(1951)*.

Bender subscribes to a belief in the principle of psychophysical identity: ". . . that the laws of the psyche and the biological organism are identical and that both have the same type of developmental problems" *(1961, p. 533)*. To her, behavior is primarily the result of a natural unfolding, an emergence of new functions which depend on the maturation of the central nervous system rather than on specific learning experiences. This follows the general philosophy of Gestalt psychologists and of those who view postnatal behavior as a continuation of embryological principles (e.g., Gesell, 1945). Bender's concept of childhood schizophrenia is that it is a result of maldevelopment of the central nervous system; in her words, "schizophrenia in childhood is a biological disorder in central integration and in maturation processes involving behavior with a lag characterized by embryonic features, especially plasticity" *(1961, p. 536)*.

Bender considers the essential cause to be an "inherited potentiality for schizophrenia," which may be triggered into a clinical syndrome by organic damage or physiological crisis in the foetal period or in early infancy, a specific syndrome which can often be detected shortly after birth. In 1947, she spoke of three common ages of onset: the first two years; between three and four and a half years; and between ten and eleven and a half years. Trauma and crises are the precipitating, but not the basic, cause.

She also feels that the parents of schizophrenic children have their own difficulties, which are a *result* of the child's problem:

The mother of the schizophrenic child . . . shows a specific mechanistic patterning due to her efforts to help the child in his distorted identification processes, to understand what is happening and to identify herself with the child. The mother bears an intolerable burden of anxiety and guilt, and is more bewildered than the child himself. She will try every mechanism for denying, evading, displacing or absolving the child's psychosis.[*]

Results of experimental studies indicate that schizophrenic children function on a significantly lower developmental level in some basic psychophysical behavior patterns than nonschizophrenic children *(Berkowitz, 1961; Pollack, 1958; Pollack and Goldfarb, 1957a; 1957b; Pollack and Krieger, 1958)*. Berkowitz interpreted her findings as consistent with Bender's theory of a maturational lag *(1961)*. There still remains the question whether such disturbances should be considered merely secondary to the severity of the mental disorganization, part of the total symptom picture rather than the

------

[*]Bender, *op. cit.*, p. 52.

explanation. R. K. Safrin carried out a careful study of differences in visual perception and in visual-motor functioning between 39 hospitalized schizophrenic boys and 57 nonpsychotic boys from schools and after-school centers. Mental ages and IQs were significantly lower for the psychotic boys than for the nonpsychotic boys. She found a strong relationship between MA and performance on the Bender Gestalt Test, the WISC Block Designs, and Cornell-Coxe Memory for Designs. Group differences on the tests were nullified when control for the differences in MA was instituted. Further analyses indicated that the considerably greater incidence of neurological deviations observed among the psychotic group was also a function of differences in maturational development. When the incidences of neurological deviations were compared for limited mental age ranges, tests of significance suggested no differences. In other words, psychotic children are more retarded in their over-all maturational development than nonpsychotic children, and differences between them in such psychophysical functions as visual perception and visual-motor performance as well as in nervous system functioning appear to be primarily related to differences in functional mental age. She interpreted her findings as *not* supporting Bender's theory of an organically determined maturational lag *(1964, p. 45)*. She felt that psychotic children show immaturity in the over-all biological and mental maturational processes and proposed that psychosis be studied in terms of deviations in ego development. In this she follows the approach of D. Beres who analyzed the schizophrenic symptoms in terms of arrest or regression in the ego functions of reality testing, regulation and control of instinctual drives, object relationships, thought processes, defense functions, autonomous functions such as

motility, and the synthetic functions *(1956)*.

Hypotheses Based on the Parent-Child Relationship

Emphasis on constitutional predisposition. Most psychologically oriented theories mention the child's predisposition to infantile psychosis. Some authorities consider predisposition more important than the role of the parents; others consider it less important. In her original paper on symbiosis, M. S. Mahler took the position that parental psychopathology is the major factor in the genesis of symbiotic psychosis *(1952)*. Later, she considered the cause basically intrinsic, rather than extrinsic:

These children are constitutionally vulnerable and pre-disposed toward the development of a psychosis. It is the very existence of the constitutional ego defect in the child that helps create the vicious circle of a pathogenic mother-child relationship, by stimulating the mother to react to the child in ways that are deleterious to his attempts to separate and individuate. *(Mahler and Gosliner, 1955.)*

There have been efforts to be more precise about the nature of the "constitutional vulnerability." Child analysts, in particular, have made use of Freud's comments on the importance of the protective barrier: ". . . *protection against* stimuli is an almost more important function for the organism than *reception of* stimuli" *(1920, 1955, p. 27)*. He pointed out the importance of being able to sample the outer world in small quantities; it is this function of the sense organs which characterizes highly developed organisms. Ekstein and J. Wallerstein described the ego of borderline psychotic children as

. . . characterized by a specific vulnerability or hypersensitivity in response to both inner and outer stimuli. We may conceptualize this difference, i.e., from normal children, by comparing the ego of border-line children to a delicate permeable membrane through which the primary process penetrates with relative ease from within, and which external forces puncture easily from without. *(1954, p. 349.)*

This is similar to the idea proposed by L. Bergman and S. Escalona, who observed unusual sensitivities in five infants who later became psychotic and suggested that these infants were forced to precocious ego development in order to compensate for their "thin protective barrier" *(1948)*. Because of its prematurity, this ego development is not a secure one, and it breaks down under trauma, paving the way for psychotic development. S. K. Rosenfeld and M. P. Sprince also use this concept of an inadequate protective barrier to help explain the earliest stages of infantile psychosis:

. . . one of the points which has emerged is that our [borderline] children find it difficult to inhibit stimuli. They seem to be swamped by them, and are unselective in their choice of what is relevant and what is irrelevant. We think that the inability to inhibit and select stimuli, a circumstance leading to distractability as described by Piaget (1936) on an intellectual level, may extend to reactions to emotional stimuli . . . It may be that this incapacity to select and inhibit interferes with the differentiation between self- and object-representation. It probably goes back even further and influences the very first step in reality testing, namely, the distinction between what is inside the infant's own body and what is outside *(1963, p. 623).*

There is no doubt that these youngsters are supersensitive and that they collapse under trauma which most children survive without sinking. It is less clear how much of this is constitutional and how much is the result of ineffective maternal care. Unfortunately, the opportunities for close study of infants

before the onset of infantile psychosis are virtually nonexistent.

Emphasis on Parental Psychopathology. The James Jackson Putnam Center Staff has been identified with the "schizogenic" mother concept. In her original statements, Beata Rank remarked that one assumed that these atypical children had suffered gross emotional deprivation and that this hypothesis required an examination of the mother's personality *(1949)*. Later, she modified this by acknowledging a biological and hereditary predisposition, although she did not consider it sufficient cause for the child's disturbance. She noted three important factors in the etiology of "atypical" development *(1955):*

1. The relationship between mother and child was profoundly disturbed in the first two years. This disturbance antedated the appearance of atypical behavior in the child. All areas of emotional interchange in the relationship were highly ambivalent.
2. The early relationship between the father and the child was disturbed.
3. Many of the atypical children had suffered an unusual number of respiratory and gastrointestinal illnesses during infancy. In a considerable number of cases, the outbreak of symptoms followed specific traumatic events, such as separation from, or loss of, a parent, the birth of a sibling, and so on. These were the proverbial straw on the camel's back, and resulted in a massive breakdown.

The cases reported by Rank and her colleagues *(Putnam et al., 1948; Pavenstedt, 1955)* abound in evidence of maternal difficulties: "On the surface, [these mothers] may give the impression of being well-adjusted; not too rarely they are highly intellectual, prominent people. Close investigation reveals that the majority of them are immature and narcissistic, with precarious social contact" *(Rank, 1949, p. 131).* In cases personally known to the author, there are a few in which the environment was sufficiently patho- logical to explain the child's autistic disturbance. Donny is a case in point:

Donny was first seen in a child psy- chiatry clinic when he was almost four. He was an only child, and a handsome youngster. He spoke clearly, but totally ignored anything that was said to him. What he said was an echo—"Don't touch that, son; it might be hot." But then he would proceed to touch the hot radiator. He neither watched nor listened to any- thing. In one observation hour, his activ- ities were three: he raced back and forth from one end of the playroom to the other, staring at the floor. Apparently the shadows and patterns on the floor fascin- ated him. He touched and backed away from the radiator and various water pipes, and then touched them again. And he let blocks dribble through his fingers.

His early development was at least nor- mal. He smiled at 2 months, sat at 5 months, and walked alone at 13 months. He began to use words at 13 months, and was speaking short sentences before 21 months. His mother reported a feeding problem from earliest infancy, and she had been unable to toilet train him despite strong punitive measures (about which she felt very guilty). She had set out to break him of his stubbornness, and gave as an example an incident which had occurred when he was 13 months old. At dinner, he had repeatedly touched her plate, and she had slapped his hand over and over, until she realized that it was becoming red and swollen, but to no avail. She was always afraid of spoiling him, and so let him cry for many hours. She had insisted on his saying "please"; she considered him hard to handle and "infuriating." She commented, "I never thought of him as a baby. He always seemed to understand what I was saying to him and to know everything." There was no doubt that she had little idea of "normal" behavior for young children and that she had had un- reasonable expectations. When he did not cooperate, she became furious.

There had been a number of separations. Donny's mother was hospitalized for a week because of a miscarriage when

Donny was 18 months old, and he had shown a marked reaction. When he was 21 months old, the family moved and he spent a week with one relative and a week with another.

The first sign of his disturbance was his refusal to answer questions. At the same time he became secretive, and paid no at- tention to his mother's requests, and echoed her reprimands. She did not seek help, however, until her own mother com- mented, after an interval of several months, that Donny was saying less and that it was mostly nonsense. He seemed withdrawn and restless.

Donny was observed over a period of two and a half years. At the age of six and a half, he behaved much as he had on the first visit. His most outstanding quality was his detachment. He would come when someone called his name, but would re- main only briefly before returning to his stereotyped activities. He sang to himself (he had a great love of music), and he raced back and forth as if on a well-worn path, retracing his steps in a small area. Periodically, he crouched, examining the floor tiles with great care; he smelled, mouthed, and banged small objects that he found by chance. His play did not take any organized form and he did not differ- entiate between objects. As far as one could see, he had no preference for one person over another, and gave no sign of recognizing his parents.

Because of the history of regression after normal development in the first year, Donny was hospitalized for neurological study. Electroencephalographic examina- tions showed varying degrees of abnormal- ity, and the neurologist raised the possi- bility of a postencephalitic behavior disorder. Donny was unmanageable at home and was placed in the state school for the retarded. Later, his mother was hospitalized for an acute schizophrenic ill- ness.

Any child with a mother like Donny's would have become emotionally dis- turbed. Whether this explains his re- gression is moot, but it is reasonable to think that he had to block out people in order to defend himself against their impossible demands. In addition, the organic pathology may have so weakened his ego that he could cope with his traumatic environment only by regressing. Donny's case is also interesting in connection with the Bergman-Escalona hypothesis: He had unusual sensitivity (to sounds, as well as his fondness for music), he was precocious (he spoke early and stacked blocks at the age of one year), he experienced trauma (separations and a psychopathological relationship to his mother), and the culmination was the breaking down of all his ego functions (i.e., psychosis).

Kanner and L. Eisenberg are less definite than the Putnam Center staff about cause-and-effect relationship. Kanner's original statement of cause was an "innate inability to form the usual biologically-provided affective contact with people, just as other children come into the world with innate physical and intellectual handicaps" *(1943, p. 250)*. Their observations about the parents of psychotic children are frequently quoted, however. Kanner observed that an unusually high proportion of autistic children had intelligent, obsessive, and cold parents. In order to test the possibility that some hidden selective factor tended to bring only these parents in for consultation, he and Kanner compared the parents of 50 autistic children with the parents of 50 nonautistic private patients. They found that the control group had considerably less education and professional status and that "one does not find the dramatically evident detachment, obsessiveness and coldness that is almost a universal feature of parents of autistic children" *(1956, p. 8)*. They point out however, that 10 per cent did *not* fit the stereotype, that those parents who did fit the description had raised other, nonpsychotic children, and that other, equally cold parents did not produce autistic children. They also observed that the child's unresponsiveness might be partly responsible for the parents' apparent coldness, but they nevertheless feel that the coldness suggests the presence of a dynamic experiential factor in the genesis of autism. They quote cases to illustrate the mechanical maternal care and the absence of emotional warmth in the early history of some autistic children. Eisenberg added to the information on parental contribution with his study of the fathers of 100 autistic children. Eighty-five were "seriously disturbed" in their paternal role, a disturbance characterized by a coldly mechanical attitude toward marriage and child-rearing *(1957)*.

Much has been written about the parents of psychotic children. The diversity of opinion is illustrated in three papers presented as a workshop on "Parents of Schizophrenic Children" at the 1958 convention of the American Orthopsychiatric Association. Lewis B. Klebanoff, using a questionnaire type of inventory, failed to find any differences between the attitudes of mothers of schizophrenic children and those of retarded brain-damaged children *(1959)*. A. H. Esman, M. Kohn, and L. Nyman *(1959)*, reporting their clinical observations of the families of 11 schizophrenic children, found that almost all the parents were severely disturbed. They cautiously remark, however, that some disturbances in the family patterns might have been a reaction to the child's difficulty. I. Kaufman *et al.*, in a clinical study of the pathology of 38 schizophrenic children and their parents, proposed a fourfold classification of the parents' psychopathology. Although specific manifestations may differ, these authors state firmly that the etiology of childhood schizophrenia lies within this disturbed parent-child relationship *(1959, p. 471)*.

Goldfarb studied the parents of schizophrenic children hospitalized at the Henry Ittleson Center. As expected, the normal control subjects had superior family lives. When he analyzed the families in terms of categories of schizophrenia, he found important differences. In the schizophrenic group, the most aberrant children (Goldfarb's "organic" category) tended to belong to the families considered most adequate on a psychological basis; the least aberrant (Goldfarb's "nonorganic" category) tended to belong to the families judged least adequate. In a later study, Goldfarb and Donald Meyers (1962) found twice as many schizophrenic mothers of the nonorganically psychotic children as compared to mothers of organically psychotic children (44 and 21 per cent, respectively). This raises the possibility that genetic factors are a cause of "nonorganic" schizophrenia, but Goldfarb and Meyers cautiously point out that:

. . . these findings do not prove that genetic factors are *not* involved in childhood schizophrenia. However, they do point to the fact that the presence of schizophrenic parents in the families of schizophrenic children cannot in itself be taken to prove the genetic hypothesis, because these families with schizophrenic parents are also relatively inadequate families from the psycho-social viewpoint.[*]

These reports are only a few of many, but they illustrate the problems involved. In evaluating any such study, one must consider the definition of childhood schizophrenia used, the nature of the control group (if any), the representativeness of the sample of parents, and the methods of evaluating parental psychopathology. There is a tremendous difference between the techniques of Klebanoff, who used the Parental Attitude Research Instrument (PARI) with two groups of little-known parents of hospitalized children, and those of Esman and Kaufman, who

used treatment interview material obtained in weekly sessions over a period of years, with no control group.

Even with control groups, it is difficult to evaluate the results. If no differences are found, it may be because of faulty methods of evaluation; if identifiable differences are found, how do we know whether they are reactions to the child's problem (*Erickson, 1950; Peck, Rabinovitch, and Cramer, 1949; and Bender, 1955*), or causal (Kanner, the Putnam Center staff, and Kaufman *et al.*)? And if the parents are responsible, is there a genetic transmission of schizophrenia or is it passed on in the household? Investigations in this area give abundant evidence of the human equation in research; even the most conscientious researcher seeks, and is likely to find, confirmation of his personal beliefs.

Emphasis on Multiple Causation. Some experts believe that childhood schizophrenia (or infantile psychosis) is not a separate entity and, therefore, cannot be attributed to a single cause. Goldfarb suggests that the "single cause" prejudice has resulted in apparently mutually exclusive and conflicting theories of etiology. Discussing the two most significant biases—the purely somatic and the purely psychogenic—Goldfarb likens the situation to the one which prevailed in the study of mental retardation several decades ago. Mental retardation was first thought to be a matter of heredity, then a matter of environment, but it is now recognized as a possible result of either or of both (*1961*). And, although the vivid reports given by Kanner and Eisenberg convey the impression that they hold the parents to be wholly responsible, their theoretical position is in fact similar to Goldfarb's. Eisenberg suggests that "just as intellectual inadequacy [i.e., mental retardation] may be the outcome of structural [i.e., organic] limitation, *or* of cultural deprivation, so may affective inadequacy reflect organic dysfunction, affective deprivation or a combination thereof" *(1956, p. 23).*

Goldfarb considers childhood schizophrenia (the author prefers the term "infantile psychosis," which indicates something of the seriousness and nature of the symptoms without making it the same disease as that which affects older people) only a symptomatic classification, and attempts to make subdivisions on the basis of presenting symptoms and etiology. His conceptual model for the study of childhood schizophrenia implies a temporal sequence of events, beginning with causes and proceeding to primary and secondary effect. He states his theoretical position as follows:

The diagnosis of childhood schizophrenia is a gross signal to the observer of the presence of profound impairments in essential adaptive functions (Step 3) . . . Childhood schizophrenia obviously is not a unitary, etiologically specific and positive disease entity, relentlessly unfolding itself; it is merely a label indicating that the child deviates dramatically from the normal in ego-functioning, that he lacks normal guides for self-regulation, for achieving self-identity, and for differentiating himself from the world outside himself (Step 3). Aside from the deficits in ego, one notes clinically a panic-inducing stage of strangeness and a complicated variety of compensatory adjustments for finding constancy (Steps 4–5).*

Conceptual Model for the Study of Childhood Schizophrenia

1)† Parental inadequacy and perplexity lead to an absence of positive reinforcements and, in turn, to stimulus confusion which in turn increases parental perplexity, which may produce
2)† a deviant child
3) with an ego deficiency caused by the absence of normal guides for self-directed action and self-regulation; and with a defect in self-identity, diffusion of boundaries of self and non-

self, and thus producing for the child a pronounced
4) absence of predictable expectancies, with an ultimate loss of referents and anchors, which produce
5) catastrophic feelings of strangeness and unfamiliarity, and then
6) panic (primordial anxiety), in an often-vain seeking for sameness and constancy.

†1 and 2 may be either primary or secondary.
SOURCE: Goldfarb, *op. cit.,* p. 28.

In this model, the primary cause may be either the intrinsic disorders of the child, or the extrinsic pathology arising from distortions in family relationships. Again, quoting Goldfarb:

Just as many causal factors are likely, so each child's impairments are probably due to varying combinations of multiple contributing factors. These combinations theoretically may be considered along a continuum. At one end of the continuum, somatic inadequacies within the child are the primary basis for the ego deficits. At the other end of the continuum, the important etiologic factor is disturbance in the child's experiences within his family. One can demonstrate the etiologic model by ranking a hypothetical group of children in order of the presumed relative weights of somatic and familial factors leading to the abnormality. This schematic model, although theoretical, accords with actual clinical experience. At one end, for example, would be the child who gives definite evidence of brain damage and, on the basis of observation, comes from a normal family. At the other end would be the child with no evidence of somatic abnormality who was reared in a manifestly deviant family atmosphere.**

Research Findings

Goldfarb's report is based on clinical and experimental study of 26 schizophrenic children admitted to Ittleson Center for residential treatment and a control group. His report is not primar-

---

*Goldfarb, *op. cit.,* p. 27–28.

**Goldfarb, *op. cit.,* p. 29.

ily concerned with treatment, but brief mention is made of the need for clear-cut adult responses and directives, understandable rewards, and definition of boundaries in order to give schizophrenic children a definite structure. He describes the dangers of "adult perplexity" and the need for organization and structure, in order to insure predicability for the children. Spatial boundaries of movement were precisely delineated; the day's activities were carefully scheduled to stress the structure of time, and the responsibilities and roles of various adults were outlined. The ratio of adults to children was better than 2 to 1, which gives an indication of the expense of the therapeutic program.

The Ittleson Center patients were 18 boys and 8 girls, of 6 years and 6 months to 11 years and 2 months. The schizophrenic children did not differ from the normal ones in height and weight, or in auditory, visual and tactile acuity. They were, however, uniformly inferior to normal children in perceptual processes involving figure-ground discrimination and configurational closure, in conceptual functions which required abstraction and categorization, in speech and communicative ability, and they were very deficient in motor capacity. The schizophrenic child's behavioral impairment at perceptual and conceptual levels was reflected in his confusion about time, space, person, and his own body scheme. This confusion seemed to contribute to his uncertainty about his personal identity and his inability to differentiate self from nonself; this led in turn to anxious feelings of unfamiliarity. (A literary account of the confusion and panic experienced by a schizophrenic boy is contained in a little book, *Jordi*, by T. I. Rubin, 1960.)

The Ittleson Center staff sought to divide the schizophrenic group according to Goldfarb's model. The psychiatrists considered 16 of the subjects to be in the "organic" group, and found no clinical evidence of physiological deviation in 10. Independently, on the basis of neurological examination and history, 17 were classified as "organic" and 9 as "non-organic." Psychiatric and neurological judgments agreed about 21 of the 26 cases of schizophrenia.

The psychological data showed the control group to be superior, the "non-organic" schizophrenics were next, and the "organic" schizophrenics were the most impaired. The mean IQ's on the WISC give a rough index of this: for the normal group it was 101.8; for the "non-organics," 91.7; and for the "organics," 62.2. Some 70 physical, neurological, behavioral, mental, motor, and perceptual tests were given to all the children. It was recognized that the functions tested were often interrelated, and a factor analysis was made to determine the underlying variables. The study confirmed the existence of Goldfarb's "organic" and "non-organic" subgroups. He reiterates his belief that "childhood schizophrenia" is ambiguous, in that it includes at least two broadly different pathologies which are distinguishable partly by etiology and partly by performance. But the numbers studied were few, and he feels that testing should be standardized in order to provide more data.

The more one investigates child behavior, the more one realizes that identical behavior can be the result of radically different causes. The same rule seems to apply to psychotic symptoms. After the initial stage of precise, descriptive diagnosis, the clinician searches for historical and social causation. Although there is no need to apologize for reasonable doubt about cause, there is great danger in arriving at a premature conclusion.

Treatment and Follow-Up

Theoretically, one seeks the cause of a disorder in order to prescribe treatment and means for prevention, and it is natural that the treatment of infantile psychosis varies with the particular concept of cause.

Physical Therapy

According to Bender, the goal of treatment is to "nudge" evolutionary and developmental processes. She attempted to use treatments used for adult schizophrenics and reported the results of metrazol shock and electroshock in some 100 cases of childhood schizophrenia, aged four and older *(1947)*. In 1955, she reported on a 34-month-old child given nine electric shock treatments, and concluded that electric shock did not hurt the child, and that children were less disturbed by it, emotionally and intellectually, than adults. None of the shock treatments had curative effects, but it was her opinion that the children were more vigorous and better able to respond to psychotherapy, training, and education. W. J. Freeman and J. W. Watts *(1947)* reported on 11 psychotic children, including one four-year-old, who had prefrontal lobotomies: In their judgment, the therapeutic value of lobotomy proved to be limited *(1951)*. Such drastic measures have been quietly dropped from the therapeutic inventory. Drugs have been tried *(Fish, 1960; Freedman, 1958)*, but they have been less successful with children than with adults.

Educational Therapy

Remedial education and training seem to have replaced physical therapy as the major method of treatment of those who take an organic viewpoint. J. M. and Marie-Anna May described therapy at their residential center for autistic children as "a job of education, habilitation, analogous to putting braces on a polio-stricken child, or teaching Braille to a blind person" *(1959, p. 437)*. They describe the first step of residential treatment as the "loving contact period," when efforts are made to diminish the child's anxiety and give him confidence in the residential staff. When the child feels comfortable, the training starts. It is peripheral in the sense that one works from the outside in. By forcing the child, albeit gently, to perform certain acts, he is enabled to discontinue some of his autistic habits and build up a repertoire of new responses.

On the training of autistic children, Goldstein emphasized what he refers to as "concrete and situational determination": "these children 'learn' only by doing: through specific movement and activities they can be brought into contact wtih a desired task" *(1959, p. 549)*. This approach is based mainly on the view that psychosis is a cognitive disorder. Conditioning experiments, involving concrete rewards such as candy, and equally concrete punishment such as mild shocks, have been carried out at a number of centers (usually residential).

Combined Therapy

In educational therapy, little attention is paid to the causal role of personal relationships, although it is considered; in combined therapy, however, it is the basis of treatment. The Putnam Center has had extensive experience in coordinated treatment of parent and child; as a matter of policy, the child is kept at home and treatment is entirely on an out-patient basis. Parents are seen less often than the child, but mothers are seen at least weekly and fathers have individual or group psychotherapy or counseling. Since the premise is that infantile psychosis results from a profound disturbance in the parent-child axis during the first years of life, "the therapeutic philosophy is aimed toward helping the mother and father strengthen their function as parents, particularly in relation to the psychotic child."[*] Putnam stated that therapeutic success depends

---

[*]Reiser, *op. cit.*, p. 847.

largely on the parents' capacity to understand some of the psychological factors that have played a role in etiology, and also in their capacity to change, insofar as these factors have sprung from their own personality and attitudes *(1955)*.

Treatment of the Child

Rank has described two phases of psychotherapy of the atypical child: In the first, the therapist acts as a parent substitute, but is more understanding and more emotionally consistent than the real parent, in an effort to make restitution for past frustrations. "We meet the child's needs at whatever level he presents himself, avoiding frustrations wherever possible and providing a maximum of gratification" *(1955, p. 499)*. In the second phase, the therapist helps the child to take the necessary steps toward socialization, that is, she helps him to postpone immediate gratifications and to establish tender personal relationships. Rank gives no indication of her success, beyond remarking on the seriousness of the disorder and the slow pace which is necessary. Mahler's prognosis for symbiotic psychosis is guarded. "It is important to let the child test reality very gradually at his own pace. As he cautiously begins this testing of himself as a separate entity, he constantly needs to feel the support of an understanding adult. Such continual infusions of borrowed ego-strength may have to be continued for a lifetime" *(1952, p. 302)*.

Ekstein and J. Wallerstein describe the special difficulties encountered by the therapist:

The world of every child, his mode of thought and perception, differs markedly from that of the adult therapist. And it is necessary in the therapy of all children to devise and create ways of living oneself in the world of childhood. This difference and the attendant difficulties in understanding and communication increase seven-fold in work with the borderline

and psychotic child. His psychological world is not only alien to the logical adult mind of the therapist, but is characterized by a fluidity of ego organization which can hardly be captured in the therapist's conscious recollection of his own childhood. This wide gulf separating patient from therapist has faced us with formidable problems of many kinds. *(1954, p. 368.)*

In a later paper dealing specifically with the autistic child, Ekstein warns that anyone treating psychotic children must be prepared for frustrations of a unique sort. He cites the case of a three-year-old autistic girl, one of whose symptoms was echolalia. The technique used to establish contact was the therapist's imitation of the child, so that the child saw and heard herself mirrored in his actions and words *(1959)*. This report illustrates the kind of ingenuity that the therapist must employ in order to break through the autistic barrier. Mahler stresses the autistic child's dislike for direct human contact and the consequent need to lure him "out of his shell" with music, rhythmic activities, and other pleasurable stimuli of the sense organs. He must be approached gradually with the bait of inanimate objects, always keeping in mind that demonstrations of affection which one might expect to be reassuring are of no avail; indeed they are often contraindicated for these children *(1952)*.

I. H. Weiland and R. Rudnik summarize the observations of others, as well as their own experience with some 30 autistic children in residential treatment. They note a striking repetition in the proposals for the treatment of child psychotics: all stress the need to establish an "exclusive, need-satisfying relationship between the therapist and the child" *(1961, p. 549)*. In other words, the therapist must be useful to the child in a direct, immediate way that the child can quickly appreciate. The therapist must not provide merely a symbolic gratification; her value to the child must be real and concrete. Weiland and Rudnik compare this approach with that of C. B. Ferster and Marian K. DeMyer, who condition autistic children to respond to mechanical vending machines. Initially, the therapist herself is not unlike a super-efficient candy machine (1962). Weiland and Rudnik state that most of their autistic patients learned to tolerate—and eventually even make use of—the therapist for specific purposes, but they point out that this does not constitute a genuine social relationship because they are not aware of the therapist as a person. The child is not concerned about what the therapist might think or feel, but only about what she will do to, or for, him. The authors consider this a parallel, playlike relationship, and feel that it represents the maximum level of many of their patients. The child develops a stereotyped pattern of responding to others; he wants to repeat a particular activity. It is the activity in which he has invested his interest. Bobby, for example, enjoyed coming to the Mental Development Center but did not care who played with him, as long as the place, the toys, and the routine were the same.

Experience with the residential treatment of such children led Weiland and Rudnik to draw a number of conclusions regarding the etiology of most of the autism they observed. They felt that the children's course in treatment and their failure to progress beyond the parallel playlike relationship indicated that they suffered from an *absence* of relatedness, rather than from an active defense against it. Weiland and Rudnik do not argue that there must be an innate affective deficiency (Kanner's original hypothesis), but they suggest that the symptom may be created by a lack of exposure to, or an absence of, crucial experience in the first six months of infancy. They relate the irreversibility of the damage done to the child with "imprinting" experiments performed on animals, which demonstrate the permanent effects of deprivation at crucial periods (1961, pp. 555–56).

They are careful to point out that the genesis of autism is not the same in every case, and that in a few it develops as a defense against overwhelming traumatic experience. But there is little doubt that children with a history of traumatic relationships, who then retreat from people, have a better prognosis than those who have never related adequately to others.

Follow-up Reports

In general the prognosis for psychotic children is not encouraging. One can expect some limited improvement in social conformity and adaptability, but one inevitably feels that much of the child's potential has been wasted. Many children achieve a level at which their deficiencies and strong points come closer together, often within the range of the mentally retarded. Community classes and institutions for the retarded continue to include autistic children, since this is the only place where they can be accepted. Considering our information about treatment, training designed for the retarded is often the most practical solution, and it is certainly better than nothing.

Long-term follow-up studies do not show the superiority of any one therapy. Eisenberg and Kanner report on 120 cases in which there had been no therapeutic intervention. About one-third had achieved at least a minimum social adjustment to school and community life. Of 50 children followed up for a mean period of five years, none developed hallucinations; the major pathology continued to be an inability to relate normally to others (1956).

A more formal follow-up study was made of 80 autistic children (age nine or older) who had been known to the Children's Psychiatric Service at Johns

Hopkins Hospital for at least four years (*Eisenberg, 1956*). Of the 63 who were traced (34 in full-time residential settings and 29 at home), 3 had achieved a "good" adjustment; 14, a "fair" adjustment; and 46 a "poor" adjustment. This study failed to reveal any relationship between psychotherapy and adjustment, but Eisenberg remarked on the prodigious efforts made both by the school and the parents of the children who improved: "We cannot escape the feeling that the extraordinary consideration extended to these patients was an important factor in the amelioration of their condition" (*1956, p. 18*).

The second important prognostic factor was the degree of disturbance in language function. Eisenberg chose the presence of useful speech at the age of five as a line of demarcation, dividing the series into 32 "speaking" and 31 "non-speaking" children. Half of the first group achieved a fair-to-good social adjustment, but only 1 out of 31 non-speaking children was so classified. Useful speech is an index of the extent of autistic isolation, since its presence indicates some interchange with other people. Eisenberg found that those children who did not emerge from their autism were severely retarded in adolescence, and he regards such retardation as the inevitable result of the inability to incorporate the viewpoints of others and to substitute logic for primitive thinking.

Bender and her colleagues have reported a number of follow-up studies, many of which confirmed the original diagnosis. A follow-up study of 120 children diagnosed as schizophrenic indicated that two-thirds of them were later diagnosed by other physicians as having adult schizophrenia. Ninety-four were in institutions and 26 were making some sort of adjustment in the community (*1952*). The proportion in institutions is larger than that reported by Eisenberg, which may reflect any or all of the following factors: (1) a larger number of disturbed children initially; (2) less effective treatment procedures; (3) a lower socioeconomic level.

Janet L. Brown and D. G. Reiser (*1963-a*) reported on the follow-up of 125 children who were evaluated or treated, or both, at the Putnam Center before the age of five. The study was done from 5 to 17 years after treatment ceased, and the age of the subjects at the time of the follow-up was 9 to 22 years. Sixteen had made good social and intellectual adjustments; 34 had some peculiarities (e.g., shyness, isolation, lack of social awareness) but had been able to attend school. Of the remaining 75, 45 were severely retarded, arrested, or irreversibly regressed. Thirty-five per cent had been in regular school, 32 per cent in special schools, 25 per cent in custodial settings, and 6 per cent had stayed at home (*1963-b*). Brown also compared the clinical histories of the 20 most successful cases with the 20 least successful. Complete absence of speech after age *three* occurred only in the poor outcome group. That group was also less able to make appropriate use of toys, while the group with the best outcome was generally more fearful (*1960*). The finding about speech confirms Eisenberg's observations, but the fact that three years, rather than five, was the significant line of demarcation suggests that Brown's sample was more advanced from the beginning.

The fact that all 40 children had had some treatment provided an opportunity for studying the effect of variations in the treatment situation. The age of the child at the start of treatment, the number of years in treatment, the number and the experience of the therapists, the unit treatment, the treatment of the father—none of these made any appreciable difference. In general, the children who were extremely regressed or arrested did not improve; those who had better contact, less primitive preoccupations and a more mature level of functioning continued to improve. In Brown's judgment, this suggested that treatment may act as a catalyst, accelerating ego development and integration in cases where the process is already partly under way. She also observed that it is very difficult to alter the direction of response from the total, or almost total, withdrawal which was seen in the worst cases to a positive reaching out *(1960)*. Reiser comments that "in our experience, children originally designated as having psychosis of infancy who responded less well to therapy were those with the highest incidence of demonstrable neurologic and electroencephalographic abnormalities."[*] This evidence increases the likelihood that there are two groups of psychotic children (Goldfarb's "organic" and "non-organic" subcategories) who seem different initially and who respond to different forms of treatment.

The theoretical issues involved in childhood psychosis are far more important than the social significance of the disturbance. Infantile autism, in particular, challenges many long-accepted theories on child development. In spite of research and study, the essential mystery still remains: how is it that a very young child will exclude the stimulation of human contact but still respond alertly and retentively to objects? It is not a matter of general withdrawal; it is a highly selective exclusion which sometimes entails great discrimination between the animate and the inanimate. No theories yet advanced have explained this unusual selectivity.

One wonders how autistic children learn as much as they do, since so much of learning depends on the social rewards which are conspicuously absent in their lives. Observation of their learning could be of great value, and we could learn much about the early stages of personal relationships as they slowly evolve in therapy. As of now, even without this research, autistic children have contributed far more to psychology than psychology has been able to contribute to them.

References for Chapter 11

Bailey, P., *Intracranial Tumors.* Springfield, Ill.: C. C. Thomas, 1933.

Bellak, Leopold (ed.), *Schizophrenia: A Review of the Syndrome.* New York: Logos Press, 1958.

Bender, Lauretta, "Childhood Schizophrenia," *American Journal of Orthopsychiatry,* XVII (1947), 40–56.

——, "The Brain and Child Behavior," *Archives of General Psychiatry,* IV (1961), 531–48.

——, "The Development of a Schizophrenic Child Treated with Electric Convulsions at Three Years of Age," in Gerald Caplan, *Emotional Problems of Early Childhood* (1st Ed.). New York: Basic Books, Inc., 1955.

——, "Twenty Years of Clinical Research on Schizophrenic Children with Special Reference to Those under Six Years of Age," in Gerald Caplan, *Emotional Problems of Early Childhood,* (1st Ed.). New York: Basic Books, Inc., 1955.

——, *et al.,* "Schizophrenia in Childhood: A Confirmation of the Diagnosis," *Transaction of the American Neurological Association,* LXXVII (1952), 67–73.

——, and W. Helme, "A Quantitative Test of Theory and Diagnostic Indicators of Childhood Schizophrenia," *Archives of Neurology and Psychiatry,* LXX (1953), 413–27.

Beres, David, "Ego Deviation and the Concept of Schizophrenia," *Psychoanalytic Study of the Child,* Vol. XI, New York: International Universities Press, Inc., 1956.

Bergman, P. and S. Escalona, "Unusual Sensitivities in Very Young Children," *Psychoanalytic Study of the Child,* Vols. III, IV. New York: International Universities Press, Inc., 1948.

Berkowitz, Pearl H., "Some Psychophysical Aspects of Mental Illness in Children," *Genetic Psychology Monographs,* LXIII (February, 1961), 103–48.

Bradley, Charles, *Schizophrenia in Childhood,*

---

[*]Reiser, *op. cit.,* p. 844.

New York: The Macmillan Company, 1941.

———, and M. Bowen, "Behavior Characteristics of Schizophrenic Children," *Psychiatric Quarterly*, XV (1941), 296–315.

Brown, Janet L., "Prognosis from Symptoms of Preschool Children with Atypical Development," *American Journal of Orthopsychiatry*, XXX (1960), 382–91.

———, and D. E. Reiser, "Patterns of Later Development in Children with Infantile Psychosis." Paper presented at Fortieth Annual Meeting of American Orthopsychiatric Association, Washington, D.C., March, 1963-*a*.

———, "Follow-up Study of Preschool Children of Atypical Development (Infantile Psychosis): Later Personality Patterns in Adaptation to Maturational Stress," *American Journal of Orthopsychiatry*, XXXIII (1963-*b*), 336–38.

Coghill, G. E., *Anatomy and the Problem of Behavior.* Cambridge: The University Press, 1929.

Des Lauriers, L. and F. Halpern, "Psychological Tests in Childhood Schizophrenia," *American Journal of Orthopsychiatry*, XVII (1947), 57–67.

Despert, Louise, "Differential Diagnosis between Obsessive-Compulsive Neurosis and Schizophrenia in Children," in Hoch and Zubin, *Psychopathology of Childhood.* New York: Grune & Stratton, Inc., 1955. Proceedings of the Forty-Fourth Annual Meeting of the American Psychopathological Association, New York, 1954.

Eisenberg, L., "Emotional Determinants of Mental Deficiency," *Archives of Neurology and Psychiatry*, LXXX (1958), 114–22.

———, "The Autistic Child in Adolescence," (1956) in Charles Reed, Irving Alexander, and Silvan Tomkins, *Psychopathology: A Source Book.* Cambridge, Mass.: Harvard University Press, 1958.

———, "The Fathers of Autistic Children," *American Journal of Orthopsychiatry*, XXVII (1957), 715–25.

———, and L. Kanner, "Early Infantile Autism: 1943–1955" (1956) in Charles F. Reed, Irving E. Alexander, and Silvan S. Tomkins, *Psychopathology: A Source Book.* Cambridge, Mass.: Harvard University Press, 1958.

Ekstein, Rudolf, *On the Acquisition of Speech in the Autistic Child.* Paper delivered at the annual meeting of the American Psychoanalytic Society, Atlantic City, N.J., 1959.

———, K. Bryant, and S. Friedman, "Childhood Schizophrenia and Allied Conditions, in L. Bellak, *Schizophrenia: A Review of the Syndrome*, New York: Logos Press, 1958.

———, and J. Wallerstein, "Observations of the Psychology of Borderline and Psychotic Children," *Psychoanalytic Study of the Child*, Vol. IX. New York: International Universities Press, Inc., 1954.

Erickson, E. H., *Childhood and Society.* New York: W. W. Norton & Company, Inc., 1950.

Esman, A. H., M. Kohn, and L. Nyman, "The Family of the Schizophrenic Child," *American Journal of Orthopsychiatry*, XXIX (1959), 455–60.

Ferster, C. B. and Marian K. DeMyer, "A Method for the Experimental Analysis of the Behavior of Autistic Children," *American Journal of Orthopsychiatry*, XXXII (1962), 89–99.

Fish, B., "Drug Therapy in Child Psychiatry," *Comprehensive Psychiatry*, I (1960), 55–61, 212–27.

Frank, Lawrence K. *et al.*, "Personality Development in Adolescent Girls," *Monographs of the Society for Research in Child Development, Inc.*, XVI, No. 53 (1953), New Orleans: Child Development Publications.

Freedman, A. M., "Treatment of Autistic Schizophrenic Children with Marsilid," *Journal of Clinical and Experimental Psychopathology*, XIX (1958), Suppl. 1, 138–45.

Freeman, W. J. and J. W. Watts, *Psychosurgery in the Treatment of Mental Disorders and Intractable Pain* (2nd Ed.). Springfield Ill.: Charles C. Thomas, Publisher, 1951.

———, "Schizophrenia in Childhood: Its Modification by Prefrontal Lobotomy," *Digest of Neurology and Psychiatry*, XV (1947), Institute of Living, 202–19.

Freud, S., *Beyond the Pleasure Principle* (1920), Standard Edition, Vol. XVIII, ed. and trans. by James Strachey. London: The Hogarth Press, Ltd., 1955.

Friedman, Gloria, "Conceptual Thinking in Schizophrenic Children," *Genetic Psychology Monographs*, XLIII (1963), 149–96.

Gesell, A., *The Embryology of Behavior.* New York: Harper & Row, Publishers, 1945.

Goldfarb, William, *Childhood Schizophrenia.* Cambridge, Mass.: Harvard University Press, 1961.

———, "Self-Awareness in Schizophrenic Children," *Archives of General Psychiatry*, VIII (1963), 47–60.

———, and M. M. Dorsen, *Annotated Bibliography of Childhood Schizophrenia and Related Disorders in the English Language through 1954*. New York: Basic Books, Inc., 1956.

———, and Donald Meyers, "Psychiatric Appraisals of Parents of Schizophrenic Children," *American Journal of Psychiatry*, CXVIII (1962), 902–9.

———, and I. Mintz, "Schizophrenic Child's Reactions to Time and Space," *Archives of General Psychiatry*, V (1961), 535–43.

Goldstein, K., *After-Effects of Brain Injuries in War*. New York: Grune & Stratton, Inc., 1942.

———, "Abnormal Mental Conditions in Infancy," *Journal of Nervous and Mental Diseases*, CXXVIII (1959), 538–57.

Harms, Ernest, "Childhood Schizophrenia and Childhood Hysteria," *Psychiatric Quarterly*, XIX (1945), 242–57.

Hill, D., "EEG's in Children," *EEG Clinical Neurophysiology*, I (1952), 113.

Kanner, Leo, "Autistic Disturbance in Affective Contact," *Nervous Child*, II (1942–1943), 217–50.

———, *Child Psychiatry* (3rd Ed.). Springfield, Ill.: Charles C. Thomas, Publisher, 1957.

———, "Early Infantile Autism," *Journal of Pediatrics*, XXV (1944), 211–17.

———, "Parents' Feelings About Retarded Children," *American Journal of Mental Deficiency*, LVII (1953), 375–83.

———, "The Specificity of Early Infantile Autism," *Zeitschrift für Kinderpsychiatrie*, XXV (1958), 108–13.

———, "To What Extent is Early Infantile Autism Determined by Constitutional Inadequacies?" *Proceedings of the Association for Research on Nervous and Mental Diseases*, XXXIII (1954), 378–85.

Kaufman, I. *et al.*, "Four Types of Defense in Mothers and Fathers of Schizophrenic Children," *American Journal of Orthopsychiatry*, XXIX (1959), 460–73.

Kennard, M. and S. Levy, "The Meaning of Abnormal Electroencephalograms in Schizophrenia," *Journal of Nervous and Mental Diseases*, CXVI (1952), 413.

Klebanoff, Lewis B., "Parental Attitudes of Mothers of Schizophrenic, Brain-injured and Retarded, and Normal Children,"

American Journal of Orthopsychiatry, XXIX (1959), 445–55.

Kluever, H., *Behavior Mechanisms in Monkeys*. Chicago: University of Chicago Press, 1933.

Koegler, R. R. and Edward G. Colbert, "Childhood Schizophrenia. Role of the Family Physician," *Journal of the American Medical Association*, CLXXI (1959), 1045–50.

Kraepelin, E., *Psychiatrie*. 5 Aufl. Leipzig: Meiner, 1896.

Lane, Ellen A. and George W. Albee, "Childhood Intellectual Differences Between Schizophrenic Adults and their Siblings," *American Journal of Orthopsychiatry*, XXXV (1965), 747–54.

Mahler, M. S., "On Child Psychosis and Schizophrenia: Autistic and Symbiotic Infantile Psychosis," *Psychoanalytic Study of the Child*, Vol. VII. New York: International Universities Press, Inc., 1952.

———, and B. J. Gosliner, "On Symbiotic Child Psychosis," *Psychoanalytic Study of the Child*, Vol. X. New York: International Universities Press, Inc., 1955.

May, J. M. and Marie-Anne May, "Treatment and Education of the Atypical Autistic Child," *American Journal of Mental Deficiency*, LXIV (1959), 435–43.

Mehr, H. M., "The Application of Psychological Tests and Methods to Childhood Schizophrenia," *The Nervous Child*, X (1952), 63–94.

Meyer, A., *The Commonsense Psychiatry of Adolf Meyer*, ed. and trans. by Alfred Lieb. New York: McGraw-Hill Book Company, 1948.

Morris, D. P., E. Soroker, and G. Burruss, "Follow-up Studies of Shy, Withdrawn Children: Evaluation of Later Adjustment," *American Journal of Orthopsychiatry*, XXIV (1954), 743–55.

Myklebust, Helmer R., *Auditory Disorders in Children*, New York: Grune & Stratton, Inc., 1954.

New York University Film Library, *Clinical Aspects of Childhood Psychosis*. Produced by the Institute of Psychiatry, University of London, Maudsley Hospital, London. New York: 26 Washington Place.

Ohio Department of Mental Hygiene and Correction, "Outpatient Psychiatric Clinics and Mental Hospital Community Service Units, Annual Report, Year Ended June 30, 1963." Columbus, Ohio.

Orton, S. T., *Reading and Writing and Speech Problems in Children.* New York: W. W. Norton & Company, Inc., 1937.

Pavenstedt, Eleanor, "History of a Child with an Atypical Development, and Some Vicissitudes of his Treatment," in Gerald Caplan, *Emotional Problems of Early Childhood.* New York: Basic Books, Inc., 1955.

Peck, H. B., R. D. Rabinovitch, and J. B. Cramer, "A Treatment Program for Parents of Schizophrenic Children," *American Journal of Orthopsychiatry,* XIX (1949), 592.

Pollack, M., "Brain Damage, Mental Retardation and Childhood Schizophrenia," *American Journal of Psychiatry,* CXV (1958), 422–26.

———, and W. Goldfarb, "The Face-hand Test in Schizophrenic Children," *AMA Archives of Neurology and Psychiatry,* LXXVII (1957-*a*), 635–42.

———, "Patterns of Orientation in Children in Residential Treatment for Severe Behavior Disorders," *American Journal of Orthopsychiatry,* XXVII (1957-*b*), 538–52.

———, and H. P. Krieger, "Oculomotor and Postural Patterns in Schizophrenic Children," *AMA Archives of Neurology and Psychiatry,* LXXVIII (1958), 720–26.

Putnam, Marion C., "Some Observations on Psychosis in Early Childhood," in Gerald Caplan, *Emotional Problems of Early Childhood.* New York: Basic Books, Inc., 1955.

———, *et al.,* "Roundtable 1947: Case Study of an Atypical Two-and-a-half Year Old Child," *American Journal of Orthopsychiatry,* XVIII (1948), 1–30.

Rank, Beata, "Adaptation of the Psychoanalytic Technique for the Treatment of Young Children with Atypical Development," *American Journal of Orthopsychiatry,* XIX (1949), 130–39.

———, "Intensive Study and Treatment of Pre-school Children Who Show Marked Personality Deviations or 'Atypical Development,' and Their Parents," in Gerald Caplan, *Emotional Problems of Early Childhood.* New York: Basic Books, Inc., 1955.

Reiser, David E., "Psychosis of Infancy and Early Childhood, as Manifested by Children with Atypical Development," *New England Journal of Medicine,* CCLXIX (1963), 790–98, 844–50.

Rimland, Bernard, *Infantile Autism.* New York: Appleton-Century-Crofts, Inc., 1964.

Ritvo, S. and S. Provence, "Form Perception and Limitation in Some Autistic Children," *The Psychoanalytic Study of the Child,* Vol. VIII. New York: International Universities Press, Inc., 1953.

Rosenfeld, S. K. and M. P. Sprince, "An Attempt to Formulate the Meaning of the Concept 'Borderline,'" *Psychoanalytic Study of the Child,* Vol. XVIII. New York: International Universities Press, Inc., 1963.

Rubin, Theodore Isaac, *Jordi.* New York: The Macmillan Company, 1960.

Safrin, Renate Kersten, "Difference in Visual Perception and in Visual-Motor Functioning Between Psychotic and Nonpsychotic Children," *Journal of Consulting Psychology,* XXVIII (1964), 41–46.

Sarason, S. and T. Gladwin, "Psychological and Cultural Problems in Mental Subnormals: A Review of Research," *Genetic Psychology Monographs,* No. 57 (1958), 3–290.

Scheerer, M., E. Rothman, and K. Goldstein, "A Case of Idiot Savant: An Experimental Study of Personality Organization," *Psychological Monographs,* LVIII (1945), No. 4, 63.

Schilder, P., *Image and Appearance of the Human Body.* New York: International Universities Press, Inc., 1951.

Stroh, George, "On the Diagnosis of Childhood Psychosis," *Journal of Child Psychology and Psychiatry,* I (1960), 238–43.

Weiland, I. H. and R. Rudnik, "Consideration of the Development and Treatment of Autistic Childhood Psychosis," *Psychoanalytic Study of the Child,* Vol. XVI. New York: International Universities Press, Inc., 1961.

Werner, H. and A. A. Strauss, "Pathology of Figure-Background Relationships in the Child," *Journal of Abnormal and Social Psychology,* XXXVI (1941), 236–48.

12

JUVENILE DELINQUENCY

Delinquents are involved in such a wide range of behavior—from the most trivial infraction of rules to the most serious antisocial offense—that it is hardly possible to say anything significant about them as a group, except that most of them are adolescent boys. This variety of behavior contrasts with other areas of childhood psychopathology (e.g., psychosis) in which the behavior is fairly homogeneous even when the causes may be diverse.

The following newspaper item gives some idea of the diversity of offenses, corresponding personality problems and causes which are included under the rubric of delinquency (Identifying data have been deleted and names altered):

Three Mentor boys were found delinquent during Juvenile Court hearings Thursday. Judge Brown ordered a 60-day suspended sentence in the Juvenile Detention Home for one 16-year-old boy charged in connection with purchase of a "girly" magazine and a pack of cigarettes. The boy was also placed on indefinite probation. Painesville police claim the boy bought a copy of the magazine and cigarettes at Smith's. Store owner pleaded innocent to charges of contributing to the delinquency of a minor in connection with the case.

A second 16-year-old boy was ordered to spend 60 days in the detention home and placed on indefinite probation in connection with stealing two cars and running away. He wrecked one car in New Philadelphia, Ohio, in mid-June. He ran from police, stole another car and drove to Winston-Salem, N.C., where he was arrested three blocks from the police station. A commitment to Boys' Industrial School was suspended. The boy spent 33 days in detention prior to his hearing.

A third Mentor boy, 15, was committed to the temporary care of the County Welfare Department. A commitment to Boys' Industrial School and a 60-day detention home term were suspended by the judge. The boy spent 21 days in detention prior to a hearing. He ran away from home and was arrested by Dayton police in connection with trying to cash an $85 forged personal check. Police report the boy swallowed some brass pellets while in custody. He was treated at Dayton Hospital. He told authorities he ran away because of conditions at home. A sister is already in the custody of the Welfare Department. A parent was called "emotionally disturbed" by authorities. *

This news story makes it very clear that "delinquency," as used here, is a legal, and not a psychological or medical term. The first boy was guilty only of being 16; had he been two years

---

*Quoted from the Painesville (Ohio) *Telegraph*, August 1, 1964. Reproduced by permission.

older, no crime would have been committed. The second boy resembles the aggressive, amoral boy usually thought of as the typical delinquent. The third boy, who tried to provide himself with an illegal means of escaping from what may have been an intolerable home life, was sufficiently disturbed to attempt suicide.

In the area of juvenile delinquency, the questions of who, how much, and why lead into technical, legal, and administrative practices, socioeconomic problems, and the complex psychological factors which affect an adolescent's moral sense and his ability to control himself. Legal, sociological, and psychological experts do not seem to be describing the same phenomenon when they write about delinquency. To add to the confusion, there is an abundance of lay opinion on the subject. Juvenile delinquency belongs to the public domain; according to Roul Tunley, a national poll indicated that—apart from peace and national survival—Americans are more interested in juvenile delinquency than in any other problem *(1964)*.

It is generally believed in the United States that juvenile delinquency is a greater social blight here than anywhere in the world. But Tunley, a journalist who participated in a worldwide study of delinquency, reports that it is Sweden that has the highest juvenile delinquency rate. And, both in terms of the present rate and the rate of increase, the official reports coming from Great Britain read much like those in the United States *(Eighth Report, Children's Department, London, 1961)*. Tunley concluded that "from Moscow to Manila, and from Turin to Tokyo, delinquency as bad as, or worse than, ours does exist" *(1964, p. 43)*.

Alarm over a country's unruly and intractable adolescents is universal; the more civilized the nation, the more alarmed it becomes. Juvenile delinquency seems to increase in direct pro-portion to the complexity and prosperity of a society, and countries which are on the move, abandoning old ways and adopting new, find that juvenile delinquency is the unwanted dividend of progress and change.

Defining the Term

Generally, definitions of the term "juvenile delinquency" fall into two categories: psychological and legal. K. R. Eissler makes a strong case for the psychological definition, commenting that "Whether certain behavior is delinquent or not is entirely dependent on the motivation which lies behind that particular behavior. No external feature can ever be used as a reliable index of delinquency" *(1955, p. 5)*. Eissler would include behavior which is not legally delinquent. His psychological criteria (e.g., infringement of values, aggression) would be hard to apply, partly because moral standards vary and partly because establishing the diagnosis would require intensive individual study. However, his criteria serve to remind us that much thoughtless or cruel behavior is not punishable by law, although it may sometimes be more vicious than legal offenses.

Legally, the term "delinquency" applies to offenders (i.e., those who have committed a legal offense) who are younger than the statutory age limit, which varies from 16 to 20 years. A child adjudged a delinquent may have committed an act for which an adult would have been adjudged a criminal, or his offense may be one which is not applicable to adults (e.g., incorrigibility, waywardness, or truancy). Statutes vary from state to state and from community to community. The Michigan law defines a delinquent as "any child under the age of seventeen who violates any law of the state or any city or village ordinance, or is incorrigible, or knowingly associates with thieves, vicious or immoral persons" or who is guilty of indulging in any one or sev-

eral of sixteen other kinds of taboo behavior *(Carr, 1950)*. Under Michigan
law, a delinquent is any child committing such a violation, whether or not
the offense is ever detected.

Lowell J. Carr subdivides the legal
definition of a delinquent into five
parts, each involving a group smaller
than that preceding it. The first, "legal
delinquents," includes all those who, at
one time or another, commit delinquent
acts. This is perhaps half the teen-age
population. The second, "detected
delinquents," are those who are caught
in the act. The third, "agency delinquents," are those who are brought to
the attention of some authority such as
the police. The fourth, "alleged delinquents," are those who are brought before a court. The "ajudged delinquents,"
the smallest group, are those found
delinquent under the law. Carr estimates this group to be 75 per cent to
90 per cent of the alleged delinquents.
The literature deals almost exclusively
with the last three categories: agency
delinquents, alleged delinquents, and
adjudged delinquents.

Statistical Aspects of Juvenile Delinquency

Sources of Data

The most extensive data on police
contacts with juvenile and adult offenders are in the *Uniform Crime Reports* which are published annually
by the Federal Bureau of Investigation. In a voluntary system, each contributing law enforcement agency is
responsible for compiling its own crime
report with the assistance and guidance of the F.B.I. As of 1963, the reporting agencies covered 92 per cent of
the national population with 98 per cent
coverage of the metropolitan areas and
only 77 per cent of the rural areas. The
second major source of data is the
Children's Bureau of the United States
Department of Health, Education, and
Welfare, which prepares special re-

ports as well as an annual statistical
report on juvenile court cases. In order
to get a representative nation-wide
picture, selected juvenile courts are
asked to report; the 1963 data are based
on the reports of 502 courts. Beginning
in 1957, traffic offenses were separated
from delinquency cases so that figures
before and after this year are not directly comparable. It must be remembered that figures on delinquency are
meaningless unless we know whether
they refer to arrests (i.e., agency delinquents), court cases (i.e., alleged delinquents), or convictions (i.e., adjudged delinquents).

Prevalence

The F.B.I. reported that 788,762 persons under 18 years were arrested in
1963 *(Uniform Crime Report, 1963,
Table 21)*. Between 45 and 50 per cent
of the juvenile offenders taken into
custody by the police are referred to
juvenile court jurisdiction. The Children's Bureau reported that a total of
601,000 cases were handled by juvenile
courts in 1963 and it was estimated
that 518,000 children were involved
(Children's Bureau Report, 1963). This
represented 1.9 per cent of the population aged 10 through 17 years, and this
figure is often cited as the prevalence
rate. Another way of viewing the size
of the problem is to consider the proportion of our youth who will be alleged or adjudged to be delinquent. It
has been estimated that one boy in
every five will appear in court at least
once between the ages of 10 and 17
years.

Increase in Delinquency

The annual increase in the number
of juvenile delinquents is partially due
to the increase in the number of children belonging to the age group at
risk, but the rise is disproportionately
great, as we can see from Figure 2. In
1963, for example, 8 per cent more
delinquents appeared in court than in

Figure 2

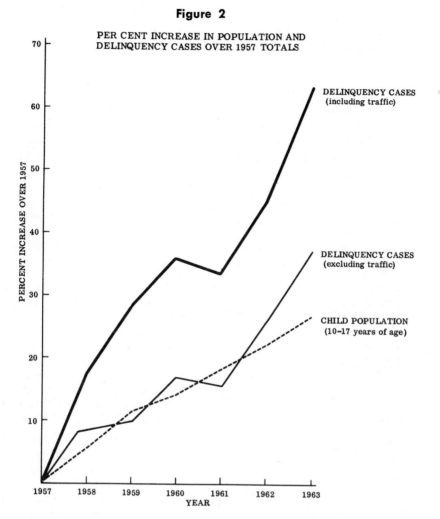

PER CENT INCREASE IN POPULATION AND
DELINQUENCY CASES OVER 1957 TOTALS

1962 although the relevant population increase was only 4 per cent. The juvenile court statistics of the Children's Bureau show a sharp increase during World War II, followed by a drop, and then by a steady increase since 1949 (except for a slight decrease in 1961). In the past decade, delinquency has increased twice as fast as the child population.

Ratio of Juvenile to Adult Crime Rate

With respect to reported crimes, the F.B.I. reports steady increases, for example, a 10 per cent increase in 1963 over 1962. Since 1958, the over-all crime rate has increased five times faster than the population growth. Of the total arrests in 1963, 17 per cent were juvenile offenders. The increase in arrests has been greater for delinquents than for adult offenders when all offenses are included; arrests for serious crimes has increased at about the same rate for both juvenile and adult offenders. No one has ventured a definitive statement as to whether the crime rate for juveniles is increasing at a more rapid rate than the crime rate for adult persons. There is no way of knowing who was responsible for the large number of reported but unsolved crimes.

Related Factors:

Age. Statutory age limits affect the average age of children brought to court. Where the jurisdiction of the juvenile court extends to age 18, the average age is 15.7 years; where the maximum is age 16, the average is 14.3 years. Figures relating age to incidence must be interpreted with this in mind.

Geographical Distribution. Both the F.B.I. and the Children's Bureau report that the rates of juvenile delinquency in urban areas are about three times those of rural areas. Urban courts now handle about two-thirds of all our delinquents, although delinquency in rural areas has been increasing.

Sex. Official crime is largely a male problem. In general, male arrests are eight times the female arrests. Between five and six times as many male as female juveniles are arrested and about four times as many boys as girls appear in juvenile courts. However, both the F.B.I. and the Children's Bureau note that arrests of girls are increasing at a faster rate than that for boys. The charges brought against girls and boys differ—almost half the boys are apprehended for property offenses, while more than half the girls are charged with specifically juvenile crimes such as running away, incorrigibility, or sexual offenses.

Categories of Offense. About 50 per cent of those coming to juvenile court are either first offenders or are charged with relatively minor offenses. The data on police arrests show that juveniles accounted for about half the thefts charged in the country but only a small proportion of crimes of violence. The frequency of offenses against persons increases with age, as does the frequency of certain offenses against property (i.e., robbery, fraud, and forgery), but the rate of arrests for burglary and larceny decreases with age. Arrests for auto theft reach a peak at 15 (*Perlman, 1963*).

Interpretation of Statistics

Experts repeatedly warn against taking statistics on juvenile delinquency at face value (*Perlman, 1957; Mannheim, 1940; Gibbens, 1961 a*). Some of the important factors which may produce statistical artifacts are:

Methods of Enforcement. The number of delinquent acts reported depends, first of all, on the vigilance and adequacy of the police force, but matters of policy also affect the official records. When a middle-class child gets into trouble, the complaining citizen is more apt to turn to the child's parents than to the police on the assumption that the parents will pay for the damages and try to prevent a recurrence. Similarly, when a minor complaint is brought to the police, they often take it directly to the parents so that there will be no official record. This milder approach to the offending child whose parents have status in the community explains some of the disparity in the delinquency rates among different economic groups and between rural and urban areas.

Legal and Judicial Changes. Statistics on delinquency are affected by changes in statutes or ordinances, the establishment of a curfew for minors, for instance, or extending the age limit of a court's jurisdiction will increase the number of delinquents reported.

T. C. N. Gibbens points out that the courts themselves can profoundly affect the incidence of delinquency (*1961 a*). Placing large numbers of offenders at liberty may increase the commission of delinquent acts. Variations in judicial attitude toward the conviction of young offenders change the reported facts. Reporting practices are another important factor, for example, the change in reporting traffic offenses. In the year of 1963, there were 366,000 juvenile traffic violations compared to 601,000 delinquency cases. In all likelihood, traffic violations accounted for approximately one-third the delinquency cases reported prior to 1957. One oft-repeated recommendation is that reporting procedures should be made uniform so that data will be comparable from year to year and place to place ("*Role of the Federal Government*," 1961).

Public Awareness. T. C. N. Gibbens (*1961 a*) feels that public awareness has an important effect on the statistics. The police, who are initially responsible for the available statistics, are also subject to public criticism when they do not make arrests. Increased public awareness leads directly to increase in reported incidence. The two forms of crime which attract the greatest attention—sex crimes and crimes of violence—are also those which are thought to be the least well detected. One reporter stated that, at most, only 5 per cent of all sex offenses are reported or detected (*Radzinowicz, 1957*). Greater sophistication and awareness of a problem may be the cause of an increase in figures, rather than an actual change in its occurrence.

Fluctuations, Cycles and Trends. Over a period of time, a statistical series reflects four kinds of fluctuations: (1) a long-term trend; (2) a cyclical pattern (i.e., rhythmic ups and downs); (3) seasonal variations; and (4) other fluctuations caused by accidental or unforeseeable factors (e.g., changes in laws).

Even for the short period of which we have some record, definite cycles in

Figure 3

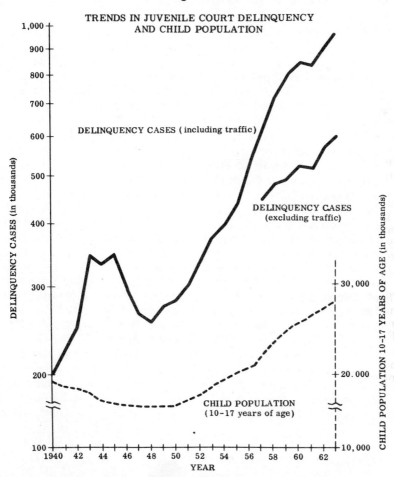

TRENDS IN JUVENILE COURT DELINQUENCY
AND CHILD POPULATION

juvenile delinquency have been identified *(Carr, 1950)*. The figures of the
Cuyahoga County Juvenile Court are
often cited because they were first issued in 1909. They show that delinquency reached an all-time high of 6.6
per cent in 1919. By 1921, the rate had
dropped to 3.8 per cent, and the record
low was 2.1 per cent, in 1939. In 1948,
a year often used as a basis for comparison with the present, the rate was
2.7 per cent; in 1962 it was 3.1 per cent.
This is a significant increase, but it is
still considerably lower than the 1919
figure. These figures are thought to
reflect long-term cycles; if so, the
present high rate of delinquency can
be expected to fall over a period of
time.

There are more statistics about juvenile delinquency, however, than
about other areas of psychopathology.
They are undoubtedly of great value
even though they must be interpreted
with caution.

Classification and Typology

At the outset, it was stated that delinquency is a symptom rather than a
disease. Even as a symptom, it is difficult to define, and when one tries to
classify delinquency in terms of etiology, the problem becomes even greater.
Numerous typologies have been presented, but none has gained general
acceptance. The only point of agreement is that we need some way of
differentiating categories of delinquency according to its seriousness, and
its chronicity and its motivation.

One criticism is the amount of emotional disturbance manifested; boldly
put, "Some juvenile delinquents have
personal problems and some do not."
This criterion is, however, controversial. For example, Eissler's definition
presumes that all delinquents have a
personality difficulty. Those with a
sociological point of view believe that

psychiatrists and clinicians have overemphasized psychopathology and un-
deremphasized the extent to which
delinquent behavior may inhere in
some social environments. W. C. Kvaraceus and Walter B. Miller, for example, state that:

. . . from the point of view of the delinquent, most delinquent behavior is pur-
posive and adjustive. From the vantage
point of middle-class norms and status,
such behavior is frequently seen as maladjustment. But in looking at this same behavior from the child's point of view, one
can see that the child is frequently using
it as a means of adapting or adjusting in
accordance with his essential frame of
reference. *(1959, p. 33.)*

These authors estimate that only
one fourth of the delinquent youngsters have "demonstrable emotional
disturbances," and that "the preponder-
ant portion of our 'delinquent' population consists of essentially 'normal'
lower-class youngsters" *(1959, p. 55)*.
Unfortunately, the authors cite no statistics and do not define a "demonstrable emotional disturbance" which
would have to be demonstrated by the
kind of careful individual assessment
relatively few delinquents ever receive.

In another classification scheme different terms are used for the same
ideas. R. L. Jenkins and Sylvia Glickman, after studying 300 boys at the
New York State Training School, proposed three main "patterns of personality organization": (1) the socially
delinquent; (2) the emotionally disturbed, and (3) the unsocialized aggressive *(1947)*. Reviewing their findings, Jenkins observed that only a few
boys fit the second category, "the emotionally disturbed." The "socially delinquent" behavior was interpreted as
adaptive, since these crimes were conceived as a way of achieving desired
ends. The social delinquents, according to Jenkins, had been schooled in

delinquency. The "unsocialized aggressive" behavior was interpreted as maladaptive, in that the crime was little more than an impulsive response to frustration *(1957)*.

Although it is impossible to put individual cases of delinquency into airtight categories, it is imperative to make some psychological differentiations. The following classification, proposed by the author, contains Jenkins' major categories but subdivides his "emotionally disturbed" group.

Delinquency, in the author's opinion, is repeated antisocial behavior which may or may not get the child into legal difficulty. It is a disorder in the functioning of the superego, caused by any or all of the following:

1. The absence of a superego because of early neglect, deprivation and failure to establish meaningful relationships at the earliest level (also called the "psychopath" and the "unsocialized aggressive").

2. Identification with socially inadequate models, incorporation of antisocial values, inabilty to achieve satisfaction in socially acceptable ways because of either deficiencies in ego functions or lack of opportunity, or both (the "normal" delinquent; the "socially delinquent").

3. Lacunae in superego resulting from the conscious sanctioning by the parents of behavior which they pronounce to be wrong.

4. Weakness of the superego in coping with instinctual desires (e.g., as in the narcissistic, hysterical person who "does it now, regrets it later").

5. Abeyance of the superego because the delinquent behavior is an unconscious means of expressing aggression toward the parents or of acting out a special unconscious fantasy, or is a way of obtaining punishment for an unconscious sense of guilt ("neurotic delinquency").

The author feels that some of these categories will overlap, as do most classifications. It should also be noted that it would be impossible to assign percentages to these classifications, for this would require that every delinquent be subjected to clinical examination, and usually, it is only the middle or upper-class delinquent who receives such attention.

Before discussing the specific categories, some general observations are in order. Those made here are based on youngsters who have been involved in *repeated,* antisocial acts which have brought them to the attention of the psychological staffs of juvenile courts, detention institutions, and treatment centers. These observations have little, if any, relevance for the one-time offender who is usually and quite properly lost from official sight.

Physical Characteristics

C. Lombroso introduced the concept of "the criminal man" who was morphologically different from the normal man, and described many anatomical differences, particularly in cranial structure *(1911)*. Many years later, Lawson Lowrey *(1944)* stated succinctly that "it may be said that no distinctive type of criminal [brain] has been proven to exist" *(1944, p. 803)*.

Although anatomical theories have been abandoned, biological and constitutional aspects of delinquency continue to receive some professional attention. S. and E. Glueck *(1956)* and W. H. Sheldon *(1949)* have shown that delinquents are more muscular, or mesomorphic. Gibbens found that boys in English detention homes tended to be muscular *(1961-b)*. It is probable that a constitutional predisposition to be active does make some youngsters susceptible to delinquency if the social and psychological climate in which they live is also conducive to delinquency. Gibbens also mentions the decreasing age of puberty as another biological feature which may contribute indirectly to the rising number of delinquents. Recent evidence suggests that menarche is occurring earlier today than it did 50 or 100 years ago. In 1900, the average American girl reached menarche at 14; the current average is 13 years of age *(Tanner, 1955)*. Although adolescents are attaining adult status physically at an earlier age than previous generations, society is tending to keep young people dependent longer. This discrepancy between earlier physical maturity and later social maturity leads to a conflict between the generations which may manifest itself as delinquent behavior.

Psychological Characteristics

The psychological characteristics of delinquents are of greatest interest to most experts, and the studies dealing with their *intellectual functioning* are legion. C. M. Louttit *(1957)* has reviewed the numerous reports on the intelligence of delinquents and has concluded that there is a consistent trend toward decreasing the percentage of feeble-minded in the delinquent population. Investigations published during the period from 1910 to 1914 reported that an average of 50 per cent of all delinquents were feeble-minded. Fifteen years later, the percentage had dropped to 20 per cent. In the first edition of Louttit's work, seven studies of IQ distribution, made between 1925 and 1935, are reported. They show that 13 per cent of delinquents had IQ's below 70. But the five studies quoted in the third edition, printed in 1957, show that about 5 per cent have IQ's below 70. The mentally retarded, as a group, contribute only their fair share to delinquency; thus mental retardation cannot be considered a major etiological factor *(Wheway, 1958)*.

In general, the delinquents tested in courts and institutions have average IQ's in the high 80's and low 90's *(Louttit, 1957)*. However, such low scores could be simply another sign of the disturbance which is initially responsible for the delinquency—that is,

an associated symptom rather than a causal factor.

Another associated symptom is severe *academic retardation*. H. Peck reported that 75 per cent of a sampling of a juvenile court population were at least two years retarded in reading and that half of these were over five years retarded *(1958)*. Elsewhere Peck states:

Our experience indicates that delinquent children generally do not value academic achievement and that the so-called "acting out" is a direct expression of a need for achievement along what are to them socially necessary and feasible lines. The child of low socio-economic status is handicapped by several factors in his effort to learn to read: he is deficient in pre-school readiness experience. Attitudinally, he is unprepared for school living and learning. His use of oral English is poor, and in view of the sub-cultural de-emphasis of verbal communication, his interest in language skills is minimal. *(Peck et al., 1955, p. 30.)*

A number of observations have been made on *deficiencies in language skills*. In a discussion of group treatment for potentially delinquent boys and girls, the workers commented:

At first we found the extreme inability or reluctance of these adolescents to verbalize bewildering and frustrating. To understand how they felt or what they were thinking, we had to depend upon the language of motor expression. Having learned in their life experiences to distrust words, the boys in turn observed more closely what we did, than what we said. *(Stranahan, Schwartzmann, and Atkin, 1957, p. 526.)*

These observations of mental inefficiency (e.g., acting rather than talking, lack of interest in intellectual knowledge) belong in the theoretical framework of ego functioning and the nature of the ego ideal; they are specific aspects of what happens when ego controls are weak and sublimations are not established. The symptoms themselves create more frustration and this, in turn, stimulates aggressive reactions. It is difficult to rehabilitate a teen-age delinquent because his academic weakness severely limits his vocational opportunities.

Looking at this cluster of symptoms from a developmental point of view, it is important to consider certain factors: (1) the fate of aggression; (2) the capacity to identify with others; (3) the ability of the conscience to withstand the desire for pleasure; and (4) the capacity of the ego for delaying gratification and finding socially acceptable substitutes. Functionally these are interrelated. For example, aggressive feelings towards others are inhibited when one has identified with them, a powerful factor in the establishment of conscience. And if the ego is unable to tolerate a reasonable amount of frustration, there is a flux of aggression to be dealt with. Without some ability to tolerate delay, the individual does not sublimate, he continues to act on his impulses, like a young child. Since such behavior is usually disappointing and trouble-making, the individual is thus further frustrated and his aggression is further increased. Although they are obviously interwoven, the four factors are treated separately here for the sake of simplicity.

Fate of Aggression

Delinquency is aggression turned outward, toward a rule of society, the authority of the parent, or another individual (as when the delinquent steals from someone or does him bodily harm). It was pointed out in Chapter 3 that psychopathology can be differentiated according to whether it is directed inward or outward. Aggression directed against the self, called "autoplastic," is seen in neurotic and psychotic disorders; Eissler uses the hysterical symptom of conversion as an illustration of this: An angry person may be unable to express his anger, so that the aggressive reaction does not find release. But a short time later, he may

develop a headache, the effect of this undischarged energy. The headache is an autoplastic disorder. Delinquency, on the other hand, is primarily "alloplastic"; the individual aggressively tackles the external situation *(1955)*.

The problem of aggression in delinquency is more than a question of direction, however; it is also a question of quantity. Fritz Redl and David Wineman, explaining why they chose to call their study of delinquent boys *Children Who Hate,* write:

Among all the troubles that are usually summarized under the term "delinquency," the most serious seem to be the ones which involve large quantities of *Hate.**

Much of the hate can be understood as a reaction to personal problems (e.g., parental rejection or mistreatment) or social problems (e.g., poverty, social inequality, disorganization, or crowding), but sometimes the origin, the extent and the intensity of the hate is incomprehensible. Nevertheless, the hate may be naked and primitive, if the child's aggressiveness has never been tempered by a strong personal attachment.

Identification with Others

Usually, the motive for a single delinquent act is clear. The delinquent wanted pleasure or momentary excitement, and he took the shortest available route to that goal. Such an explanation, however, raises the question of why more people do not commit antisocial acts. One answer is that they fear humiliation or punishment, by society or through feelings of guilt. B. L. Diamond suggests that the most powerful deterrent is the capacity for *identification with others* who would suffer from this antisocial behavior. In

---

*Quoted from Fritz Redl and David Wineman, *Children Who Hate* (New York: The Free Press of Glencoe) 1951, p. 20. Reproduced by permission of The Macmillan Company.

order to have compassion for others or to feel an ethical or moral obligation to them, one must be able to identify with them. Diamond points out that most people are able to find some excuse for cheating on their income taxes or taking advantage of errors made by large stores or corporations; the golden rule breaks down when there is no identification with the victim. In such depersonalized situations, even the most normal person may act delinquent *(1961)*.

It is rare, however, to find a delinquent youngster who has no capacity for identification with others. The question is: With whom does he identify? Unfortunately, it is usually with the powerful attacker rather than the helpless victim. Delinquent behavior makes it possible to identify with the tough guys. Albert K. Cohen says that: "Delinquency, like marbles, jazz, poker, or politics, is not merely something which may be learned from others. It is usually something that people do together, something invented, elaborated and transformed in group interaction, and its very meaning to the participants depends upon the group setting" *(1957, p. 786)*. As a member of a gang, the adolescent in search of an identity has a sense of power and independence which he cannot create on his own. The aggressive gang leader is admired because he is masculine, fearless, and strong. But the members of the gang are weak and are afraid of revealing this, so it is imperative that they show no compassion for their weak victims.

Pathology of Conscience

Conscience, or the superego, (as we noted in Chapter 3) represents a relatively advanced stage of personality development. One can function biologically without it, but it is unlikely that one can go through life unscathed socially. All delinquent behavior involves an absence or laxity of conscience, either total or temporary. Occasionally, the delinquent's conscience may be so defective that he conforms only to the standards of his particular group and deviates almost completely from those of society. We except, of course, and are not discussing, those whose antisocial behavior is a protest against social injustice and those who are motivated by instincts of self-preservation or real physical need. When these offenders are judged, the exceptional nature of their acts or motives should be taken into consideration.

The superego is composed of: (1) the ego ideal, (i.e., the values, standards, and aspirations of the individual); (2) self-observation; and (3) self-control through an internal system of reward and punishment (i.e., pride and guilt). It is particularly in the ego ideal that society's influence can be seen: the kind of person the child wants to be is determined largely by the kind of parents he has and his relationship with them, but it is also influenced by the world in which he finds himself. The adolescent turns to other adolescents in order to develop a set of standards, and to some degree they are all rebelling against the standards of their parents. At this point, a youth may find for himself a partner in crime, someone his own age who encourages his inclination toward delinquency. In some environments, delinquency rates are significantly higher. These are likely to be economically marginal areas, where the residents are transients and where cultural and ethnic groups are mixed. Cultural heterogeneity does not automatically result in cultural conflict and delinquency, however. Both the highest and the lowest delinquency rates occur in minority groups (i.e., the Negro and the Chinese, respectively). Tradition and the attitudes of society may determine whether one is proud or ashamed of such a difference, and this leads to different patterns of reaction. But only a minority of children become delinquent, even in high-delinquency areas. Environmental factors are obviously filtered through the medium of the family; thus, to fully understand delinquency, the psychological experiences of the individual child must be examined.

The formation of the superego and its dependence on identification and on auto-aggression were described in Chapter 3. The capacity for identification must exist; It is in this regard that autistic and retarded chlidren are handicapped. There must also be socially acceptable people with which the child can identify; if they are not present or are inadequate, identification becomes more difficult, as it does for children deprived of early maternal care or the shelter of a complete family. The urban Negro child suffers especially from the lack of a normal family life. The family is apt to be centered around the mother and supported by her. Her children may be fathered by different men, whose roles in the family are inconsistent and unpredictable. D. J. Bordua describes the psychological aspects of this situation:

The lower class boy spends the major part of the first twelve years in the company of and under the domination of women. He learns during that time that women are the people who count, that men are despicable, dangerous, and desirable. He also learns that a "real man" is hated for his irresponsibility and considered very attractive on Saturday night. He learns, too, that if he really loves his mother, he will not grow up to be "just like all men," but that, despite her best efforts, his mother's pride and joy will very likely turn out to be as much a "rogue male" as the rest. In short, he has sex-role problems. *(1961, p. 129.)*

The boy, lacking a permanent father, turns to his friends, but to test and prove his masculinity in accordance with neighborhood values, he has to engage in feats that involve delinquent behavior. As an adult, the Negro boy will have a problem maintaining his masculine status, not only because of his family structure but also because of the emasculating pressure of white society, against which effective retaliation is impossible *(Kardiner and Ovesey, 1951)*. If diligence, thrift, and politeness will not ensure his respectability and independence as an adult, what reason is there for a Negro child to practice them?

These considerations—and a great many more—are part and parcel of sociological theories of the causes of delinquency. It is this author's contention that the relationship between these sociological conditions and the development of the child's personality may be viewed in terms of its effect on the formation of the superego. For example, the fatherless child will suffer a serious distortion of the Oedipus complex; although he still cannot have his mother as a love partner and still has rivals for her affection, his aggression is diffuse, spread over a number of male figures and untempered by attachment to one particular man. The aggression remains outwardly directed, unfused because of a lack of opportunity to identify with a loved father figure. The absence of a father does not alleviate the Oedipal conflict; on the contrary, it reduces the chances of a satisfactory resolution of it.

Weakness of Ego Function

Redl and Wineman have provided the most exhaustive discussion of this topic, rightfully emphasizing the importance of being both precise and specific in describing the ways in which the delinquent ego is faulty *(1951)*. To say that a child has a "strong" or "weak" ego is to say almost nothing, since the ego includes so many behavioral functions. Redl and Wineman describe 22 "tasks" of the ego in which their severely delinquent subjects were deficient.

Listed as the first task, and perhaps the most encompassing one, is "frustration tolerance." Very little frustration is needed to upset the equilibrium of the truly delinquent ego; even waiting for a traffic light to change can be intolerable.

The second item on their list is "coping with insecurity, anxiety and fear." The mildest fears or anxieties are sufficient to break down the delinquent's control; the authors describe the "newness panic" these youngsters experience when they are faced with anything unfamiliar.

Closely related to the preceding is "disorganization in the face of guilt." Delinquent youngsters rarely experience guilt, but Redl and Wineman point out that, when they do, the youngsters are devastated and cannot use the feeling as an instrument for future control.

What the authors call "sublimation deafness" is another major deficiency in ego function:

> With our children, it was easy to see how often the "natural voice" of situations and things would be out-yelled by the screams of their inside urges and impulses. It seems that they were "deaf" to the natural challenge of life around them, while sensitively geared to the push of their impulsivity from within.[*]

So the youngsters destroyed materials, broke up organized games and activities, and were unable to profit from educational or recreational opportunities.

E. Davidoff and E. Noetzel *(1951)* also describe the differences between delinquents and normal children at play. The normal child, offered puppets with which to put on a play, usually is interested and eager to manipulate them, and helps to create a plot for the show. The delinquent youngster, however, is apathetic or, at best, unable to plan and organize the show. This poverty of the ego helps explain the boredom of delinquent youngsters and their frantic search for excitement. They have been unable to channel their

primitive impulses, partly because they cannot stand the delay which is always involved in finding an acceptable substitute. The ordinary life of the adolescent palls; the teen-age canteen is a terrible "drag," school athletics or club activities are too "tame," hobbies are nonexistent, academic pursuits are valueless, and so on. The delinquent so often explains his behavior on the basis that he had "nothing to do" and that he was "looking for kicks" that the naïve reformer may conclude that playground equipment and recreation supervisors are the solution. But the confirmed delinquent will not show up. He may call such facilities "baby stuff" but, underneath, he is unable to accept the rules, the competition, and even the elementary problem of waiting his turn. He is so impatient that he excels at little, whether it is mental, mechanical, or physical.

In their list of ego weaknesses, Redl and Wineman include several which might be subsumed under the general category of perception of reality. For instance, they describe "forgetting" or failing to perceive one's responsibility for events as the "evaporation of self-contributed links in the causal chain."[*] An illustration of this was provided by a 13-year-old boy whose only reaction to being caught stealing was to be indignant at his victim for carrying so much money and thereby tempting him. It is partly this failure to perceive cause and effect which prevents the delinquent from learning from experience. Redl and Wineman point out that the same phenomenon exists when they learn that some experiences are pleasant:

> . . . they, too, seem to be soaked up so greedily when they occur that little trace is left for later reality assessment. Thus, it took our youngsters an exceedingly long time before the harmlessness of some adults, the pleasure promise of some program possibility, would "sink in," and it

---

[*]Redl and Wineman, *op. cit.*, p. 93.

[*]Redl and Wineman, *op. cit.*, p. 108.

took an equally laboriously built-up chain of well-interpreted situations of "cause and consequence" before the idea that certain kinds of fun had better be forfeited would even begin to make sense.*

Another aspect of poor perception of reality is the delinquent's magical thinking. One reason why he is so often caught, but fails to learn from the experience of punishment, is simply that he never expects to be caught. He wishes, and so expects, to be undetected and unpunished. Frequently, his fantasies are purely infantile magic. A number of conversations recorded by Edward R. Murrow for the documentary film "Who Killed Michael Farmer?" makes this shockingly clear. One of the leaders of the gang, the one who actually did the killing, describes his fantasy of being Mighty Mouse with the excited pleasure one might expect from a four-year-old. Such infantile dreams of glory make the adjustment to reality almost impossible for the physiologically mature youngster. Murrow's 50-minute tape, which is available from NBC, dramatizes the psychology of gang delinquency. The interviews reflect the boys' dependence on each other for self-respect, their immaturity, their narcissistic fantasies, their feelings of deprivation and boredom, their lack of intellectual resources, their susceptibility to group contagion, their lack of self-control, and the strength of their aggressive urges. The tape also points up the failure of the community to take effective action even after the danger had become apparent.

There is another side to the pathology of the delinquent ego. In some ways it is remarkably strong, notably in its rigidity and impermeability to outside remedial efforts. The delinquent can be extremely clever about manipulating circumstances or people to gain his goals and he can be equally clever about explaining away his responsibility after the fact. Redl and

Wineman's work illustrates this defensive armory of "children who hate," that is, the ways they protect their self-gratifying behavior by warding off anyone who tries to alter their socially unacceptable gratifications. It is this feature more than any other which has caused many workers to despair and to consider the possibility of innate badness.

However, the children whom Redl and Wineman studied were "unsocialized aggressive" delinquents with the most severe degree of pathology. One should not lose sight of the variations in delinquency and the great differences among delinquents.

The Concept of Psychopathic Personality

The "psychopathic personality," a term now obsolete, is the "unsocialized aggressive" of the author's first category. In 1903 Adolf Meyer introduced the diagnosis "constitutional inferiority" and many similar terms have since come and gone (e.g., "constitutional psychopathic state," "psychic constitutional inferiority," "psychopathic personality" and "sociopathic personality").

Jack Wallinga remarked that "psychopath" is "the harshest label one can affix to an individual about whom one wants to convey a feeling of pessimism or hopelessness" *(1959, p. 364).* This feeling of hopelessness he refers to results from the implication that there is a constitutional basis for the problem, from the long-term nature of the disorder, from the presumed absence of conscience, and from the conviction that the psychopath will never be able to enter into a meaningful relationship with another person, at least not one in which personal sacrifices are demanded. These depressing conclusions are based on observable behavior, except for the constitutional predisposition, which has been the subject of much argument. Psychologists have

---

*Redl and Wineman, *op. cit.,* p. 127.

repeatedly examined family trees, trying to relate delinquency to heredity, particularly in the early studies which reported a high proportion of feeble-mindedness. J. S. Roucek quoted figures showing that 50 to 68 per cent of delinquents had criminal parents *(1958)*. Fifty years ago, such finding would have been taken as evidence of hereditary transmission of some kind of moral insanity, without taking into consideration the kind of environmental deficiencies created by criminal parents.

The diagnostic term "psychopathic personality" is, in one sense, the descendant of the term "moral insanity" introduced by J. C. Prichard in 1835. Earlier, Benjamin Rush had defined "moral derangement" as a condition in which "the understanding . . . is in a sound state," but "the will becomes the involuntary vehicle of vicious actions, through the instrumentality of the passions" *(1812, p. 262)*. Such "vicious actions" included murder, theft, lying, and drinking. Rush's opinion is that "in all these cases of innate, preternatural moral depravity, there is probably an original defective organization in those parts of the body, which are occupied by the moral faculties of the mind" *(1812, p. 358)*.

One of the most famous recent descriptions of the psychopath is that given by R. Cleckley; he described chronic, aggressive, uninhibited behavior which failed to respond to the most intensive therapy; failure to benefit from previous experience; inability to form affectionate ties; and the absence of recognizable feelings of guilt. An important additional characteristic was the general superficiality of thinking and judgment. The psychopath was described as living for the moment, disregarding the future, constantly seeking gratification, and refusing to tolerate frustration *(1941)*. In his original presentation, Cleckley did not seem to be impressed by the importance of the life experience of his patients, but implied that some kind of innate factor was

the explanation of their intractability in treatment.

This constitutional factor was for five years (1949–1953) the most hotly contested issue at Round Table discussions on the subject of psychopathic behavior in children at the annual meeting of the American Orthopsychiatric Association. At the first meeting, opinions represented widely-separated points along the "constitution or environment" continuum: Louis Lurie stated firmly that:

. . . the psychopath is a psychopath primarily by virtue of his specific constitutional structure. This psychopathic state may remain dormant indefinitely. On the other hand, various psychogenic or somatogenic factors may activate this condition or state, and thereby give rise to the type of behavior which characterizes the so-called psychopathic delinquent. *(The Psychopathic Delinquent Child: Round Table, 1949, p. 226.)*

At the other extreme, Frederick Allen emphasized early personal relationships:

A child, by his negative behavior, creates a chain reaction which feeds on itself and shrouds the early beginnings of such behavior in mystery. Explanations focus more and more on the individual's containing within himself all the causes for his mounting difficulties, because he seems to have no feeling and remains untouched by efforts to modify his behavior. *(ibid., p. 236.)*

Allen suggests that the responsibility for the problem is projected onto the child first by his parents and then by society, including therapists, making it entirely the child's burden. He discusses a nine-year-old "psychopath" in terms of the interaction between the mother's ambivalent feelings toward the boy (even before his birth) and the boy's aggression, which the mother constantly struggled to control. Allen describes the child as vigorous, active, and accelerated in physical development—characteristics which might please another mother but which only increased the conflicts of this one. Allen comments that "the fact that psychogenic factors are not obvious is in no sense proof of their absence. The very insidious way in which these factors operate serves to disguise their existence" *(ibid., p. 240)*.

At the next meeting, David Levy proposed a distinction between the "deprived psychopath" and the "indulged psychopath":

In terms of superego structure, it is weak in the deprived psychopath because of a deficiency in the process of identification. It is weak in the indulged psychopath because the identification is so strongly represented by the indulgent loving mother. The deprived psychopath is defective in the capacity to develop standards. In the indulged psychopath, standards are well understood but taken lightly. *(Psychopathic Behavior in Infants and Children: Round Table, 1950, p. 252.)*

Here, the psychogenic factors seem paramount, and Levy's statement could easily be rephrased in terms of social learning. The child continues to repeat throughout his life that which was rewarding in infancy. The neglected child receives no rewards for good behavior and the indulged child does not learn self-control because he is rewarded indiscriminately. Frederick G. Thorne illustrated the operation of these processes in an article entitled "Etiological Studies of Psychopathic Personality: The Ego-inflated, Defectively Conditioned Type" *(1947)*. This type is similar to Levy's "indulged psychopath."

Ben Karpman in the final symposium on this subject, questioned the validity of the traditional diagnosis of "psychopath" and suggested that psychopathic patterns develop in the first two years of life and become so firmly established that they are immutable *(Psychodynamics of Child Delinquency: Round Table, 1953)*. "Psychopath," as a diagnostic term, has been replaced by such terms as "unsocialized aggressive" and "antisocial character disorder," as our increased understanding of the effects of early infantile experience has made constitutional disposition a less valid hypothesis.

In the 1940's, accumulated evidence showed that early maternal deprivation affected the personality of many children in an unalterable way, which is indistinguishable from constitutional defects. J. Bowlby specifically related maternal deprivation and delinquency *(1944)*. In delinquents especially, early separation from the parents may presage a lifelong pattern of rejection, all the more serious because it is repeated and reemphasized. All the clinical material on serious delinquents refers to undisguised parental rejection. Redl and Wineman, for example, comment on the casualness with which the parents of their subjects surrendered them for treatment, without a backward glance or second thought, in marked contrast to the parents of neurotic children *(1957)*. Because they had no positive relationship with their aggressive children, these parents felt no anguish at parting with them. Ivy Bennett, comparing delinquent and neurotic children, found that her 50 delinquent subjects had experienced frequent interruptions of their relationships with their mothers before the age of seven years, and interruptions in the father-child relationship at all age levels. Such separations were much less frequent for the neurotic subjects. The most significant age of separation appeared to be the second year *(1960)*. These observations have been confirmed in countless studies of seriously delinquent children.

Early and consistent rejection, then, and open hostility, reinforce the child's natural aggression. Parental attempts to correct and control the child are perceived as attacks and increase his hostility. Such early imprinting is difficult to undo, for two reasons: First, the child's fear and suspicion of people is firmly entrenched; second, his aggressive behavior elicits rejection by his environment, proving to him that rejection is all he can ever expect. In spite of changing diagnostic terms and etiological theories, this form of delinquency, rooted in early rejection, remains difficult to treat and prognosis is poor.

Gang Delinquency

The child who is a member of a delinquent gang may be, to some extent, following the patterns of behavior common to his particular social class. The Children's Bureau, in its *Report to the Congress on Juvenile Delinquency (1960)* observes that some delinquency is "normal" in that it develops from the child's identification with his own neighborhood or with some special group within it. The sociologists and cultural anthropologists who deal with this category of delinquency speak in terms of "class," "culture," and "caste," and emphasize group, rather than individual, behavior.

Sociologists have observed that there is an excess of juvenile delinquents in certain areas, over and above what can be accounted for by more stringent law enforcement. The Children's Bureau Report describes such neighborhoods as characterized:

. . . not only by physical deterioration, but by very great heterogeneity of background and moral standards, by lack of neighborhood solidarity, by lack of opportunities for youth to participate meaningfully in the kinds of activities that are available for children in more favored neighborhoods, and by the presence of "successful" members of the underworld, who are regarded as heroes to be emulated. These circumstances of life are often associated with unstable families, and a high incidence of illegitimacy and deser-

tion, leading both to maternal employment with inadequate provision for the needs of children, and to the lack of a father-figure to provide guidance and affection for the young child. *(1960, p. 5.)*

In these neighborhoods, there is little control of juveniles in the home and little effort is made to exclude them from activities which, by law and by custom, are reserved for adults (e.g., smoking, drinking, and sexual intercourse). The pattern here is parental neglect rather than parental rejection which characterizes the developmental history of the unsocialized aggressive.

The "Functional" Theory: Miller

The idea that delinquency is a "normal" or probable aspect of some cultural situations is most explicitly stated by Walter Miller, a cultural anthropologist. He writes that there is a "lower-class culture" which operates in relation to a consistent, coherent, and rational set of norms and values which have grown out of the realities of economic and social functioning, and that such a culture is organized around six focal concerns: "Trouble, Toughness, Smartness, Excitement, Fate and Autonomy" *(1958, p. 7)*. Miller suggests that much of the behavior found in this culture is not deliberately antisocial or systematically criminal and that its antisocial nature is the unintentional consequence of habitual patterns of behavior which appear to be reasonable within their own context. For example, in many sections of the country a mother is not eligible for financial assistance for her children if her husband is living with her, even if he is unemployed. Thus, she may feel forced to conceal his presence from the authorities, in order to be able to continue to feed and clothe her children. "Much of the delinquency of lower-class youngsters may be seen as an attempt by the acting individual to adhere to forms of behavior and to achieve standards of value as they are defined within this type of community" *(Kvaraceus and Miller, 1959, p. 63).*

Miller finds that status within the street-corner group is purchased by fighting, assault, theft, and demonstrations of skill and daring. This finding is supported by the previously mentioned interview with the gang responsible for killing Michael Farmer; repeatedly, the boys declared that it was more important to keep their "rep" than to refrain from going along with the gang. As one of the boys put it, "People will respect me for what I've done; they'll say 'There goes a cold killer.'" According to Miller, the "ego ideals" (e.g., toughness) of the lower-class adolescent are actually functional. The boy knows he will need these qualities later, when he is a longshoreman, a truck driver, or the like. Miller does *not* consider the values and way of life of these delinquents a reaction to deprivation or a direct expression of class conflict or of frustrated ambition.

Other sociologists do not stress the "normality" of the delinquent pattern as a natural part of lower-class culture to quite the same degree. They speak; instead, of "deviant subcultures," specifically, the adolescent gang. Everyone recognizes the teen-age gang, its characteristics, its propensity for trouble, and the extent to which a member will go in order to retain his status within it. Many questions have been raised regarding the gang as a social unit, and the reason why it persists in certain urban neighborhoods. Sociologists treat the gang structure as something to be understood in itself, much as the psychiatrist tries to understand the dynamics of the individual delinquent, and there is as much difference of opinion about the gang among sociologists as there is among psychiatrists about the delinquent.

The "Reaction-formation" Theory: Cohen

Cohen and Richard Cloward and Lloyd Ohlin *(1960)* agree in that they consider the delinquent gang a social deviation and a pathological one, but their concepts of the origin of gang culture are quite different. Cohen views group delinquency as characteristically "non-utilitarian, malicious and negativistic" *(1955, p. 25).* In his opinion, it serves no practical purpose beyond that of flouting authority and discharging hostility (making gang values sound maladaptive rather than functional, as in Miller's description.) Cohen suggests that the gang adopts this behavior, not because it is unimpressed by middle-class standards but because it is very much impressed. But middle-class standards are unattainable, so the gang turns against them outwardly: "The hallmark of the delinquent sub-culture is the explicit and wholesale repudiation of middle-class standards and the adoption of their very antithesis" *(1955, p. 129).* He hypothesizes that these aspirations "linger on, underground, as it were, repressed, unacknowledged, but an ever-present threat to the adjustment which has been achieved at no small cost" *(1955, p. 132).* This concept is comparable to the individual mechanism of reaction-formation, which involves espousing inclinations and feelings which are actually the opposite of what the person truly wants. Cohen depicts the working-class boy as often unhappy, frustrated, and angered by his position in life and as finding in delinquency an active solution for these feelings:

The delinquent sub-culture of the working-class boy has these primary functions; first, of establishing a set of status criteria in terms of which the boy can more easily succeed, and second, of enabling him to retaliate against the norms at whose impact his ego has suffered, by defining merit in terms of the opposite of those norms and by sanctioning aggression against them and those who exemplify and apply them. *(1955, p. 168.)*

Thus, delinquency is functional—not, as in Miller's definition, because it is adaptive to cultural reality, but because it acts, like a neurotic symptom, to relieve tension and conflict.

The "Illicit Means" Theory

Cloward and Ohlin state that "the most crucial elements of a delinquent sub-culture are the prescriptions, norms, or rules of conduct that define the activities of a full-fledged member" *(1960, p. 13)*. They describe three types of delinquent subcultures: The gang based on criminal values (which has been organized primarily for the illegal acquisition of material gain); the gang based on violence (i.e., the fighting gang); and the gang based on the consumption of drugs. Cloward and Ohlin label these "criminal," "conflict," and "retreatist," respectively. Their theory of causation posits problems of adjustment that arise when there is little opportunity to reach desired goals. The frustration creates pressures which result in the formation of delinquent subcultures. The authors employ the concept of *anomie,* or anomy, originally proposed by Durkheim *(1951)* and extended by Merton *(1957)*. Briefly, this term refers to a state of lawlessness, a condition in which social norms no longer control men's actions. Durkheim emphasized the need for society to keep the social goals of its members within the limits of possible achievement, in order to avert tension, frustration, and deviant behavior. Merton viewed anomy as a result of the lack of relationship between goals and legitimate possibilities of attainment, rather than of unlimited aspirations alone. "Anomy," so defined, implies delinquent or antisocial behavior.

Cloward and Ohlin point out that all American children are exposed to the same promises of material success, prestige, and so forth, but that they are not given equal opportunities to achieve them. Education, in particular, is the key to this success, but it is difficult for a family which is struggling to subsist to prepare a young child for school or to become interested in his intellectual growth and development. The poorly prepared child, unencouraged and unstimulated at home, finds school difficult and unrewarding. It is a frustration, rather than a tolerable means to a desirable end and, by the time he reaches adolescence, higher education and the doors it opens are truly remote.

Cloward and Ohlin summarize their main hypothesis as follows:

The disparity between what lower-class youths are led to want and what is actually available to them is the source of a major problem of adjustment. Adolescents who form delinquent sub-cultures, we suggest, have internalized an emphasis on conventional goals. Faced with limitation on legitimate avenues of access to these goals, and unable to revise their aspirations downwards, they experience intense frustration; the exploration of non-conformist alternatives may be the result. *(1960, p. 86.)*

The authors also discuss the boys' defenses against the feelings of guilt which result from finding "non-conformist alternatives." The delinquent finds that the setup is not fair and withdraws his allegiance to approved modes of conduct. This then justifies any action he decides to take. This explanation of the lack of feelings of guilt and the stubborn resistance to correction that the conscience has been "bought off" by rationalization.

Cloward and Ohlin describe the various routes taken by delinquent groups to achieve the aspirations of the individual members; in the "conflict" subculture, for example, violent behavior is the "illicit means" used to attain the self-respect desired. In each case, gang opinion is substituted for the opinion of society.

Other Theories

Herbert Bloch and Arthur Niederhoffer describe the gang as "satisfying deep-seated needs experienced by adolescents in all cultures" *(1958, p. 17)*, thus emphasizing the problems of adjustment common to all adolescents. The "Chicago school" *(Shaw and McKay, 1942)*, attributes delinquency to the cultural conflict between immigrants and their children, to the presence of adult criminal groups, and to the slum conditions which make it difficult for parents to control their children. Under such conditions, they say, delinquency can become a group tradition, transmitted from the older boys to the younger.

Study of the various sociological theories leaves one with a stronger impression of similarities than of their differences. They need not be considered alternative explanations of gang delinquency. They seem to coalesce in a complex of interrelated social causes which create the social phenomenon of a delinquent subculture.

Individual Delinquency

We turn now to the types of delinquency which are idiosyncratic to a family or to an individual. These are Jenkins and Glickman's "emotionally disturbed" children and those included in the author's third, fourth, and fifth categories. Understanding delinquency on the basis of the individual should not be considered in conflict with the sociological approach. The sociological theories do not explain why only a minority of children who live in high-rate areas have police records nor does it explain the occurrence of delinquency among children in privileged circumstances. Albert Bandura and Richard Walters suggest that the so-

ciological factors may not themselves be causative agents: "their primary importance may lie in the fact that they provide conditions under which the psychological factors conducive to the development of antisocial behavior may more readily operate" *(1959, p. 4)*. In this section, we are concerned with the delinquent youngster who has no obvious environmental disadvantage. It may well be that the psychology of these exceptional cases is the same as that which is so greatly magnified by adverse social situations.

There are some distinguishing features of delinquents in the broad category of "emotionally disturbed." Most delinquency perpetrated as an individual offense—rather than in cooperation with a gang—is of a neurotic variety. The reverse does not necessarily follow. Although delinquency may represent a solution for an internalized conflict, the choice of symptom may be facilitated by partners available to share the guilt and excitement. The neurotic delinquent has a functioning conscience which is evidenced by feelings of guilt and remorse or sporadic conscientiousness. The delinquency is at least in part alien to the adolescent's ego ideals. Also, the neurotic delinquent usually has a history either of neurotic symptoms or of such emotional disturbances as chronic depression or attacks of diffuse anxiety and uneasiness. Finally, the nature of the offense often gives some clue as to the underlying cause. Running away, firesetting, and certain sexual offenses strongly suggest that neurosis is present.

None of these criteria provides undeniable proof that the delinquent is neurotic, but they should serve as signals that psychological study of the child is in order.

In the disturbed delinquent, the unconscious plays a major role in symptom determination, and distinctions can be made by whether it is the child's or the parent's unconscious which is primarily responsible for the child's anti-social behavior. If it is the parent's, he has unconsciously sanctioned lacunae in his child's superego; if it is the child's, we are dealing with a classical internalized neurosis, one in which the delinquency results from unconscious aggression, guilt, or fantasy.

Sanctions for Superego Lacunae

Adelaide Johnson first used the term "superego lacunae" in 1947; it was immediately accepted by clinicians and used as a diagnostic formulation. She defined the character problems involved as "those of adolescents in conflict with parents or some other external authority because of an acting-out of forbidden, antisocial impulses. There is rarely a generalized weakness of super-ego . . . but rather a lack of super-ego in certain circumscribed areas of behavior, which may be termed super-ego lacunae" *(1947, p. 225)*. These lacunae correspond to similar defects in the parent's superego, so that the parents find vicarious gratification in the child's behavior and usually manage, albeit unconsciously, to convey to the child that they sanction the behavior. Johnson recounts many examples of such parental sanction. One parent accompanied his orders to the child with dire warnings of what would happen if they were disobeyed or checked constantly to see they were being carried out. Excessive vigilance, strongly suggests that the child will be disobedient. The child may actually behave as his parents seem to expect (i.e., disobediently). The parent who anxiously expects a daughter to "get in trouble" is likely to see his or her fears (or are they wishes?) come true. One suspects that unconscious pleasure lies behind the facade of conscious anxiety, especially if the parent acts smug about seeing his dire predictions materialize. Johnson discusses running away. Frequently, the parent actually originates the idea. The child says, "I hate you

all!" The parents reply, "Well, why don't you just pack your bag and go live some place else if you think we're so awful?" Some parents even pack the child's suitcase for him. Usually the child is terrified but not contrite, and feels obliged to save face.

Parents betray themselves in other ways. In describing his child's misbehavior, for example, the parent may betray admiration for his offspring's cunning and daring. He may feel he is expressing only disapproval, but the child is able to sense the hidden pride in his father's suppressed smile or amazed voice. Sometimes parents simply ignore evidence of misbehavior and accept a transparent lie. One 12-year-old boy brought home three new bicycles. He explained to his parents that they had been left behind in the park and that he was "holding" them for the owners. When school officials called some weeks later with a complaint against the boy for stealing, his parents expressed great surprise. In such situations, parents often react with incredulity or disbelief, revealing the defects in their own moral judgment.

Parents sometimes seduce their children into lying or stealing, often by casually borrowing money within the family without keeping a record. Suddenly, the child is borrowing from someone outside the family, that is, stealing, but no one can understand how it could have happened. A similarly seductive setup is one in which right and wrong are gauged in terms of what one can get away with, of whether or not one is caught, or of what people will say. This attitude enables the child to conclude that it is being detected that is wrong, not the act itself.

The mother who asks her child to confess to some misbehavior about which she is already informed is often only teaching the child to lie to her. She may express disappointment that she caught him lying, but she herself has lied to the child in leading him to think her ignorant of some matter she already knew about. In her discussion of treatment of youngsters with antisocial tendencies, Johnson stresses that it is important that the therapist be scrupulously honest, law-abiding, and firmly on the right side.

Often, unconscious parental condoning of a child's antisocial acts serves a dual purpose. It gratifies the parents' forbidden impulses and his hostility to the child who "gets what's coming to him." Sometimes only one child in the family is singled out for this role; he is cast as the black sheep, and obligingly fulfills his assigned part. He may be expected to follow in the footsteps of one or another family member. If the child acts on an impulse or wish of which the parent was never conscious—that is, one which the parent did not admit in his own childhood and which was not indulged in by any other member of the family, the parental impulse is so strongly repressed that it is difficult for him to acquire any insight into his own responsibility for its perpetuation in the child.

D. J. Carek, W. J. Hendrickson, and D. J. Holmes described many ways in which parents communicated unconscious approval to delinquent adolescents hospitalized at the Neuropsychiatric Institute in Ann Arbor. As a child improved, his parents became increasingly anxious and sought to sabotage or disrupt the treatment program. The authors were impressed by the compelling intensity and chronicity of the parents' need for vicarious fulfillment and the unconscious nature of the determinants of their need. The child's behavior, the authors felt, represented a good compromise for the parent; it provided an avenue for the release of forbidden wishes without causing guilt, since, after all, the parent was not the one who was committing the forbidden act *(1961)*. Such psychological interaction necessitates at least simultaneous treatment. Frequently,

physical separation of parent and child facilitates the necessary psychological separation.

In a report based on 11 years of experience with 57 children of 6 to 10, E. N. Rexford described some of the therapeutic difficulties arising with families of children referred to the Thom Child Psychiatric Clinic for aggressive, destructive, antisocial behavior. The Clinic staff felt that, on the whole, the mothers were the more adequate and responsible parents, although casework with them was difficult and frequently ineffective. The contact with fathers was deemed even less satisfactory; apparently, the sanction of the fathers was conscious and deeply entrenched. Rexford remarks that ". . . the over-whelmingly predominant character structure of fathers of antisocial young children we have seen over the past eleven years is that of a passive, restricted and hostile man, strongly allied with his obstreperous son, firm in his belief that aggressive behavior of whatever kind or degree is evidence of desirable masculine self-assertion and is not to be curbed" *(1959, p. 215).*

The research study of Albert Bandura and Richard Walters confirms these clinical observations. Their data were obtained from interviews with 52 adolescent boys and their parents. All the boys were from stable families and lived in neighborhoods with a low rate of delinquency. Half the boys had histories of aggressive antisocial behavior. The major differences were in the father-son relationship. The fathers of the aggressive boys showed less warmth to, and were more rejecting of, their sons than were the control fathers. The fathers encouraged their sons' aggression outside the home although they were very nonpermissive of aggression toward themselves. Also, the fathers of the aggressive boys were considerably more permissive of adolescent heterosexual behavior than were the fathers of the controls. In this study, the mothers of the aggressive boys placed fewer limits on their sons' behavior in the home than did the control mothers. In contrast to the vacillating inconsistency of their mothers, the fathers of the aggressive boys were harsh and punitive, thus providing the boys with predominantly aggressive and punitive models for identification. The authors felt that the disruption of the relationship between these boys and their fathers had begun long before the boys' aggression had brought them into conflict with school and legal authorities (1959). The delinquency of these youngsters was rooted, not in early maternal rejection but in later paternal rejection and the development of supposedly masculine ideals.

Unconscious Aggression

Kate Friedlander, a child psychoanalyst, has written the most complete presentation of neurotic manifestations of delinquency (1947). Delinquent behavior, when it is neurotic in origin, has the same pattern as other neurotic symptoms (see Chapter 9). The delinquent behavior is usually of a solitary nature and has a specific structure. The kleptomaniac, for example, repeatedly steals objects for which she (kleptomaniacs are usually females) has no use. She feels an irresistible impulse to take the object; when caught, she is embarrassed and unable to explain her behavior. Sometimes only particular objects are stolen, or under particular circumstances, or from particular people. One of Friedlander's patients, a ten-year-old girl, stole money from her mother's purse—a symbolic taking by force of the affection the mother had not given freely. According to the author, the girl also felt that the mother had deprived her of the means of being a boy. The feeling of deprivation was unconscious and justified only in fantasy, but the stealing served to symbolically satisfy both the instinctive urge and the demand of the superego

for punishment. Like every other neurotic symptom, it was a compromise.

Acting Out a Fantasy

The child's attempt to act out a fantasy may take various forms. Friedlander cites the case of a 16-year-old boy who was an inveterate thief, although he had no real need for money and did not want to be given it. What he wanted was to plan the theft (and the subsequent exposure) because of the excitement involved. Stealing, and everything connected with it, satisfied a strong impulse. Describing one occasion when he did not steal, the boy used the same terms that adolescents use when they describe their struggle against the desire to masturbate. This boy had a long history of masturbation which culminated in obsessional masturbation when he was 10. As a result, he believed he had damaged his brain and thus could do nothing worthwhile; he intended, he said, to become a marvelous crook and to stop feeling inferior to other boys. This was his conscious intention, but the stealing contained the excitement and pleasure which were originally connected with masturbation.

There are antisocial actions which are more obviously related to sexual gratification—exhibitionism, voyeurism, transvestism, homosexuality, and especially rape and promiscuity. The first four are sexually perverse. They are relatively rare among delinquents, and are easily recognized as stemming from emotional problems which require treatment. When the sexual problem is totally transformed, or is displaced to an activity to which it seems unrelated, the neurotic element is hard to detect. Still, some fantasy may be acted out.

Pyromania is sometimes an acting out of a fantasy. Pyromaniacs are unable to explain why they set fires, except for the "thrill of it," and they seem powerless to resist the compulsion. I. Kaufman, L. W. Heims, and

D. G. Reiser studied 30 boy pyro-maniacs as part of a research program in juvenile delinquency at the Judge Baker Guidance Center. They found their subjects to be much more se-verely disturbed than previous literature had ever suggested. This, however, may have been a function of their method of selecting cases. Their group consisted of 10 fire-setters from each of three sources: an outpatient guid-ance clinic, a residential treatment facility for delinquent boys, and the children's unit of the state hospital. Overtly psychotic or borderline chil-dren made up more than two-thirds of the total sample, and the personality problems encountered were diffuse. From psychological test data, social service interviews, and psychiatric in-terviews, the authors concluded that these children were *not* sexually aroused by fires, but were involved in more primitive problems—destroying or being destroyed (1961). Destruction by fire is often viewed by children as the fate of those who are helpless or who are trapped by someone more powerful.

The pathological liar and the im-postor are also sometimes acting out a fantasy. Frequently, the fantasy is de-rived from what Freud called the "fam-ily romance," an almost universal day-dream of youngsters between 8 and 14. The youngster imagines that he was brought to his mother and father when he was a baby, and that his real par-ents are very important people (*see Freud, 1909, 1959; Friedlander, 1947*). This fantasy is usually worked out in great detail, its emphasis being on a reunion with the imaginary parents. When the child is not satisfied with daydreaming and lives out his fantasy, the extent of the delusion may bring him close to the amnesia or "dissocia-tive reaction" of the hysteric, almost to the point of autohypnosis. Such cases are rare and do not often reach juvenile court, but vestiges of such fantasies can be seen in the usual de-linquent who becomes king of a gang. The gang delinquent, however, is part of a group, and his reasons for wishing to confer a higher status on himself are clearer. The neurotic delinquent func-tions alone; he has much less justifica-tion in reality; he is less aware of what he is doing; and he feels more guilty when he becomes aware of what he is doing.

"Criminals from a Sense of Guilt"

Freud (*1916, 1957*) was the first to describe a specific neurotic mechanism which may lead to criminal behavior. He showed that there are offenders who are driven by unconscious guilt and who feel considerably relieved after committing a crime, especially after they are punished. (For an ex-ample of this, see Chapter 3.) The dis-tinguishing feature of such offenders is that they make detection and punish-ment inevitable. Parents often marvel at the stupidity of the child who leaves so much evidence, but treatment usu-ally reveals that the child was feeling guilty about some secret (a wish, a fantasy, or a sin like masturbation), and committed the antisocial act for the express purpose of being caught and punished. In other words, the guilt feelings *precede* the antisocial behav-ior and are the cause of it. These cases rarely come to the attention of the au-thorities; the crime is usually not serious, the parents mete out the de-served punishment, and the child is duly contrite and remorseful. If, how-ever, an exception does reach the court, it is important that this diagnostic possibility be borne in mind. One is much more likely to encounter this situation in casework; it is one which may provoke considerable anxiety in parents who view the behavior as a precursor of serious criminality.

The principle of overdetermination of behavior is worth emphasizing here again. In one delinquent act, the child may simultaneously be expressing unconscious aggression against the parents, jealousy of a sibling, working out of sexual tensions by displacing them, living out a fairy-tale fantasy, and seeking the punishment which will relieve his guilt.

Treatment and Control

Juvenile delinquency was not considered a special problem until the nineteenth century. Before then, children who broke the law were punished like adults. The first institution for juvenile delinquents of which we know was the Hospice of San Michele in Rome, opened by Pope Clement XI in 1703. Designed on monastic lines, it was meant to teach wayward boys discipline and a trade, and its entrance bore the inscription, "It is insufficient to restrain the wicked by punishment, unless you render them virtuous by corrective discipline." Delinquents were put into two categories: those under 20 who had received a court sentence for some crime and incorrigibles who were handed over by their parents. Chained by one foot, the boys worked in strict silence at spinning or knitting. Intractable boys were put in solitary cells.

The first separate penal institution for juveniles in this country was New York City's House of Refuge, opened in 1825; the first such state institution was opened in Massachusetts in 1847. After that, state institutions for delinquent boys and girls multiplied rapidly, most of them being established before 1875. These were essentially prisons where hard work and rigid discipline were emphasized. In 1899, however, the first juvenile court was established in Chicago, in accordance with a law which also provided that delinquents be treated in the same manner as neglected or dependent children. By 1917, only three states remained without juvenile court legislation.

The clinical approach to juvenile delinquency began in 1909, when Dr. William Healy established the Psycho-pathic Laboratory (now known as the Illinois Institute for Juvenile Research), which operated under the aegis of the Chicago Juvenile Court. Soon after, the reform school became a training school, and juvenile delinquency became a psychological, as well as a social, problem.

The Juvenile Court

The approach of the juvenile court has been called "individualized justice;" it recognizes the "individuality of a child and adapts its orders accordingly," and it is a "legal tribunal where law and science, especially the science of medicine and those sciences which deal with human behavior, such as biology, sociology and psychology, work side by side" *(Standards for Specialized Courts, Children's Bureau, 1954, p. 1)*. Its purposes are remedial and, to a certain extent, preventive rather than merely punitive. More than 3,000 juvenile courts, by no means uniform in their methods and practices, have been established since the turn of the century.

These courts generally treat juvenile offenders in one of two ways. In either case, a preliminary investigation is made. An individual case may then be handled informally; that is, principally by the social caseworker and the counseling staff, rather than by the judge. The alternative, the authorization of a formal petition, is determined by the seriousness of the allegation, the previous history of the delinquent, and the attitudes of the parties involved *(Sheridan, 1962)*. This first screening varies considerably in different jurisdictions, but it usually requires the combined efforts of both lawyers and psychologists or social workers. "The decisions made at intake affect individual and community rights—the right of the community to be protected, the right of the child and family to personal freedom and privacy, and at the same time the right of the child and family to receive the services of the state for care, protection and treatment" *(Sheridan, 1962, p. 156)*.

The effectiveness of a juvenile court depends upon whether there are sufficient resources to provide "individualized justice;" child welfare agencies, family agencies, child guidance clinics, employment counseling services, special services in schools, recreational facilities and child placement agencies are essential. According to the Children's Bureau *(Role of the Federal Government, 1961)*, one or more of these is lacking in all but five counties in the United States and few communities have adequate local services. Some courts have, therefore, established their own facilities. In 1955, for example, there were 17 court psychiatric clinics *(Bloch and Flynn, 1956)*.

Whether controlled by the court or separately organized and administered, psychiatric and psychological services are usually provided on a part-time basis and are largely advisory and diagnostic. Surveys indicate that the recommendations of clinical staffs are usually acted on whenever possible *(Zuckerman, 1954)*. Some courts have extended their functions far beyond diagnosis and adjudication; the Cuyahoga County Juvenile Court, for instance, has experimented with group therapy programs and work rehabilitation programs *(Juvenile Court of Cuyahoga County Annual Reports, 1961 and 1962)*.

Probation

Almost half the delinquents formally handled in 1963 were placed on probation *(Juvenile Court Statistics, 1963)*. Thus, probation has become a kind of treatment, and the importance of the probation officer has become great. His responsibilities may include making a preliminary investigation of the child and family, presenting the case before the judge, arranging for the carrying out of the court's order, and giving probationary supervision. In Cuyahoga County, only one-third of the probation officer's time is devoted to probationary supervision.

In 1959, it was estimated that there were 3,572 probation officers in juvenile courts in the United States, but that more than twice that many were needed *(Russell, 1960, p. 7)*. Gladys M. Krueger reported that 85 per cent of our probation officers are college graduates and that about one in ten has a graduate degree in social work *(1959)*. Their greatest problem is their work load—over 95 per cent of the probation officers have work loads in excess of the recommended standard established by the National Probation and Parole Association. This standard is an average of 3.2 hours per child per month for *all* work connected with the case, including travel time. The time now available to probation officers is 1 hour per child per month. Under the circumstances, perhaps one should not classify probation as "treatment." It is certainly difficult to evaluate its potential efficacy.

About 20 per cent of all children on probation violate the terms and are brought back to court; from 30 per cent to 40 per cent of children who have been on probation commit new offenses within a few years. Of those who successfully complete the probation period, 75 per cent to 80 per cent never return. The few studies we have indicate that recidivism declines when the probation officers are well trained and have small case loads.

Correctional Institutions

The detention home is a special jail where children await their court hearings. Separate detention of juveniles began almost simultaneously with the juvenile court at the beginning of this century but, although all the states have separate courts for juveniles, more than 2,500 counties (of approximately 3,100) have no separate detention facilities for juveniles. In those detention homes which do exist, children are often held unnecessarily and for lengthy periods, chiefly because the police departments and courts are understaffed.

On June 30, 1963, approximately 38,500 children were living in public training schools for delinquent children, an increase of 7 per cent over 1958. Since this increase is less than the increase in delinquency during the same period, it is obvious that other kinds of programs are being used more extensively than institutional care. In about one-fifth of the cases formally brought to court, the child is committed to the custody of an institution, with an average stay of 9.5 months (*Statistics on Public Institutions for Delinquent Children, 1963*). Approximately one-fourth of the children committed in 1963 had been admitted previously. This "returnee rate" is directly related to the size of the institution; those institutions with less than 150 children had a returnee rate of 17.1 per cent compared with an over-all returnee rate of 26 per cent. Unfortunately, most institutions have populations of over 150, and are also overcrowded.

One purpose of a training school is to rehabilitate the youngster, primarily by giving him experience in community living. The training school is expected to show the delinquent that acceptable forms of social recognition and of personal satisfaction are available to him. Such schools also have well-defined custodial responsibilities; they are expected to control the child for the period of commitment and to prevent a recurrence of his antisocial conduct. Since his commitment has resulted from his wrongdoing, the child arrives at the school fearful and distrustful. "Mindful of the community's expectations, and of the children's fears, and cognizant of the need for treatment, training, re-education and rehabilitation, training schools for delinquents are attempting to provide some of the most difficult services to administer in the entire child welfare program" (*Institutions Serving Delinquent Children,*

Children's Bureau, 1957). But the training schools receive only the most difficult cases and for short periods, and are almost always grossly understaffed. It is surprising that they are as successful as they are.

Selective Short-term Treatment Institutions

Three types of institutional treatment may be clearly distinguished: the standard correctional institution for serious offenders; the more specialized intensive treatment institutions for long-term treatment of juveniles with severe disorders; and the short-term institutions, for treatment for those who cannot be at liberty but who are not sufficiently delinquent or disturbed to warrant long periods of detention.

One short-term program is conducted at Highfields, now a New Jersey state institution (started privately, in 1950) which is designed for 16 and 17-year-olds with no previous history of commitment. About 20 boys are in residence at a time; the ratio of staff to boys is about 1 to 3.3, somewhat better than the usual ratio in correctional institution. The average stay is slightly less than four months. Considerable freedom is allowed the boys: they make trips to town and spend some weekends at home; there is no censorship of their mail or telephone calls, and they are not walled or fenced in. The program includes outside employment and nightly group therapy sessions. L. W. McCorkle, Albert Elias, and F. L. Bixby call these sessions "guided group-interaction":

Guided group-interaction makes assumptions about the kinds of socializing experiences delinquents need and can use if they are to achieve their usefulness as responsible citizens. It assumes that the delinquent will benefit from a social experience where, in concert with his peers and the leader, he can freely discuss, examine and understand his problems of living, without the threats that had been so common in his previous learning experiences. It further assumes that the mutual "give and take" of group discussion stimulates the delinquent to some understanding of the relationship between what takes place in this learning situation and his immediate problems of living. *(1958, p. 74.)*

After it had been in operation five years, the Highfields program was evaluated. Of the 240 boys who completed the recommended period, 83 per cent were considered successes and 17 per cent became recidivists. This is about half the recidivism of delinquents in conventional institution, although the success is partly due to a selective admissions policy. However, when the results were compared with those of the Annandale Reformatory, in New York, and the special variables were taken into account, the Highfields group still had substantially fewer recidivists in the first three years following release *(McCorkle, Elias, and Bisby, 1958)*. This speaks well for the program, particularly since the cost is no greater than in a conventional institution (i.e., $516 per boy for four months of treatment between 1952 and 1955).

Intensive Treatment Institutions

The work of August Aichhorn is of great importance in the development of institutions for intensive treatment. Aichhorn, a teacher in the Viennese elementary schools, became interested in wayward children and was made superintendent of a reformatory in Vienna. Some of his therapeutic concepts are reflected in the closing remarks of his study, *Wayward Youth:*

I cannot close this book without once more stressing the great importance of the workers in this field. You have seen that a character change in the delinquent means a change in his ego ideal. This occurs when new traits are taken over by the individual. The source of these traits is the worker. He is the important object with whom the dissocial child or youth can retrieve the defective or non-existent identification and with whom he can experience all the things in which his father failed him. With the worker's help, the youth acquires the necessary feeling relation to his companions which enables him to overcome the dissocial traits. The word "father-substitute," so often used in connection with remedial education, receives its rightful connotations in this conception of the task.

What helps the worker most in therapy with the dissocial? The transference! And especially what we recognize as the positive transference. It is above all the tender feeling for the teacher that gives the pupil the incentive to do what is prescribed and not to do what is forbidden. The teacher, as a libidinally-charged object for the pupil, offers traits for identification that bring about a lasting change in the structure of the ego ideal. This in turn effects a change in the behavior of the formerly dissocial child. We cannot imagine a person who is unsocial (himself) as a worker in this field. We assume therefore that the ego ideal of the child will be corrected through the worker's help in bringing him to a recognition of the claims of society and to participation in society.[*]

More recently, Redl and Wineman have reported on 19 months of operation of Pioneer House in Detroit. Their valuable study describes the intensive treatment of five extremely aggressive preadolescent boys. Like many others (see Chapter 16), the authors stress the importance of the total environment in establishing a "milieu therapy"; every staff member of Pioneer House, down to the kitchen help, is said to make an important contribution to treatment. "Programming for ego support" is arranging for play that will reduce overexcitement, frustration, and overstimulation, but which will, at the same time, provide opportunities for emotional expression. The surface management of the child's behavior may entail ignoring

---

[*]Quoted from August Aichhorn *Wayward Youth* (New York: The Viking Press, Inc., 1935), pp. 235–36. Reprinted by permission of the publisher.

the child, setting limits on his activity, circumventing and forestalling difficulties, treating difficult situations with humor, using rewards and punishments, and so on. The authors give many illustrations of on-the-spot therapy, which is actually conducted on a catch-as-catch-can basis because such children cannot bring meaningful material to an office interview for later discussion.

Some of the greatest difficulties in treating delinquents arise from the community, and the fate of Redl and Wineman's work is classic. Pioneer House was closed for lack of funds; its inmates were subjected to new rejections and traumas which gradually undermined possible therapeutic gains; and it is not possible to evaluate the potential efficacy of their methods, or indeed, of intensive residential treatment of delinquent children.

Intermediate Forms of Treatment

Various methods of treating delinquents have been attempted. The California Youth Authority instituted one project which emphasized probation. Each probation officer had only eight cases and saw each delinquent as often as once a day *(Stark, 1963)*. The California Youth Authority was also the first to experiment with work camps; since 1950, such camps have been established in about 20 states. These are minimum security institutions, varying in size, program, structure, admissions policy, and type of government sponsorship *(Cary, 1964)*. Such camps should be of great value, for they provide a transition between school and work; and lack of opportunity for paid employment is an important factor in delinquency.

The half-way house is patterned on those established for discharged mental patients *(Kennedy, 1964)*. Here, temporary living quarters are provided for the delinquent leaving the institution, to help him make the adjustment to

living as a respectable member of the world outside. These are just a few of the experimental ventures which reflect the spirit currently pervading the field of juvenile delinquency.

Prediction and Prevention

Treatment and control of juvenile delinquents is designed not only to prevent recidivism, but also to reduce the number of first offenses. Since delinquency is preceded by childhood, a considerable amount of time is theoretically available for prevention. These efforts are of two sorts: first, identification and treatment designed to curb potential delinquents; and, second, community action programs designed to change those aspects of an environment which are conducive to delinquency. In a preventive program geared to individuals, it is necessary to identify the predelinquent and to institute treatment before he has run afoul of the law.

Prediction Tools

The prediction tables developed by Sheldon and Eleanor Glueck have aroused a good deal of public and professional interest. In their original study 500 delinquents from two correctional schools in Massachusetts were matched with nondelinquents in age, intelligence, racial origin, and socioeconomic level. Three prediction tables were used. One was based on five factors of family and social background; the second was based on five traits of underlying character structure, as determined by Rorschach tests; and the third was based on five traits of personality and temperament, as derived from psychiatric interviews. The authors, who were interested primarily in the early identification of potential delinquents, selected factors which were applicable to pre-school children. These, of course, had largely to do with family relationships. The five factors based on the family and social background were therefore weighted, and the authors arrived at a "social prediction score" which indicated the probability that a given child would commit a crime *(1950)*.

The KD Proneness Scale, another attempt to predict delinquency, was developed by Kvaraceus. The child responds to 75 multiple-choice questions which embody points of difference between known delinquents and children considered nondelinquent. The differences are personality differences, differences in home and family background, and differences in school experiences. A check list of 70 items, covering the same areas, is also filled out by a teacher or some other adult who knows the child well *(1953, 1955)*.

Validation of Prediction

The Gluecks were hopeful that "with the use of such devices, it ought to be possible to determine, at the point of school entrance, even before the display of most of the overt symptoms of what appears to be a tendency to persistent antisocial behavior, which children are probably headed in the direction of delinquency."* After reviewing retrospective studies and applying the Social Prediction Tables to known delinquents, Eleanor Glueck concluded that 9 out of 10 could have been correctly identified at the age of six *(1960)*. In a reexamination of the Glueck data, E. Herzog stated that "there seems good evidence that the majority of those who become delinquent will be among those assigned a high score for probable delinquency by this method. The question still to be answered is whether the majority of those assigned a high probability score will in fact

*Quoted from E. Glueck and S. Glueck *Delinquents in the Making* (New York: Harper & Row Publishers) 1952, p. 203. Reproduced by permission.

become delinquent" *(1960, p. 3)*. She concludes with the following summary of evidence:

1. Certain measures can identify *groups* of children from whom the majority of future delinquents are likely to come.
2. In doing so, these measures highlight conditions that are damaging to all children.
3. These measures are not capable of identifying individual "pre-delinquents" within the more vulnerable groups. *(1960, p. 1.)*

The Glueck Social Prediction Tables have since undergone various revisions. Maude Craig and Selma Glick followed 240 boys of 5½ to 6½ until they reached 17. They had applied the original Glueck table to the boys at the beginning of the study, and concluded that the table tended to overpredict delinquency *(1963)*. They then limited the Glueck table to the following three factors, which they found to be the most accurate and reliable:

1. *Discipline by the Father:*

. . . the fathers were generally more inclined than the mothers to be overstrict with the boys. . . . The most marked difference between the disciplinary practices of the parents of the delinquents and those of the non-delinquents is found in the considerably greater resort of the former to physical punishment.*

2. *Supervision by the Mother:*

The delinquent boys were certainly victims of a far greater laxity on the part of their mothers than the [control group], for in six of ten instances among the delinquents, as compared with one in ten among the non-delinquents, they paid little attention to the boys' misbehavior . . . A considerably greater portion of the mothers of the delinquents than of the non-delinquents were inconsistent in their disciplinary practices, swinging erratically

*Glueck and Glueck, *op. cit.*, pp. 66–67.

from laxity to over-strictness without apparent reason.[*]

In an analysis of the Cambridge-Somerville Youth Study data *(1959)*, the McCords emphasized the special importance of consistency. Discussing the development of conscience, they state: ". . . affection establishes the necessary base; the parents' model furnishes the content of conscience, and consistency insures the internalization of this content" *(1959, p. 200)*. They suggest that in terms of teaching conforming behavior, "consistency can, apparently, even be a substitute for affection" *(p. 199)*. Similar conclusions were also reached in the previously mentioned Bandura-Walters study.

3. *Cohesiveness of Family:*

A far lower proportion of such families than those of non-delinquents evinced strong affectional ties among the members, shared joint interests, took pride in their homes, and felt themselves to be "one for all and all for one."[**]

With these three factors only, Craig and Glick were able to rate 239 of their 240 subjects as having been probable, possible, or unlikely future delinquents. They found that such ratings would have been 85 per cent accurate in predicting delinquency (4 out of 27 where delinquency would have been predicted did not become delinquent) and 96 per cent accurate in predicting non-delinquency (7 out of 193 whose non-delinquency would have been predicted later proved to be delinquent). The 19 "possible" delinquents were divided about evenly between delinquency and nondelinquency.

This ten-year study demonstrates that reliable prediction can be based on social and family factors rather than on individual personality. The authors concluded that the findings "show the justification and need for eradicating the family pathology, and enriching family life as a primary step in the prevention of delinquency" *(1963, p. 261)*.

Practical Application of Prediction Measures

There is, nevertheless, some question as to the practicality of the prediction tables. First, social factors are not readily observable. Given a group of children entering kindergarten in a crowded urban school, which families should be investigated? And how is the information to be obtained? One can hardly walk once into a child's home and expect to walk out with reliable data. A trained person would have to spend considerable time establishing the ratings. Assuming it done, however, we are still left with the problem of finding the means of "eradicating family pathology and enriching family life." It is precisely in such families that the parents are most resistant to help, most distrustful of authority, and least reliable. It would be difficult to intervene effectively, short of removing the children from their families. There is no way of forcing cooperation when one is dealing with future contingencies.

Individual Programs

Various efforts have been made to provide intensive casework services for potentially delinquent children and their families. These are usually special neighborhood units organized by existing agencies to make services more accessible to families in need.

The best-known example of such a program is the Cambridge-Somerville Youth Study. For approximately eight years *(1937 to 1945)*, an effort was made to prevent delinquency in a group of 325 underprivileged boys between the ages of six and ten, by guidance, counseling, and therapy. Each boy was matched with a control subject, and assigned to one of ten counselors.

---

[*]Glueck and Glueck, *op. cit.*, p. 66
[**]Glueck and Glueck, *op. cit.*, p. 54.

Therapy ranged from a friendly big-brother type of relationship to formal interviews such as are conducted in child guidance clinics. In most cases, treatment consisted of talks between the family and the counselor, trips for the children, and whatever medical, dental, or welfare assistance was required. Some counselors tutored the boys, others provided links with welfare and family agencies. The boys and their families were generally encouraged to attend church. Each counselor did whatever he thought would be best, with the result that there was considerable variety in the efforts made.

H. Witmer and E. Powers *(1951)* and H. L. Teuber and Powers *(1953)* reported follow-up evaluations. Three years after treatment was terminated, Powers secured official police and court records, and found that as many treated boys as control subjects had delinquency records. A few more controls than treated boys had committed serious crimes, but the difference was slight. Although the guidance and the other services had not proved effective with the boys who became chronic delinquents, the authors felt that some favorable results had been achieved with boys who had sought the friendship of adults, thus giving the counselor an opportunity to offset parental inadequacies *(Witmer and Powers, 1951)*.

In 1955, William McCord, J. McCord, and J. K. Zola resumed the follow-up of these same boys, and published a new analysis of certain data. Within the experimental group itself, the 12 boys who had received "intensive" treatment (i.e., treatment involving an intimate relationship between boy and counselor during two years of weekly contact) were each matched with another boy of similar parentage, discipline, personality, and home atmosphere, who had received more general, impersonal treatment. Only 6 of the 12 boys receiving intensive treatment had committed a crime, as compared with 11 of the 12 matched subjects. The number of subjects involved is too small to permit generalization, although the difference is statistically significant: $X^2 = 3.9$; d.f. $= 1$; $p < .05$. Still these results buttress the theory that a personal relationship (the transference described by Aichhorn) is crucial *(p. 39)*. Intermittent contacts, however friendly, have little influence on the delinquent personality.

Community Action Programs

Community programs created in an effort to prevent delinquency include:

1. *Organized recreational activities.* Perhaps the earliest large-scale preventive efforts were supervised recreational programs (e.g., the Police Athletic League, the Boys' Clubs, city-financed playgrounds, and YMCA's).

2. *Detached worker service.* These programs attempt to redirect the aggressive or delinquent behavior of members of adolescent clubs and groups by providing them with a leader who is a skilled social group worker or recreation leader. The worker goes to the gang rather than waiting for the individual youngster to voluntarily leave the group and join existing programs.

3. *Neighborhood centers.* Settlement houses (e.g., New York's Henry Street Settlement House) stand somewhere between organized recreational activities and detached worker service. They provide the physical locale and professional staff for programs which include delinquency prevention among their many goals.

4. *Parent education programs.* Various agencies, including settlement houses, organize groups of parents for discussion of a wide range of subjects related to child rearing, family life, and community problems that contribute directly or indirectly to delinquency.

5. *Youth training programs.* Adolescents who have left school are given training in good work habits, and guided into jobs with employers who are cooperating with the delinquency prevention program. There are also special education programs to encourage dropouts to return to school for further training and education.

6. *Area projects.* The area project approach

is an attempt to improve the environment through the efforts of adults living in such neighborhoods, supplemented by professional help *(Konopka, 1959; Kobrin, 1959)*. The enactment of federal legislation for delinquency prevention and control stimulated a variety of such community projects. For example, Community Action for Youth in Cleveland included pre-school nurseries, services for teen-age mothers and day care for their children, tutoring of school children, employment training programs for high school dropouts, work with small groups of pre-adolescent boys, summer schools, and other projects within the school system.

Although a discussion of delinquency customarily concludes with a plea for more study and research, this author holds the contrary opinion. Delinquency is no longer a mystery, and a good deal is known about preventing it. But the rights of parents are still jealously guarded and, without their cooperation, little can be done. Unfortunately, the parents least interested in their children are also those least interested in the intervention of some outside authority. The taking of effective action is further complicated by the division of public opinion over whether juvenile offenders should be punished or treated. Too many people feel that the psychological approach to juvenile delinquency will only result in mollycoddling the offender and speeding the day when society's barricade against crime will no longer stand. Stern punishment is still viewed by some as the only solution for badness, despite overwhelming evidence to the contrary.

References for Chapter 12
Books and Articles

Aichhorn, August, *Wayward Youth*. New York: The Viking Press, Inc., 1935.

Bandura, Albert and Richard H. Walters, *Adolescent Aggression*. New York: The Ronald Press Company, 1959.

Bennett, Ivy, *Delinquent and Neurotic Children: A Comparative Study*. London: Tavistock Publications, 1960.

Bloch, Herbert A. and Frank T. Flynn, *Delinquency*. New York: Random House, 1956.

———, and Arthur Niederhoffer, *The Gang: A Study in Adolescent Behavior*. New York: Philosophical Library, Inc., 1958.

Bordua, D. J., "Delinquent Subcultures: Sociological Interpretations of Gang Delinquency," *Annals of the American Academy of Political and Social Science*, No. 338 (November, 1961), 119–36.

———, "Sociological Theories and Their Implications for Juvenile Delinquency," *A Report of the Children's Bureau Conference*, 1960.

Bowlby, J., *Forty-four Juvenile Thieves: Their Characters and Home Life*. London: Bailliere, Tindall & Cox, Ltd., 1944.

Carr, Lowell Juilliard, *Delinquency Control*, Revised Edition. New York: Harper & Row, Publishers, 1950.

Carek, D. J., W. S. Hendrickson, and D. J. Holmes, "Delinquency Addiction in Parents," *Archives of General Psychiatry*, IV (1961), 51–56.

Cary, Lee J., "Classifying Work Camps for Young Offenders," *Crime and Delinquency*, X (1964), 167–71.

Cleckley, H., *The Mask of Sanity*. St. Louis: The C. V. Mosby Company, 1941.

Cloward, Richard and Lloyd E. Ohlin, *Delinquency and Opportunity, A Theory of Delinquent Gangs*. New York: Free Press of Glencoe, 1960.

Cohen, Albert K. "Sociological Research in Juvenile Delinquency," *American Journal of Orthopsychiatry*, XXVII (1957), 781–88.

———, *Delinquent Boys: The Culture of the Gang*. New York: The Free Press of Glencoe, 1955.

Craig, Maude M. and Selma J. Glick. "Ten Years Experience with the Glueck Social Prediction Table," *Crime and Delinquency*, IX (1963), 249–61.

Davidoff, E. and E. Noetzel, *The Child Guidance Approach to Juvenile Delinquency*. New York: Child Care Publications, 1951.

Diamond, B. L., "Identification and the Sociopathic Personality," *Archives of Criminal Psychodynamics*, Special Psychopath Issue (1961), 456–65.

Durkheim, Emile, *Suicide: A Study of Sociology*, ed. George Simpson, trans. J. A. Spaulding and George Simpson. New York: The Free Press of Glencoe, 1951.

Eissler, K. R., "Some Problems of Delinquency," in *Searchlights on Delinquency*, K. R. Eissler, ed., 2nd Edition. New York:

International Universities Press, Inc., 1955.

Freud, Sigmund, *Family Romances* (1909), Standard Edition, Vol. IX, ed. and trans. by James Strachey. London: The Hogarth Press, Ltd., 1959.

———, *Some Character Types Met within Psychoanalytic Work: (III) Criminals from a Sense of Guilt* (1916), Standard Edition, Vol. XIV, ed. and trans. by James Strachey. London: The Hogarth Press, Ltd., 1957.

Friedlander, Kate, *The Psychoanalytic Approach to Juvenile Delinquency.* New York: International Universities Press, Inc., 1947.

Gibbens, T. C. N., *Psychiatric Studies of Borstal Lads.* London: Oxford University Press, 1966 b.

———, *Trends in Juvenile Delinquency.* Geneva: World Health Organization, 1961 a.

Glueck, E., "Efforts to Identify Delinquents," *Federal Probation,* XXIV, No. 2 (1960), 49–56.

Glueck, S. and E. Glueck, *Delinquents in the Making.* New York: Harper & Row, Publishers, 1952.

———, *Juvenile Delinquents Grown Up.* New York: The Commonwealth Fund, 1940.

———, *One Thousand Juvenile Delinquents.* Cambridge, Mass.: Harvard University Press, 1934.

———, *Physique and Delinquency.* New York: Harper & Row, Publishers, 1956.

———, *Predicting Delinquency and Crime.* Cambridge, Mass.: Harvard University Press, 1959.

———, *Unraveling Juvenile Delinquency.* New York: The Commonwealth Fund, 1950.

Herzog, E., "Identifying Potential Delinquents," *Juvenile Delinquency, Facts and Facets,* Vol. V. Washington, D.C.: United States Department of Health, Education and Welfare, Children's Bureau, 1960.

Jenkins, R. L., "Motivation and Frustration in Delinquency," *American Journal of Orthopsychiatry,* XXVII (1957), 528–38.

———, and Sylvia Glickman, "Patterns of Personality Organization among Delinquents," *The Nervous Child,* VI (1947), 329–39.

Johnson, Adelaide, "Sanctions for Super-ego Lacunae of Adolescents" (1947), in K. R. Eissler, ed., *Searchlights on Delinquency.* New York: International Universities Press, Inc., 1949.

Kardiner, A. and L. Ovesey, *The Mark of Oppression.* New York: W. W. Norton & Company, Inc., 1951.

Kaufman, I., L. W. Heims, and D. E. Reiser, "A Re-evaluation of the Psychodynamics of Fire-Setting," *American Journal of Orthopsychiatry,* XXXI (1961), 123–37.

Kennedy, Robert F., "Half-way Houses Pay Off," *Crime and Delinquency,* X (1964), 1–7.

Kobrin, S., "The Chicago Area Project: A 25 Year Assessment," *Annals of the American Academy of Political and Social Science,* No. 322 (1959), 19–29.

Konopka, G., "Coordination of Services as a Means of Delinquency Prevention," *Ann. Amer. Acad. Pol. Soc. Sci.,* No. 322 (1959), 30–37.

Krueger, Gladys M., "Survey of Probation Officers, 1959," *Juvenile Delinquency, Facts and Facets,* Vol. 15. Washington, D.C.: United States Department of Health, Education and Welfare, Children's Bureau, 1960.

Kvaraceus, W. C., "Prediction Studies of Delinquent Behavior," *Personnel and Guidance Journal,* 34 (November, 1955), 147–49.

———, *KD Proneness Scale and Checklist.* New York: Harcourt, Brace & World, Inc., 1953.

———, and Walter B. Miller, *Delinquent Behavior, Culture and the Individual.* Washington, D.C.: National Education Association 1959.

Lombroso, C., *Crime: Its Causes and Remedies,* trans. H. P. Horton. Boston: Little, Brown & Co., 1911.

Louttit, C. M., *Clinical Psychology of Exceptional Children,* 3rd Edition. New York: Harper & Row, Publishers, 1957.

Lowrey, Lawson G., "Delinquent and Criminal Personalities," in J. McV. Hunt, *Personality and the Behavior Disorders,* Vol. II. New York: The Ronald Press Company, 1944.

McCord, William, J. McCord, and J. K. Zola, *Origins of Crime.* New York: Columbia University Press, 1959.

McCorkle, L. W., Albert Elias, and F. L. Bixby, *The Highfields Story.* New York: Holt, Rinehart & Winston, Inc., 1958.

Mannheim, H., *Social Aspects of Crime in England between Wars.* London: George Allen & Unwin, 1940.

Merton, R. K., *Social Theory and Social Structure,* Revised & Enlarged Edition. New York: The Free Press of Glencoe, 1957.

Meyer, Adolf, "Arrest of Development in Adolescence," *Proceedings of the National Education Association,* 1903, p. 813.

Miller, W. B., "Lower-Class Culture as a

Generating Milieu of Gang Delinquency," *Journal of Social Issues*, XIV, No. 3, (1958), 5–19.

Mohr, Peter, "Die Forensische Bedeutung der Psychopathen," *Schweizer Archiv für Neurologie und Psychiatrie*, LX (1947), 244–268. Quoted in Wm. McCord and Joan McCord, *Psychopathy and Delinquency* (New York: Grune & Stratton, Inc., 1956).

Peck, H., "Delinquency: A Laboratory for Public Health Psychiatry," *American Journal of Orthopsychiatry*, XXVIII (1958), 134–46.

———, et al., "A New Pattern for Mental Health Services in a Children's Court," Round Table. *American Journal of Orthopsychiatry*, XXV (1955), 1–50.

Perlman, I. R., "Reporting Juvenile Delinquency," *National Probation and Parole Association Journal*, III (1957), 242–49.

———, *Statistical Aspects of Antisocial Behavior of the Minor in the United States*. Children's Bureau for the United States Report to the Twelfth Pan-American Child Congress, Buenos Aires, Argentina, December, 1963.

Prichard, J. C., *A Treatise on Insanity and Other Disorders Affecting the Mind*. London: Sherwood, Gilbert, and Piper, 1835.

Radzinowicz, L., *Sexual Offenders*. Cambridge, Mass.: Harvard University Press, 1957.

Redl, Fritz and David Wineman, *The Aggressive Child*. New York: The Free Press of Glencoe, 1957.

———, *Children Who Hate*. New York: The Free Press of Glencoe, 1951.

Roucek, J. S., *Juvenile Delinquency*. New York: Philosophical Library, Inc., 1958.

Rush, Benjamin, *Medical Inquiries and Observations upon the Diseases of the Mind*, 3rd Edition. Philadelphia: J. Grigg, 1827.

Russell, Bernard, "Current Training Needs in the Field of Juvenile Delinquency," *Juvenile Delinquency, Facts and Facets*, Vol. VIII. Washington, D. C.: United States Department of Health, Education and Welfare, Children's Bureau, 1960.

Rexford, E. N., "Anti-social Young Children and their Families," in L. Jessner and E. Pavenstedt, eds., *Dynamic Psychopathology of Children*. New York: Grune & Stratton, Inc., 1959.

Shaw, C. R. and H. D. McKay, *Juvenile Delinquency and Urban Areas*. Chicago:

University of Chicago Press, 1942.

Sheldon, W. H., *Varieties of Delinquent Youth*. New York: Harper & Row, Publishers, 1949.

Sheridan, W. H., "Juvenile Court Intake," *Journal of Family Law*, University of Louisville School of Law, II, No. 2 (1962), 139–56.

Stark, Heman G., "A Substitute for Institutionalization of Serious Delinquents," California Youth Authority Experiment, *Crime and Delinquency*, IX (1963), 242–48.

Stranahan, Marion, Cecile Schwartzman, and Edith Atkin, "Group Treatment for Emotionally Disturbed and Potentially Delinquent Boys and Girls," *American Journal of Orthopsychiatry*, XXVII (1957), 518–28.

Tanner, J. M., *Growth at Adolescence*. Springfield, Ill.: Charles C Thomas, 1955.

Teuber, H. L. and E. Powers, "Evaluating Therapy in a Delinquent Prevention Program," in *Psychiatric Treatment*, Vol. XXI, Proceedings of the Association for Research in Nervous and Mental Diseases. Baltimore: The Williams & Wilkins Co., 1953.

Thorne, Frederick C., "Etiological Studies of Psychopathic Personality: The Ego-Inflated, Defectively Conditoned Type," *Journal of Consulting Psychology*, XI (1947), 299–310.

Tunley, Roul, *Kids, Crime and Chaos: A World Report on Juvenile Delinquency*. New York: Dell Publishing Co., Inc., 1964.

Wallinga, Jack V., "The Probation Officer's Role in Psychiatric Cases," *Journal of Criminal Law, Criminology, and Police Science*, L (1959), 364–67.

Wheway, Jane P., "Intelligence and Delinquency," *Durham Research Review*, II (1958), 208–14.

Witmer, H. and E. Powers, *An Experiment in the Prevention of Delinquency: The Cambridge-Somerville Youth Study*. New York: Columbia University Press, 1951.

———, and E. Tufts, *The Effectiveness of Delinquency Prevention Programs*. Washington, D. C.: United States Department of Health, Education and Welfare, Children's Bureau, 1954.

Zuckerman, Stanley B., "The Clinical Psychologist in the Juvenile Court and Youth Authority Program," in Eli A. Rubinstein and Maurice Lorr, eds., *Survey of Clinical Practice in Psychology*. New York: International Universities Press, Inc., 1954.

American Orthopsychiatric Association Symposia

"The Psychopathic Delinquent Child," Round Table, 1949, Karpman, B., *et al.*, *American Journal of Orthopsychiatry*, XX (1950), 223–65.

"Psychopathic Behavior in Infants and Children: A Critical Survey of the Existing Concepts," Round Table, 1950, Karpman, B., *et al.*, *American Journal of Orthopsychiatry*, XXI (1951), 223–72.

"A Differential Study of Psychopathic Behavior in Infants and Children," Round Table, 1951, Karpman, B., *et al.*, *American Journal of Orthopsychiatry*, XXII (1952), 223–67.

"Psychodynamics of Child Delinquency," Round Table, 1952, Karpman, B., *et al.*, *American Journal of Orthopsychiatry*, (1953), 1–69.

"Antisocial Acting Out: Symposium, 1954," Lippman, H., *et al.*, *American Journal of Orthopsychiatry*, XXIV (1954), 667–96.

"Psychodynamics of Child Delinquency: Further Contributions," Round Table, 1953, Karpman, B., *et al.*, *American Journal of Orthopsychiatry*, XXV (1955), 238–82.

Official Reports

Annual Report for 1961: The Juvenile Court of Cuyahoga County. Cleveland: 1962.

Annual Report for 1962: The Juvenile Court of Cuyahoga County. Cleveland: 1963.

Federal Bureau of Investigation Uniform Crime Report, 1962. Washington, D.C.: United States Department of Justice, 1963.

Federal Bureau of Investigation Uniform Crime Report, 1963. Washington, D.C.: United States Department of Justice, 1964.

Institutions Serving Delinquent Children: Guides and Goals. Washington, D.C.: United States Department of Health, Education and Welfare, Children's Bureau, 1957.

Juvenile Court Statistics, 1963. Children's Bureau Statistical Series No. 79. Washington, D.C.: United States Department of Health, Education and Welfare, Children's Bureau, 1964.

Eighth Report, Children's Department. London, 1961.

Report to the Congress on Juvenile Delinquency. Washington, D.C.: United States Department of Health, Education and Welfare, Children's Bureau and the National Institute of Mental Health, 1960.

"Role of the Federal Government in Combating the Juvenile Delinquency Problem," *Hearings before the Subcommittee to Investigate Juvenile Delinquency of the Committee of the Judiciary.* United States Senate, 87th Congress, Part 9. Washington, D.C.: United States Government Printing Office, 1961.

Standards for Specialized Courts Dealing with Children. Washington, D.C.: United States Department of Health, Education and Welfare, Children's Bureau, 1954.

Statistics on Public Institutions for Delinquent Children, 1963. Children's Bureau Statistical Series No. 78. Washington, D.C.: United States Department of Health, Education and Welfare, Children's Bureau, 1964.

13

MIND AND BODY

Our chapter title is borrowed from Flanders Dunbar, who used it to describe the approach to physical illness which she named "psychosomatic medicine" (1947). The chapter material is divided into two major parts: one dealing with the emotional effects of physical defects or illnesses and one dealing with the emotional causes of somatic symptoms, particularly of the psychosomatic diseases of childhood. This division may suggest that one always knows which came first, the emotion or the illness, but this is not so; it is more of a question of the relative weighting of the two factors. The most organic illness often has a precipitating psychological factor; psychogenic factors have been reported even for the common cold (Despert, 1944; Saul, 1938). Conversely, there is always a significant somatic predisposition to psychosomatic illnesses, perhaps most obvious in the allergic sensitivity which underlies eczema and asthma.

Some topics which theoretically might have been discussed in this chapter are covered elsewhere. For example, anorexia nervosa, obesity, chronic constipation, fecal impaction, and megacolon, are discussed in Chapter 6. Enuresis is occasionally classified as a psychosomatic illness, although the logical basis for such categorization seems weak. The psychological conse-

quences of brain lesions and neurological disorders have been touched on in Chapters 7, 8, and 9. Two common neurological disorders, epilepsy and cerebral palsy, may appear in a symptom complex, associated with mental retardation or hyperactivity and perceptual disturbances; on the other hand, they are sometimes only somatic. To the extent that cerebral palsy is associated with mental retardation, 40 per cent of the time, according to Greenbaum and Buehler (1960); 55 per cent, according to Hohman and Freedheim (1958), it is covered in Chapter 8. Its orthopedic aspects are included in the discussion of other orthopedic disabilities in this chapter.

Part I:

Emotional Reactions to Somatic Events

The Role of Transitory Physical Illness

Even the best cared for and healthiest children become physically ill. At such times, the child also becomes susceptible to thoughts and feelings which are associated with his illness. In the following discussion of the emotional side-effects of transitory illness, we do not mean to convey the impression that a child is emotionally scarred for life from a bout with flu, mumps, or whatever, for the emotional sequelae usually fade away.

The child's illness or injury is superimposed on a psychological substrate consisting of his concern about the integrity of his body, his fantasies, and his inability to verbalize. It thus acquires meanings above and beyond the medical reality and arouses strong feelings around any combination of the following facets of illness:

1. Fear of the physical symptoms of the illness.
2. Fear of pain.
3. Reactions to the change in the emotional climate.
4. Reactions to nursing and treatment.
5. Speculation about the cause of the illness.

Fear of Physical Symptoms of the Illness. It is easy to observe the anxiety which children feel about such out-of-control symptoms as vomiting and diarrhea. Not only are these symptoms uncomfortable, but children are also concerned about the messiness and the possibility of being scolded for it—especially younger children, whose toilet training is sufficiently recent that they can recall being censured for messes for which they felt no more responsibility than for the diarrhea. Physical changes (e.g., swellings, discolorations, or skin eruptions) worry the slightly older child, who fears that his body will change even more drastically or that it will never return to normal. The child's problem is further complicated by his reluctance to put his worst fears into words, lest he thereby make them come true. The result is that he is often left without the reassurance which one could freely offer him if one but knew what he feared.

Fear of Pain. Sensitivity to pain differs at different times and in different children. The experience of pain depends a good deal on the content in which it occurs and the child's interpretation of the event. A slight hurt inflicted by another child or adult is often felt much more grievously than a self-inflicted one, because the injury from the other person is viewed as an aggressive attack. The child is angry as well as hurt, and he may also be anxious about a repetition of the attack. In any event, he may fear permanent damage—slight bleeding may give him the idea that all the blood will ooze out of his body, a bruised limb may seem broken, and so on. Anxiety derived from fantasy is at its height in the child of three to seven, whose every wound must be tenderly bandaged.

Reactions to the Change in Emotional Climate. Anna Freud points out that there are few parents who do not, imperceptibly or grossly, change their own attitude toward the child when he is ill (1952). Most parents become more indulgent providing extra attention, extending special privileges, offering presents and treats and sometimes allowing the child to sleep with them so that they can keep close watch. There are a few parents who react in the opposite way, however. Because of their own anxiety about illness, they are faintly repelled and even withdraw from the child, waiting for nature to take its course. The indulged child may find it hard to relinquish the secondary gains of illness; the neglected one may feel that he has displeased his parents and have an obscure sense of guilt about having been sick.

Reactions to Nursing and Treatment. When illness is protracted or requires hospitalization, the child's body must be inspected and handled in a number of unusual ways. The really sick child is dressed, undressed, fed, cleaned, washed, and helped to urinate and defecate; in short, he is treated like a baby. His nakedness is exposed to nurse and doctor, a situation which embarrasses most hospitalized adults, as well as most children, but the child's modesty is less respected.

Georges Simenon in his novel, *The Bells of Bicetre*, gives a vivid picture of the thoughts, feelings, and emotions of a man recovering from a stroke. His doctors complain about his lack of trust, his withdrawal, and refusal to help himself in the recovery period *(1963, 1965)*. Children, as well as adults, react differently to the passivity and regression inherent in being nursed. For children, the mastery of self-feeding, going to the toilet alone, independent washing and dressing, and so forth, are newly acquired steps in ego development *(Anna Freud, 1952)*. The loss of these abilities, even though temporary, means an equivalent loss in ego control, a pulling back toward an earlier and more passive phase. Children who have built up strong defenses against their passive tendencies resist this enforced regression and are difficult to care for; others lapse back without any fight *(1952)*. Many mothers report that, after an illness, their young children have to be retrained in their toilet habits, weaned once more from spoon feeding, or encouraged not to cling.

Medication also poses a problem. The child's fear of shots goes beyond the pain involved and into the realm of fantasy. Some children fear that the needle will break and remain forever stuck in their skin, some fear it will make a hole and let out all their vital juices. The needle looks very long and suspiciously like a dagger with all the potentials of a dangerous weapon. It it not what actually happens that frightens the children; it is their fear of what *might* happen.

Swallowing is sometimes difficult for the sick child, but if the mother has been told to "force fluids" (to avoid dehydration), she will use any tactic, frightening or forceful, to accomplish this end in order to ensure her child getting well. During convalescence the mother may find herself urging unwelcome food on a child. Unfortunately, the ensuing conflict may make even a minor illness the starting point of a prolonged eating difficulty. Enemas may be prescribed or catheterization may be indicated. These events may be traumatic to the child; he may be too sick or frightened to resist, but he experiences them as attacks on his body.

Speculations about the Cause of the Illness. As we have mentioned before, children believe that everything occurs for a reason. Someone made it happen. The crucial question is, Who is the guilty party?

Young children tend to attribute their illness to their all-powerful parents; older children are more likely to blame themselves. Parents often use the threat of illness or injury as the reason for their demands or prohibitions. The 1937 Stanford-Binet includes this question for 11-year-olds: "Give two reasons why children should obey their parents," and one of the most common is, "So you won't get hurt or sick." They certainly can also believe the converse—that when they do become sick or hurt, it is because they did not obey their parents or because their parents did not act to prevent the calamity. The child may reveal his suspicion that his parents are responsible by being irritable with them, or he may show that he holds himself responsible by behaving very well.

The mysteriousness of germs, what they look like and where they come from, is yet another source of anxiety. Since germs are linked with dirt, the ill child may betray his anxiety by a spurt of excessive cleanliness which usually abates with the reassurance of a period of good health.

Emotional Effects of Illness

Although the period of emotional convalescence could probably be aided and abetted with some awareness of the psychological factors involved, there is no denying that most children recover from transitory illnesses without obvious emotional ill effects. There is, however, some evidence to suggest that there may be sequelae of a more lasting nature than appears on the surface. The researches of Lillian Wagenheim suggest that contraction of the usual childhood diseases before the age of five contributes to IQ variability and to learning problems. For example, she found a significant relationship between early contraction of such diseases as measles, chicken pox, German measles, and mumps and later reading achievement in boys. She found that the most critical age is two years, but did not find any clear reason for this relationship. It is possible that there is organic involvement of the brain, although neurological complications are thought to occur in only 1 per cent of persons contracting measles, for instance. But Wagenheim proposes the alternative hypothesis that the illness is viewed as a punishment for hostile feelings. Around two or three, the child is first aware of his aggressive feelings and the unfortunate consequences which result from carrying them into action. He can easily link illness with badness, and because of the limitations in the child's language and thought, the fantasy is difficult to correct *(1954, 1959)*. Such studies need replication; if the findings are confirmed, further exploration would be in order to define the nature of the cause and effect relationships.

The factors which contribute to the emotional side-effects of transitory illness are even more cogent in serious illness. Parental anxiety is more intense; nursing is complicated and prolonged; and fears of possible long-range physical effects are more realistic. In addition, most of the serious illnesses have unique features regarding causation, permanent effects, and medical care which may well create psychological complications. The discussion which follows is intended to be representative rather than inclusive.

Juvenile diabetes. Diabetes has been discussed from the psychological standpoint perhaps more than any other disease, excluding those considered psychosomatic. The major concerns have been: (1) the relationship between the emotions and the medical course of the diabetes; and (2) emotional reactions to the management of the illness *(Falstein and Judas, 1955)*.

Many problems attend dietary restrictions and the daily injections of insulin. It is usually the mother who must withhold the prohibited foods and inflict the pain, and this places an extra strain on her relationship with the child. One can readily appreciate the difficulty of controlling without arousing resentment or apprehensive passivity. And, if the diabetes is out of control because too much sugar or too much insulin has been given, the mother cannot escape a feeling of guilt. The child, too, may feel guilty. The cause of the illness is usually obscure to him since it cannot be seen. Many children relate it to oral excesses, "eating too many sweets," something which all children are warned against. Other children may relate the illness to genital functioning, since frequency of urination and enuresis are common early symptoms and the urine is analyzed so often. In the last decade or so, there has been an increasing awareness of the need to explain the illness to the children, to minimize their fantasies and to engage their intelligent cooperation rather than their passive submission. There has also been a tendency to relax the earlier rigidity of dietary control.

One study of the intelligence of diabetic children is especially interesting in the light of Wagenheim's findings. Marvin Ack, Irving Miller, and William Weil found a significant negative difference in the Stanford-Binet Intelligence Scale scores of diabetics, as compared with their siblings, but only in children who acquired the disease before they were five. These investigators suggested two explanations, one is physiological: "It does not seem unreasonable that the young diabetic may have some loss of IQ as a result of early metabolic disturbances that do not produce damage in later childhood *(1961, p. 769)*. Their alternative theory concerns the impact of a chronic illness on the immature ego. The authors propose that the youngster suffers a disruption of his self-image; hence:

. . . the child feels himself damaged, different and worthless, and this attitude becomes translated into feelings of inadequacy in intellectual endeavors. It also seems that the diabetes disrupts the normal growth of independence, both mental and physical, so that the child does not feel capable of adequate, independent functioning. *(1961, p. 769.)*

Another study, of children with rheumatic fever, confirmed the importance of the age of onset. Richard Reinhart also found that children who incurred this illness before six had IQ's slightly, but significantly below their siblings. Physiological explanations seemed less likely in the case of rheumatic fever and he postulated a relationship with anxiety *(1963)*.

Rheumatic Fever. The psychological aspects of *rheumatic fever* are quite different from diabetes. Recovery is usually complete, but the possibility of permanent heart damage looms large during the acute phase of the illness. Reinhart found that children who had contracted rheumatic fever early showed more than normal anxiety (on the Sarason Anxiety Scales) some years later *(1965)*. I. M. Josselyn, Albert Simon, and E. Eells found that anxiety in children convalescing from rheumatic fever was of considerable psychological and physiological importance. The heart changes which accompany anxiety are easily confused by the child with the heart damage he fears, and it is possible that anxiety places additional strain on the already damaged heart. Rest and restriction of action is

much less effective if the child is tormented by anxious fantasies which are increased, if anything, by inactivity *(1955)*. Essentially the same problem exists for children with congenital heart conditions. Again, doctors now allow much more freedom, relying on the child's natural fatigue to restrict him rather than on arbitrarily imposed rules and regulations.

Hemophilia. William Browne, Mary Mally, and Ruth Kane reported on hemophiliacs who frequently developed hemorrhages while exposed to emotionally stressful situations. They concluded that for the 28 boys in their group, physical trauma accounted for only a minority of the bleeding episodes, and that most episodes appeared to be associated with the boy's anticipation of increased activity or independence *(1960)*. On the other hand, Ake Mattsson and Samuel Gross observed 35 hemophilic children and after two years concluded that bleeding after physical trauma was far more common than spontaneous bleeding (which might be presumed to be psychogenic). These authors were impressed by the generally good adaptation which their patients and families had made to the illness; only 8 were judged to be poorly adjusted either because of extreme passivity or unnecessary risk-taking behavior. Like many authors, the authors emphasized the relationship between parental acceptance of the disease and the successful adjustment of the child patient *(1966)*. A special complication is the mother's feeling of guilt because of her responsibility for the genetic transmission.

Tuberculosis. Tuberculosis is special in that there are few overt symptoms, even in gravely ill children. The child has a vague, mysterious sense that something is dreadfully wrong, and his isolation can easily give him the impression that the contagion resulted from a lack of cleanliness. Sarah Dubo found a morbid preoccupation with death in all the 25 children she studied *(1950).*

Convulsive disorders. The National Health Education Committee estimated that in 1955 some 1,500,000 persons were afflicted with convulsive disorder, i.e., about 5 children in 1,000. Many more persons have had a single convulsion, usually associated with a high fever in childhood. Although convulsions may be a symptom of organic brain damage, occurring in association with such other symptoms as mental retardation or cerebral palsy, we are considering only idiopathic convulsive disorder, that is, convulsions of unknown origin which are not accompanied by other symptoms.

It had been thought there was an "epileptic personality" characterized by irascibility, impulsiveness, and egocentricity *(Clarke, 1918),* but considerable doubt has recently been cast on this concept *(Deutsch and Wiener, 1948; Tizard, 1962).* The Rorschach has been used extensively to study the personality of epileptics, perhaps because Rorschach himself described a specific epileptic protocol *(1942).* Barbara Tizard reviewed 20 of these studies and observed that in very few was intelligence a controlled variable and that many involved epileptic subjects from institutions. The few well-controlled Rorschach studies yielded contradictory results *(1962).*

Epilepsy has a definite repercussion on the personality, but there does not seem to be any specific clinical picture. A child cannot fail to react to a condition which is socially stigmatizing, strikes out of the blue, causes embarrassing out-of-control behavior (such as wetting), and limits his freedom of action. Some states even now have laws forbidding the marriage of epileptics, and most forbid them to drive automobiles. Between attacks, there is nothing which marks the epileptic as different. Still, even though the attacks may be infrequent or controlled by anticonvulsant medication, the child lives with the knowledge of his susceptibility, which is usually a dark family secret.

There are those who would classify epilepsy as a psychosomatic, rather than a neurological, disorder. In this they concur with Sigmund Freud, who assumed that the epileptic is characterized by preformed organic channels of discharge which are used (thus causing seizures) when normal outlets for emotional tension are inhibited or blocked *(1928, 1961).* This theory accounts for the stimulus (e.g., emotional interference, anxiety-creating situations and tension-producing conditions), but not for the response (i.e., the seizure). Therapy should include both aspects—that is, medication should be given to raise the threshold for the response and counseling should be given to reduce the stimuli. L. Deutsch and L. L. Weiner stated the following objectives of psychotherapeutic treatment of the epileptic child: (1) removing acute emotional disturbance; (2) giving additional support in handling normal difficulties; and (3) reconditioning which enables the child to accept the limitations imposed by his illness while helping him to make the most of his capacities. Unfortunately, the medical and psychotherapeutic approaches are rarely combined, particularly in convulsive disorders.

Most of the few detailed clinical reports of epileptic activity and the sequence of events leading to it have been contributed by Louis Gottschalk *(1953; 1955; 1956).* While he did not deny the existence of neurological factors, Gottschalk found that psychological factors also influenced the form and frequency of the seizures. In his opinion, the *grand mal* had no symbolic significance, though it could be at times precipitated by emotional conflict. This opinion was based on neurological considerations—that is, on the fact that no integrated functioning of the cortex is possible during *grand mal*—as well as on his own clinical data: "A grand mal seizure is a kind of mass reflex which is the end product of a potential series of noxious stresses [trauma, electric shock, drugs, metabolic disturbances, emotional problems] to the organism, but it is not specific to any one kind of stress" *(Gottschalk, 1956, p. 379)*. However, he suggested that:

. . . in less generalized forms of epileptic discharge, such as in psychomotor epilepsy and related automatisms or in certain manifestations of petit mal epilepsy and especially in "psychic equivalent seizures," it is likely that epileptic manifestation may symbolize in microcosmic forms some aspects of the subject's old and recent emotional conflicts. *(1956, p. 379.)*

The ten-year-old boy whom Gottschalk treated suffered psychomotor seizures following frustration and anger. The boy also underwent another kind of spell, which consisted of staring and shaking his arms. He was not aware of any emotion or frustration before the onset of a staring spell, only a compulsion to look through a window screen. The subsequent visual stimulation prompted a loss of consciousness and shaking. Treatment revealed this to be a hysterical conversion phenomenon, remediable by psychotherapy. The symptom complex condensed and symbolized both the peeping which the boy had earlier engaged in, when he tried to discover what his parents were doing in their bedroom, and his guilty fear of his love for his mother and his resentment of his father. The boy was able to report, just before or during a seizure, thoughts and feelings that were highly unacceptable to himself; and, in the course of his communication with the therapist, his seizure was modified. Thus, it became apparent that there was some integrated cortical activity going on which gave these attacks meaning and symbolic significance.

Gottschalk pointed out that other boys, with similar conflicts and psychological mechanisms, do not have seizures. Both the hysterical character disorder and the paroxysmal cerebral functional disorder were necessary to produce the clinical syndrome.

Emotional Implications of Hospitalization and Surgery

Most children are hospitalized at one time or another, but prior to the 1930's, little attention was paid to the emotional effect on the child. Now, although the study, diagnosis, and treatment of the child's physical illness are still the primary concerns of a hospital staff, his emotional needs have also become of interest.

This interest has been stimulated by a number of clinical and experimental studies of illness made by thoughtful pediatricians *(Prugh et al., 1953)*, by analytically oriented child psychiatrists *(Jessner, Blom, and Waldfogel, 1952)*, and by pediatricians trained in child psychiatry *(Senn, 1945)*. In this discussion of hospitalization, we will review only those findings which are unique to the hospital situation.

One of the most complete investigations is a five-year study carried out by Lucie Jessner, Gaston Blom, and Samuel Waldfogel *(1952)*. Their subjects were 143 children who underwent tonsillectomy and adenoidectomy at the Massachusetts Eye and Ear Infirmary. The children and parents were interviewed at the time of admission and observed during the 24-hour period of hospitalization. Sixty-two of the children were given psychological tests *(Rubin, 1951)*. Mothers and children were seen in later interviews (about 40 children were followed for three to four years) and sufficient follow-up material was collected on 136 of the cases to permit classification of the postoperative reaction.

Of the 136, about 20 per cent were classified as having *severe* postoperative reactions, that is, marked or persisting emotional sequelae. The reactions covered the gamut of possible emotional symptoms: eating, sleeping, and speech disturbances; tics and mannerisms; fears; and regressive behavior (e.g., increased dependency, wetting, and soiling). These reactions were evenly distributed in relation to age and sex. The most significant relationship found was that between previous neurotic tendencies and severity of postoperative reaction. The authors felt that a tonsillectomy was not likely to be a permanently harmful experience except for already disturbed children. But they also concluded that a tonsillectomy was an important and stressful experience for each child, activating the basic fears of abandonment, mutilation, and death.

The four main foci of anxiety were: separation from the parents and exposure to the strange hospital surroundings; the anticipation of the narcosis; the operation itself; and the fear of needles. Age was an important determinant of which was uppermost in the child's mind. Anxiety about hospitalization and separation was greatest in the youngest children; the 5 to 10-year-olds worried most about the operation itself; the fear of the anesthesia was greatest in the 10 to 14-year-olds. The young adolescents were particularly frightened by the prospect of losing control under anesthesia. In addition, the authors collected much clinical information regarding the fantasies of the children. These included having a baby or changing sex. Another study, based on psychiatric interviews with six children prior to herniorrhaphy, confirmed the importance of fantasies (*Falstein, Judas, and Mendelsohn, 1957*). A repair of a hernia is even more susceptible of misinterpretation because of its proximity to the genitals and the difficulty in giving a realistic, simple explanation.

Clinical observations have eventuated in recommendations for minimizing the emotional impact of hospitalization and surgery. Proper *preparation* is usually considered most important—many hospitals have booklets for the children and several have been published commercially (*Sever, 1953*). The importance of a thorough, realistic explanation of what the child will experience is professionally acknowledged, although parents often try to spare the child by painting a rosy picture of the hospital. It is hard for parents to realize that their child's anticipatory anxiety will actually help him to assimilate the real experience. The value of anxiety is indicated by the statement of Jessner, Blom, and Waldfogel that "acknowledgement of fear and expression of anxiety in play and talk tended to enhance assimilation" (*1952, p. 168*). Suppression, denial, and overcontrol of fear were observed "to collapse with a bang" in the hospital, and lack of overt anxiety was a poor prognostic sign. Emma Plank gives some excellent details about preparation, emphasizing the importance of play as the child's natural way of working through feelings. She makes the interesting point that some cute solutions actually cloud the situation:

I am not sure about gadgets, like space helmets, that may arouse all sorts of hopeful fantasies in children—only to have them awaken with pain. It seems to me that with these we are using a gimmick to secure a child's cooperation under false pretenses rather than with the child's understanding and trust in our honesty. (*1963, p. 810.*)

Of course, preparation need not include details about the surgery itself or anything which the child will not perceive; for the child, the important facts are what will occur before the operation and what he will see and feel when he awakens.

The second major point in psychological management is the *minimization of the separation anxiety*. This entails unrestricted visiting privileges for the parents, allowing the mother to stay with her young child, and parental participation in ward care. The hospitalized child feels deserted at the very time he is in the most need of maternal support. It is often suggested that the child bring something of his own along, as a tie to home and as a sign of his own identity. Attempts are also made to avoid unnecessary strangeness in the hospital, for instance, by allowing the child to wear some of his own clothing. Boys are sensitive to hospital gowns, which seem to be made for girls and are therefore regarded with suspicion.

The third recommendation is the *provision of special play opportunities,* especially for children hospitalized for longer periods. Constance Impallaria has described the use of social group work and the medium of play to help child patients to understand and withstand the real pain and suffering of hospital procedures. In the group, aided not only by the worker, but by the other children who have similar problems, the child is able to play, act, and talk out his secret anger, fear, and suffering *(1955).*

A fourth recommendation is the *sensitization of hospital personnel* to the emotional aspects of medical care. This has usually been accomplished by some sort of collaboration between the psychiatric and the pediatric staffs, and should intimately involve the nurses. And the fifth area of psychological recommendations deals with *techniques of inducing anesthesia and with medical procedures.*

One indication of the seriousness with which doctors are beginning to view the emotional needs of the hospitalized child is that two doctors, one in England and another in America, have written books on the subject *(Dimock, 1960; Robertson, 1962).* James Robertson is also the author of a 60-minute film entitled, "A Two-Year-Old goes to the Hospital." (Distributed in the United States by New York University.)

A major investigation was carried out by Dane Prugh *et al.,* at the Children's Medical Center in Boston, to evaluate the effectiveness of a psycho-logical program of ward management. The subjects were two groups, of 100 children each, admitted to a medical ward for an average of a week. The control subjects were hospitalized under traditional circumstances; the others were exposed to an "experimental type of ward nursing practice" which permitted more parental visiting and more individualized and supportive attention. Fifty of each group were followed up for six months following discharge.

The experimental group showed a significantly lower percentage of *severe* reactions (14 per cent as compared with 36 per cent in the control group). The authors also found an important relationship between severity of reaction and age. Children of three and less suffered the highest incidence of severe reactions (37 per cent in the experimental group and 50 per cent in the control group). The effect of the experimental program was greatest on the older children: *No* child of six to twelve in the experimental group had a severe reaction, whereas 27 per cent of the control group had severe reactions. The study also confirmed Jessner's findings about the importance of pre-hospital adjustment in the child's capacity to weather the hospital stress. *(Prugh, et al., 1953).*

During the acute phase of their illness, many children show remarkable strength and courage. Parents and nurses are therefore surprised by the unreasonable displays of temper and anxiety which erupt after the pain and realistic danger have passed. The following anecdote illustrates a phobic reaction which did not appear until six months after the traumatic medical experience.

At the age of six, Mark was rushed to a hospital with the possible diagnosis of spinal meningitis. For four days, he was isolated and confined to bed by continuous intravenous injections. For the first two days he was under close surveillance. At two-hour intervals, the staff examined him to see if there was any change in the distribution of a skin rash. Within 48 hours, spinal meningitis was ruled out, and he convalesced until his temperature returned to normal.

Mark's behavior was quiet and subdued in the hospital. Physicians and nurses commented on his "goodness" and "gentlemanliness" and considered him a model patient. However, following one of the physical examinations, in quiet desperation, Mark asked his mother what was really wrong with his penis. He had not understood the skin examinations and had related them to what he felt to be the most vulnerable and questionable part of his body. On another occasion, he paled and showed considerable distress. He said nothing to the doctor, who was there, but it was soon apparent that he had considerable pain in his swollen hand. He had said nothing because he believed that a nurse had caused the needle to slip out of the vein when she bathed him and that she would be angry if he "told on her." He also feared the pain of the reinsertion of the needle.

There were no immediate reactions after he was discharged. In fact, he bragged a bit to his friends about all the shots he had had. If anything, one would say he enjoyed the prestige of a harrowing experience which he had survived manfully. But about six months later, when it was time to keep a routine appointment for a polio immunization, Mark became nauseated, faint, and suffered acute panic. The appointment was postponed, and the delay was used to explore the reasons for his anxiety. There was much discussion about shots, doctors, and hospitals, and slowly it emerged that Mark was grievously indignant at his doctor for hospitalizing him "for nothing." His anxiety sprang from his expectation that the doctor would return his anger. And any child knows that it is unwise to get doctors, who have so many fearsome weapons at their disposal, angry at you. He was reassured that the doctor was not a mind reader, and would not be angry, anyway. Mark kept the deferred appointment with only ordinary trepidation, but commented that when he grew up, he would be a lawyer who only sued doctors. In fantasy, he was able to allow his aggressive feelings expression without anxiety.

The story is further complicated by the fact that the boy's father was also a doctor and that these events occurred during the normal Oedipal period. Some of his feelings about the doctor were in all probability a displacement from those toward his father. Nevertheless, the incident, in and of itself, illustrates an incipient phobia, prompted by reality but greatly compounded by fantasy.

Professional people who work with physically healthy children are usually not aware of the importance of hospitalization or surgery in the emotional development of a child. They often assume that recovery is the end of the matter. But the child's physical and emotional history are not independent. Sometimes the psychological events connected with illness contribute heavily to neurosis and help to explain behavior otherwise very mysterious in origin. A good history will include all the child's experience with illness, his age at the time, and his reaction to the event.

Emotional Effects of Physical Disabilities

It was previously thought that each physical disability was associated with specific mental and personality characteristics. This view is reflected in the classic work, *Psychology of the Physically Handicapped (Pintner, Eisenson, and Stanton, 1941)*, in which the psychological characteristics of each disabled group are catalogued as if they were inherent in the disability. In a more recent work, *Physical Disability: A Psychological Approach* the emphasis is placed on understanding the factors which act as intervening variables between any physical handicap and its psychological manifestations. Beatrice Wright, the author, states as a basic principle that *"somatic abnormality as a physical fact is not linked in a direct or simple way to psychological behavior"* (1960, p. 373). She also states that "there are far fewer psychological experiences peculiar to persons with physical disabilities than an offhand guess might indicate" *(p. 3)*, and consistently points out the generality of the psychological principles involved and their applicability to physically normal persons. A term which appears frequently in the literature on physically handicapped is "somatopsychology," a term somewhat awkwardly defined by R. G. Barker and B. A. Wright: "[The somatopsychological] relation deals with those features of physique that affect the psychological situation of a person via his body as a tool for behavior and as an object with social significance to himself and others" *(1954, p. 419)*. The variability of psychological correlates of disability, then, is to be understood in terms of differing experiences which result in differing attitudes.

One statement which is repeatedly encountered is that the handicap *per se* has less influence on emotional adjustment than the parental and peer group attitudes to which the handicapped child is exposed. This has been said of cerebral palsy *(Haring, 1959)*, of facial deformities *(MacGregor et al., 1953)*; of acquired physical disfigurements *(Watson and Johnson, 1958)*; of mixed organic handicaps *(Carter and Chess, 1951)*; and of blindness *(Cole and Taboroff, 1955)*. The child tends to adopt the same attitudes toward his disability that his parents or associates demonstrate. He also perceives and imitates the defenses against anxiety utilized by his parents. Summing up, Wright states that the attitudes of parents toward their disabled children tend to be extreme, with overprotection occurring more frequently than overt rejection *(1960, p. 376)*. The most frequently seen patterns are oversolicitude, rejection, pressing for accomplishments beyond the child's abilities, and inconsistency *(Barker and Wright, 1954)*.

But it would be a mistake to conclude that the personality of the handicapped is determined solely by parental attitudes. A handicapped child, like any other child, observes himself and compares himself with other children. Some of the difficulties of self-evaluation are revealed in Harway's study of the level of aspiration. She compared 80 orthopedically handicapped and 40 physically normal children of at least average intelligence, aged 7 to 13. The handicapped children tended to maintain their aspirations at a higher level than their achievement and to ignore their previous failures. But there was considerable overlapping between the two groups, and only a minority of the handicapped were unrealistic in setting goals for themselves. One cannot say, therefore, that the handicap acts directly to distort the child's self-concept and sense of reality.

The handicapped child may have fantasies about the cause of his disability and fears about what further damage might occur. A research study which gives indirect evidence of this was carried out by William Cruickshank. He administered a sentence completion test to two groups, each of over 200 adolescents. One group was physically handicapped by various types of orthopedic, cardiac, and neurological disorders; the other consisted of physically normal adolescents of similar socioeconomic background. The handicapped group revealed more fears and feelings of guilt than did the control group *(1951)*.

It has been clinically observed that handicapped children are fearful of new experiences and new situations *(Carter and Chess, 1951)*. Some explanation for this can be found in the anomalous social position of the physically disabled, well described by Vivian Harway:

. . . the physical handicapped person is described as occupying a marginal and ambiguous position between physical independence and physical helplessness, due to the absence of a clear line of demarcation between physical normality and physical disability. The handicapped individual may frequently find himself in situations where he experiences uncertainty as to the ground on which he stands. Accepting the values of the dominant group (the physically normal), he feels attracted by many of the same goals and satisfactions sought after by the non-handicapped. However, he can never be sure that such goals are within his capacity. The goal may have strong positive attractions, and yet the fear of embarrassment or failure will act as a strong negative barrier impelling the individual away from the goal and toward the safety of identification with the values of the physically helpless. For some handicapped individuals, the strength of the barrier between them and normals may be exaggerated. Their withdrawal seems to be an acceptance of the negative judgment of others and a devaluation of themselves. For others, this barrier may be denied in a vigorous but unrealistic rejection of the disabled status. Even for the handicapped person who attempts to be realistic and plan behavior and activities which are possible for him (i.e., exploit to the fullest the potential of the overlapping normal and handicapped situations), there is often the frustration of society's not accepting his evaluation of his capabilities.*

Kathy, who had been seriously handicapped since birth by amyotonia, described her fears and questions about starting junior high school in the language of an 11-year-old.

I don't know how it is going to be in the new school and I am afraid. I guess that is normal but it is more for me because of my handicap. People say I am pestery and chicken. One of my friends, at least she used to be my friend, teased me about being a crybaby. I don't know how I am going to get around. There is an elevator but I don't know where it is. If I had a wheelchair it might be better. Then the kids would know to be careful and not to crowd me. It would be fun if it was an electric chair and the kids would like

to see it. They might even be jealous. But then people would stare at me if I were in a wheelchair. They would think I couldn't walk and that I was really *crippled*.

The kids will all be going places I can't go, you know, up to the shopping center. They all go there, I don't know what they do. I think it is really silly to just hang around like that. But I am always alone, I always have to come in late or leave early and they see my mother come to pick me up. My mother doesn't understand at all. I finally got her to let me have my hair cut in bangs, but they are wispy, like me. And I got some dresses which are not so babyish but I always have to be careful that my back support doesn't show. I guess it would scare the kids if they saw that. My mother doesn't know how important these things are, I suppose because she is pretty old. I would like to have someone to talk to, but they are always leaving me and going off to that shopping center. And I suppose they will be having boy friends and dates. Of course, I am not interested in anything like that, but I don't know if I can have babies.

As Kathy said herself, her fears were normal but greatly intensified by the reality of her physical limitations. She was ambivalent about attracting attention by a wheelchair and unhappily weighed the pros and cons. Although she herself was far from puberty, the interests of her friends made her worry about what she could expect as an adult woman. Above all, she complained of loneliness, something which her loving parents could not change. On the other hand, her ability to recognize and verbalize her feelings and to cope with them realistically reflected the attitudes of her parents.

Physicians, physical therapists, occupational therapists, and others who work closely with physically handicapped children and their families must be careful to consider the total life situation of the child—family, friends, school, play, work, as well as the physical problems. Especially in conditions

---

*From: Self-Evaluation and Goal-Setting Behavior in Orthopedically Handicapped Children," by Vivian T. Harway in *Readings on the Exceptional Child*, edited by E. Philip Trapp and Philip Himelstein. Copyright © 1962, Appleton-Century-Crofts, Inc. Reprinted by permission of Appleton-Century-Crofts.

of life-long disability, there is a danger that the physical rehabilitation regimen will take away energy needed for other activities. It also may become another source of conflict and guilt. Failure to improve may be interpreted by parents and child as their own fault. For psychological rehabilitation, handicapped children and their families need information, sympathy, encouragement, and someone to share the responsibility for making decisions.

The studies of the *sensorially handicapped* bear out the expectation that sensory defects, particularly if they are congenital or acquired very early, will have a more pervasive influence on the child's personality and mental development than other disabilities. The loss of one of the major senses limits the ability to learn, to perceive reality, and to establish personal relationships. The differences between the blind and deaf and the normal have been observed by comparing scores on conventional tests; performance of experimental tasks; developmental experiences; and clinical observations and interview data. Conventional test reports were published mainly in the twenties and thirties; these were followed by reports of experimental procedures; since 1955, the discussions of sensorially handicapped subjects have been embedded in developmental theory or clinical contexts.

Multitudinous studies have been made of the measurable intelligence of the blind and deaf (although not of the orthopedically handicapped, for one does not expect to find an intellectual deficit unless the motor problem is of neurological origin). The results are difficult to summarize, even contradictory, but this is not surprising since the tested populations have been varied, or even not fully described, and the age of onset has not been a controlled variable. Nor are we certain about the tests used. Standard intelligence tests have to be modified to allow for the lack of sight or hearing, and it

is questionable how far they can be changed and still be comparable to conventional test results.

D. H. Crowell's summary (*Chapter 12 in Louttit, 1957*), included a total of 19 studies in which the Hayes-Binet Intelligence Test and the Wechsler Bellevue Verbal Scale were given to a total of 3,178 blind children in residential schools. Their mean IQ's were between 92 to 108, not significantly different from the average except that the distribution tended to be bimodal. It appeared that fewer blind children were of average intelligence and more were superior or inferior than the general population.

There has been more extensive investigation of the intelligence of the deaf, than of the blind, one reason being the greater number of deaf. Individual performance scales or nonverbal techniques were used. Crowell (*Chapter 12 in Louttit, 1957*) summarizes 21 studies (reported between 1921 and 1953) of 9,530 deaf subjects. The results are inconsistent and, again, it is difficult to compare the studies because different sampling and testing techniques were used. R. Pintner, an author of one of the special nonverbal tests for the deaf and a major investigator in this field, concluded that the average IQ for deaf children was 91 on performance scales, 86 on nonverbal group tests, and 88 on the Goodenough Draw-A-Man test (*Pintner, Eisenson, and Stanton, 1941, p. 126*). L. A. Tyler concluded that "deafness, when it is congenital and complete, constitutes more of an intellectual handicap than blindness" (*1956, p. 428*).

Both the blind and deaf are educationally retarded. Experiments do not substantiate the theory that the blind are innately superior in other ways. They bring no special talent to the academic situation; on the contrary, they begin school later and read less and, as we know, academic achievement depends largely on reading. The learning problems of the deaf begin with the learning of language, and other mental problems evolve from this. "Comparisons of the deaf with the hearing child in educational achievement show the former to be greatly retarded" *(Pintner, Eisenson, and Stanton, 1941, p. 148)*—an average of three or four years. Children who become deaf after the age of four have much higher educational achievement scores than those who are born deaf or who become deaf during their first few years.

Studies of performance of experimental tasks have been mainly studies of perception (i.e., of other senses than the deficient one) and of concept formation. An interesting study, because it shows the overflow from one function to another, is an investigation of the *visual* perception of *deaf* children. Helmer Myklebust and Milton Brutten employed many of the experimental procedures used by H. Werner and A. Strauss (i.e., the Marble Board Test, the Figure-Ground Test, the Rubin Vase-Profile, the Goodenough Draw-a-Man, and the pattern reproduction test) on 55 institutionalized deaf children between 8 and 11 and 55 hearing children from a nearby orphanage. The deaf children were inferior in all the experimental tasks, although the two groups were matched in IQ on the Chicago Non-Verbal test. The authors felt that a deficiency in abstraction was the underlying cause for the inferior perceptual functioning of the deaf child. However one explains it, these children did more poorly on visual and visuomotor tasks, although their handicap was an oral one. The subgroups were small in number, but there was some indication that those born deaf had suffered the most. Apparently, there is significant interplay between auditory and visual stimulation in infancy, although the mechanics of this interaction are hard to specify:

The endogenous deaf child was most atypical in the primary perceptual process of figure-ground articulation . . . It was suggested that the sensory deprivation which the endogenous child invariably sustained from birth exerted a severely consequential impact upon this basic structuring of the visual perceptual field. *(1953, 118.)*

The conceptual thinking of the deaf has been explored via sorting tasks, such as the Weigl form-color test, the sorting tests of Goldstein and of Halstead, and the Wisconsin card-sorting test. P. Oleron *(1953)* reviewed these studies and stated that they all indicate that the deaf have difficulty with conceptual thinking. The deaf subjects use fewer categories for sorting and do not spontaneously shift their basis of categorization. They tend to become lost in irrelevant or superficial details and to neglect the more general principles. When they try to explain (verbally) the basis of their sorting, they only describe the object or what they have done, without speaking of the general concept involved (e.g., color, number, or material):

The mental processes of the deaf are characterized by an especial concern for observed data, which data guide them in accomplishing the tasks set before them. This attitude becomes an obstacle when they are confronted with tests demanding a certain level of abstract thinking . . . it indicates a stage of incomplete development, similar to an earlier stage found in normal children. *(Oleron, 1953, p. 309.)*

The facilitating power of language is interesting. There was a relationship between the degree of success in sorting and the ability to relate verbally the reasons for the sorting. It is hard to say which comes first, the word or the concept, but certainly each aids and abets the other. H. McAndrew studied these conceptual difficulties under the rubric of "rigidity" and used other measures (i.e., satiation time, level of aspiration, and the Rorschach) to compare groups of 25 deaf, blind, and normal adolescents. The Rorschach could only be administered to the deaf and to the normal, who were asked to write down their responses. The deaf gave fewer responses (less than one per card), and these tended to be simple, whole responses which suggested magical repetition or perseveration. All in all, their Rorschach records resembled those of younger children. Verbalization confirmed the simple, childish type of communication found by F. and G. M. Heiders in 1941, in their investigation of the language and sentence structure of the deaf. In general, the studies showed the deaf to be more disadvantaged and more rigid, in all the measures used, than the blind. The blind scored somewhere between the deaf and the normal. McAndrew concluded that rigidity is a positive function of the degree of isolation, and that the deaf are more isolated than the blind, who are, in turn, more isolated than normal people (*1948, 1962*).

The third category of reports on the sensory handicapped consists of theoretical discussions of developmental differences, specifically in relation to the concept of "sensory deprivation." Children with congenital sensory handicaps are natural subjects for research into the effects of sensory deprivation, and attempts have been made to relate observations on such blind and deaf children to findings with experimental subjects. The first experiments of A. H. Riesen *et al.* (1951) and of D. O. Hebb (1937) showed that laboratory animals reared from birth in various states of isolation exhibited conspicuously aberrant behavior when they were exposed to a normal environment. A great number of studies which followed indicated that an impoverished environment in infancy, one which offers limited stimulation and little opportunity for exploration, produces an adult organism less able to discriminate, less able to solve problems, with less curiosity, and with less integrative capacity (*Bruner*,

1961). The next step was to study the effects of sensory deprivation on human adults (*Solomon et al., 1961*). Isolation for periods as short as 48 hours impaired intellectual functioning, produced hallucinations, resulted in depersonalization, and disturbed the perception of the subjects. A variety of effects have since been reported, and a number of variables have been defined (*Cohen et al., 1961*).

The most important finding is that social isolation is more devastating than sensory deprivation alone (*Riesen, 1961, p. 36*). Harold Michel-Smith and George Klein (*1962*) have both picked up this point, in relation to deaf and blind children, respectively. According to Michel-Smith:

When deafness occurs in early childhood, it causes an obvious interference with language functions, and consequently, with the entire function of communication. It is suggested, therefore, that it is this over-all disturbance in communication and the resulting isolation from the environment, not the sensory deprivation itself, from which the psychological problems of the deaf child spring. His problems lie not only in his frustrations and disabilities in communication with his environment, but also in the compounding of the disorder by the frustrations and disabilities of other individuals in his environment in communicating with him. (*1962, p. 291.*)

Klein says much the same thing about the blind:

It is in relation to the second kind of deprivation—restrictions of environmental contact—that the effects of blindness and of any other physical defect are to be assessed, these effects being not a direct consequence of the blindness itself, but reflections of an environmental insufficiency which in one way or another does not allow the individual to utilize compensatory input channels to sustain the synthetic function. (*1962, p. 84.*)

For the blind child, whose mental capacity is intact, it is possible for the environment to provide the feedback of information about reality which the eyes ordinarily provide. Someone, usually his mother, brings him into tactile contact with objects and provides him with verbal information about the felt world. If, however, the mother is unaware of her responsibility or is emotionally depressed, the child suffers twice—from sensory deprivation and from social isolation.

The fourth category of reports on the sensorially handicapped is clinical. Intensive clinical studies of the blind or deaf are few and far between, and observations about their personalities have been based mainly on children in residential schools, the effects of institutionalization not being separated from the effect of the sensory defect. The author is not familiar with any intensive study of an individual deaf child.

There are, however, two detailed reports of the treatment of blind children. Nyla Cole and Leonard Taboroff have described the treatment of a congenitally blind adolescent girl. As is usual in case histories, there were other trauma: hospitalization at five for osteomyelitis; tonsillectomy at eight; residential school placement from six to fourteen years; facial disfigurement; and markedly immature parents. The girl's dependence on others to assist her in perceiving reality was clearly shown in the course of therapy. Moreover, she expressed the ubiquitous fantasy that the defect had been caused by something bad which she or her mother had done.

A lengthier treatment of a congenitally blind, three-year-old girl was reported by Eveline Omwake and A. J. Solnit *(1961)*. Ann, one of prematurely born twins, developed retrolental fibroplasia (formerly a common cause of blindness in premature infants). Her mother was depressed and a good share of Ann's care was left to a nurse who considered her hopelessly retarded. By the age of three, Ann had developed an inhibition against touching objects.

She did nothing for herself; she did not even walk. She was not toilet trained, her vocabulary was meager, and she was described as autistic and retarded. Over a period of five years, she improved to the point of demonstrating average intelligence and considerable creativity, and spontaneously expressed appropriate feelings. The authors give a vivid picture of the infantile anxieties which had been aroused by listening and touching alone and of the psychological conflicts which had forced her to retreat into autism. The report reveals her fantasy life, her expanding knowledge, and the increasing ability to cope which she gained by acting out dramatic productions which she devised. Not until her fourth year of treatment (when she was six) did the subject of her blindness come up spontaneously. And then she wanted to know how the blindness started, why it started, and how long it would last. The title of the report, "It Isn't Fair," is the statement Ann made when she was six and a half. Discussion of her resentment was followed by further dramatic improvement.

Perhaps the greatest insight into the early development of the blind is provided in an article by Dorothy Burlingham, based on observation of a number of blind nursery school children at the Hampstead Clinic in London. Burlingham also used material from work with the mothers and psychoanalytic material drawn from the treatment of five children of four to eleven.

With respect to motility, retardation and restriction of muscular achievement, she observed, are "the order of the day":

In the absence of vision, the blind baby is not stimulated in the same manner to reach out toward people or inanimate objects . . . The baby is not guided by the mother's look or her expression of pleasure in his activity and therefore lacks some of

the incentive to repeat achievements . . .
All the children under our observation
show the so-called blindisms, i.e., rhythmic
movements of the body, rubbing the eyes,
knocking of the head with the hands,
swaying and rocking. There is little or no
thumb sucking in our nursery, although
the normal amount of masturbation can be
seen.*

About verbalization, Burlingham
wrote that the blind child "finds uses
for speech that the seeing do not require, that is, for orientation, to collect
characteristics for differentiating between persons, to discover some mark
by which an object can be recognized."** Blind children also seem to
enjoy playing with words more than
sighted children. Their speech is welcomed and encouraged by their mothers, because it provides a longed-for
contact with the children and reassures
them that the children are not retarded
as well as blind. But the mothers sometimes do not realize that some of what
they say is meaningless to children who
cannot see. The mother or teacher must
have the child feel, hear, or smell the
object mentioned. Burlingham also confirms the observation of Omwake and
Solnit that talking of blindness is a relief to the children. As long as their
blindness is surrounded by an aura of
taboo, it has an inhibiting effect.

The ability to express their thoughts,
fantasies, and disappointments about
blindness has a liberating effect on the
children so that they are able to verbalize
other affect-laden subjects . . . The acceptance of their blindness increases the children's curiosity about other matters and
allows them to use their intelligence to
draw conclusions.***

On the emotional side, Burlingham

observed that it is more difficult for
blind children to achieve independence. It is hard for both the child
himself and his caretaker to relinquish
dependent protection. Their fear of
abandonment is also greater:

. . . blind children are often treated like
inanimate objects, picked up and dumped
where convenient . . . [They] have learned
from experience how dependent they are
on those with sight, into how many
dangers they run, and how many of their
wishes are unobtainable on their own . . .
The phase of conflict between dependence
and independence . . . has to be immea-
surably longer with the blind. With them
it is less a stage of development than a
continued testing of their own powers of
accomplishment as well as of adult reaction to what they are doing. (1961, pp.
129–31.)

Observation of these children at the
school showed relatively little aggressiveness. The signs of aggression noted
by the teachers were abortive or were
merely verbal; they neither reached nor
harmed the offending object. This is
partly because the children could not
see the object at which they were
angry, but it is at least in part attributable to their feeling of dependency
and fear of retaliation.

We have reported the work with the
blind in some detail because it is an
excellent example of exploiting an experimental situation provided by nature rather than an artificial one contrived in the laboratory. The absence
of a major sense has manifold effects
which infiltrate all aspects of intellectual and emotional development and
illustrate the interrelatedness of functions. This material should not be
viewed solely from the standpoint of
understanding the blind child, but also
for its implications about the role of
vision in normal development. Burlingham's observations, a far cry from test
surveys, help to explain the multifaceted origins of the differences be-

---

*Quoted from Dorothy Burlingham, *Some
Notes on the Development of the Blind* (New
York: International Universities Press, Inc.)
1961, pp. 123–25. Reprinted by permission.
   **Burlingham, *op. cit.*, p. 134.
***Burlingham, *op. cit.*, p. 142.

tween the blind and the sighted and provide us with some clues as to how to mitigate the differences.

Accident Proneness

Accident proneness lies on the border between somatic reactions caused primarily by the emotions and the converse—emotional reactions to somatically caused illness. Many accidents are, of course, truly unpreventable. On the other hand, many accidents reflect a failure of the ego function of self preservation.

Industry has long been concerned with this problem. One of the earliest studies, that of M. Greenwood and H. M. Woods, showed that, among sample populations of adult workers, more people had no accidents and fewer people had many accidents than chance alone could account for *(1919).* E. M. Newbold, using the accident records of some 10,000 industrial workers, confirmed the existence of differing individual susceptibility to accidents. Other studies *(Fabian and Bender, 1947; LeShan, 1952-a and 1952-b; Marcus, 1960)* have since confirmed these early findings and have shown that any person may become accident prone under stress. These studies have given rise to the accident-proneness hypothesis, which is simply that certain individuals tend to have repeated accidents.

The human being is unique in that he must learn to protect himself. Unlike other animals, he cannot trust his instincts. In the Vineland Social Maturity Scale, the item "Avoids Common Dangers" is placed at the three-year level. Most of this basic learning is acquired from the mother; the child learns to care for himself as she has cared for him. But the function of self-preservation can fail for a number of reasons. A neglected child has no model to follow and an overindulged and overprotected child may not assume responsibility for himself. Expressing oneself in deeds, rather than in fantasies, thought, or words, is a major cause of accident-proneness, according to Liselotte Frankl *(1963).* Such children do not delay, but rush pell-mell into action without considering the risks. This is normal in the toddler, but it is soon toned down by experience. The persistence of such impulsivity is probably partly constitutional, but there are children who retain this pattern of behavior despite painful experiences, because of the anxiety they would feel if they stopped to think.

Lanny, the product of a very disturbed, impulse-ridden family with many sociopathic tendencies, had been witness to, or involved in, some dozen minor accidents in his eight years. These included the accidental killing of two pet birds, a bruised penis from too-strenuous rocking on a rocking horse, serious cuts and falls, and so on. He had undergone surgery twice, at five and at six. He was extremely fearful and had nightmares. He was enuretic, he soiled, and he was retarded in school.

Lanny made only limited progress in psychotherapy, partly because of the psychopathology of his parents. It was also very difficult for him to work on his problems, because the mere mention of a fear set him to hopping around in search of escape. His most frequent defense, besides flight, was identification with the aggressor. This led to bizarre behavior, such as growling like a lion in kindergarten.

When he was seven, intensive treatment was discontinued, but he did not discuss this event before or after it occurred. One might have thought he lacked any feeling for his therapist. But a year later, he caught sight of her and rushed toward her. In his haste, he tripped and cut his lip. As usual, his feelings had caught him by surprise, and he had no recourse except immediate, unthinking, action.

Accident proneness can be more complicated and stem from more involved inner conflicts than this, however. Some of these conflicts were mentioned in connection with the development of the superego. Turning aggression inward, for example, is demonstrated in its simplest form by the young child who hits himself when he is angry at his mother. In the next stage, the child is unconscious both of his anger and of its object, but he somehow provokes an injury to himself which serves to relieve his feelings of guilt. And when he is hurt, he becomes the recipient of pity rather than of censure. Sigmund Freud described this as well as any later author:

It is well known that in the severer cases of psychoneurosis instances of self-injury are occasionally found as symptoms and that in such cases suicide can never be ruled out as a possible outcome of the psychical conflict . . . Many apparently accidental injuries that happen to such patients are really instances of self-injury. What happens is that an impulse to self-punishment, which is constantly on the watch and which normally finds expression in self-reproach or contributes to the formation of a symptom, takes ingenious advantage of an external situation until the desired injurious effect is brought about . . . They betray the part which the unconscious intention plays by a number of special features—e.g., by the striking composure that the patients retain in what is supposed to be an accident. *(1901, 1960, pp. 178–79.)*

In her analysis of the genesis of accident proneness, Lisolette Frankl discusses the special problem of accidents involving adolescents. She relates the high incidence of automobile accidents during adolescence to the psychology of the period. The need to fight, to prove one's fearlessness, and to flirt with danger becomes a cause of automobile accident when displaced to the relationship between cyclists or drivers on the road *(1963)*.

Research in this field has suffered by the failure to differentiate the causes of susceptibility to accidents. Most studies are comparisons of accident-prone children with "safety-prone" children, in an attempt to demonstrate group differences. The situation would be improved by comparing children within a limited age range. A typical study, although more thorough than most, was made by a team which included a psychiatrist, a psychologist, a pediatrician, and a social worker. They concluded that:

. . . the accident pattern appears here to be related to emotional problems but not to a specific diagnostic category. It would seem to be analogous to a symptom such as enuresis. In terms of learning theory, accidents would be a response to emotional disturbance, a stimulus which, under different circumstances, might evoke a different response. The conditions under which this behavior [i.e., accidents] would occur include a hyperactivity which may be constitutional, a tendency to express tension through physical activity, and disturbed family relationships. *(Marcus, et al., 1960, p. 54.)*

This helps to explain the "response," or choice of symptom (although "disturbed family relationships" are found in every form of psychopathology). The "stimulus," however, or the emotional disturbance, varies from child to child: identification with a neglectful parent, simple avoidance of anxiety, involuted hostility, seeking of punishment, expression of a passive wish to be nurtured as a helpless child, or a perverted denial of danger.

Part II:

Emotional Causes for Somatic Symptoms

In this section, we move from what has been called "somatopsychology" to what are commonly termed "psychosomatic" conditions. Flanders Dunbar, who made this term a popular one, was a pioneer investigator of the emotional components of organic diseases *(1938)*. At that time, the medical profession was ready for psychosomatic investigations. W. B. Cannon's research into the psychological effects of acute emotion *(1936)* had predisposed the doctors, and psychoanalysis was breaking down the hitherto sharp distinctions between the mentally abnormal and the normal.

The journal *Psychosomatic Medicine* was first published in 1939 and, in 1942, a society for research into psychosomatic problems was inaugurated. The earliest text on the subject, by Edward Weiss and O. S. English *(1943)*, was closely followed by Dunbar's book on psychosomatic diagnosis *(1943)*. The major premise of the psychosomaticists is "that bodily changes may be brought about by mental stimuli, by emotion, just as effectively as by bacteria and toxins, and that physiological changes accompanying emotion may disturb the function of any organ in the body" *(Dunbar, 1943, p. 9)*. All the authors decry either-or thinking, and urge that one think in terms of a proportion of psychological to organic factors. Psychosomatic medicine is not put forward as a specialty in itself, but rather as an approach to medicine which involves "the simultaneous application of physiological and psychological techniques to the study of illness in an effort to make a definitive diagnosis and in preparation for comprehensive medical care" *(Weiss and English, 1943, p. 3)*.

Somatic symptoms with major psychological causes can be subdivided into three categories: (1) temporary physical changes related to acute emotional states; (2) somatic reactions expressing an inner conflict in symbolic form; and (3) tissue changes and organic disease resulting in part from long-standing emotional problems.

In the first category belong all the physical changes which prepare the person for fight or flight when he is afraid or angry (see Chapter 3). These changes—in muscle tension, secretion, circulation, respiration, and concentration of sugar in the blood—are largely the result of innervation of the autonomic nervous system. When the emotion disappears, the corresponding physiological process also abates, and the body returns to its former state. The second category includes somatic symptoms of an hysterical structure (see Chapter 10). The resulting inability to perceive, to feel, or to move is a compromise solution between an unconscious wish associated with the function of the affected organ and the anxiety aroused by the wish. The last category is psychosomatic disease, also called "organ neurosis" by Otto Fenichel *(1945)* and "psychophysiologic autonomic and visceral disorder" by the American Medical Association. Psychosomatic diseases develop in two phases: first, there is a functional disturbance caused by a chronic emotional disturbance; later, the chronic functional disturbance gradually leads to tissue change and to organic disease.

Disturbances of the gastrointestinal system were the first to be examined in the light of their psychological components by the psychosomaticists. Everyday experience provides *prima facie* evidence of the effect of feelings on the whole of the alimentary tract: dryness of the mouth, choking of the throat, tightening of the stomach, nausea and vomiting, and cramps and diarrhea are commonly observed physiological effects of emotional stress. One of the early experiments was that of S. Wolf and H. G. Wolff. As the result of an accident, a laboratory helper developed a gastric fistula which permitted a direct view of the lining of his stomach and a sampling of the gastric contents. It was thereby possible to relate the man's emotions, gauged by daily interviews and experimentally induced states, to his gastric condition *(1947)*.

It is fallacious to assume that, because a physical ailment can arise from emotional events, therefore it *must* be psychogenic. It is possible for peptic ulcers to have causes entirely independent of the emotions. However, it is now widely agreed that emotional factors are of great importance in the causation or perpetuation of peptic ulcer.

Theoretical Concepts of Psychosomatic Medicine

The theoretical concepts of psychosomatic medicine, derived from work with adult patients, are of four main kinds *(Kaplan and Kaplan, 1959).* The first two are "specificity" theories: one of these theories is that a specific type of personality gives rise to a specific psychosomatic disease; the other is that a specific type of conflict leads to a specific psychosomatic reaction. The nonspecific theoretical approaches to psychosomatic medicine include the theories of H. G. Wolff, G. F. Mahl, Hans Selye, and various animal experimentalists such as H. Liddell and W. H. Gantt. They do *not* believe that there is a correlation between the type of psychological stress and the body organ which is somatically affected. The distinction between the two nonspecific theories is whether or not the physiological responses are to be considered a biological regression to an earlier state of physiological functioning.

The theory that a specific personality type incurs a specific disease is Dunbar's. After a five-year study of some 1,600 patients admitted to the Department of Medicine of Presbyterian Hospital, in New York, she developed a series of "personality profiles" considered typical of coronary occlusion, hypertensive cardiovascular disease, anginal syndrome, rheumatic fever and rheumatoid arthritis, rheumatic heart disease, cardiac arrhythmias, and diabetes. For a quick thumbnail description she offered the following:

Coronary occlusion and hypertensive cardiovascular disease seem to occur particularly frequently among *top-dogs* and *would-be-top-dogs.* Anginal syndrome is a frequent finding among *prima donnas* or *big frogs in small puddles.* Rheumatic fever and rheumatic heart disease occur among *teacher's pets* and *martyrs.* Patients with cardiac arrhythmia, although they have something of the prima donna, give the impression of being *children in the dark.* Patients with diabetes can generally be characterized as *muddlers.* (1943, p. 578.)

It is interesting to note that a group of patients with fractures were originally selected as Dunbar's control group. In her opinion, however, this group did not prove to be so normal, and she prepared a psychological profile for the patients with fractures, as well. She suggests that these profiles can be useful in the diagnostic process and that they should be used like a laboratory test for establishing the medical diagnosis. Her theory is now only of historical interest because there is considerable evidence to show it is an oversimplification. However, the impact of her early statements is attested to partly by the frequency with which they are denied. Many later studies of these diseases start out with the statement that "no specific personality type was found."

The concept that a specific conflict is responsible for a specific disease is Franz Alexander's, and is held by other members of the Chicago Institute for Psychoanalysis:

A mysterious and vague correlation between personality and disease does not exist; there is a distinct correlation between certain emotional constellations and certain vegetative innervations. Whatever correlation is found between personality type and somatic disease is only of relative statistical validity and often incidental . . . The true psychosomatic correlations are between emotional constellations and vegetative responses. *(Alexander, 1950, p. 75.)*

The major premise of this concept is that every emotional state has its own physiological syndrome. Alexander differentiates two attitudes: (1) a preparation to deal with an anxiety-producing situation by meeting it actively; and (2) a retreat from it by increased dependence. In Alexander's opinion, the first emotional attitude is accompanied by increased sympathetic excitation and the second by increased parasympathetic excitation. Within these two large categories, specific responses to different emotions can be distinguished.

On the basis of his experience with the psychoanalysis of psychosomatic patients (plus hypotheses derived from psychoanalytic theory and from physiology), Alexander describes a number of dynamic patterns which he feels lead specifically to peptic ulcers, ulcerative colitis, bronchial asthma, and hypertension. Many of these revolve around frustration or repression of passive, dependent longings. In the patient with peptic ulcers, for instance, the initial repression of "oral-receptive longings" may be followed by an overt reaction formation of great activity. But beneath the surface, the patient is unconsciously "hungry for love," and ulcers are the physiological consequence of his psychological needs. The patient with bronchial asthma is expressing his passive longing for dependence in his pathological breathing. His asthma is an unconscious cry for help, an attempt to "suck in" his mother and so avoid separation from her. The hypertensive patient has hostile, competitive tendencies, which are frustrated by failure or fear of retaliation, so that he later experiences a consequent increase in dependent longing. This is followed by a reactivation of the hostile competitiveness, accompanied by anxiety and inhibition, and hypertension finally results. This complicated sequence of drives and defenses would be very difficult to establish without a complete anamnesis and an intimate knowledge of the patient.

Dunbar, and Alexander even more, recognize that not all persons who fit a personality profile or experience a specific conflict develop a specific disease. They agree that there must be somatic

compliance, a susceptibility of the body organ to disease. However, they feel that there are specific correlations between the psychology and the resultant organic response.

The trend, however, has been away from specific and toward more general concepts (Prugh, 1963). Wolff suggests that the physiological changes in psychosomatic disorders are derived from unconditioned protective reaction patterns (e.g., vomiting) which get rid of noxious physical substances. By the process of conditioning, these reactions patterns are later associated with, and aroused by, psychological stimuli (1950). Selye injected cortisone into animals and produced disease states resembling colitis, arthritis, nephritis, and other syndromes. He views these as "diseases of adaptation," the by-product of the organism's effort to adapt to stress, physical or psychological (1955). Kaplan and Kaplan have also proposed a nonspecific theory: "If a patient's psychological defenses are inadequate to reduce his excited or anxious state, so that he is left in a chronic state of emotional tension, then a variety of psychosomatic diseases may be produced in constitutionally susceptible individuals as a result of chronic tension" (1959, p. 1094). Roy Grinker (1953), M. Schur (1955), J. J. Michaels (1944), T. S. Szasz (1951), and S. G. Margolin (1957) have interpreted psychosomatic symptoms as a reactivation or regression of an infantile pattern, "the emergence of responses of undifferentiated, fluctuating, primitive nature, appropriate to the infant's physiological state but productive of pathological organ function in the child or adult" (Prugh, 1963, p. 300).

Julius Richmond and Seymour Lustman (1955), who have studied the autonomic functioning of the newborn, argue against these explanations of psychosomatic disorders as biological regressions. They point out that the normal state in infancy is not that of physiological vagotonia, which is the condition that obtains in psychosomatic gastrointestinal disturbances. They believe that even if a physiological regression did occur, it would not explain the abnormal tissue responses (e.g., in peptic ulcers, ulcerative colitis, or rheumatoid arthritis) for which there is no physiological paradigm in the healthy human infant (*Grossman and Greenberg, 1957*). The continuing controversy about these physiological mechanisms will have to be resolved in terms of physiological rather than psychological data.

Constitutional Predisposition

Since all psychosomaticists acknowledge the importance of a constitutional susceptibility, we will review the material on individual differences in the neonatal period. This is as close to "constitutional" as one can get, and the findings are relevant to the entire field of psychopathology. Constitution is the x factor which helps to explain the choice of symptom as well as why one child develops a symptom in response to pressures which leave another child unaffected. However, our review is necessarily a brief one.

Many of the early researches into child development were studies of the behavior of newborn infants as a group, with little attention to individual differences. One of the first to describe differences in spontaneous activity was Margaret Fries, a pediatrician who became a psychiatrist. In her original description of "congenital activity types," she proposed a standard method of observation (rather than measurement) and criteria by which to judge a youngster to be "active," "moderately active," or "quiet." Children of different activity types require different kinds of maternal handling, according to Fries. The quiet child needs more than an average amount of stimulation and patience. The active child needs more reassurance and fares badly under restraint, which stimulates aggressiveness and other traits like stubbornness and rebelliousness (*1944*). In a later article (*1953*), she hypothesizes a relationship between congenital activity types and personality disorders (*1953*).

Brownfield also reported on activity and sensory differences of normal infants during the first week in the hospital nursery. Her ratings of the spontaneous activity of 100 infants fell into a bell-shaped curve. Quiet babies slept more and vocalized less than active babies. The active babies were very vocal and active, and awoke before feedings. There was a correlation between spontaneous activity and response to an auditory stimulus. She concluded that quiet babies are less sensitive to hunger and other stimuli, but drew no conclusions regarding potential psychopathology.

Stella Chess *et al.* described "primary reaction types," deriving their classification mainly from interviews with parents of some 110 children who were followed from birth. They developed nine three-point rating scales of "reactivity":

1. "Activity-Passivity" in motor behavior.
2. "Regular-Irregular" in sleeping, eating, and so forth.
3. "Intense-Mild" in quality of response.
4. "Approach-Withdrawal" in response to new situations.
5. "Adaptive-Nonadaptive" in terms of quickness to modify behavior.
6. "High-Threshold–Low-Threshold" of sensitivity.
7. "Positive Mood–Negative Mood."
8. "Selectivity-Nonselectivity" in terms of discrimination.
9. "Distractibility-Nondistractibility."
(1960, pp. 436–37.)

Although the ratings are not deemed reliable until the third month of life, Chess views the observed behavior as evidence of "primary" (or constitutional) reactivity because it is so consistent from this age on. She states that "the determination of the existence of the primary reaction pattern in the infant bears significantly on one of the basic unresolved problems in child psychology, that of individuality" *(1960, p. 437)*. Chess and her co-workers are also concerned with practical application. They distinguish between "undesirable characteristics," which are largely psychodynamic in origin and therefore capable of basic change, and aspects of the primary reaction pattern which are not modifiable. Accordingly, they recommend that parents be helped to understand and accept these intrinsic differences, so that they can work around them rather than attack them head on.

There have been many experimental investigations of differences in autonomic functioning, both under natural conditions and in response to stimulation, and a great deal of attention is given in the published reports to methodology, instrumentation, exact condition of the infant, methods of stimulation, methods of recording response, and so on. Infants have been stimulated tactilely, orally, and by partial immersion in water, and their heart rates, skin temperatures, pupillary dilations, and motor behavior have been measured.

The possibilities for individual variation appear almost infinite. To begin with, there is considerable normal variation in such activities as the heart rate. Second, there are significant individual differences in autonomic reactivity. In their original study of three-day-olds, Richmond and Lustman found that changes in skin temperature and cardiac rate in response to a variety of stimuli followed a normal distribution curve, with clearly defined hyperreactors and hyporeactors at the extremes *(1955)*. Third, there are differences in the duration of the responses. Fourth, there are differences in the babies' ability to become habituated to a stimulus *(Bridger, 1962)*. Fifth, the infants' reactivity alters when experimental conditions are altered. For example, sucking on a pacifier makes most infants less responsive to a stress, but the degree of change differs in individual babies *(Bridger, 1962)*.

The current neurophysiological research into the individual differences among the newborn and the effect of the infant's state on his reactivity provides exciting glimpses of the possibilities of bridging the gap between physiology and psychology. But is it well to take note of some of the problems entailed in assessing an infant's constitution through observation and experiment.

The first major problem is that of evaluating the reliability of the observed individual differences—that is, their consistency over a period of time. Brownfield's study contained some measure of the stability of individual differences within the neonatal period *(1956)*, and Bridger and Reiser demonstrated that certain cardiac responses are reliable for two days *(1959)*. Most of the studies, however, are of a single type of response, and there are reasons for questioning the stability of the observed behavior. First, some differences in response are due to differences in the maturity of the nervous system which result from different lengths of gestation. Ten of the three-day-old infants studied by Richmond and Lustman did not respond to stimulation, and the authors considered this an indication of the immaturity of the autonomic nervous system *(1955)*. It is possible, thus, that in a few days these infants would have reacted very differently. Second, the baby may be temporarily affected by the anesthesia given the mother during childbirth. T. B. Brazelton found that medication of the mother: (1) prolongs the state of disorganization typical of the baby's first few days; (2) affects the child's responsiveness to feeding; and (3) delays his gain in weight *(1961)*. The relative maturity of the nervous system and the effect of anesthesia are probably only transitory, but they affect measurements of behavior made in the first few days.

Assuming for the moment that the measured behavior is stable; where do individual differences arise? Undoubtedly, heredity contributes a large part, but the fetal environment and birth are perhaps equally important. M. F. Ashley-Montagu, who reviewed the possible prenatal influences (1962), pointed out that the common endocrine pool of the mother and fetus forms a neurohumoral bond between them which allows nervous changes in the mother to affect the fetus. He quotes the work of L. W. Sontag and others at the Fels Institute, which showed that emotional disturbance of the mother produces a marked increase in the activity of the fetus. The Fels Institute workers found that if the mother undergoes severe emotional stresses during pregnancy, especially during the latter part of pregnancy, her child may be a hyperactive, irritable, squirming infant who cries for his feeding every two or three hours. There is also abundant evidence of the effect of poor nutrition on the fetus. Such evidence comes from experiments with animals (Masland, 1961) and, indirectly, from correlations between fetal abnormalities and socioeconomic status. A series of retrospective investigations by B. Pasamanick and his co-workers has posed the possibility that there is "reproductive continuum" between neonatal death, cerebral palsy, epilepsy, and mental retardation, behavioral disorders, and learning disabilities. Pasamanick believes that much psychopathology in children is organic and that minor damage is sufficient to disorganize the child's behavioral development and to lower his threshold for stress. He is particularly impressed by the fact that most abnormalities of pregnancy and most neuropsychiatric disorders occur in the lower strata of our society (1961). Another study, somewhat related, found behavioral differences between normal and traumatized newborn infants (Graham, Matarazzo, and Caldwell, 1956).

Neonatal differences, as we have already remarked, bear on psychosomatic theory specifically and on personality development theory in general. Seymour Lustman described "inherent autonomic endowment . . . as one of the nuclear apparatuses from which the primitive ego emerges" (1956, p. 97). From the earliest age, different infants experience life differently, according to their sensitivities. Lustman links the differences in sensitivity to perceptions of sucking, for example, citing three infants whose reactions were very different. He mentions that there were infants who reacted intensely to stimulation of every part of their bodies, even though their lips proved to be the most sensitive zone. An infant who hyperreacts to anal stimulation might, though following the usual sequence, move more quickly into the area of anality, or perhaps by virtue of greater sensitivity, develop defensive measures at an earlier than usual age. It seems logical to assume that delay, deprivation, overindulgence, weaning, and toilet training will be experienced by each child in accordance with his individual sensitivity and responsiveness. In addition, of course, his mother's personality and her reaction to his idiosyncrasies will add a vast number of variables to the situation.

Parent-Child Interaction in Psychosomatic Disorders

Although the role of parents and the nature of their relationships with their children are important in every area of childhood psychopathology, these topics completely dominate the area of psychosomatic disorders in childhood. It is assumed that psychosomatic disorders in childhood have their origin in the preverbal period, when somatization is the only outlet for emotions and also when the relationship between mother and child is paramount. Psychosomatic illnesses, if they appear in childhood at all, usually occur early.

Such illnesses are among the few complaints which occasion universal concern and for which the pre-school child is likely to be referred for psychiatric assistance. A psychosomatic illness, unlike other behavioral problems, cannot pass as a sign of immaturity. Another reason why the relationship between mother and child is so much stressed is that the mother is inevitably intensively involved in the care of the ill child. In reading the reports of mothers' roles in these conditions, it is hard to tell how much of this is the effect of the illness on the mother.

One of the strongest protagonists of the view that mothers are responsible for their children's psychosomatic symptoms was Margaret Gerard. In a clinical study of 38 children with ten types of psychosomatic disorders, she found that all the mothers were narcissistic, interested in their children only as self-enhancing assets, resented the care their children required, and seldom enjoyed their children. She felt that most of the mothers had rejected their children and that some had been physically cruel. She remarked that, in these cases, traumatic events had focused the mother's attention on the functioning of specific organs. In effect, she suggested that the rejection of the mother was not total, but was focused on specific physiological functions of the child:

Emphasis of focus of the mother's rejection upon particular physiological functioning in the early months may be the differential etiological feature between schizophrenia and psychosomatic disorders and between the specific different organ neuroses. For instance, mothers of ulcerative colitis cases seem to reject and be especially irritated at the time of the diarrheal bowel illness; mothers of coeliacs and megalocolons are irritated and anxious with constipation and thus impose enemas; of duodenal ulcers rejects any feeding irregularities and dependencies; . . . of rheumatic arthritis react to the helplessness and the need to be held and supported, by

rough handling, and so on. *(Gerard, 1953, pp. 93–94.)*

Rejection of some aspect of the maternal role is viewed as the common denominator among the mothers of psychosomatic children.

The largest single investigation of the role of the mother in psychosomatic disorders of children was published as a book by A. M. Garner and C. W. Wenar, psychologists at the University of Illinois. These authors adhere to the nonspecific concept of Grinker *(1953)*, and accordingly treated all the psychosomatic conditions (bronchial asthma, rheumatoid arthritis, ulcerative colitis, peptic ulcer, and atopic eczema) as one group. Their essential argument follows the thesis of Gerard (the psychiatric consultant involved in their study) that the mother, for individual reasons, is "unable to assist her infant effectively in developing and integrating the smooth muscle patterns of somatic response—breathing, digestion, elimination, for example— which enter into the behavioral repertory of the healthy infant" *(1959, p. 11)*. The major hypothesis is that "mothers of children who develop psychosomatic disorders lack 'motherliness'" *(p. 168)*. "Motherliness" is defined as "maternal gratification of the infant's needs for body care and pleasurable stimulation in ways that also provide the mother herself with satisfaction" *(p. 15)*.

Four predictions were based on this hypothesis:

1. If the mothers of children with psychosomatic disorder are lacking in "motherliness," then the mother-infant relationship in the first year of life will be distorted. The mother's fantasies regarding pregnancy and childbirth will reveal distortions, overemphases, [and so forth].

2. If the infant has received inadequate mothering, then his later attitude toward maternal figures will be one of ambivalence, characterized by feelings of rage, fear, and mistrust, along with longings for tender protection. More specifically, a

child's fantasies about being mothered will be characterized by a decrease in positive feelings and an increase in negative and ambivalent feelings. [The child] should be mistrustful of affection which is offered him, while his unfulfilled longings for closeness should intensify his interest in primitive, sensory experience.

3. If the infant has been damaged at the earliest level of forming interpersonal relationships, then he will show in his later social behavior, distance, inhibition, and inability to relate spontaneously.

4. The present mother-child interaction will show mutual frustration of need.*

Garner and Wenar's subjects, 78 children between six to twelve years, divided into three groups of 26 each. One group consisted of children who were hospitalized for psychosomatic diseases; the second was a group of neurotic children drawn from the out-patient clinic of the Institute for Juvenile Research in Chicago; the third was a group of chronically ill children suffering from nonpsychosomatic illnesses. Apparently some children of this third group were hospitalized and some were not. The mean IQ's of all three groups were between 104 and 107, and the groups were also matched for sex, race, socioeconomic status, and family constellation. No special inducement was offered the mothers, and the rate of attrition was considerable. The numbers in each group who completed all the procedures were 16, 14, and 15, respectively.

The mothers were asked to tell a story about 20 pictures depicting different aspects of infant care, pregnancy, or birth and to rate a number of items concerning the first year of the child's life. They also had a series of interviews with the social worker. Thirty judges characterized the interview material in terms of 84 items. The procedures for the children included the Stanford-Binet Vocabulary, the Kent

quick test of intelligence, the Goodenough Draw-A-Man, the World Test, the Rorschach, the Garner Illness Fantasy Technique, and observation of some special situations designed to evaluate the child's need for sensory stimulation, his response to a gift, and his spontaneous play in the company of his mother.

Few statistically significant differences were found among the groups of mothers. The mothers of the psychosomatically ill children recalled fewer negative feelings about pregnancy than the other mothers, however. The authors emphasize the high expectations which these women had had. But they also recalled few positive feelings about the actual training and care of their infants. From the totality of the interviews, the thematic material, the item ratings, and the direct observation ratings, the authors concluded that:

. . . the psychosomatic mothers might be epitomized as follows: they are ambitious controlling women who have high expectations for their child during pregnancy but find the actual caretaking of the infant unrewarding or disagreeable; because of their emotional investment, however, they are irresistably drawn to this ungratifying activity to the point of becoming entangled in a close, mutually frustrating relationship.*

The mothers' heightened expectations during pregnancy reflected their overinvestment in specific goals other than giving pleasure to, and receiving pleasure from, the infant. For example, a mother may have wanted to have as many babies as her sister had. But, once the infant has arrived, she gets little out of caring for him: "Caretaking and training are done either in a wooden manner or with distaste, and the infant is clearly regarded as an irritant or a source of concern, anxiety, and frustration." (p. 161). Lack of motherliness, as predicted, was the dominant characteristic of the mothers of children with psychosomatic diseases.

*Quoted from A. M. Garner and C. W. Wenar, The Mother-Child Interaction in Psychosomatic Disorders. (Urbana, Illinois: University of Illinois Press) 1959, p. 21. Reproduced by permission.

*Garner and Wenar, op. cit., p. 160.

The authors found two types of such mothers. One type is a shrewd, complex, and cold, manipulative woman who gives to the child only on condition that his behavior be congruent with the image of her as a good mother. The other type is overactive, unstable, and disorganized. The reports on the children will be reviewed in the next section; briefly, they tended to bear out the predictions made at the start of the study.

In general, this investigation received favorable comment for the effort to adhere to scientific procedures, but criticism was directed at the underlying theory (*Sundberg, 1961*). Clearly, the authors' convictions must, to some extent, have influenced their choice of psychological instruments and the variables selected for comparison. Since the data was obtained five to ten years after the fact, the mothers' recall may have been influenced by the children's later medical difficulties. Only predictive research, starting from the beginning of the child's life, would answer the questions about original cause, and large numbers of children would have to be observed in order to pick up the small proportion who develop psychosomatic disorders in childhood. Freud once described the dilemma involved in psychoanalytic prediction, and it seems to fit this case as well:

So long as we trace the development (of a mental process) from its final outcome backwards, the connection appears continuous, and we feel we have gained an insight which is completely satisfactory or even exhaustive. But if we proceed the reverse way, if we start from the premises inferred from the analysis and try to follow these up to the final result, then we no longer get the impression of an inevitable sequence of events which could not have been otherwise determined. We notice at once that there might have been another result, and that we might have been just as well able to understand and explain the latter. (*1920, 1955, p. 167.*)

A second study of psychosomatic

disease, made by Gaston Blom and Babette Whipple, bears out our observation about the relevance of one's theoretical position to the basic design of research. They believe in the specificity of psychosomatic disease; accordingly, in their investigation of emotional factors in children with rheumatoid arthritis, they chose children with a different psychosomatic disorder, asthma, as the control group. Eight males and twelve females in each category were matched. The mean age of the children in both groups was nine years, but the children who had asthma had been ill an average of three years longer. In addition, the arthritic children had had more and lengthier periods of hospitalization. These differences were unavoidable because they are inherent in the diseases. The procedures were much simpler than those used by Wenar and Garner. Briefly, scales were applied to the clinical records. The scales were, however, constructed with great care, over a period of four years, by a highly qualified research team.

A total of 67 scales—20 related to feeding, 24 to separation, and 23 to depression—was constructed. The only statistical differences were found on the scales which measured depression. Fourteen of the twenty mothers whose children had rheumatoid arthritis were described as having depressed character traits, in comparison with only five of the mothers whose children had asthma. The authors state:

Our evaluation of these early scales indicated that the following differences probably were not fortuitous: that mothers of children with rheumatoid arthritis as compared with the mothers of asthmatic children often showed depressed character traits, expressed fewer feelings and more rarely spoke of their own past; they were pessimistic about the child's disease and were masochistic in their care of the child; more of them had sustained a loss of a key person during their pregnancy with or in the infancy of the arthritic child. (*Blom and Whipple, 1959, p. 146.*)

Unfortunately the raters knew the

diagnosis of each child, but the authors were fully aware of this and prepared procedure for cross-validating their results. Their detailed description of their procedures is a lesson in experimental design well worth the reading. In contrast to the psychophysiological experiments on neonatal behavior, it is unusual for clinical-psychological investigators to follow the procedures worked out by someone else. This means that every study has to stand on its own merits with little verification or refutation from other sources.

Other reports of the role of parents in psychosomatic diseases of children have been less systematic and less dependent on clinical observation. Repeatedly, one finds statements to the effect that the mother has an overly close relationship with the child. From an analysis of the TAT records of 19 children with ulcerative colitis, Bettie Arthur concluded that:

. . . the "mother-child relationship is a highly cathected one and constitutes the fulcrum upon which swing the other family relationships" (1963, p. 543).

This has also been said of mothers of phobic children and children with symbiotic psychosis, however. Is it a matter of degree? Is it even possible that effect has been confused with cause? Perhaps mothers are drawn into unusually close relationships with children who are physically ill, severely anxious, or excessively dependent. Perhaps the mother becomes anxious, and feels a responsibility to be doing something for the child. Whether her efforts are helpful or harmful would be another question.

The allegation that the relationship between the mother and child is too close appears to contradict the thesis of maternal rejection proposed by Gerard and, to some extent, by Garner and Wenar. Psychodynamically, however, there is no contradiction: One group of authors emphasizes the underlying feelings of rejection as the cause of the overt overinvolvement and

views it as a defense (i.e., a reaction formation) against the unconscious hostility. The excessive anxiety which leads to overprotection is thought to originate in the mother's conflict.

Stuart Finch and John Hess, who observed the parents of 17 children with ulcerative colitis, support this line of reasoning:

A striking observation by the social worker was the inability of all these parents to express overt hostility in an appropriate manner . . . In all cases, the mothers appeared dominating and controlling toward the patient, regardless of sex. The child was the object of hostility and rejection by the mother, that was rarely overtly expressed. The mothers reacted consciously in the opposite fashion, demonstrating extreme, though superficial, concern for the child and demanding complete submissiveness from him. The mothers also had a tendency toward seductiveness for their sons. In many cases, the mother's negative attitude was shown in her apparent need for illness in the child; thus providing an opportunity for her to demonstrate her concern for the youngster. (1962, p. 821.)

It should be obvious to the reader from the above quotation, how right the psychology may be but how difficult to prove objectively. One can record behavior, but it is perilous to impute to it unconscious motives without having made a thorough clinical study of the individual. And then the lengthy case history which results is met with skepticism in scientific circles because it is only one case, and possibly an exceptional one. The dilemma of how much depth to sacrifice for the sake of larger numbers is a constant one in psychological research.

Psychological Characteristics of Children with Psychosomatic Disease

Less has been said about the children than about their mothers. In general, children with psychosomatic diseases are viewed as more disturbed than neurotic or chronically ill children (Garner and Wenar, 1959). Finch and Hess assess their subjects (children with ulcerative colitis) as suffering from severe psychopathology, often close to psychosis, and requiring long-term therapeutic measures *(1962)*. Interestingly enough, Garner and Wenar found that both their groups of physically ill children expressed fantasies of a bad mother more than the neurotic children. Although their mothers were highly rated in "motherliness", the organically ill children portrayed a "terrifying picture of the destructive power of the mother." In all probability, this reflects the child's assumption of the mother's omnipotence and, therefore, of her responsibility for his suffering.

Blom and Whipple reported that children with rheumatoid arthritis were more depressed than asthmatic children, were more inhibited in physical activity, had fewer interests, responded more slowly to the therapist, and controlled their feelings more. This conclusion makes the asthmatic children sound less disturbed than the arthritic, but the finding may be a function of the variables which were selected for measurement. The personality characteristics they found in child arthritics have also been reported for adult arthritics: obsessional patterns, marked emotional constriction, and depression. The authors also noted that the children reacted to emotional crises with intense autonomic activity: "Typically, they were also unable to express their emotions, had primitive aggressive fantasies, and difficulty in forming relationships with other people and in achieving separateness from their mothers" *(Blom and Whipple, 1959, p. 126)*.

The concept of "emotional constriction" has been applied to all the psychosomatic disorders. Garner and Wenar found that the psychosomatic group gave fewer color responses to the Rorschach items than either of their other two groups. This constriction is also indicated by their less elaborated and more impersonal fantasies. Somatic symptoms seem to provide an avenue of discharge which obviates the necessity for other outlets.

In their discussion of the course of treatment of hospitalized ulcerative colitis patients, Finch and Hess substantiate the impression of constriction and inability to verbalize:

It was difficult for them to speak of feelings, at times so difficult that one suspected that they were incapable of recognizing and identifying their own feelings. It seemed impossible for these children to exist except in terms of good or bad. Every thought, feeling or piece of behavior was judged in this light . . . Direct expressions of hostility were rare and when they occurred they were followed by almost panicky efforts to undo and to atone. *(1962, p. 824.)*

These authors also comment on the similarity between children and adults who suffer from ulcerative colitis. Both exhibit "obsessive-compulsive character traits and were constricted, defensive, guilty, and covertly hostile" *(1962, p. 822)*. These children are also described as chronically depressed, and one wonders how much of this is the secondary effect of chronic illness. Both ulcerative colitis and rheumatoid arthritis patients are in frequent pain, while asthmatic patients are well between attacks. One would expect the one group to be depressed by the constant discomfort and the other to be anxious in anticipation of another surprise attack.

The clinical evidence is somewhat ambiguous about the children's ability to establish relationships. Finch and Hess felt that their subjects established superficial relationships which were demanding, infantile, and easily transferred from one person to another. "It was as if they had a bottomless pit into which endless amounts of love could disappear" *(1962, p. 824)*. The symbiotic relationship with the mother is fraught with anxiety and ambivalence on the child's side. Many observations have been made about the psychosomatic child's anxiety about separation. Finch and Hess, who studied children with ulcerative colitis, and Leonard Taboroff and William Brown, who studied children with peptic ulcer syndrome, reported that the onset of symptoms was related to a real or fantasized disruption of a close and important re-relationship, usually with the mother *(1954)*. However, Finch and Hess view the birth of a sibling, starting to school, illness, extreme hostility, independent accomplishment, and the onset of puberty as all symbolizing separation. These events have other aspects of psychological stress besides the frustration of dependency needs.

Separation anxiety has traditionally been viewed as the key problem in asthma. Thomas French and Franz Alexander interpreted the asthmatic attack as, first and foremost, a reaction to the danger of separation from the mother; second, as the equivalent of an inhibited and repressed cry of anxiety or rage; and third, as revealing that the danger of losing the mother has its source in some temptation to which the child is exposed *(1941)*. It has been said that the role of the asthmatic attack is to control the mother, to keep her tied to the child by a means for which the child cannot be blamed.

In view of these observations, it may seem paradoxical that many asthmatic children improve when they are away from home. Lucie Jessner, *et al.* observed some 65 asthmatic children who improved in the hospital and suffered a relapse when they returned home. The chose 28 of these children (14 boys and 14 girls between five and sixteen) for intensive study. In their fantasies, the authors felt, the children revealed the double edge of the wish to be close to the mother; that is, they feared the closeness they wished for. Their fantasies expressed a wish for total shelter and protection which meets all needs, even breathing. But such total surrender is as frightening to them as it is desirable, it symbolizes helplessness, frustration, and death as much as it does satisfaction and safety. Such profoundly regressive oral wishes are akin to those expressed by psychotics, but the asthmatic has usually erected more adequate defenses against them *(1955)*.

Asthma may be a vehicle for the simultaneous expression of the desire to surrender and the desire to rebel, a conflict which is intensified when the child is with his mother and lessened when he is away from her. In Jessner's opinion, this conflict, although to some extent universal, is extremely intense and of central significance for the asthmatic child. Mere physical separation brings only temporary relief. The aim of psychotherapy, then, would be to achieve a genuine differentiation between mother and child, so that they can both tolerate being together as well as apart.

Also, the secondary gains of the asthmatic attacks may be less for the child away from home. The mother is not there to respond with anxiety and solicitude and the attack has no purpose in the expression of unconscious aggression against her. The aura of anxiety with its reciprocal effect on mother and child is less in the hospital than in the home.

Virtually no reference is made to sexual conflicts in the literature on psychosomatic diseases. The crucial problems seem to originate during what psychoanalysts view as the "oral" and "anal" phases of development, and in problems of ego differentiation and independence which inhere in these developmental periods. Somatization, the child's defense against anxiety, also reflects the immaturity of his ego. This does not mean that the child with a psychosomatic disease has *no* sexual problems or ego functions belonging to later periods of development, but rather that the earlier problems have retained considerable strength and that the child has retained his capacity to react somatically.

It is easy to appreciate the fearsome complications that arise in the wake of psychosomatic disease. First, there are the original physiological and psychological predispositions which combine with physiological and psychological events to precipitate the psychosomatic disease. The subsequent illness and treatment occasion psychological reactions in the child like those following any physical illness. The child's relationship with his mother, which probably contained pathogenic elements from the start, becomes more complicated. The illness can be used by the child as an escape from all sorts of conflictful situations and as a weapon against his mother or anyone else who might threaten to frustrate him.

Yet, the illness never can be treated solely on a psychological basis. The physical danger is real and always present. It is usually unwise to combine both treatments in the same person, but it is imperative that the doctor and the psychotherapist work together, often in conjunction with a third person who counsels the mother. In this respect, it is comparable to the treatment of a learning problem where an educator is involved as a necessary third party. It is always hard to manage a troika, and it is difficult to find therapists from three different fields who have the time and ability to work together on a single case.

The psychosomatic situation contains all the pathogenic elements of neurosis and physical illness in childhood, but we know very little about preventing it. Perhaps the only generally useful advice that can be given is that parents should be taught the usefulness of verbalizing emotions, whether their own or those of their child. Such guidance would be most helpful in the first two or three years of a child's life.

References to Chapter 13

Ack, Marvin, Irving Miller, and William B. Weil, "The Intelligence of Children with Diabetes Mellitus," *Pediatrics,* XXVIII (1961), 764–70.

Alexander, Franz, *Psychosomatic Medicine.* New York: W. W. Norton & Company, Inc., 1950.

Arthur, Bettie, "Role Perceptions of Children with Ulcerative Colitis," *Archives of General Psychiatry,* VIII (1963), 536–45.

Ashley-Montagu, M. F., *Prenatal Influences.* Springfield, Ill.: Charles C Thomas, Publisher, 1962.

Barker, R. G. and B. A. Wright, "Disablement: The Somatopsychological Problem," in E. D. Witthower and R. A. Cleghorn, *Recent Developments in Psychosomatic Medicine.* Philadelphia: J. B. Lippincott Company, 1954.

———, ———, and Mollie R. Gonick, "Adjustment to Physical Handicap and Illness: A Survey of the Social Psychology of Physique and Disability," *Social Science Research Council Bulletin,* No. 55 (1953).

Bergmann, Thesi, *Children in the Hospital.* New York: International Universities Press, Inc., 1965.

Blom, Gaston E. and Babette Whipple, "A Method of Studying Emotional Factors in Children with Rheumatoid Arthritis," in Lucie Jessner and Eleanor Pavenstedt, *Dynamic Psychopathology in Childhood.* New York: Grune & Stratton, Inc., 1959.

Brazelton, T. B., "Psychophysiologic Reactions in the Neonate. I. The Value of Observation of the Neonate," *Journal of Pediatrics,* LVIII (1961), 508–12.

Bridger, Wagner H., "Sensory Discrimination and Autonomic Function in the Newborn," *Journal of Child Psychiatry,* I (1962), 67–82.

———, and M. F. Reiser, "Psychophysiologic Studies of the Neonate: An Approach Toward the Methodological and Theoretical Problems Involved," *Psychosomatic Medicine,* XXI (1959), 265–77.

Browne, William, Mary Mally, and Ruth Kane, "Psychosocial Aspects of Hemophilia: A Study of Twenty-eight Hemophilic Children and Their Families," *American Journal of Orthopsychiatry,* XXX (1960), 730–41.

Brownfield, E. D., "An Investigation of the Activity and Sensory Responses of Healthy Newborn Infants." Unpublished doctoral dissertation, Cornell University, 1956.

Bruner, J. S., "The Cognitive Consequences of Early Sensory Deprivation," in P. Solomon *et al., Sensory Deprivation.* Cambridge, Mass.: Harvard University Press, 1961.

Brunschwig, Lily, "A Study of Some Personality Aspects of Deaf Children," *Contributions to Education,* No. 687. New York: Bureau of Publications, Teachers College, Columbia University, 1936.

Burlingham, Dorothy, "Some Notes on the Development of the Blind," *Psychoanalytic Study of the Child,* Vol. XVI. New York: International Universities Press, Inc., 1961.

Cannon, W. B., *Bodily Changes in Pain, Hunger, Fear, and Rage,* 2nd Edition. New York: Appleton-Century-Crofts, Inc., 1936.

Carter, Victor and Stella Chess, "Factors Influencing the Adaptations of Organically Handicapped Children," *American Journal of Orthopsychiatry,* XXI (1951), 827–37.

Chess, Stella, *et al.,* "Implications of a Longitudinal Study of Child Development for Child Psychiatry," *American Journal of Psychiatry*, CXVII (1960), 434–42.

Clarke, L. P., "Treatment of the Epileptic, Based on a Study of the Fundamental Makeup," *Journal of the American Medical Association*, LXX (1918), 357–62.

Cohen, S. I., *et al.*, "Problems in Isolation Studies," in P. Solomon *et al.*, *Sensory Deprivation*. Cambridge, Mass.: Harvard University Press, 1961.

Cole, Nyla J. and Leonard H. Taboroff, "The Psychological Problems of the Congenitally Blind Child," *American Journal of Orthopsychiatry*, XXV (1955), 627–43.

Coolidge, J. C., "Asthma in Mother and Child as a Special Type of Intercommunication," *American Journal of Orthopsychiatry*, XXVI (1956), 165–78.

Cruickshank, William, "The Relation of Physical Disability to Fear and Guilt Feelings," *Child Development*, 22 (1951), 291–98.

Despert, J. Louise, "Emotional Factors in Young Children's Colds," *Medical Clinics of North America* (1944), pp. 603–14.

Deutsch, L. and L. L. Wiener, "Children with Epilepsy: Emotional Problems and Treatment," *American Journal of Orthopsychiatry*, XVIII (1948), 65–73.

Dimock, Hedley G., *The Child in the Hospital*. Philadelphia: F. A. Davis Company, 1960.

Dubo, Sara, "Psychiatric Study of Children with Pulmonary Tuberculosis," *American Journal of Orthopsychiatry*, XX (1950), 520–28.

Dunbar, Flanders, *Emotions and Bodily Changes*, 2nd Edition. New York: Columbia University Press, 1938.

———, *Mind and Body: Psychosomatic Medicine*. New York: Random House, 1947.

———, *Psychosomatic Diagnosis*. New York: Paul B. Hoeber, 1943.

Erickson, F. H., "Play Interview for Four-year-old Hospitalized Children," *Monographs for Research in Child Development*, No. 23, (1958).

Escalona, Sibylle, "The Study of Individual Differences and the Problem of State," *Journal of Child Psychiatry*, I (1962), 11–37.

Fabian, A. A. and L. Bender, "Head Injury in Children: Predisposing Factors," *American Journal of Orthopsychiatry*, XVII (1947), 68–79.

Falstein, Eugene I. and Ilse Judas, "Juvenile Diabetes and Its Psychiatric Implication,"

American Journal of Orthopsychiatry, XXV (1955), 330–43.

———, ———, and Robert S. Mendelsohn, "Fantasies in Children Prior to Herniorrhaphy," *American Journal of Orthopsychiatry*, XXVII (1957), 800–7.

Fenichel, Otto, "The Psychoanalytic Theory of Neurosis," *Organ Neuroses*. New York: W. W. Norton & Company, Inc., 1945; Chapter 13.

Finch, Stuart M. and John M. Hess, "Ulcerative Colitis in Children," *American Journal of Psychiatry*, CXVIII (1962), 819–26.

Fitzell, G. T., "Personality Factors and Certain Attitudes toward Child Rearing among Parents of Asthmatic Children," *Psychosom. Med.*, XXI (1959), 208–17.

Frankl, Liselotte, "Self-preservation and Accident Proneness." Paper presented at the Cleveland Psychoanalytic Society, Cleveland, March, 1963.

French, Thomas and Franz Alexander, "Psychogenic Factors in Bronchial Asthma," *Psychosomatic Medicine Monograph*, I, No. 4 (1941); II, Nos. 1, 2 (1941).

Freud, A., "The Role of Bodily Illness in the Mental Life of Children," *Psychoanalytic Study of the Child*, Vol. VII. New York: International Universities Press, Inc., 1952.

Freud, Sigmund, *Patricide in Dostojewski* (1928). Standard Edition, Vol. XXI, ed. and trans. by James Strachey. London: The Hogarth Press, Ltd., 1961.

———, *Psychopathology of Everyday Life* (1901), Standard Edition, Vol. VI, ed. and trans. by James Strachey. London: The Hogarth Press, Ltd., 1960.

———, *The Psychogenesis of a Case of Homosexuality in a Woman* (1920), Standard Editon, Vol. XVIII, ed. and trans. by James Strachey. London: The Hogarth Press, Ltd., 1955.

Fries, M. E., "Psychosomatic Relationships between Mother and Infant," *Psychosomatic Medicine*, VI (1944), 159–62.

———, and P. J. Woolf, "Some Hypotheses on the Role of the Congenital Activity Type in Personality Development," *Psychoanalytic Study of the Child*, Vol. VIII. New York: International Universities Press, Inc., 1953.

Gantt, W. H., *Experimental Basis for Neurotic Behavior*. New York: Paul Hoeber, 1944.

Garner, A. M. and C. W. Wenar, *The Mother-Child Interaction in Psychosomatic Disorders*. Urbana, Ill.: University of Illinois Press, 1959.

Gerard, Margaret W., "Genesis of Psychosomatic Symptoms in Infancy," in F. Deutsch, *The Psychosomatic Concept in Psychoanalysis.* New York: International Universities Press, Inc., 1953.

Gottschalk, Louis A., "Effects of Intensive Psychotherapy on Epileptic Children," *Archives of Neurology and Psychiatry,* No. 70 (1953), pp. 361–68.

———, "Psychologic Conflict and Electroencephalographic Patterns," *Archives of Neurology and Psychiatry,* No. 73 (1955), pp. 656–63.

———, "The Relationship of Psychologic State and Epileptic Activity," *Psychoanalytic Study of the Child,* Vol. XI. New York: International Universities Press, Inc., 1956.

Graham, F. K., R. G. Matarazzo, and B. M. Caldwell, "Behavioral Differences Between Normal and Traumatized Newborns: II. Standardization, Reliability and Validity," *Psychological Monographs,* No. 70 (1956), 17–33.

Greenbaum, M. and J. A. Buehler, "Further Findings on the Intelligence of Children with Cerebral Palsy," *American Journal of Mental Deficiency,* LXV (1960), 261–64.

Greenwood, M. and H. M. Woods, "The Incidence of Industrial Accidents, with Special Reference to Multiple Accidents," *Industrial Fatigue Research Board Report* (London), 4 (1919).

Grinker, Roy, *Psychosomatic Research.* New York: W. W. Norton & Company, Inc., 1953.

Grossman, H. J. and N. H. Greenberg, "Psychosomatic Differentiation in Infancy: 1. Autonomic Activity in the Newborn," *Psychosomatic Medicine,* XIX (1957), 293–306.

Haring, Norris G., "A Review of Research on Cerebral Palsy and Emotional Adjustment," *Exceptional Children,* XXVI (1959), 191–94.

Harway, Vivian T., "Self-evaluation and Goal-setting Behavior in Orthopedically Handicapped Children," in E. Philip Trapp and Philip Himelstein, *Readings on the Exceptional Child.* New York: Appleton-Century-Crofts, Inc., 1962, pp. 568–82.

Hebb, D. O. "The Innate Organization of Visual Activity: I. Perception of Figures by Rats Reared in Total Darkness," *Journal of Genetic Psychology,* LI (1937), 101–26.

Heider, F. and G. M. Heider, "Studies in the Psychology of the Deaf: No. 2," *Psychological Monographs,* LIII, No. 242 (1941).

Hohman, L. B. and D. K. Freedheim, "Further Studies on Intelligence Levels in Cerebral Palsied Children," *American Journal of Physical Medicine,* XXXVII (1958), 90–97.

Impellaria, Constance, "The Hospitalized Child: The Contribution of Social Group Work," *American Journal of Orthopsychiatry,* XXV (1955), 306–12.

Jessner, Lucie, "Some Observation on Children Hospitalized During Latency," in Lucie Jessner and Eleanor Pavenstedt, *Dynamic Psychopathology in Childhood.* New York: Grune & Stratton, Inc., 1959.

———, Gaston Blom, and Samuel Waldfogel, "Emotional Implications of Tonsillectomy and Adenoidectomy on Children," *Psychoanalytic Study of the Child,* Vol. VII. New York: International Universities Press, Inc., 1952.

———, et al., "Emotional Impact of Nearness and Separation for the Asthmatic Child and His Mother," *Psychoanalytic Study of the Child,* Vol. X. New York: International Universities Press, Inc., 1955.

Josselyn, I. M., Albert Simon, and E. Eells, "Anxiety in Children Convalescing from Rheumatic Fever," *American Journal of Orthopsychiatry,* XXV (1955), 109–20.

Kaplan, H. I. and H. S. Kaplan, "Current Theoretical Concepts in Psychosomatic Medicine," *American Journal of Psychiatry,* CXV (1959), 1091–97.

Kessler, Jane W., "The Impact of Physical Disability on the Child," *Physical Therapy,* XLVI (1966), 153–59.

Klein, George S., "Blindness and Isolation," *Psychoanalytic Study of the Child,* Vol. XVII. New York: International Universities Press, Inc., 1962.

Langford, W. S., et al., "Pilot Study of Childhood Accidents: Preliminary Report," *Pediatrics,* XI (1953), 405–15.

LeShan, L., "Dynamics in Accident Prone Behavior," *Psychiatry,* XV (1952-a), 73–80.

———, "The Safety Prone," *Psychiatry,* XV (1952-b), 465–68.

Liddell, H., "The Role of Vigilance in the Development of Animal Neuroses," in Hoch and Zubin, *Anxiety.* New York: Grune & Stratton, Inc., 1950.

Lipton, E. L., A. Steinschneider and J. B. Richmond, "Autonomic Function in the Neonate: II. Physiologic Effects of Motor Restraint," *Psychosomatic Medicine,* XXII (1960), 57–64.

———, ———, "Autonomic Function in the Neonate: III. Methodological Considerations,"

Psychosomatic Medicine, XXIII (1961), 461–71.

———, ———, "Autonomic Function in the Neonate: IV. Individual Differences in Cardiac Reactivity," *Psychosomatic Medicine,* XXIII (1961), 472–84.

Louttit, C. M., *Clinical Psychology of Exceptional Children,* 3rd Edition. New York: Harper & Row, Publishers, 1957.

Lowenfeld, Berthold, "The Effects of Blindness on the Cognitive Functions of Children," *The Nervous Child,* VII (1948), 45–54.

Lustman, Seymour, "Rudiments of the Ego," *Psychoanalytic Study of the Child,* Vol. XI. New York: International Universities Press, Inc., 1956.

Mac Gregor, F. C., *et al., Facial Deformities and Plastic Surgery: A Psychosocial Study.* Springfield, Ill.: Charles C Thomas, Publisher, 1953.

Mahl, G. F., "Anxiety, HCL Secretion, and Peptic Ulcer Etiology," *Psychosomatic Medicine,* XII (1950), 158–69.

Marcus, W., *et al.,* "An Interdisciplinary Approach to Accident Patterns in Children," *Monographs of the Society for Research in Child Development,* Vol. XXV, No. 2 (1960).

Margolin, S. G., "Psychotherapeutic Principles in Psychosomatic Practice," in E. D. Wittkower and R. A. Cleghorn, *Recent Developments in Psychosomatic Medicine.* Philadelphia: J. B. Lippincott, Co., 1957.

Masland, R. L., "Researches into the Prenatal Factors that Lead to Neuropsychiatric Sequelae in Childhood," in G. Caplan, *Prevention of Mental Disorders in Children.* New York: Basic Books, Inc., 1961.

Mattsson, Ake and Samuel Gross, "Social and Behavioral Studies on Hemophilic Children and Their Families," *Journal of Pediatrics,* to be published, 1966.

McAndrew, H., "Rigidity and Isolation: A Study of the Deaf and Blind" (1948), in E. P. Trapp and P. Himelstein, *Readings on the Exceptional Child.* New York: Appleton-Century-Crofts, Inc., 1962.

Michaels, J. J., "A Psychiatric Adventure in Comparative Pathophysiology of the Infant and Adult," *Journal of Nervous and Mental Diseases,* C (1944), 49–63.

Michel-Smith, Harold, "Sensory Deprivation: A New Approach to Emotional Problems of the Child with a Hearing Loss," *Journal of Speech and Hearing Disorders,* XXVII (1962), 290–94.

Myklebust, Helmer and Milton Brutten, "A Study of the Visual Perception of Deaf Children," *Acta Oto-Laryngologica Supplemtum* CV (1953).

National Health Education Committee, *Facts on the Major Killing and Crippling Diseases in the U.S. Today.* New York: The National Health Education Committee, 1955.

Newbold, E. M., "A Contribution to the Study of the Human Factor in the Causation of Accidents," *Industrial Fatigue Research Board Report* (London), 34 (1926).

Oleron, P., "Conceptual Thinking of the Deaf," *American Annals of the Deaf,* XCVIII (1953), 304–10.

Omwake, Eveline and A. J. Solnit, "It Isn't Fair: The Treatment of a Blind Child," *Psychoanalytic Study of the Child,* Vol. XVI. New York: International Universities Press, Inc., 1961.

Pasamanick, B. and H. Knoblock, "Epidemiologic Studies on the Complications of Pregnancy and Birth Process," in G. Caplan, *Prevention of Mental Disorders in Children.* New York: Basic Books, Inc., 1961.

Pintner, R., J. Eisenson, and Mildred Stanton, *The Psychology of the Physically Handicapped.* New York: Appleton-Century-Crofts, Inc., 1941.

Plank, Emma, "Preparing Children for Surgery," *Ohio State Medical Journal,* LIX (1963), 809–11.

———, *Working with Children in Hospitals.* Cleveland: Press of Western Reserve University, 1962.

Prugh, Dane G., "Toward an Understanding of Psychosomatic Concepts in Relation to Illness in Children," in A. J. Solnit and S. A. Provence, *Modern Perspectives in Child Development,* New York: International Universities Press, Inc., 1963.

———, *et al.,* "A Study of the Emotional Reactions of Children and Families to Hospitalization and Illness," *American Journal of Orthopsychiatry,* XXIII (1953), 70–106.

Reinhart, Richard A., "Some Relationships between Early Rheumatic Fever, Intelligence, and Anxiety Scores," *Journal of Child Psychology and Psychiatry,* VI (1965), 243–51.

Richmond, Julius B. and Earle Lipton, "Some Aspects of the Neurophysiology of the Newborn and Their Implications for Child Development," in Lucie Jessner and Eleanor Pavenstedt, *Dynamic Psychopathology in Childhood.* New York: Grune & Stratton, Inc., 1959.

———, ———, and A. Steinschneider, "Observations on Differences in Autonomic Nervous System Function between and within Individuals during Early Infancy," *Journal of Child Psychiatry*, I (1962), 83–91.

———, and Seymour Lustman, "Autonomic Function in the Neonate: I. Implications for Psychosomatic Theory," *Psychosomatic Medicine*, XVII (1955), 269–75.

Riesen, A. H., "Excessive Arousal Effects of Stimulation after Early Sensory Deprivation," in P. Solomon *et al., Sensory Deprivation*. Cambridge, Mass.: Harvard University Press, 1961.

———, *et al.*, "Chimpanzees' Vision after Four Conditions of Light Deprivation," *American Psychologist*, VI (1951), 282. An abstract.

Robertson, James, *Hospitals and Children*. London: Victor Bollancz, Ltd., 1962.

Rorschach, H., *Psychodiagnostics*. Bern: Huber, 1942.

Rotter, J. B., "A Study of the Basis for Individual Differences in a Level of Aspiration Situation." Unpublished doctoral dissertation, Indiana University, 1941.

Rubin, E., "An Experiment in the Prediction of Children's Reactions to Stress by Means of Psychological Test Measures." Unpublished doctoral dissertation, Boston University, 1951.

Saul, Leon, "Psychogenic Factors in the Etiology of the Common Cold and Related Symptoms," *International Journal of Psychoanalysis*, XIX (1938), 451–70.

Schur, M., "Comments on the Metapsychology of Somatization," *Psychoanalytic Study of the Child*, Vol. X. New York: International Universities Press, Inc., 1955.

Selye, Hans, "Stress and Disease" (1955), in Charles Reed, Irving Alexander, and Silvan Tomkins, *Psychopathology: A Source Book*. Cambridge, Mass.: Harvard University Press, 1958.

Senn, M. J. E., "Emotional Aspects of Convalescence," *The Child*, X (1945), 24–28.

Sever, J. A., *Johnny Goes to the Hospital*, Boston: Houghton Mifflin Company, 1953.

Simenon, Georges, *The Bells of Bicetre*. Les Anneaux de Bicetre (1963). New York: Harcourt, Brace & World, Inc., Signet Book (1965).

Solomon, P., *et al.*, eds., *Sensory Deprivation*. Cambridge, Mass.: Harvard University Press, 1961.

Sontag, L. W., "The Significance of Fetal Environmental Differences," *American Journal of Obstetrics and Gynecology*, XLII (1941), 996–1003.

Sperling, M., "The Role of the Mother in Psychosomatic Disorders in Children," *Psychosomatic Medicine*, XI (1949), 377–85.

Sundberg, Norman, "She Loved Me, She Loved Me Not, My Mother," *Contemporary Psychology*, VI (1961), 219–20. A review of A. M. Garner and C. Wenar, *The Mother-Child Interaction in Psychosomatic Disorders.*

Szasz, T. S., "Oral Mechanisms in Constipation and Diarrhea," *International Journal of Psychoanalysis*, XXXII (1951), 196–203.

Taboroff, Leonard H. and William H. Brown, "A Study of the Personality Patterns of Children and Adolescents with the Peptic Ulcer Syndrome," *American Journal of Orthopsychiatry*, XXIV (1954), 602–10.

Tizard, Barbara, "The Personality of Epileptics: A Discussion of the Evidence," *Psychological Bulletin*, LIX (1962), 196–210.

Tyler, L. A., *The Psychology of Human Differences*. New York: Appleton-Century-Crofts, Inc., 1956.

Wagenheim, Lillian, "The Effect of Childhood Diseases on IQ Variability," *Journal of Consulting Psychology*, XVIII (1954), 354.

———, "Learning Problems Associated with Childhood Diseases Contracted at Age Two," *American Journal of Orthopsychiatry*, XXIX (1959), 102–9.

Watson, E. Jane and Adelaide Johnson, "The Emotional Significance of Acquired Physical Disfigurement in Children," *American Journal of Orthopsychiatry*, XXVIII (1958), 85–98.

Weiss, Edward and O. S. English, *Psychosomatic Medicine*. Philadelphia: W. B. Saunders Company, 1943; 3rd Edition, 1957.

Werner, H. and A. A. Strauss, "Pathology of Figure-Background Relation in the Child," *Journal of Abnormal and Social Psychology*, XXXVI (1941), 236–48.

Wolf, S. and H. G. Wolff, *Human Gastric Function*, 2nd Edition. New York: Oxford University Press, Inc., 1947.

Wolff, H. G., "Life Stress and Disease: A Formulation," in H. G. Wolff, S. Wolf, and C. C. Hare, *Life Stress and Bodily Disease*. Baltimore: Williams & Wilkins, Co., 1950.

Wright, Beatrice A., *Physical Disability: A Psychological Approach*. New York: Harper & Row, Publishers, 1960.

14

PSYCHOTHERAPY FOR CHILDREN

Our discussion of clinical problems contained many references to the treatment of specific conditions, the methods employed, and the results. In this chapter, we are concerned with the techniques of therapy, the theories underlying different therapeutic approaches, and the problems of evaluating the results. No reference is made to drug therapy or physical treatment of any kind, because it is assumed that these would not be employed by nonmedical workers. Our focus is on direct work with children; work with parents is discussed in Chapter 15.

As the reader will soon see, there are many kinds of psychological treatment, and they are based on widely differing premises concerning the origin of pathology. Futhermore, there is no empirical evidence that any one method is better than the others; in fact, there is as yet no statistical proof that psychotherapy is better than leaving the child alone. There is no doubt, however, that psychotherapy in various guises is here to stay: People will continue to ask for advice and help as they have done since time immemorial, and professionals working with children will have to make decisions and recommend courses of action. They cannot take refuge in citing published differences of opinion; they must take some sort of stand regarding an individual problem which comes to their professional attention. Therefore, this chapter concludes with a number of miscellaneous, but practical observations based on clinical experience.

Historical Development of Child Psychotherapy

The Emergence of Dynamic Psychotherapy

In his historical chronicle of the evolution of psychotherapy, Walter Bromberg remarks that even in distant centuries there were attempts to heal the demented by magic charms, herb medicines, and exorcism of demons. In Bromberg's opinion, modern medicine came to grips with mental healing in the eighteenth and the nineteenth centuries, and Mesmer was the first medical psychotherapist. In 1765, Mesmer stated his theory that the celestial bodies act on human beings through a kind of fluid which he called "animal magnetism," and Mesmerism soon became an influential cult, complete with gadgets, costumes, and showmanship. Although it was officially branded as quackery by contemporary medical societies, it had to be acknowledged that Mesmer achieved cures, and one of the prominent physicians of Paris, Charles d'Eslon, prophetically explained them as the effect of "none other than imagination itself, whose power is as extensive as it is little known" *(Bromberg, 1954, p. 173).*

The work of Mesmer proved to eighteenth-century Europe that one man can affect another. The undeniable transference of thought was said to occur through rapport between patient and physician. Although the nature of this relationship was erroneously interpreted, the power of rapport was never forgotten. Mesmerism was recognized as hypnosis by succeeding generations and stripped of its trappings. The literature on the subject during the 1880's was mainly devoted to inquiries into the nature of hypnosis. H. Bernheim asserted that hypnotism was no more than an intensification of normal suggestion. And suggestion, said Bernheim, is a ubiquitous force, used by the mother to persuade her child, used by the teacher to influence his pupil, and used by the state to control its citizenry.

One therapeutic approach, employed by the "Nancy School," was simply to use the authoritative weight of the physician to talk the patient out of his ills. Bromberg's quotations indicate that they had the same problems in child psychopathology as we have now, but the reported results were sensational. Lazy children were converted into industrious children; idiots were taught to read and write in two months:

Stupid children are made gifted by this discovery of hypnotism with mere verbal suggestion and instruction. By this process children become mere machines, and their studies may be directed the way their parents incline . . . The confirmed bad habits of years' standing are now also cured by hypnotism. It is claimed that in fifty years more such a thing as a chronic drunkard will be unknown. *(Bernheim, 1889, p. 187.)*

Exhortative and inspirational psychotherapy was practiced well into the twentieth century and still has its place. One of the most famous practitioners of this century was Coué, who put the burden of cure on the patient's will power. In an effortless singsong way, but with great faith, the patient told himself, "Day by day, in every way, I am getting better and better" *(1923).* Bromberg observes that a century of experience with hypnosis established its usefulness and that a century of experimentation revealed that its secret lies in the patient's suggestibility. However, suggestibility did not explain all: It was necessary to introduce the concept of a second consciousness to explain the ability of the hypnotized subject to remember events which he could not recall in his normal mental state, as well as his performance, in his normal state, of acts which had been suggested to him while he was hypnotized. This second consciousness became the unconscious whose properties were first elaborated by Freud. (See Chapter 1.) Psychoanalysis became the new method of treating neuroses, although it was greeted with the same violent repudiation as its forerunners.

Evolution of Child Guidance

The child guidance movement was a result of the convergence of many forces. First, there was a new interest in child psychology at the turn of the century. The feminist movement which worked for many social reforms was thereby opening the way for the "Century of the Child" *(Key, 1909).* Laws against child labor were sponsored and passed. As compulsory education gained ground, children with problems could no longer be hidden away at home. In fact, judging from the reports of their activities, the first clinic created specifically for children (by Lightner Witmer, at the University of Pennsylvania, in 1896) was primarily concerned with the adaptation of children to the school situation. The first great American child psychologist, G. Stanley Hall, planned the first journal of child psychology to be an "international record of *educational* literature, institutions, and progress" *(1891)*.

A second great influence was the mental hygiene movement in America, initiated by the publication of *The Mind that Found Itself (Beers, 1908)*. To disprove the age-old dictum, "Once insane, always insane," became the unceasing objective of Clifford Beers and a growing corps of mental hygienists. And it was only a step from mental hygiene for adults to mental hygiene, or guidance, for children.

Third, the psychiatrists known as "the Boston group" were viewing mental disorders as maladjustments of personality rather than as diseases of the nervous system. Adolf Meyer, for one, felt strongly that all possible factors should be taken into consideration—original endowment, special personality traits, home influences, habits, stresses of the environmental situation, and bodily ailments. And his use of the developmental history led Meyer to an interest in childhood and in early prevention: "In harmony with my dynamic conceptions of most mental disorders, I had to reach out more and more toward a broader understanding of the patients, which led me to a study of the family settings and by and by also of the place where the individual first becomes a member of the community, the school." *(Meyer, 1928, p. 16)*. Psychiatric social work is thought to have had its beginnings when Adolf Meyer persuaded his wife to visit the homes of his adult hospital patients to inquire into their emotional histories and to gather data about their personalities and their illnesses. She also prepared the families for the patient's return home. This interest in the families and in the childhood experiences of adult patients paved the way for a similar interest in the families and experiences of child patients.

By 1921, there were a number of clinics for children, attached to mental hospitals, courts, schools, social agencies, and colleges, but only a few could have been called "child guidance clinics." Child guidance clinics (first established under that name in 1922 by the National Committee for Mental Hygiene and the Commonwealth Fund) emphasized a team approach to the diagnosis and treatment of children's problems. The clinic team included a psychologist and case worker who worked under the direction of a psychiatrist. In the early years provision was made for physical examination of the patients as well. The child guidance team was a first interdisciplinary endeavor and as such, was radical for its time. The disciplines were well defined in role and function: the psychiatrist had over-all responsibility and carried out the treatment; the case worker counseled the parents; the psychologist performed diagnostic tests. Professional roles have changed so that there is now much more overlapping in function. In most clinics, the social workers and psychologists, as well as the psychiatrists, treat children, in addition to their traditional roles. Bernice T. Eiduson has taken sharp issue with the traditional clinic structure on the basis that it has led to intellectual inbreeding and rigidity of professional "habits," whether they are effective or not *(1964)*. Fritz Redl, too, has complained that "the holy trinity of the child guidance team" is obsolescent because of its exclusive emphasis on one form of treatment, useful for some but not all disturbed children *(1962)*. Traditional clinic practices have also been criticized on the basis of their inefficiency and waste of valuable professional time (see Chapter 17). All these criticisms do not negate the fact that treatment of children must be accompanied by services to their parents. Also, experience in an interdisciplinary clinic setting provides an invaluable apprenticeship for the beginner in any of the many professions helping children.

The American Orthopsychiatric Association, inaugurated in 1924, has become the professional organization for child guidance workers. (The term "orthopsychiatry" was coined, by analogy with "orthopedics," to express the idea of "straight-mindedness" through therapeutic intervention at an early stage to prevent further difficulties.) Initially, only psychiatrists, psychologists, and social workers who had had clinical experience in child guidance clinics were eligible for membership. There has been a movement to change the membership requirements to include any professional person working with disturbed children, e.g., pediatricians, psychiatric nurses, teachers of emotionally disturbed children, group workers, and so forth.

Development of Child Psychoanalysis

Most of the published reports of the treatment of children have been written by psychoanalysts or psychoanalytically oriented psychologists and caseworkers. The volumes of the *Psychoanalytic Study of the Child,* which have appeared annually since 1946, are invaluable sources of discussion of theory and reports of practice in child psychopathology.

The first published report of psychoanalytic treatment of a child describes the phobia of Little Hans, which was treated by his father with the guidance of Freud *(1909, 1955),* but it was some time before children were treated directly. It is important to recall the basic differences in theory and practice between the two leading exponents of child analysis, Melanie Klein and Anna Freud (see Chapter 1).

In 1926 and 1927, Anna Freud gave a course of lectures at the Vienna Institute of Psychoanalysis on the technique and theory of child psychoanalysis and the indications for such treatment. In these lectures, Anna Freud contrasted her point of view with that of Melanie Klein, who held that every infant undergoes phases of grave abnormality and that ideally, mental health could best be safeguarded by early and universal child analysis. According to this view, the individual experience of the child is not crucial in the production

of a neurosis, nor is speech essential in the treatment. The technique is based on the interpretation of the child's play which is considered the equivalent of free associations in adult patients *(1955).* The analyst "tells" the child what his play means. In contrast, Anna Freud, and what is sometimes called "the Vienna school" of child psychoanalysis (as opposed to "the English school" of Klein) restricts the treatment of psychoanalysis to exceptional children. They consider work with the family and the educational role of the analyst to be much more important than does the English school. Interpretation of play and unconscious conflicts is much more conservative; more attention is given to the ego defenses; and the child's participation is much greater. Our discussion of the psychoanalysis of children follows the general approach of Anna Freud. In the author's opinion, many of the basic tenets of the Kleinian school are contrary to what we know about the importance of experience and maturation in child development.

Because of the continuing controversy about nonmedical persons practicing psychotherapy (which, of course, includes psychoanalysis), the facilities for training child analysts are very limited. The major training center, particularly for lay therapists, is Hampstead Clinic in London under the direction of Anna Freud. In 1963, the American Association for Child Psychoanalysis was incorporated and includes in its membership child psychoanalysts with a nonmedical as well as a medical background.

Theories and Techniques of Individual Psychotherapy

A therapist proceeds on the premise that what has been done to a child can be undone and that what has been lacking can be supplied. Choice of technique will depend on the therapist's explanation for the pathological behavior. Since one's understanding of symptoms evolves from one's view of normal development, it is logical to find that systems of therapy reflect the systems of personality theory described in Chapter 1. There are two general categories: the various psychodynamic therapies derived from psychoanalysis in one or another form and the behavior therapies derived from learning theories. Many workers, mainly psychologists, have attempted to synthesize psychodynamic and learning theory schools of thought (*Dollard and Miller, 1950; Mowrer, 1950; and Breger and McGaugh, 1965*), but the individual psychotherapist usually follows the one or the other. It has been suggested that behavior therapy is more appropriate to the training and practice of the clinical psychologist (*Franks, 1965*), but most child therapy is of the psychodynamic variety.

In the psychodynamic therapies the relationship between the psychotherapist and his patient is considered crucial. With different emphases, all these therapies involve some release of emotions, some use of play, and some effort to re-educate the child through corrective experiences and verbal explanations. The variations within the psychodynamic approach are well represented in Helen Witmer's presentation of reports on ten children treated by as many different therapists. In conclusion, she described the fallacy of simple labelling:

Other comments that might be made about these records could call attention to the fact that treatment methods are so much more varied and so much less stylized than much of the literature about child psychiatry would lead one to expect. It is popularly supposed that treatment can be categorized as Freudian, Rankian, Adlerian, and so on. These records suggest that in the actual practice of child psychiatry these terms lose much of their meaning. The underlying theory on which certain psychiatrists base their work may have been stated by one or another of the masters. Other psychiatrists draw inspiration from more than one source. In working with a child, however, none of the therapists used "textbook" patterns. Instead they responded sensitively to the children's needs as they perceived them, and they applied their knowledge in such diverse ways that the influence of the "schools" seems almost transcended by principles that are common to all psychotherapy. . . .

Finally, note will have been made of the fact that there are no magic words, no set patterns of procedure, no formulae by which the psychotherapy of children is accomplished. The phrases that are so often used in describing treatment techniques ("interpret the transference," "make the unconscious conscious," "get out the aggression," and so on) seem almost inapplicable to these cases, so remote are they from the reality of therapist and patient working together on a problem. The truth, of course, is that phrases like these are abstractions, very useful for scientific analysis but never intended to guide the practitioner in his minute-to-minute words and deeds. . . .

If it has been demonstrated that there are rules to this game (psychotherapy) but that each person must find his own way of using them—his own way of putting himself and his knowledge at the service of the patient—our aim will have been accomplished.[*]

There is a danger, when one categorizes the theories and techniques of therapy, that the shorthand symbols, the clichés and jargon of therapy, will be taken as its sum and substance. The beginner needs to know theory and needs technical advice, but these are not enough to make a good therapist. In this regard, the child therapist is like a parent—if he relies on intellectual comprehension only, his responses are slow, indecisive, unclear to the child, and lack the empathic quality which is the catalyst of treatment. However,

[*]Quoted from Helen L. Witmer, *Psychiatric Interviews with Children*. (New York: Commonwealth Fund, 1946), p. 442–43. Reproduced by permission.

there is little one can do, between the covers of a textbook, beyond presenting the abstract symbols.

Relationship Therapy

Relationship therapy is interesting because of its similarities to later therapies which go by entirely different names. It evolved from the psychoanalytic philosophy of Otto Rank at about the same time as the techniques of Melanie Klein and Anna Freud evolved from Sigmund Freud's psychoanalytic philosophy. Rank's view that the source of therapy lies in the understanding and constructive use of the patient's reaction to the therapeutic situation was the starting point for the development of procedures which were very influential in child guidance and social casework. The term "relationship therapy" was coined by John Levy in 1938. The geographical center of the school has been Philadelphia, because of the leadership of Frederick Allen, who was psychiatrist and director of the Philadelphia Child Guidance Clinic from 1925 to 1956, and of Jessie Taft, of the University of Pennsylvania School of Social Work. Taft, in 1933, and Allen, in 1942, wrote the first two books on the psychotherapy of children published in America.

In contrast to the methods involving hypnosis or suggestion, Taft and Allen both stressed the importance of the patient's active participation; indeed, Taft chose the word "therapy" in preference to the word "treatment" because it implies less manipulation. She wrote:

I wish to use the English word "therapy" with the full force of its derivation to cover a process which we recognize as somehow and somewhat curative but which, if we are honest enough and brave enough, we must admit to be beyond our control. . . . One must accept one's final limitation and the right of the other [i.e., the patient], perhaps his necessity to refuse help or to take help in his own terms, not as therapist, friends or society might choose."[*]

This emphasis on the conscious cooperation of the patient implies a corresponding de-emphasis of his unconscious and his past history. Following Rank's theory, every person shared the common trauma of birth, leaving him with a permanent fear of "individuation." Since there is obviously little to interpret regarding the physical experience of birth, uncovering and interpreting the past play relatively little part in this form of treatment. The psychotherapist's focus is on the present situation; the patient's relationship to the therapist is not interpreted in terms of transference from parent figures but rather as if it were a new experience:

"He does not want a father or a mother, but he does want someone who will permit him ultimately to find himself apart from parent identifications without interference or domination; someone who will not be fooled, someone strong enough not to retaliate."[**]

Commenting on a child guidance case, Taft writes: "Interpretation there was none, except a verbalization on my part of what the child seemed to be feeling and doing, a comparatively spontaneous response to her words or actions which should clarify or make more conscious the self of the moment whatever it might be.[***] This foreshadows Carl Rogers' non-directive treatment.

The early proponents of relationship therapy placed a unique emphasis on time, sometimes sounding somewhat mystical: "The reaction of each indi-

---

[*]From *The Dynamics of Therapy in a Controlled Relationship* by Jessie Taft. Published by Dover Publications, Inc., New York 14, N.Y. at $1.75, and reprinted through permission of the publisher.
[**]Taft, *op. cit.,* p. 9.
[***]Taft, *op. cit.,* p. 28.

vidual to limited or unlimited time betrays his deepest and most fundamental life pattern, his relation to the growth process itself, to beginnings and endings, to being born and to dying."* She suggested that the human problem might be phrased thus: "If one cannot live forever, is it worth while to live at all?* This formulation leads to an emphasis on the present and a looking neither to the past (i.e., birth) nor to the future (i.e., death).

One of the techniques of the relationship therapist is the setting of a time limit for therapy, an arbitrary calendar date which is accepted by both patient and physician as a kind of deadline. The acceptance of this time limit is viewed as part of the process of accepting reality. The importance of present time can be seen in Taft's definition of relationship therapy as a "process in which the individual finally learns to utilize the allotted hour from beginning to end without undue fear, resistance, resentment or greediness . . . if he can live this hour he has in his grasp the secret of all hours, he has conquered life and time for the moment and in principle."** The process of separation at the end of each hour and at the end of treatment is a major focus of treatment, because these separations are viewed as repetitions of the original trauma, birth. In a therapeutic experience with a favorable outcome, the patient "takes over the birth fear and transforms it into an ego achievement"*** Taft viewed the therapeutic relationship as a very intense and intimate one, representing a "depth of union never risked since birth or weaning."**** The termination of this relationship "diminishes the fear of individuation, since to leave convincingly is to find that one can bear both pain and the fear of withdrawal . . . and to discover within the self a substitute for the lost wholeness."****

Rollo May's discussion of existential psychotherapy is reminiscent of Jesse Taft's writings. He defines anxiety as the "subjective stage of the individual's becoming aware that his existence can become destroyed, that he can lose himself and his world, that he can become nothing" (1958, p. 50). The internal conflict is between the security of the present and the uncertainty of the future potential. May links this reluctance to move ahead to the birth trauma and describes death as the most obvious form of the threat of "non-being." Like Taft, the existential therapists place time in the center of the psychological picture and the significance of the present existence is for self-actualization in the future. Both these writers mix philosophy with their psychology and stress man's capacity for introspection as the source of conflict as well as the source of cure.

Allen's presentation of relationship therapy has a less philosophical ring. He is equally concerned with problems of differentiation and individuation, but he uses a physiological frame of reference (e.g., the growth processes described by G. E. Coghill). The anxiety of birth is not considered as important as its biological implications: "Birth ushers in a new and final phase of differentiation."† He shared Taft's belief in the importance of the relationship: "Therapy begins when the therapist is brought into a relationship as a supporting and clarifying influence around the patient's need and desire to gain or regain a sense of his own worth."‡ He differed from Taft not only in some of his theoretical premises, but also in some matters of technique; for instance, he does not particularly recommend setting time limits for the duration of therapy. However, he also believed firmly in the active participation of the child in helping himself, and

---

*Taft, *op. cit.*, p. 13.
**Taft, *op. cit.*, p. 17.
***Taft, *op. cit.*, p. 282.
****Taft, *op. cit.*, p. 291.

†Quoted from Frederick H. Allen, *Psychotherapy with Children*. (New York: W. W. Norton & Co., 1942), p. 22. Reproduced by permission.
‡Allen, *op. cit.*, p. 47.

tended to emphasize the present, rather than the genetic development of problems and conflicts:

Only through his own participation can the changes that have been effected have meaning that can be interwoven into the fabric of his day-to-day living. When the child has been helped to affirm the value of what he is in an active, changing world, his major focus of interest has been directed ahead and away from the shackles of an outlived past.*

It is entirely possible to take exception to a person's theories and to find much to admire in his practice. In his discussion of the therapist's role in facilitating or interfering with the therapeutic process, Allen comments that "the therapist who tries too hard to maintain an 'objective' attitude may become an automaton in a relationship with a child who needs the unobtrusive warmth of a friendly human being"** On the other hand, he does not think that mere friendliness is enough. It is possible for a therapist to be too good and understanding. "An aggressive, fighting child who has been running roughshod over every limit and every person will find more anxiety roused by the therapist who is too giving and understanding on the theory that the child needs to be 'loved' because of 'affect-deprivations.'"** Such a child, Allen feels, needs a strong person, able to allow free expression of feeling and yet able to limit freedom of action. These apt observations of Allen's confirm Witmer's remarks about the way in which psychotherapists work with their patients. After years of experience, child psychotherapists do not differ so much in what they actually do with their patients, even when they afterwards relate what they have done to widely different theoretical frames of reference. In the real work with children, neither therapist nor child has the time for abstractions.

---

*Allen, *op. cit.*, p. 306.
**Allen, *op. cit.*, p. 261.

Release Therapy

Release therapy was described by David Levy *(1938; 1939)*. It depends mainly on abreaction (i.e., acting out or talking out a suppressed emotion) for its therapeutic effect. The concept of abreaction appears in Freud's earliest writings on hysterical phenomena *(Breuer and Freud, 1893, 1955)*. If the appropriate reaction was originally suppressed, the affect remains undischarged and does not lose its hold on the subconscious. Freud felt that language could be a substitute for action, that a suppressed emotion could be talked out.

In essence, Levy applied this concept of cathartic abreaction to children by substituting the medium of play for the medium of language. He viewed it as a technique specially suited to young children who had clear symptoms which had been precipitated by a specific traumatic event (e.g., an operation) in their recent past. He did not feel that it was indicated for children with chronic problems or children from disturbed environments.

Release therapy was originally related to a clear diagnostic formulation and limited to acute reactions but, unfortunately, these are the simplest of all problems and are not often brought to child guidance personnel. When they are spotted early, it is often possible to help the parents "work through" the trauma directly with the child, without direct psychotherapy. In the more modern language of ego psychology, this "working through" process would be described as an example of turning passive behavior into active (see Chapter 2). That is, the child repeats the traumatic event, but instead of having something done *to* him, he goes through the experience again on his own terms, starting and stopping it as he wishes. In this slower repetition of the event, which he is himself controlling, the child can express the feelings and fantasies which remained unexpressed in the original experience. However the problems which crowd the clinics have multiple causes and they do not lend themselves to simple abreaction.

There are many advocates of catharsis, particularly among parents and teachers. One of the most popular exponents of the belief that the key to mental health is to express one's feelings is Dorothy Baruch, who describes the "draining off" of normal aggression: "When enough of the negative feelings have drained off and have been accepted, then more positive feelings come in" (1949, p. 42). This idea of emptying out hostile feelings, thus leaving a vacuum which will automatically be filled by "warm and good positive feelings," sounds very much like catharsis. It also sounds very simple. Parents and teachers have only to permit the child to express his emotions, safely, by words or by play.

Baruch credits the nondirective approach of Carl Rogers for the term "reflection," which she uses a good deal (Baruch, 1949, Preface). The idea of reflecting the child's feelings and thereby giving him words for his feeling and permission to express it was described by Taft. The recommendation to drain off unpleasant emotions by allowing free expression of them is linked with the philosophy of permissiveness in child rearing, the dangers of which were mentioned in our discussion of immaturity (see Chapter 7). Nevertheless, now and again a child therapist operates on this theory, and with the same disappointing results, although these therapists sometimes call it "release therapy" and believe that they are following Levy or Freud.

Play Therapy

Some of the earlier writers on the subject of play discussed it as a way of gaining an understanding of children (Conn, 1939). It was J. C. Solomon who first published articles dealing with play as a technique of treatment (1938; 1940).

Work with children invariably involves play, but therapists make different uses of it. Kleinian analysts use it for symbolic interpretations of unconscious conflicts. Allen remarks that play is the child's natural form of expression, a language that brings him into a communicating relationship with others and with the world in which he lives. The play is regarded not as the "port of entry to the past and to the unconscious," but as an indication of what the child is feeling in the here and now (1942). In Allen's view, the therapist should follow the lead of the child and offer only general guidance in helping the child express himself (1942). Other therapists, (e.g., Levy, 1939) deliberately plan the play materials and steer the games. Family dolls may be made to carry on conversations that are built around specific situations which are thought to be the source of the child's fear or other difficulty. Such purposeful use of play is, of course, designed to set the stage for abreaction and catharsis.

Virginia Axline discusses play in the context of nondirective therapy. It is neither planned in advance (in the fashion of Levy, Conn, and Solomon) nor is it symbolically interpreted (in the fashion of Klein). Like Taft and Allen, she considers the nature of the relationship that is created between the therapist and the child to be the deciding factor in the success or failure of the therapy. The following list is a brief restatement of her eight basic principles (1947, p. 75):

1. The therapist must develop a warm friendly relationship with the child.
2. The therapist accepts the child exactly as he is.
3. The therapist establishes a feeling of permissiveness in the relationship.
4. The therapist is alert to recognize the feelings and to reflect the feelings back to the child so that he gains insight into his behavior.

5. The therapist maintains a deep respect for the child's ability to solve his own problems.
6. The child leads the way; the therapist follows.
7. The therapist does not attempt to hurry the therapy along.
8. The therapist establishes only those limitations that are necessary to anchor the therapy to the world of reality and to make the child aware of his responsibility in the relationship.

Axline emphasizes the naturalness and spontaneity of play therapy. In her view, it is not necessary for the child to be aware that he has a problem; he may benefit without being aware that he has done anything more than play. There are no diagnostic interviews, and interpretation of the play is ruled out "as far as it is possible to do so." The child's disturbed behavior is attributed to blocking by exterior forces, i.e., the criticalness and domination of adult persons. With this concept of cause, it is surprising that so little is said about the work with the parents and so much reliance is placed on the curative effects of the relatively few hours with the therapist. In the therapeutic relationship, the child reveals his "true self"; he is accepted, he grows in self-confidence and "he is more able to extend the frontier of his personality expression."[*] Like Allen, she stresses the child's potential for growth. In this they follow the maturational theory of development which was discussed in Chapter 1.

The crux of nondirective play therapy lies in the complete acceptance of the child; of course, he must have some feeling for the therapist or the therapist's acceptance of him would have no significance. In Carl Rogers' introduction to Axline's book, which is directed especially to teachers and workers in schools, he writes that it is, "on the surface, an account of the way in which a teacher has come to function as a therapist, to release the curative forces which exist within each individual."[**] This treatment approach would seem most useful for mild developmental disturbances. In his summary of relevant researches in the field of play therapy, A. G. Woltmann commented that all the studies were based on data collected during comparatively brief contacts with supposedly normal children (1952). It is doubtful that one could rely only on the therapeutic powers of acceptance and the natural drive for growth to help the majority of emotionally disturbed children referred for treatment.

Child Analysis and Analytically Oriented Psychotherapy

These treatments are most commonly employed in child guidance clinics. Anna Freud, in a brief exposition (1946-a), describes an introductory phase during which the psychoanalyst tries to induce in the child the readiness and willingness for treatment which are usually missing. Through a variety of techniques which depend on the particular situation, the psychoanalyst tries to help the child to gain insight into his problem and to be eager to change it. This is the point at which adherents of some other schools would begin, but the psychoanalyst considers it a milestone.

The child psychoanalyst sees her patients three, four, or five times a week. This promotes an intense relationship and a continuity of the flow of material; it also makes it unnecessary for the patient to remain long alone with the anxiety which may be aroused by treatment. He can look forward to seeing his therapist the next day, and so has less need to erect defenses against his anxiety.

Psychoanalytic techniques vary with the age and ability of the child, with

---

[*]Quoted from Virginia M. Axline, *Play Therapy* (Boston: Houghton Mifflin Company, 1947), p. 24. Reproduced by permission of the publisher.

[**]Axline, *op. cit.*, p. vii.

the nature of his symptoms, and with his general character. Children are much more likely to bring daydreams than night dreams for interpretation, and often begin a sequence of make-believe situations which facilitate interpretation and understanding of their problems. Kolansky's case of the three-year-old stutterer is a good example of psychoanalytic treatment (see Chapter 7). The following material, from the psychoanalysis of Ralph, illustrates a child's way of telling about himself and his inner conflicts.

Ralph began to have psychoanalytic treatment at five, for a variety of chronic problems, including separation anxiety, enuresis, phobias, and destructive and aggressive behavior. Early in his third year of treatment he became interested in making puppets, and for almost ten months puppet play was a major occupation in treatment. Through the puppets, Ralph brought out his conflicts between his wishes and his conscience. Themes in the puppet play were linked with events in his daily life through asides.

He named the two main puppet characters Good Bob and Bad Bill. He was always Good Bob, and the therapist was Bad Bill. Good Bob was a model child; he was also bright and wealthy. Bill was a boy of poor stock, always in need of money, brains, or friends. Bad Bill was always getting into fights, was antagonistic, was a braggart, and Good Bob was the first friend he had ever had. Bill was miserably unhappy, could say so (via the therapist), and sought Bob's advice about getting along with people. Bill was always treated harshly and shabbily at home, and Bob began to advise him that love, kindness, and firmness can conquer all. Bob had a room full of jungle animals that he had tamed; he told Bill that he achieved this by training them patiently. He gave them instructions, was patient when they failed, and rewarded them when they succeeded. Bill asked if this would work with people, and Bob assured him it would—the wild animals would never have responded if he had beaten or rebuffed them.

Bob's reform (in identification with the therapist) of Bill proceeded. However, Bob began to decline into a boy who was forever having all wishes gratified. He ate sweets perpetually, went to bed when he wished, and always had money to buy what he wanted. The therapist began to challenge his being "Good Bob," inasmuch as all people have to live by rules, do without things they want, and learn to wait for some of what they desire. There began to be less contrast between Good Bob after a while (the perfection of superego) and Bad Bill (instincts out of control). Bill managed to control his behavior, and Bob's deterioration was reversed so that he no longer indulged himself constantly. Yet he continued to be fabulously successful and wealthy—he was a marvel of a baseball player and his family owned swimming pools, lakes, and amusement parks.

Bob preferred males and had no contact with girls. As "Bill," the therapist began to refer to his mother and sisters. This introduced other major points of conflict, concern, and confusion. Ralph was unable to discuss any sexual topics, pretending to know all the answers or to have no interest. But in the puppet play, Bob's mother was going to have a new baby only four months after having another baby. As Bill, the therapist challenged Bob on this and chided him for being so ignorant about "baby things" when he was expert on all other topics. Then Bob admitted his ignorance and asked Bill how long it took a baby to grow in the mother "once it was started." Ralph's repression and denial could be seen in Bob's "forgetting" these facts from day to day. Bill showed Bob that he had trouble learning about babies, surprising since he learned other things so quickly.

As time went by, Bill and Bob had many other concerns—big brothers and girl friends (when the puppets reached age 14) and entering the Armed Services (when they reached the proper age for induction at 18 years). When the therapist remarked that Bill and Bob had left the world of girl friends to enter a world of men, Ralph suggested that they go back to being 10 years old. The therapist interpreted this as a wish to regress every time he came near grown-up ideas or feelings, especially if they had to do with marrying and making babies.

The puppets indicated many conflicts that Ralph was avoiding. After they were worked out with the puppets, they could be directed back to the real Ralph. It was as if he had to know the ending before he could relate them to himself. The therapist exploited the puppets but they were Ralph's idea. Other children might not take to this mode of expression.

Play materials are provided, but nothing is contrived by the therapist. However, the psychoanalyst may enter into the play, in order to guide the child toward areas of conflict. In Ralph's case, the analyst's interpretations were made in the guise of Bill. Drawing is also often used, for in their drawings children may express specific conflicts and general personality difficulties. One nine-year-old drew only tiny figures and objects in miniature form. After a while, the therapist could show him that he saw himself as tiny and insignificant. Another boy used an exaggerated, cartoon style, making his figures ugly and monstrous. Another drew scenes of stalemates and still lives; another drew scenes of violence and explosions; yet another drew scenes of suspense and watchful waiting. Such drawings speak as loudly as words, and the child can see the truth for himself. One also uses the actual words of the child and the events of everyday life as he reports them or as the parents bring them to the psychoanalyst's attention.

What is done with this material? This depends on the stage of the analysis. It may be simple reflection (in the style of Rogers) or it may be labelling (à la Dollard and Miller) in which the therapist gives the child names for his feelings and permission to have them. The psychoanalyst may teach discrimination, by pointing out the difference between reality and fantasy, or between thought and action. There may be education when the analyst tries to explain the behavior of people or things. There may be reassurance that the child is not as bad, damaged, or stupid as he thought himself to be.

The technique which belongs uniquely to psychoanalysis is called "interpretation." Briefly, this consists of making connections for the child where he himself sees none. Sometimes these connections are between the past and the present; sometimes, between a defense and a feeling; sometimes, between a fantasy and a feeling. Taken out of the context of the total case material, it is difficult to give the rationale on which any specific interpretation is based. The timing, wording, and reasons for the interpretations involve skills which cannot be briefly communicated, but the following are typical interpretations.

Connections between the past and the present are frequently made in connection with transference. The patient feels something about, or expects something from, the therapist on the basis of previous experiences. The patient has a kind of set which he himself does not recognize. For instance:

A therapist who has been seeing a ten-year-old girl for some time starts to see a boy patient the preceding hour. Nothing is said about the new patient; in fact, the therapist is not sure if the girl is aware of the new situation. Shortly, however, the girl's behavior changes: She does not want to leave anything in the office, she is very critical of herself, and she removes all her drawings from the wall. After a while, the therapist suggests that she no longer feels so comfortable in the office because she feels she is sharing it with someone new. She does not trust the therapist to take care of her things if left behind. Further, she feels her productions are no good and believes that the therapist will not admire her any more. After identifying, or labelling, her change of heart, the therapist goes on to say that this must have been the way she felt when her younger brother was born many years ago.

Connections between a defense and a feeling are probably the most frequently offered. Varieties of defense are almost endless (see Chapter 3), and these need to be identified before major unconscious conflicts (e.g., castration anxiety, penis envy, or Oedipal rivalry) are handled:

One six-year-old boy entered psychoanalysis for a number of problems, including enuresis, occasional soiling, and aggressive behavior. Soon after, he got into a fight on his way home from school with another boy whom he described as very "big and tough." As he talked about this boy, it became clear that he had been frightened and had fought the boy in the manner that he expected the boy to fight him. He had turned his fear of attack into an act of aggression, but the other boy was really harmless. In the treatment which followed, there were countless opportunities to show that the patient acted aggressively whenever he was frightened. It was a milestone in his psychoanalysis when he could feel and recognize his anxiety without covering it up with wild behavior.

Connections between a fantasy and a feeling play a part in every interpretation, if fantasy is defined as an unrealistic expectation. However, it sometimes appears in fairly simple form:

One eight-year-old frequently complained of nausea and stomach-ache when she was in certain situations—school, her bedroom, or visiting her grandparents—but she considered the place the cause of her stomach-ache. One day, she described a visit to an amusement park but, in the midst of her gusto about the pleasures there, she suddenly had a stomach-ache and could not go on. It was possible to discover that her stomach-ache began when she thought about her trip through a fun house which contained terrifying monsters. She could see that the stomach-ache was replacing her memory of these awful things and, as she talked about them, it disappeared. This was only a small step toward finding out what memories evoked the pains in the other situations, but before this, she had not been able to imagine any possible connections between her thoughts and her pains.

Perhaps the single word "insight" best defines the goal of psychoanalysis. The therapist hopes that the child will learn enough about himself to recognize his feelings and his defenses and deal with them directly. In the process of achieving this, one tries to make the unconscious conscious to the child. Anna Freud compares it to the task of adult psychoanalysis, "to undo the various repressions, distortions, displacements, condensations, etc., which had been brought about by the neurotic defense mechanisms, until, with the active help of the child, the unconscious content of the material was laid bare" *(1946-a, p. 71).* Child psychoanalysts work above all on the past, thereby providing a cleared and improved ground for future development. This does not imply, however, that the child receives permission for anything and everything:

He [the analyst] has to allow and forbid, loosen and bind again. If he does not succeed in this, analysis becomes the child's charter for all the ill conduct prohibited by society. But if he succeeds, he undoes a piece of wrong education and abnormal development, and so procures for the child, or whoever controls its destiny, an opportunity to improve matters. *(A. Freud, 1946 a, p. 49.)*

It is important to keep in mind that psychoanalysis was devised for neurotic patients, and that neurosis is only one form of emotional disturbance (see Chapter 10). Psychoanalysis involves undoing repressions which were created by unrealistic anxiety stimulated by the parents' attitudes or the child's fantasies. Borrowing Eysenck's terms, analysis is for children who suffer from "surplus conditioned responses," rather than for those who have "deficient conditioned responses" *(1960, p. 17).* It is not the treatment of choice for children who are acting out their problems because of poor training, nor for children who are living under intolerable conditions, nor for children with weak or defective egos. Anna Freud believes that psychoanalysis should be used sparingly, for those children whose development is arrested because of neurotic conflict and for whom the hope of spontaneous recovery is slight.

Child psychoanalysts use their understanding of child development and psychopathology in many ways other than classical psychoanalysis. One example is in psychoanalytically oriented psychotherapy, in which the goal is less ambitious (*Arthur, 1952*). Briefly, the psychoanalyst tries to relieve the child of the symptoms which place him at odds with his environment. He sees him only once or twice a week, a reduction in treatment time which usually means that he more actively directs the activity during the hour and more frequently points out the child's feelings and defenses. The psychotherapist will be more selective than the psychoanalyst; he will let some things go while he concentrates on others. The treatment of the school phobia of Mary Ann is a good example of analytically oriented psychotherapy (see Chapter 10).

It is difficult to demonstrate the technical differences between psychoanalysis and psychoanalytically oriented therapy without detailed case material, but the differences derive chiefly from the objectives. The six-year-old boy who attacked when he was frightened can serve as an illustration. One may simply wish to bring the aggressive behavior to an end, and go no further than to interpret it as a defense against anxiety. The psychoanalyst would probably inquire: why should the child be expecting attack? This particular boy's anxious expectation was born out of a wish for attack, specifically for an attack that would turn him into a girl. (He had repeatedly tried to injure his genitals.) The psychoanalyst then proceeded to investigate the origin of such an overwhelming anxiety about sexual differences. Sometimes, after treatment

is begun, one changes one's objective and some of these technical differences are obliterated. The level of therapy depends on the child's needs and on what his ego can tolerate. It is not a question of reserving psychoanalysis only for the "more sick" and therapy for the "more healthy," but rather a question of the complexity and structure of the emotional illness.

Psychotherapy in the Light of Learning Theory

The psychologists' unique contribution to psychotherapy has been made in terms of learning principles which were first developed in the animal laboratory. O. H. Mowrer (*1950*) and John Dollard and Neal Miller (*1950*) were among the first to make a systematic attempt to relate learning theory to psychotherapy. Their major premise is that neurotic behavior is learned and must therefore conform to the laws of learning. Psychotherapy, then, involves unlearning through some combination of the same principles by which the maladjustment was acquired. The principle of reinforcement is analogous to Freud's pleasure principle.

Mowrer (*1939*) was the first to state the hypothesis that fear or anxiety can serve as a drive (i.e., a motive for behavior) and that reduction of fear can serve as a reinforcement (i.e., a reward). Neurotic symptoms are self-perpetuating because of the reinforcement which arises from their reduction of anxiety. Learning theorists view the source of anxiety as external: anxiety is fear of punishment by others. Considerable emphasis is put on the social conditions which impart attitudes of goodness or badness. As we mentioned in Chapter 1, the concept of drives is a major point of difference in the viewpoints of psychoanalysts and learning theorists. Learning theorists believe there are many drives, if not an infinite number, which can be arranged in a hierarchy and which develop out of each other. Sex and aggression are considered particularly important only because their expression is so often punished in our society. However, learning theorists are by no means unanimous. The differences among them are as great as among psychoanalysts.

The Dynamic View. Dollard and Miller offered few innovations in technique; on the contrary, they followed the "one type of therapeutic practice with which we are familiar—namely, the Freudian" *(1950, Preface).* Their contribution was a new look at the old therapy, a reformulation of psychoanalysis using the language and concepts of Hull's theory of learning. The psychotherapist is described as a special kind of teacher:

> . . . someone with prestige who pays favorable attention, listens sympathetically, and holds out hope by having enough faith in an eventual cure to attempt treatment. The therapist shows exceptional permissiveness; he encourages the patient to express feelings in speech (but not in direct action) in the therapeutic situation . . . By encouraging the patient to talk and consistently failing to punish him, the therapist creates a social situation that is the exact opposite of the one originally responsible for attaching strong fears to talking and thinking. The patient talks about frightening topics. Since he is not punished, his fears are extinguished *(1950, p. 230).*

The therapist does more than "decondition" the patient by accepting his bad feelings. He also helps the patient to discriminate between thoughts and actions and between his childhood helplessness and his adult situation. The reduction in fear is generalized from the therapeutic situation to the rest of the patient's life, giving him new courage. The success of his new activities reinforces his new attitudes and begins a cycle in which success begets success. In addition, the relief of "stoppage of thinking" (i.e., re-

pression) has the effect of restoring the higher mental processes, which can then be used for discrimination, reasoning, foresight, adaptive problem solving, and the like.

The Moral View. The dynamic view of Dollard and Miller can be contrasted with the moral view which Mowrer has developed over the years. Mowrer also began with the general concepts of Freudian analysis, and reinterpreted them in terms of his two-factor theory of learning. He took exception to what he called the Freudian assumptions regarding the direction and content of repression and argued that the "neurotic ego" remains dominated by the id and directs repressive action against the superego *(1953).* Ten years later, Mowrer emphasized even more strongly the role of guilt in the production of a neurosis. "There was a growing indication that in so-called neurosis we are dealing, not with a mere 'guilt complex,' but with *real* guilt" *(1963-b, p. 579).* In other words, he considers the patient's anxiety as realistic and justified. In the course of therapy, the patient reveals bad thoughts and feelings about which he ought to feel guilty and for which he ought to make restitution. "My own clinical experience leads me to believe that neurotic difficulties commonly, if not invariably, have their roots in unresolved personal guilt, rather than in the unfortunate or traumatic things which 'happen' *to us*" *(1963-b, p. 578).* He suggests that the way for the patient to feel better is to act better.

This has led Mowrer to change his psychotherapeutic techniques radically. Instead of the privacy and confidentiality traditional in psychotherapy, he recommends a "radical openness," a deliberate admission of his misdeeds, by the patient, to a small circle of friends and relatives. A confession to be followed by restitution and rectification of past misdeeds *(1963-a).* Mowrer's equation of mental illness with irresponsibility makes mental health an ethical issue. The way for persons to cease being irresponsible, and therefore sick, is for them to become responsible (i.e., to be meticulously honest, reliable, generous, cooperative, and moral). This seems like a rather harsh and narrow view of mental health and mental illness and runs counter to the thinking which prompts us to teach children to recognize and tolerate their bad thoughts, which are not really harmful unless they are converted into action.

Behavior Theory. Still a third learning approach to therapy is the mechanistic approach of J. Wolpe *(1958)* and H. J. Eysenck *(1960)*:

From the point of view of learning theory, treatment is in essence a very simple process. In the case of surplus conditioned responses, treatment should consist in the extinction of these responses; in the case of deficient conditioned responses, treatment should consist in the building up of the missing stimulus connections. *(Eysenck, 1960, p. 9.)*

Eysenck then describes methods of treatment, which he terms "behavior therapy," in contrast to "psychotherapy." To a large extent, behavior therapy is a British import, although some American psychologists have become interested in it. There are four main variants of behavior therapy: *reciprocal inhibition; negative practice; aversion therapy;* and *positive conditioning.*

Wolpe has most fully developed *reciprocal inhibition* as a therapeutic tool. Briefly, the process involves the extinction of the neurotic response X to a given stimulus S by associating S with a new response R, which is incompatible with the old neurotic response X. His technique involves "systematic desensitization based on relaxation." The relaxation responses are "taught" in order to inhibit the former anxiety responses producing the symptoms *(1958)*.

We also know this approach as *de-conditioning*, the therapeutic properties of which were first demonstrated by M. C. Jones. She reduced fear reactions in a group of children, of one to four, by coupling the feared objects with pleasant stimuli *(1924)*. A. A. Lazarus elaborated the method and applied it to a group of 18 phobic children of 3½ to 12. The treatment was short, about 9 sessions, and the results were dramatically successful. The behavior therapists uniformly report amazing success, at least amazing to a person accustomed to the slow, tortuous relearning which ordinarily takes place in psychotherapy. Wolpe, for instance, reports that 90 per cent of his patients were markedly improved (110 out of 122 patients). He treated adults with long-standing problems and apparently produced results in an average of 26 sessions *(1960)*. However, in his descriptions of how this is accomplished, he mentions hypnosis and cites instructions given by the therapist as to how the patient should feel and behave. There is also some use of electric shock (not the electroshock with which depression is treated) when the patient reports a particular fantasy or mental image. Although the theoretical explanation is by no means the same, this seems to have brought us around full circle to the authoritative therapist, and it may well be that reciprocal inhibition techniques cure in the same way as the Nancy school of suggestion therapy did.

Negative practice is a second variant of behavior therapy. The technique, first proposed by Knight Dunlap *(1932)*, is to have the patient repeat and practice the very habit of which he is trying to rid himself. This method has been used to help stutterers *(Sheehan, 1951; Case, 1960)*, and it has also been used with patients with tics *(Yates, 1960)*. The technique depends on the patient's conscious performance of an act which he usually performs unconsciously.

Aversion therapy, the third variant

of behavior therapy, is not unlike the use of electric shock stimulus in avoidance conditioning described by Wolpe. The neurotic response is made so unpleasant that the patient becomes more motivated to give it up than to retain it. An example is the antabuse therapy for alcoholics. If a patient on this drug takes an alcoholic drink, he becomes violently ill. This is presumed to condition him so that the thought, sight, smell, or taste of alcohol will eventually produce a conditioned adverse reaction.

The fourth variant is *positive conditioning,* best exemplified by the treatment of enuretics *(Mowrer and Mowrer, 1938).* Enuresis is viewed as the consequence of the lack of a conditioned response (that is, leaving the bed to go to the bathroom) which most people have acquired. The techniques were discussed before in Chapter 6 and are comparatively simple. Some device which wakens the child at the very start of urination is used, and after a while the full bladder itself becomes the waking stimulus. The rationale and published results have been summarized by H. G. Jones. He indicates that the "degree of success achieved by this method is well in excess of the spontaneous remission rate" *(1960, p. 401).* In some ways, positive conditioning procedures are very similar to those recommended in the habit training clinics for pre-school children described by Thom *(1924).*

Operant Conditioning. Basically, behavior therapy makes use of classical conditioning techniques to extinquish pathological behavior and to substitute new responses. Other investigators have applied Skinnerian operant conditioning techniques to clinical problems. Compared with classical conditioning, operant conditioning pays less attention to the stimulus and more attention to the response, especially to the effect of the response. According to this view, children behave in certain ways because in the past these acts accomplished a useful purpose. In operant conditioning, the environment is programmed to respond to the subject's behavior and reward the desired acts and ignore the others. This technique has been used in the treatment of autistic children (see Chapter 11). Although these investigations have relied on non-verbal rewards such as food and candy *(Ferster, 1961),* other writers have stressed that verbal responses are no less significant in affecting behavior *(Krasner, 1963).* Sometimes a combination of conditioning methods is used as illustrated in the treatment of a school phobia described by A. A. Lazarus (see Chapter 10). In all the conditioning techniques, the nature of reinforcement plays the major role. Behavior is motivated by the results, and the results are thought of in terms of the immediate, observable reactions of the environment.

Comparisons of Theories

In behavior therapy, the child's role is minimized and full use is made of the authoritative weight of the therapist. Interestingly enough, Eysenck *(1960)* makes light of rapport, writing that "personal relations are not essential for cures of neurotic disorder, although they may be useful in certain circumstances" *(1960, p. 11).* Apparently he believes that learning or conditioning takes place automatically, and independently of the patient's attitude toward, or feeling for, the therapist. One suspects that the patient is much impressed by the firmness and determination of the therapist and awed, perhaps even frightened, by the procedures. The spirit both of behavior therapy and the moral therapy of Mowrer is in direct contrast to that of Taft, Allen, and Rogers. The Freudian techniques and the dynamic learning approach of Dollard and Miller stand somewhere in the middle on this question of who directs the treatment—therapist or patient.

A second important issue of clear-cut

difference is in the attitude towards symptoms. Eysenck is most explicit: "Learning theory does not postulate any such 'unconscious causes,' but regards neurotic symptoms as simple learned habits; there is no neurosis underlying the symptom, but merely the symptom itself. *Get rid of the symptom and you have eliminated the neurosis*" (1960, p. 9). Traditionally, psychoanalytically oriented therapists have been loath to treat a symptom, for fear that another symptom will appear in its place in answer to the continuing unconscious conflict. Therapists who consider the symptom to be the illness claim that symptom substitution has *not* occurred, but one wonders if they have looked with a sharp eye. Sometimes an overt symptom (e.g., a tic or phobia) is replaced by a symptom of another character (e.g., an inhibition of learning or of social behavior). Such inhibitions may escape notice for a while. Nevertheless, some symptoms produce further trouble in and of themselves, and there may be justification for symptomatic treatment in such cases. The damaging effect of continued bed-wetting on the child's image of himself, and the possibility of displacement to areas far removed from enuresis (e.g., learning) was discussed in Chapter 6. There are times when relief of the symptom will permit the child to progress on his own.

A third difference in therapies, essentially a corollary of the second, is the matter of time. Learning theorists aim for efficiency and economy of effort. In comparison with relationship or insight therapists, who expect real change to occur slowly, they expect quick results. Perhaps one can eliminate a single, circumscribed symptom by a concentrated attack, but the child in a guidance clinic usually has many symptoms, diffuse character problems, or generalized inhibitions which are hard to specify. The task of identifying their separate symptoms and treating them one at a time, by behavior therapy

or whatever, would probably take nearly as long as psychoanalytic therapists take. Underneath the symptoms, one usually finds character traits which predispose the child to future symptom formation. This is not a mystical postulation of "unconscious conflict," but a readily verifiable observation. For instance, Sally (see Chapter 6) was brought to therapy on account of her incessant finger sucking. But we learned that she sucked her fingers when she felt lonely, that she felt lonely after she had been angry with someone, and that most of the time she was angry with her family and peers. Her finger sucking stopped after an accident to her front tooth, when she began to fear losing it altogether. The symptom disappeared, and this seemed sufficient reason, to her and to her parents, to stop treatment. She did not again suck her fingers, but she continued to be an unhappy, angry, and lonely girl. It would have taken much longer to help her to lessen her demands on other people, to recognize her verbal cruelty, and so on.

Another area of disagreement is the selection of patients. Many require that the patient be aware of his problem and seek help. A relationship therapist would not attempt to treat a child against his will, nor would painful topics be brought up except on the initiative of the child. Dollard and Miller discuss the importance of "selecting patients who can learn." With respect to motivation, they comment that "the prognosis is good if the patient is extremely miserable because his misery will motivate therapy, and it is bad if he is self-satisfied. It is good if the patient has enough motivation actively to seek therapy on his own, and it is bad if he must be dragged in or sent by others" (1950, p. 234). But most child patients would then have a poor prognosis! Dollard and Miller also stress the importance of a strong conscience and of language for therapeutic communication, but these are embryonic in a child. In their discussion of habits which interfere with therapy, they mention suspiciousness of the therapist, passivity, or a tendency to give up easily, but such habits are more the rule than the exception. Conditioning therapists rely mainly on an authoritarian approach and do not discuss methods of establishing rapport and enlisting the child's interest.

There are many points of contact and areas of similarity between the psychodynamic and learning theory approaches to psychotherapy, and it is possible to translate some of the language of the one into that of the other. Nevertheless, the differences are much more than semantic ones, and the individual psychotherapist must choose the general approach in which he feels most confidence. The choice probably depends more on the therapist's personality than on any rational factor. The learning theory approach is highly intellectual. The therapist observes and collects what past and present data he needs to formulate the problem. Then he maps out his treatment strategy and follows a procedure to influence the patient's observed behavior. There is more feeling in the psychodynamic theories and the therapist employs more empathy and less intellectualism. The psychodynamic theories are also more dynamic in the sense that the strategy does not follow a prescribed course but evolves gradually as the therapist becomes better acquainted with the child. In the author's opinion, the learning theory therapists are in danger of making premature conclusions and simplifying problems of child behavior. Particularly in the conditioning techniques, it would be easy to forget that a child has feelings and thoughts which he does not express at the moment but which will influence his future behavior. For the author, communication between adult and child is crucial, and it can only be achieved when the therapist is attuned to feelings which may appear in all kinds of disguises.

Theories and Techniques of Group Therapy

Historical Evolution of Group Therapy

As early as 1906, groups of physically ill persons were organized for instructional purposes and this method was gradually extended to classes for neurotic patients. In 1930, the first class of what was called "thought control" convened. This was essentially the application of suggestion therapy to a group of patients.

At about the same time, J. L. Moreno, in Vienna, started working with group dramatic productions. In 1909, he began staging written plays with children and juveniles, but he soon let them play out their problems without a prepared script. In 1911, he created a "children's theatre for spontaneity," the beginning of psychodrama. In 1927, he came to the United States, started a therapeutic theatre, and worked with groups at Sing Sing Prison and at the New York State Training School for Girls. He also developed the techniques of sociometry to study the interrelationships of individuals in groups. In his historical survey of the development of group psychotherapy, Joseph Meiers *(1945)* gives credit for the authorship of the term "group psychotherapy" to J. L. Moreno *(1931)*.

In the two decades that followed, there was a tremendous increase of interest in group therapy. Two national organizations—the American Society of Group Psychotherapy and Psychodrama and the American Group Psychotherapy Association—were formed in 1943. The official journal of the latter is the *International Journal of Group Psychotherapy*, which first appeared in 1951; since World War II, the literature has grown by leaps and bounds. Hugh Mullan and Max Rosenbaum reported that, at the end of 1955, the literature on group psychotherapy consisted of 1,700 items. They estimated the annual output at about 200 books, articles, and theses—double the 1950 figure *(1962, p. 16)*.

Social group work, at least a first cousin to group therapy, has its roots in recreation and youth groups (e.g., Girl Scouts), neighborhood settlement houses, and various voluntary self-help movements. In 1923, Grace Coyle started the first course in group work at the School of Social Work at Western Reserve University. In 1936, the American Association for the Study of Group Work was founded. This became the American Association of Group Workers, and joined the National Association of Social Workers, formed in 1955. Konopka offers the following distinctions between group work, social group work, and group therapy: *Group work* is the generic term; it includes all work with groups. *Social group work* is a method of social work which helps individuals to enhance their social functioning through purposeful group experiences. *Group therapy* is psychotherapeutic practice which is aimed at ameliorating suffering and improving the personal and social functioning of its members by arranging for specified and controlled group interaction *(1963)*. When the group worker uses his professional training and skill to work with groups of individuals who have special problems, he enters the practice of group therapy. Indeed, many times one cannot find the fine line between social group work and group therapy or between social case work and psychotherapy.

Rationale of Group Psychotherapy

It has often been said, particularly in the beginning, that the main advantage of group psychotherapy is economy. However, group psychotherapy is now viewed as more than the poor man's substitute for individual psychotherapy.

The sense of belonging to a group sometimes reduces an individual's suspicion of the therapist; for this reason, group therapy has been used in penal institutions and in hospitals for the mentally ill, whose residents are often distrustful. Moreover, group therapy has a special value, in that it stimulates social behavior. In individual psychotherapy, one depends on the patient's account of what has transpired between himself and other people. The therapist gradually becomes aware of characteristic patterns described by the patient and recognizes the patient's defenses in reporting. But this takes time and taxes the therapist's skill in sorting through the perceptual distortions of the patient. In group therapy, one can observe social behavior directly. This is informative to the therapist. It also means that each patient is soon confronted with the reactions of the other members of the group. As the patients begin to perceive that others in the group are also distorting reality, their resistance to recognizing their own projections is lessened. Sidney Levin points out that this does not happen in individual therapy *(1963)*. A therapist cannot say that he has emotional problems similar to his patient's, but a fellow member of a group can offer such support without undermining the therapeutic situation. It is in this sense that group therapy has been described as more real than individual therapy. Nathan Ackerman has made the following observations:

Group therapy is an independent method; it neither competes with nor substitutes for individual therapy. It is a more real experience than individual therapy. It is less bound to the irrationalities of the unconscious and is weighted on the side of allegiance to social reality. It is only a partial therapy for the more serious personality disorders. Its powers are sharply limited with personality disorders having deep unconscious roots. Its greatest effectiveness lies in the area of reintegration of ego patterns with consequent improvement in the level of social functioning. For some disturbances of personality it may be usefully combined with individual therapy. (In *Moreno, 1945, p. 362.*)

Before proceeding further, it should be emphasized that group therapy is not a simple matter. There is no magic in merely bringing people together. There is potential danger in group dynamics as well as potential benefit. Control can slip into the hands of a foolish or cruel participant. Feelings stimulated in the group may prompt heedless actions. Competition for the therapist's interest may lead to distorted self-exposures. Some people never lose their shyness in the group situation, but remain perpetual onlookers.

Categories of Group Psychotherapy

It should be understood at the outset that there are all types and levels of group psychotherapy, just as there are of individual therapy. The therapeutic aim, the role of the therapist, and the specific treatment methods should be adapted to the patients' needs, to the problems arising out of his social situation, and to the environment in which the therapy takes place. Meiers and Moreno have offered a classification scheme for group therapies which is here simplified to five bipolar variables which seem most important *(in Moreno, 1945, p. 507)*:

There is a tendency for the left-hand categories to appear together: the more

amorphous the group and the more incidental it is to another factor such as hospitalization or commitment, the more likely it is to be therapist-centered and symptomatic or educational in approach. If the group has been precisely structured by the psychotherapist, its activity is likely to be more spontaneous. Moreover, the groups which have been created specifically for psychotherapy, i.e., those in "derivative" situations, are more likely to have a "causal" objective. However, this is not always so. There are also many combinations. Psychodrama may be used in a mental hospital (i.e., *in situ*) with an amorphous group, but with no rehearsals and no intervention by the therapist. On the other hand, psychodrama has also been used in mental hospitals with a structured group (i.e., patients about to return home), and with the very definite objective of anticipating the return home, the answering of friends' questions, and looking for a job.

Group Psychotherapy with Children

Slavson, who has done the most psychotherapy with groups of children *(1943; 1950; 1952)*, distinguished four categories of group psychotherapy for prepubertal children: activity group psychotherapy, transitional groups, play

1. Constitution of the group

Amorphous	Structured, as in S. R. Slavson's "activity group therapy."

2. Locus of treatment

In situ, as in camps, settlement houses, or hospitals. The group members are there for reasons other than group psychotherapy.	Derivative; i.e., especially arranged situations, such as in clinics.

3. Agent of therapy

Therapist centered.	Group centered.

4. Form of therapeutic procedure

Rehearsed, planned in advance.	Spontaneous.

5. Goal of treatment

Symptomatic or re-educational, to improve adaptation to a specific social situation.	Causal, stressing the importance of insight, as in psychoanalytically oriented group therapy.

group psychotherapy, and activity-interview group psychotherapy. Slavson recommends *play group psychotherapy* for groups of three to five pre-school children, and describes it as utilizing the techniques and materials of individual play therapy. *Transitional groups* are so termed because they serve as a bridge between therapy groups or individual psychotherapy and "the social realities of the world." Slavson considers membership in a group as an educational experience, a kind of rehearsal for life:

The difference between these groups and ordinary clubs lies in the fact that their members are selected because, though almost ready for realistic social participation, they are as yet unable to enter into the competitive relations and high social pressures of the latter . . . Transitional groups offer an attenuated reality; the social demands are much greater than in therapy groups. *(1952, p. 292.)*

It is *activity group psychotherapy* which is most closely linked to Slavson's name: "The general pattern of activity group psychotherapy for small groups of no more than eight children is free acting out in a specially designed physical setting and carefully planned group milieu" *(Slavson, 1952, p. 280)*. The technique, as he describes it, sounds very much like the release therapy of David Levy *(1938)*. The therapist is as passive as the children will allow. Hostility and aggression are vented on anything and anyone *except* the therapist, but the therapist "does not call attention to it, nor does he react to it in any way" *(1952, p. 280)*. There is no plan of organization nor specific program, but arts and crafts materials and tools are supplied in order to avoid the anarchy and chaos which idleness would bring. Slavson speaks of the importance of a refreshment period and of trips and excursions as the group gains strength and control. (Some of the techniques are demonstrated in a film, "Activity Group Therapy," distributed by Colum-

bia University Educational Films, Columbia University, New York.) The therapist never prohibits, but he is quick to praise; his failure to respond to undesirable behavior "serves as action interpretation." He sets a perfect example of courtesy, thoughtfulness, and self-control, in order to make himself a figure for identification. The therapist, however, is not the sole object of identification. Other children also serve as models, and because of this it is essential that children who would have too negative an influence should not be included. Slavson states that those who gain most from activity group therapy are children who suffer from primary behavior disorders (if the hyperactivity and aggressiveness are not so intense as to disturb the group beyond a permissible degree); children with character disorders, particularly those involving constriction, faulty sex role identification, or low self-esteem; and children with neurotic traits and mild psychoneuroses. This excludes autistic children, those with severely disturbed perceptions of reality, and those whose behavior is seriously out of control.

Slavson discusses in detail the techniques of selecting a group. The idea is to achieve a balance between aggressive, active children ("instigators") and withdrawn and average children ("social neuters" and "neutralizers," respectively). In a properly balanced group, the aggressive children spur the group to regressive and challenging behavior, and the more stable, socially oriented children serve as group superegos. The therapy lies in the group activity *per se*, which pulls some out of their social isolation, curbs the aggressiveness of others, and gives the more stable children a chance to grow in self-mastery.

Activity-interview group psychotherapy is considered a combination of activity group therapy and individual interview psychotherapy. The general setting is similar, but the therapist behaves differently. The children are free to act on their impulses, as they are in activity groups, but their acts are interpreted by the therapist, who also encourages the young children to communicate to each other, and to him, their problems, difficulties, preoccupations, fears, and anxieties. The goals include not only catharsis (i.e., release), the formation of new identifications, learning to be more expressive or less active (as the case may be), but also the acquisition of insight into the reasons for behavior. The difference between activity-interview group psychotherapy and activity group psychotherapy is similar to that between release or relationship therapy and psychoanalytically oriented psychotherapy.

Psychoanalytic Group Therapy

This provides yet another example of the principle that almost every kind of individual therapy has a counterpart in group therapy. Some of the psychoanalysts who early became interested in the psychoanalysis of groups were A. Wolf *(1949)*, L. Berman *(1950)* and S. H. Foulkes in England *(1948)*. Most psychoanalysts, however, believe that psychoanalysis cannot be accomplished in groups. For one thing, the analysis of "the transference neurosis," that is, of the patient's displacement to the analyst of his feelings toward his parents is of major importance in psychoanalysis. In the group situation, several people are available for transference. The psychoanalyst is a more real person, less a "blank screen" for projection of transference feelings. However, regardless of whether the work should properly be called "psychoanalysis in groups" *(as argued by Wolf and Schwartz, 1962)* or whether it should have another name, many psychoanalysts are now working with groups of patients.

Mullan and Rosenbaum, who have written one of the most detailed discussions of the theory and techniques of psychoanalytically oriented group treatment, argue that the group is a positive and unique experience and should never be offered as a second-rate or less expensive psychotherapy. They use the term "regressive-reconstructive" therapy to describe the concept of fostering regression to earlier levels of relationships, thereby undoing repressions and preparing the ground for a healthier reconstruction of the personality. The goal is "a lasting, deep personality change of an evolving nature, which will occur in the group members and simultaneously, though to less extent, in the therapist" *(1962, p. 53)*. They feel it is appropriate for all ages, although the level and medium of communication will vary accordingly. All sorts of technical innovations have been tried—combined individual and group therapy, co-therapy (usually two therapists of opposite sex), alternate sessions (i.e., sessions without the therapist present), variations in frequency and length of sessions, and variations in size and composition of groups.

Experienced group therapists emphasize the need for specific training in group work, and most agree that it is more difficult than individual therapy. There are no generally accepted criteria of training and qualification, but Mullan and Rosenbaum recommend competence in individual psychotherapy as a prerequisite. To the usual psychoanalytic training, they would add personal group psychotherapy, didactic work, clinical seminars, and supervised group experience lasting another two or three years. Most actual training is informal and much less extensive.

Family Treatment

The family is a natural group and one with deep significance for its members. The methods of family diagnosis were described in Chapter 4 and have the same rationale as family therapy.

Alexander Gralnick has made a straightforward statement of this rationale:

If the origins of mental illness reside within the family, it would seem that the resolution of psychopathology lies there too. After all, the individual does not carry his illness in some encapsulated form, but demonstrates it in action with people, probably most acutely with members of his family. What better place then to make the most observation of pathology and to bring therapeutic influence to bear most decisively? *(1962, p. 518.)*

Gralnick points out that various authors define "family therapy" differently. Ackerman regards family therapy as only that in which the entire household participates in joint sessions with the same therapist. Work with different members of a family by separate therapists, long the custom in child guidance clinics, is usually called "collaborative treatment." Jackson uses the term "conjoint therapy" for simultaneous treatment by one therapist and reserves the term "family therapy" for "family oriented collaborative psychotherapy where family members are seen in individual psychotherapy" *(1959)*. Gralnick offers the most inclusive definition: "Family therapy is any psychotherapeutic approach to the primary patient which consciously includes other members of his family, seen either separately or jointly with the primary patient" *(1962, p. 519)*. Gralnick describes his aims in working with families of institutionalized adult psychotics as: (1) to help the family keep pace with the patient's progress; (2) to help the family to understand the psychiatrist and what he can and cannot do; (3) to help them understand the patient's distortions so that there may be more communication, tolerance, and sympathy; (4) to help the family in the aftercare of the patient; and (5) to restore a relationship with psychiatrists. These aims remind one of Adolf Meyer's purpose in sending his wife out to visit the homes of his patients, and they sound like the goals of contemporary psychiatric social workers. The statement is new in that all these efforts are to be made by one person, rather than by a team.

In the research project conducted by Bowen and his co-workers, 18 families of psychotic patients were seen in family group therapy. Seven families—fathers, mothers, patients and siblings—resided in a hospital for about a year. Each family occupied a separate ward and received group psychotherapy. No individual sessions were permitted, and the therapist tried to maintain a detached air by such devices as taking notes during the sessions. The premise of this experiment was that "psychosis is a symptom of an active process that involved the entire family. Just as a generalized physical illness can focus in one organ, so schizophrenia was seen as a generalized family problem which disabled one member of the family organism" *(1961, p. 43)*. The clinical material describing family interactional patterns is interesting, but only one of the seven families made a "fairly good resolution of parental relationship problems and the patient achieved a good adjustment . . . the [11] out-patient families did better in family psychotherapy . . . the seven in-residence father families were never able to deal with their helplessness" *(1961, p. 59)*. The social worker of the project, Basamania, concludes the papers by raising the important question of selection: Which patients should be treated individually, and which as part of a family group?

Ackerman has probably done most to apply family therapy to child patients. A psychoanalytically trained psychiatrist, he has worked closely with the New York School of Social Work and family service agencies and became interested in group therapy early. His procedure is a flexible one, in which separate sessions with the patient are interspersed with interviews in which the patient is seen jointly with members of his family. "Because the primary patient is viewed both as an individual in distress and as a symptomatic expression of family pathology, the disturbance of this patient becomes the fulcrum or entering wedge for the appropriate levels of intervention into the disorder of the family relations" (Ackerman, 1958, p. 305).

One of the cases he describes entailed a complicated mixture of individual sessions with the patient (an anxious boy of eight) and the other members of the family and sessions in which the whole family or two or three members participated. There were also visits to the home. The report reveals the depth of the therapist's understanding of the family's interrelationships; it also shows the great number of technical decisions which are made in the course of such treatment:

The planning of sessions with individuals and sessions with two or more family members must be discriminatingly timed in accordance with indications that derive from the active and flexible implementation of the principles of family diagnosis. From one stage of therapy to the next, as the balance of reciprocity in family role relations shifts and the focus of pathogenic disturbance moves from one part of the family to another, the therapist must be ready to institute corresponding shifts of the level of therapeutic intervention into the family disturbance. Family therapy is obviously complex. (Ackerman, 1958, p. 307.)

In the author's opinion, a psychotherapist would have to possess considerable experience in individual therapy before he could undertake family therapy. He has to be sensitive to his own identifications with family members, must register the conflicts and defense mechanisms of several people, and has to be able to phrase his interpretations so that they will be simultaneously acceptable to different people. If the therapist is a detached, passive observer, this would not be so difficult, but Ackerman's methods involve far more than getting the family and child together and letting them work it out.

In theoretical respects, family diagnosis and psychotherapy are an extension of the concepts of Adelaide Johnson and her co-workers, who view much child psychopathology as the result of unconscious parental conflicts, e.g., the "superego lacunae" unconsciously fostered by the parent whose delinquent youngster vicariously gratifies the parent's forbidden impulse. The family treatment plan might also be well suited to a learning theory approach to neurotic conflict, although learning theorists have not yet made much use of group treatment.

Evaluating Effectiveness of Treatment

How does one decide whether individual or group psychotherapy is indicated for a particular patient? To some extent, the answer should depend on the nature of the case and the circumstances under which treatment is possible; on the other hand, very different methods have been used under exactly the same diagnostic conditions and under roughly similar circumstances. In practice, the method is determined by the training or predeliction of the therapist, rather than by the needs of the patient. And unfortunately, we are far from the point at which we can evaluate the relative effectiveness of different psychotherapeutic methods. There are many evaluative reports, but no agreed-upon interpretations.

The most unimpressed observer of child psychotherapy is Eugene Levitt, who summarized the published studies and participated in a follow-up study of patients treated in a community child guidance clinic, the Institute for Juvenile Research, in Chicago. Levitt summarized 37 reports of the outcome of child therapy, made either at the close of treatment or any time from 1 to 27 years later. At the close of treatment, an average of 67 per cent of the children were regarded as improved; the follow-up evaluations found an average of 78 per cent improved *(1957)*. His summary agrees closely with that of Leon Lucas and Ruth Ochroch, who grouped the published reports chronologically *(1963)*. In the decade from 1930 to 1940, nine studies involving 966 children reported that 68 per cent of the patients improved; from 1940 to 1950, eight studies involving 876 children reported 78 per cent improved; and from 1950–1962 period, three studies involving 524 children reported 56 per cent improved.

At first glance, these results look positive. Levitt contends, however, that there is no significant difference between treated and untreated disturbed children. The children he would use as control subjects are often referred to as "defectors," i.e., patients who are accepted for treatment but who never report for treatment. Levitt did a series of studies which show that the defectors are similar to the patients, except for the factor of treatment itself. In his survey *(1957)*, he quotes the results of Witmer and Jane Keller *(1942)* and of L. J. Lehrman *et al.* *(1949)*. Their figure of 72.5 per cent spontaneous improvement is used as a basis on which to compare the results achieved with treated children. Later, Levitt, H. R. Beiser, and R. G. Robertson published a report on 192 patients who were treated for at least ten sessions at the Illinois Institute for Juvenile Research and compared them with 93 defectors, using some 26 variables derived from psychological tests, objective facts of adjustment, parents' ratings, self-ratings, and clinical judgments of the interviewers. The average age at the time of follow-up was almost 16 years, and an average of about 5 years had elapsed. There was no significant difference between the two

groups on *any* of the outcome variables. As Forstenzer observed in his discussion of the study *(in Levitt, Beiser, and Robertson, 1959)*, this is a veritable H-bomb in the child guidance field. Certainly, such findings cannot be ignored.

It is legitimate, however, to inquire into the methodology of evaluating the effectiveness of psychotherapy. Some of the specific questions to be considered are: (1) sampling; (2) choice of control subjects; (3) selection of data on which the evaluation is based; (4) assessment of causal relationships, and (5) the nature of the treatment under evaluation. Lawrence Kubie has criticized the lack of proper selection of patients for follow-up research (i.e., the sampling):

It is valueless to gather assembly-line statistics on heterogeneous lots of patients, young or old. To give statistics on the treatment of such unstudied samples is precisely as though one gave general statistics on the success of "surgery" when the surgery had been performed on splinters, boils, chronic osteomyelitis and cancer.

The choice of control subjects is limited. The only possible group seems to be the defectors, but there is a strong possibility that they are not comparable to the patients in some significant or even crucial way. Since the parents did not persist in their search for treatment, perhaps the children were not as disturbed or their parents were more ready to see improvement than parents of the treated group. However, such differences, if they in fact exist, have not been identified.

The difficulties of selecting data to be used as the criteria of improvement have been presented by Helen Sargent *(1960)*. At least some of the data must come from the patient or his family. Sargent points out that during treatment, probing questions are expected, but that the follow-up is a different matter. The patient by then feels entitled to a normal amount of privacy, there may be more resistance (conscious or unconscious) to direct questioning in sensitive areas and the situation is not particularly conducive to frank revelations.

Then there is the perplexing problem of what data to gather. What is meant by "cure"? Some therapists, as we have seen, regard the disappearance of a symptom as a cure. Others look for a strengthened personality, immunized against a further invasion of mental illness. Still others, including the psychoanalysts, hope for even more, a basic change which permits the fulfillment of potential "to capitalize on personal resources so as to feel free and happy, satisfy personal needs, and be an efficient, productive person" (Ackerman, 1958, p. 298). Clearly, the data selected will depend on the original emotional disturbance of the patient and the goals of the therapist. We have no agreed-upon definitions of cure and, so far, every investigator has chosen his own criteria.

When we assess the causal relationships, we often assume that we are measuring a single variable, i.e., the psychotherapy. In reality, nothing could be further from the case. Kubie states:

. . . it is impossible in such assembly-line studies to be certain that after leaving treatment different patients have had to face comparable stresses. We recognize this problem in a much simpler form in the work of a heart specialist . . . If one patient goes back home to a pick-and-shovel job, to live in a walk-up cold-water flat, whereas the other goes home to a ground-floor apartment and a sedentary job which does not subject him to excessive physical or emotional strain, the outcome will not be the same. In the same way identical neuroses of similar duration in patients of the same age and treated by the same doctor by the same method, may nonetheless face conditions which in vital respects can be profoundly different. (1962.)

Researchers assume that, when the numbers are large enough, such differences cancel each other out. This assumption may not be justified.

Perhaps the most important point is the fifth, namely, the nature of the treatment which is under scrutiny. This factor may be involved in the work of Levitt, Beiser, and Robertson (1959). Almost half their patients were treated by students or therapists with less than a year of experience, about one-third had to change therapists at least once, and only one-third were treated by therapists with more than three years of experience. No correlation was made between the experience of the therapist and the outcome, but indirect evidence that there may have been such a correlation is given in another study reported by Herman Stein (1956). This report, known as the San Francisco-New York Study, involved 488 families at 9 child guidance clinics in the two cities. Of those patients who were seen at least once, 46 per cent improved and 54 per cent did not improve. Between 76 and 79 per cent of the patients who had more than 40 interviews were improved. This number of interviews suggests that fairly experienced personnel was involved. In their review of the literature, Lucas and Ochroch (1963) observe that most of the therapy in child guidance clinics is performed by inexperienced personnel. Most of the clinics serve as a training ground for professional workers, who then take up private practices.

It must be admitted that there is no statistical proof of the effectiveness of psychotherapy; neither is there any statistical proof that it is ineffective. It seems very clear that the effectiveness of psychotherapy is not fairly evaluated when all cases are lumped together regardless of the amount or extent of therapy received. Yet Ackerman's opinion is that the reported results of child psychotherapy are much the same, regardless of the methods. He suggests that successful psychotherapy of children, currently represented by a wide range of diverse procedures, may depend as much on the sincerity and devotion of the therapist to the needs of the child as on any technical factor *(1958)*.

Training and Supervision of Child Psychotherapists

Personal Qualifications

It is obvious that there are great differences in the effectiveness of individual therapists, no matter what brand of therapy they practice, but the different schools place varying emphases on the importance of the personality of the therapist. Eysenck, for instance, says next to nothing about the personal qualifications of therapists, and his silence on the matter implies that psychotherapy requires only intellectual mastery. On the other hand, Slavson echoes Ackerman's sentiments when he states that "success in psychotherapy is achieved as much because of what the psychotherapist is as by what he does" *(1952, p. 198)*. Dollard and Miller describe a number of characteristics which they consider to be essential: the therapist must be "mentally free," so that he can permit the patient to reveal his secret thoughts and fantasies; he must be "empathic," so that he can feel with the patient and also so that he can judge when something is missing or illogical in the patient's account; he must be "restrained," so that he can subordinate his personal wishes to the strategy of treatment; and he must have a positive attitude toward the patient's capacity to change. They stress the importance of transference and countertransference feelings, and point out how difficult it is to manage these feelings if the therapist has overwhelm-ing personal difficulties or frustrations *(1950)*.

Dollard and Miller share the opinion of many that a psychotherapist should first undergo treatment himself. There are at least three reasons for this policy. First, the emotional disturbances of the therapist must be therapeutically reduced to the greatest possible extent in order that they not interfere with the treatment of his patients. The treatment also is a way of screening out unsuitable candidates. Second, the psychotherapist must acquire as much insight into himself as he humanly can, in order to be alert to his denials and projections, cognizant of his own feelings, and aware of his effect on others. Third, one learns something about the technique of a particular therapy by experiencing it directly. The therapist who is so trained can better understand the feelings of his patients and has some guidelines from his own therapist to put into practice.

It is probably unnecessary to elaborate on the importance of self-knowledge on the part of the therapist. Most people readily appreciate that continuous contact with emotionally disturbed individuals is a particular kind of strain, and that it often calls for the utmost self-discipline. The therapist must always be able to act in the patient's interest, rather than in his own. He must be able to be passive, to wait the patient out, and to tolerate delays and setbacks. A genuine desire to help people is, of course, a prerequisite, but the therapist who views himself as a savior and "fixer-upper" will soon be disappointed in himself, his technique, and his patients. This is perhaps even a greater danger for child psychotherapists, who may unconsciously be trying to be a better parent than the real parent. Should he fall into this trap, the real parent may sense the unconscious rivalry and either sabotage the treatment in order to win the contest or adopt a helpless, dependent attitude toward the all-knowing, all-giving therapist, thus making treatment interminable.

Empathy with Children

Many people who are intuitive and perceptive with adults cannot communicate with children. Slavson gives a particularly good description of what is involved in empathy with children:

For work with children a psychotherapist should not have left his childhood so far behind him that he is unable to empathize with his young patients. . . . A person with too rigid controls, inflexible and devoid of lyrical qualities and some enthusiasm, cannot make any contact with children. Children do not respond to or have confidence in the matter-of-factness, coldness, and detachment that is erroneously attributed to "maturity." The successful child psychotherapist needs to possess warmth, spontaneity, imagination, and some of the "unrational" qualities usually attributed to children themselves, except that he should have integrated these qualities into his total character so as to have them under control. *(1952, p. 199.)*

Slavson goes on to say that a child therapist should have had a difficult childhood himself, but should have solved his problems sufficiently to have gained insight and empathy when there might otherwise have been fixation and identification. The good child therapists he has known "possessed a child-like quality, which in ordinary parlance might be considered immaturity" *(1952, p. 200)*, an interesting observation which is hard for another child therapist to judge. Certainly, it is important that the child therapist enjoy children—he should be able to laugh at their jokes, share their games, follow their conversation, read their books, and watch their television programs without boredom—at least for a while. The therapist must be able to tolerate provocative teasing, unflattering frankness, meddlesome curiosity, and physical roughness as well as physical affec-

tion. By "tolerate" we do not necessarily mean "permit"; we refer to an emotional tolerance which allows the therapist to react to the needs of the child rather than to his personal discomfort.

Perhaps one of the special requirements of a child therapist is some ability to accept ambiguity, to be willing to imagine and to guess what is going on in the child's mind. Children usually hide their thoughts and feelings, and the therapist must rely a good deal on how he would feel were he in the child's place. Then, he must communicate his supposition simply, directly, and with feeling, so that the child can grasp it. Some of the techniques of talking with children are discussed later, but effective communication with children rests more on feelings than on information. Withal, however, the therapist must retain some detachment. He must be able to respond to the child's suffering and confusion without actually assuming them or being infected by them, or he will not be able to help his patient to discriminate between fantasy and reality or between past and present. Empathy requires that one be able to step into the shoes of the other, and then step out again.

Professional Training and Supervision

Child therapists come from a number of professional specialties—education, social work, psychology, and medicine. Few experts hold that medical training is essential, but some believe that the nonmedical child psychotherapist should work only under medical supervision.

Each profession has evolved standards for training in therapy which is usually introduced at an advanced stage in the professional curriculum. For example, it is the consensus of opinion among clinical psychologists that predoctoral internships cannot prepare the psychologist to assume full treatment responsibility *(Grossman, 1963)*. There simply is not sufficient time for the psychologist to obtain a general background in experimental psychology and personality theory, learn to administer and interpret diagnostic tests, carry out original research for his thesis, *and* acquire supervised experience in psychotherapy. Some postdoctoral supervision and training is needed to become a qualified independent therapist.

On the other hand, the tremendous need for psychotherapists (The Joint Commission on Mental Health and Illness estimated, in 1961, that at least 17,000,000 people in the United States needed psychotherapy) and the critical shortage of trained personnel (*Albee, 1959*) have led people to look for shortcuts in training. It has been suggested that psychotherapy should perhaps not be a specialized area of a more traditional profession. Kubie, for one, has proposed a new doctoral program which would combine those aspects of psychology and medicine needed for the practice of psychotherapy (*1955*).

The most radical innovation in training "mental health counselors" was carried out as a pilot study by the National Institute of Mental Health (*Rioch et al., 1963*). The hypothesis was that there is a large unexploited reservoir of talent among middle-aged women who are reluctant to embark on the regular training programs set up for young graduate students. Eight 40-year-old mothers, with "good general intelligence, perceptiveness, integrity, and sufficient emotional maturity to be able to operate effectively together and to cope with the stresses of psychotherapeutic work" were selected for special training (*p. 680*). There were four, almost full-time semesters, in which practical, on-the-job training was emphasized. In addition to seminars, reading seminars, and so forth, the students were placed in community agencies (i.e., clinics and school counseling services). Four judges rated tape-recorded therapeutic interviews; and the changes

in the patients were evaluated directly. There were, in all, 49 adolescent and adult patients, and the results, after the first year, were generally favorable:

. . . as therapists they have all performed some useful services to patients during this past year and none of them has done anyone any harm . . . Their greatest fault has been a tendency to follow the dictates of polite society. In other words, they pleasantly reassure, protect and sympathize when it would be better to question more deeply and seriously. A second fault is a tendency to try to deal on a surface, common sense level with problems that are soluble only by eliciting unconscious conflicts (*Rioch et al., 1963, p. 688*).

Although the directors of the study hesitated to form a final judgment about the probable effectiveness of the participants when they moved away from the protection of the group and from their supervisors, the project excited a good deal of interest.

There is general agreement that supervision is crucial. In the psychodynamic therapies, one of the supervisor's main jobs is to impress the student with the significance of the relationship between himself and the patient. As George Gardner says:

It is comparatively easy for the young student to evaluate all of the niceties and symbolism of the material he gathers in reference to the patient's own feelings in regard to the people who comprise the external world beyond the therapeutic room. On the other hand, it is extremely difficult for him continually to bear in mind that every piece of material, because of the fact that it is given to him in the therapeutic relationship, has some transference value, positive or negative, for the patient in relation to him, the student. (*1953, p. 296.*)

The relationship between supervisor and trainee is a complex one, and may even border on psychotherapy although it is generally agreed that the supervisor should avoid treating the trainee, tempting as the student's repetitive patterns may make such a course (*Gardner, 1953*). In their book on the teaching and learning of psychotherapy, Rudolph Ekstein and Robert Wallerstein pay particular attention to the "parallel process" between therapist and patient, on the one hand, and between supervisor and student, on the other (*1958*). Like therapy itself, supervision of therapy is a great deal more than the authoritative transmission of technical advice. Particularly when the patients are adults, it often seems as if the apprentice and the patient have the same psychological problems. Ekstein and Wallerstein view this as a metaphorical situation—the patient's problem in psychotherapy may be used to express the therapist's problem in supervision, and vice versa. The supervisor sees the patient only through the eyes of the student therapist, so he has the task of understanding both the patient and the therapist.

Because of the subjectivity of student reports, some training schools replace written notes with recordings or with one-way vision screens. Accurate as these devices may be, one should pause before employing them. For one thing, the patient is aware that he has an unknown audience (if a one-way vision screen is used) or that he will have one (if a tape recorder is used). For another, the objective reality may not be as important as the reality perceived and reacted to by the therapist. An objective account is sometimes useful, but most of the time the supervisor is better advised to use the material which the therapist recalls, even though it is a distillation.

Relatively little has been written about the supervision of child therapists. In B. Lubin's survey of the training of psychologists for psychotherapy, there were many more therapists whose supervised work was with adult patients (*1962*). It is the author's suspicion that some problems are encountered more frequently in the supervision of

treatment of children. It is easy for the supervisor to assume a parental role, in fact, this accords all too well with the wishes of some students. Others may react very negatively because being supervised reactivates their own rebellious feelings toward their parents, perhaps the very thing which led them into work with children. And there is no doubt that it is more difficult to report a therapy session with a child, because so much of what occurs is not verbal. The therapist's understandable difficulty in reproducing the session complicates the supervisor's task. One session usually sounds like nothing at all; it is only an emerging pattern which begins to make sense. It seems to the author that treatment of children, like diagnosing them, is more difficult than adult therapy. Those who expect child patients to be simpler, because they have less complicated defenses, or more malleable, because of their younger years, are very soon caught up short. The physical strain is greater, the regressive pull on the therapist is more, communication is more mysterious, and one has always to reckon with the environment in which the child lives.

Practical Observations

As mentioned before, treatment raises practical questions which demand practical answers. The author's comments are derived from her experience in psychoanalytically oriented psychotherapy of individual children, and no attempt is made to answer them from any other point of view. The items discussed are not intended as an exhaustive list, nor are the answers intended to be prescriptions. They should, however, convey some idea of the practical aspects of child therapy. Many of these items, particularly on the subjects of play materials and setting limits, are included in the collection of brief contributions edited by Haworth (*1964*).

All psychodynamic therapists report the same problems although their solutions differ somewhat.

Choice of Treatment

It used to be said that one should not begin treatment without first establishing a clinical diagnosis, but now one can read that "it is a fallacy that diagnosis is basic to treatment" *(Bugental, 1963, p. 563)*. The actual state of affairs is somewhere in between. There is an important relationship between diagnosis and treatment, if one means, by this, that behavior should be treated according to some understanding of its cause. But there are also no specific treatments which correspond to our present diagnostic labels. Furthermore, there is no sharp division between diagnosis and treatment. We noted earlier (Chapter 4) that diagnosis and treatment commingle, which means that one must consider the therapeutic significance of the diagnostic process itself and always be ready to change one's aims as new information is discovered.

There are two general principles to keep in mind—the rule of parsimony and the rule of availability. No matter how complicated a problem appears to be, one should first do the simplest thing and see how much it accomplishes. Psychotherapy really begins where common sense leaves off; so, before starting treatment, one should be sure that all common-sense measures have been given a fair trial. Some idea of this was given in the discussion of school phobia (see Chapter 10). In child guidance work, the obvious things have usually already been attempted, but it is always worthwhile to make certain of this.

The second point has to do with the availability of the kind of treatment one recommends. It may be worse than useless to tell an anxious parent that his child needs psychoanalysis if there is no psychoanalyst available to them, nor does it help a brain-injured child to recommend special schooling if there is none available. A diagnosis of autism or schizophrenia may be so alarming, that the child is automatically excluded from every community program and remains isolated at home. It is more important to find something which will be helpful to the child and family, even if it is not exactly what one would want. The practitioner must know local programs, their intake policies, and their waiting lists.

Diagnosis entails assessing the pathology in the environment and in the child, and determining which is paramount. If the environment is chiefly responsible, then one treats the child indirectly by counseling the parents or even by removing the child from his home (see Chapters 15 and 16). If the difficulty seems to stem primarily from a permanent weakness of the child's ego (as in mental retardation and psychosis, for example) the focus will be on environmental manipulation and parent guidance in order to give the child all possible outside support. This may involve special schooling, tutoring, and individual psychotherapy of a supportive nature, probably relationship therapy or nondirective treatment.

If the source of the child's problem behavior lies more with the child, its seriousness must be determined. How chronic, disabling, and pervasive is this problem, and how deep-rooted? It may have arisen from a developmental crisis such as toilet training, separation from home, or puberty. Such difficulties are usually transitory, and require only brief (but prompt) treatment. The situation is similar if the problem behavior is an acute reaction to a reality crisis such as illness, surgery, death in the family, a family move, desertion, or divorce. When real crises have been eliminated as causal factors, one is left with the neurotic or character disorders which seem unconnected with reality. For the treatment of these, one would choose some form of insight therapy, and one's goals would be determined by practical exigencies and the growth potential of the family and the child.

There are exceptions to these general rules. The pathology may be chiefly the child's, yet one may remove him from his home for specialized treatment or because his presence is harmful to other members of the family. And even the psychoanalytic treatment of a neurotic child will require some work with the parents, if only to ensure their cooperation. Some of these issues are discussed in greater detail in succeeding chapters.

Starting Treatment

The child needs to have an explanation of why he is seeing a psychotherapist and of what they are going to do together. Usually the explanation is made in terms of some concrete experience, something which caused him anxiety or brought him into conflict with others in the past. It is relatively easy to prepare a child who has a specific neurotic symptom, especially if it is associated with shame and anxiety. It is more difficult to prepare the child who is in trouble with authority because of his aggressiveness, lack of attention, or uncooperativeness. It must somehow be conveyed to these children that the therapist is going to try to help him with the problems he is having with other people, and that this is not a punishment. One makes the assumption that underlying most bad behavior is anxiety or, at least, that the child would be happier if he were not under disciplinary fire all the time. The therapist introduces himself as an ally of the child, not as an ally of the parents, teachers, juvenile authorities, or whatever.

The therapist should make it clear, very early and in a simple way, that he is well informed about the child's troubles, that he is interested in the child even though he cannot read, wets his bed, sometimes lies or steals, or whatever. The therapist says, in effect, "I know all the things that people think are bad about you, and I still like you very much and want to help you get over these things." This also sets an example of candor and honesty.

Very early, the therapist must review the child's past experiences and consider how they might affect the child's expectations of the therapist. If the child has seen other people for diagnosis or treatment, he may assume that his previous experience will be repeated. The therapist must explain in what way his assistance is different. He can also anticipate that the child may feel rejected if his previous "helpers" gave up or transferred him to someone else. Particularly if the patient is an adolescent, it is imperative to consider his ideas about "head shrinkers" and their ilk. Most children have picked up some ideas about psychopathology and about the kind of people who go to psychiatrists, and adolescents are particularly likely to fear insanity. Other children may fear being sent away or being reduced to helplessness by a truth serum or by hypnosis. Not all of this will come in the first few interviews, but the therapist should be on the lookout for such notions at the very beginning of treatment.

How Does Talking Help?

Let us say that the child understands why he is coming, knows that the therapist is kindly disposed toward him, and believes that all they are going to do together is talk. But how does talking help? If the child does not ask, the parents surely will. The answer should be phrased in terms appropriate to the child's age: "We usually do things because we feel something. If we can talk about the feeling, it may just go away in words." Or, "I am sure that there are a lot of good reasons for the way you feel, a lot of reasons that none of us know. If we talk together, maybe we will find them. It's like putting the pieces of a picture puzzle together."

Or, "If we talk about things, perhaps we can find some other ways for you to manage these things, ways that will not bring you so much trouble."

Such remarks will not immediately convince a child of the therapist's wisdom and usefulness, however. Selma Fraiberg described one little girl of six, who received the offer of help with rather more open-mindedness than is usual in children. But after a few visits, she became bored with the toys and restless with the whole setup, and decided to do acrobatics. In the middle of a headstand, she challenged Mrs. Fraiberg with the statement: "You said you knew how to help children when they are afraid." The therapist greeted this with a pleased, affirmative reply. The girl then asked, "Well, then, why don't you do it?" *(1952).* The only way to answer this is to humbly admit that it will take both workers, the child and the therapist, a long time—maybe almost as long as it took to become afraid in the first place. The child is naturally hopeful that the therapist has some quick, magical cure. Explanation to the contrary will be disappointing, but it is also somewhat reassuring to the child to learn that psychotherapy is not mind-reading and that he is as important to the process as the therapist. A child can well understand an analogy between treatment and learning to ride a bicycle, or to read a book, or something else appropriate to his particular age level.

What to Do During the Hour

Very seldom can a child simply sit and talk for a full session. Some play or diversion is almost a necessity. The toys may be provided by the child or by the agency, but one needs less equipment than is commonly thought. The author does not favor special therapy toys (i.e., amputated dolls), but prefers solid, ordinary, and familiar toys. Cars, trucks, toy soldiers, family dolls, paper and crayons, scissors and Scotch tape, small building blocks, model clay, small toy guns, and the like permit the child to invent his own games. Surprisingly few children like puppets and dollhouses, although they are often part of the play therapy room's armamentarium. Balls, darts, and the like require too much room and are too easily misused.

The therapist should avoid engaging in something which requires intense concentration (like model building, playing chess, or checkers) or allowing the child to create something so elaborate or large that it cannot remain intact from one session to the next. Dismantling and putting the toys away should be done during the session; if the child has some favorites, they may be kept in a special drawer or box for him. The therapist should be interested and helpful in the child's play, but not too expert nor too involved. Some therapists find that an activity such as knitting helps them to stay relaxed during these periods of time, but this will not work if the activity is not a fairly mechanical one. Above all, the therapist should accede to the natural interests of the child, in order to establish a natural, relaxed situation in which the child can use the materials expressively.

Setting Limits

Sometimes it seems as if child patients are divided into two main camps—those who are so passive and limp that the therapist is always trying to stir them up and those who are so aggressive and on the go that the therapist is always trying to control them. In therapy, most children eventually become less extreme, but rarely do they become radically different. In the long run, the overcontrolled, unresponsive, and passive child may be more difficult to treat, but the new therapist (like a teacher) is more likely to worry about the aggressive child whose behavior immediately forces her to take a stand. The beginner often feels uneasy about setting limits, fearing that it will interfere with rapport, or that it will seem unaccepting, or even fearing that she will not be able to enforce the limits she has set.

The rules and regulations should be made clear to the child, and he should understand that they apply equally to everyone. There are rules about behavior in the building and in the therapy room. The child must wait in a certain area, and not wander into other offices or bother the receptionist. The parents and therapist should be scrupulously punctual, so that the waiting time of both the child and the therapist is as brief as possible. Still, a child may create a commotion by refusing to enter the therapy room or by leaving it during the appointment hour. If this behavior stems from anxiety, the therapist must try to allay the anxiety. More than likely, the child is anxious about being separated from his mother and does not want to admit it. It may be necessary to have the parent in the therapy room for a few sessions, or it may be possible to help the child to verbalize his concern that his parent may leave him and his reasons for so fearing. If he is teasing, or testing the limits of the situation, he is best handled by cool firmness. This may require some extra help, for example, someone who impersonally enforces the rules by promptly taking the child back to the waiting room each and every time. The therapist must not drag or chase the child. If the child is so young that he does not have enough judgment to avoid common dangers (e.g., stairs, the street), then the problem is more one of training than of therapy. In all such maneuvers, the therapist is being watched by the anxious (or even surreptitiously pleased) parents, and he should try to behave as he wants the parents to behave with the child at home. His behavior is an important demonstration for both child and parent.

In the office, the general rule is to permit nothing which could damage the furniture or the walls or which could hurt the patient or the therapist. It is also good to be prepared with more specific rules—no climbing on the window sills, no matches (this includes the therapist), and no noise so loud that it will bother others in their offices. Whatever rules are necessary should be stated early, and with no equivocation. It is always easier to relax a too-rigid rule than to establish one after the fact, for the child who has provoked the ruling will think it is discriminatory, or that the therapist is afraid or angry, or that the therapist does not really mean it.

Spitting, name calling, using loaded water pistols, and so on are not harmful or destructive, but they are hard to take. It is probably wise to stop this kind of behavior early, because it is likely to be a prelude to more aggressive behavior. This child should be told that he is being provocative, that he is trying to find out what will happen. He can be reassured that retaliation is not forthcoming, but that the therapist will have to stop him soon because such behavior will get them nowhere and may end in a quarrel.

Nevertheless, many beginners find it hard to control aggressive, teasing behavior, and a few pointers may be of help. First, avoid any seductions. The office should be reasonably neat, and there should be no evidence of out-of-control behavior (such as scribbling on the wall). Office equipment should be reduced to a minimum, so that there is little such a child can throw or bang. If the aggression reflects anxiety, as it often does, an interpretation of this as a defense will probably help. In stopping a child, one should say, "I know you think I am angry," (or, "I know this makes you angry,") "but I can't let you do this because it wouldn't help you." Therapists often ask about physically restraining a child. It may sometimes be necessary, but is potentially dangerous. The child may enjoy the physical excitement of a tussle and provoke a repetition. Another last resort is to terminate the session early. This also may boomerang. The child may set out to discover how much the therapist will take before sending him away. So this should be done sparingly, and never threatened. If it becomes absolutely necessary, the therapist should indicate that it is regrettable and that "we will try again next time." The most important general principles are: (1) to convince the child that the restrictions are essentially for his benefit, i.e., for his own safety and to allow him to remain in this kind of therapy; and (2) to act with conviction and firmness *before* becoming irritated and angry—such emotions will lend a hollow ring to one's reassuring words.

Loyalty Conflict

As the child becomes more at home in therapy, begins to enjoy the sessions, and starts to like the therapist, he may share some of his feelings and home experiences. Often, after a particularly happy hour or an especially intimate confidence, the child suddenly becomes uncomfortable. He may feel guilty about feeling fond of someone other than his parents, or feel that he has told tales out of school, or feel that it is bad to tell his secrets to someone who is not a member of his family. This resistance comes as a surprise to the inexperienced therapist, and it is hard to recognize it unless the therapist has had the possibility in mind. Dealing with the conflict depends on the specific situation to which it arose. It may be that the parents will need to give the child explicit permission to talk about the family with the therapist, explaining that this is not the same as talking with a stranger, and the therapist may also need to reassure the child that he can be fond of her without loving his parents one bit less, and that his parents understand (i.e., that they are not jealous).

As a general rule, the therapist must guard against criticizing the parents or endorsing the child's indignation over something they have done. One can say that the child's indignation is understandable—perhaps the parents did not fully understand the situation, or perhaps the child did not explain well enough to his mother or father, or perhaps the parents' action was their way of showing their love and concern. But too-hearty agreement with the rebellious child is likely to make him feel uncomfortable when he returns home. The therapist, although on the child's side, does not want to interfere with or complicate his relationship with his parents.

On Being a Real Person

As the child develops strong feelings for the therapist, he becomes curious and wants to know more about him. Simple, straightforward answers, with no elaborations or unasked-for-details, are best. Persistent questioning will probably lend itself to interpretation in terms of the transference. For instance, if the child asks many questions about the location of the therapist's home, the age of the children, and so on, he probably would like to be part of the therapist's family in the same fashion that he feels jealous of his own family members. Of course, the therapist should not answer questions about other children who come for therapy; the patient can understand that all one's patients are entitled to privacy and confidentiality. Care should be taken that the child does not encounter written material that he is not allowed to read; it is much better to keep records and papers outside the therapy room or in a clearly demarcated area.

Using Outside Information

Anyone working with children has access to information from the parents, from the school, and so on. The child more or less expects the therapist to acquire such information, but even so, the child should be informed of every such visit or telephone call. This does not mean that the child should be told everything that transpired, but he should know with whom the therapist has been in contact, when, and why. It should be made clear to the patient that it is most desirable that he himself be the chief source of information, but it should also be made obvious to him that his parents and teachers may need to understand something about him in order to help him.

Rarely is it wise to directly confront a child with one's knowledge that he has done something bad. Using such information judiciously is very difficult, but one may introduce the event late in a therapy session by saying, "I think you are so restless (or whatever) today because you are wondering if I know that such-and-such happened yesterday. Your mother told me, and I was sorry to hear about it. Perhaps you would feel better if we could talk about it."

When the patient is an adolescent, the problem is even more difficult and one must be even more careful to avoid confrontation. Ordinarily, work with an adolescent's parents is carried by another therapist, and one makes very little, if any, direct use of outside information. If the adolescent (and to some extent this is also true of younger children) believes that you are in cahoots with his parents, he will fear that you will tell them everything he says. It is important that the parents and teachers gain some general understanding of the child's problem from the therapist, but one should not confide specific information except with the child's permission. Sometimes he is relieved, and glad to grant the permission, because he wants to have a clear conscience and to have his parents' help in avoiding further trouble. For example, children at first feel intensely guilty about sexual experimentation, but are later glad to have their parents' help in fending off future temptation. In such cases, it is imperative that the therapist be sufficiently

well acquainted with the parents that he does not divulge such information until they are able to accept it and use it to the child's advantage.

Probing "The Unconscious"

One naturally wants to find the hidden reasons which underlie the overt behavior of a child, and with this aim the therapist pursues the child with questions or suggestions. However, there is an art to questioning a child. "Why?" seldom elicits a logical answer. It is better to draw the child out by asking for more minute, and seemingly irrelevant, details. If a child says that his teacher picks on him and one asks, "Why do you think so?" the child will reply, "I just know it." If you ask, "Why doesn't he like you?" he will answer, "I don't know." It would probably be more profitable to ask, "What do they say to you?" or "What do they do nice for the other children?" These questions agree with the child's contention for the moment, and do not put the child in a defensive or argumentative mood. Also, he can probably give some more details, not regarding external reality, but his perception of it. Every question should be put in such a way that the child is bound to have some answer. It is the therapist's task to find the whys, and he must be resigned to the unavoidable detours by which his goal is reached.

Children rarely offer memories in the course of treatment, but the therapist may introduce past events that the parents have told him about. He may encourage the child to check with his parents, in order to stimulate his recollection of something significant, or use such historical information to explain some present reaction. The therapist must keep the child's history in mind and search out the relationships between past and the present, because a child does not usually reminisce. It is sometimes useful to phrase something *as if* it were in the past: "Perhaps a long time ago, you used to feel very mad at your brother when he took up so much of your mother's time," or to say that you have known other children who felt angry, or hurt, or were afraid in certain situations. It is easier for most children to admit a bad feeling by attributing it to the past or to someone else.

Interpretation of Play

Play should not be interpreted early in the course of treatment. Children normally play aggressively, are concerned with broken items, reveal feelings of jealousy and wishes to be grown-up, and so forth. It is easy to jump in and make something out of the play, but this may make the child self-conscious, uncomfortable, and very cautious about how he plays. It is much better to bide one's time and wait for definite patterns to evolve, patterns which are unique to this child rather than to his age. For instance, boys like to play cowboys, with lots of killing, ambushes, stolen treasures, and so on. However, if there is a particular wrinkle which the child always brings into the classical game, it can be identified and perhaps used for discussion or even interpretation. One boy always had the sheriff turn out to be a bad guy in disguise. The therapist suggested that perhaps he did not trust people and felt that people who look good may be bad underneath. One such game would mean nothing; the rigid repetition is the cue that it has special psychological significance.

Common Resistances

Some of these have already been mentioned, in connection with the starting of treatment and with the loyalty conflict. There are some others which are more likely to appear later in treatment. One is equating the therapist with the devil and resisting therapy on the basis that it offers permission to do bad things which are not condoned by the parents. The therapist who has been too quick to offer reassurance may find the patient turning against him. A good example is dealing with anxiety around masturbation. If the child confesses such activities and the therapist says quickly, "Don't worry, everyone does it and it doesn't hurt anyone," the child frankly does not believe it. Such reassurance flies in the face of all the child's experience. The therapist is much better advised to proceed slowly, to deal with the child's specific anxiety, and to try to get the parents to agree that masturbation is harmless.

Resistance may also arise out of the child's reluctance to give up the therapist. The child figures, "If I didn't have this problem, I wouldn't have this friend." The reverse of this is more difficult to deal with. The child who does not want to get involved in discussion of motives and reasons will relinquish the symptom and make a "flight into health," thus escaping treatment. One sees this sometimes after a single visit which seems to have scared the child out of something—wetting, a phobia, or some pernicious habit.

Treating the Symptom

Ordinarily, one does not want to focus narrowly on a specific symptom. It lends itself to just such resistances as those mentioned above, and the parents may also consider the treatment as a way of achieving a very specific improvement and terminate it prematurely. Suppose a child is being treated because of a learning problem, and his next report card shows improvement. If the entire treatment is predicated on his marks, some patients and their parents would consider this sufficient reason to stop. As soon as possible, one wants to put the treatment on a more general basis—the child's passivity, his inability to maintain a steady pace, or some other aspect of his problem which is not subject to quick or capricious changes. This also helps to dampen the enthusiasm for quick transference cures, cures which occur *only* because of the relationship with the therapist. In such cases, the child gives up a symptom because of the therapist's interest, but the danger is that he will revert as soon as the therapist's interest is withdrawn. If the therapist goes on record as being more interested in understanding the child's problem than in effecting a quick cure, there is less chance of merely temporary improvement.

Again, one should point out that there are exceptions. Sometimes relief of a symptom is sufficient to bring a change in self-concept and thereby start a benign cycle wherein success begets more success. This may be considered less than ideal, but it is not to be spurned.

Ending Treatment

The decision to conclude treatment is sometimes fortuitous. The therapist leaves, the child graduates to a new school, the parents' move, or whatever. However, when the decision can be made solely on psychological grounds, it is surprising how difficult it may be. There always seems to be more that one could do. The parents and child have come to depend on the therapist, and the therapist has worked through the difficult phases and naturally enjoys the smoother sailing of the later phases. It is hard to stop. At this point, the therapist should ask himself, "Is this child as well off psychologically as other children of his age?" "Does he have sufficient freedom now to keep progressing on his own?" "If I met him now, would I recommend treatment?" The answers should provide some of the rational bases for the decision.

It is imperative that the therapist decide with the patient about termination and allow considerable time for this final phase. One can expect new anxieties, even regressions. The reader may recall that the termination date is crucial in relationship therapy, but anxiety about termination is of great importance in therapy of any form. The author is of the opinion that termination should not be sudden and complete; the child and parent should be encouraged to return for friendly visits, or even more help, if they feel the need. Surprisingly, it is often the parents who are most fearful. They may unconsciously feel that the therapist succeeded with their child where they could not, and that they will fail again when they are on their own. The assurance of the therapist's continued interest and support is often sufficient to help them to resume total control.

References to Chapter 14

Ackerman, Nathan W., "Some Theoretical Aspects of Group Psychotherapy," in J. L. Moreno, *Group Psychotherapy: A Symposium*, New York: Beacon House, 1945.

———, *The Psychodynamics of Family Life.* New York: Basic Books, Inc., 1958.

Albee, George W., *Mental Health Manpower Trends.* New York: Basic Books, Inc., 1959.

Allen, Frederick H., *Psychotherapy with Children.* New York: W. W. Norton & Company, Inc., 1942.

Arthur, Helen, "A Comparison of the Techniques Employed in Psychotherapy and Psychoanalysis of Children," *American Journal of Orthopsychiatry*, XXII (1952), 484–99.

Axline, Virginia M., *Play Therapy.* Boston: Houghton Mifflin Company, 1947.

Baruch, Dorothy, *New Ways in Discipline.* New York: McGraw-Hill Book Company, 1949.

Beers, Clifford, *The Mind that Found Itself.* New York: Longmans, Green & Co., Inc., 1908.

Berman, L., "Psychoanalysis and Group Psychotherapy," *Psychoanalytic Review*, XXXVII (1950), 156–63.

Bernheim, H., *Suggestive Therapeutic: A Treatise on the Nature and Uses of Hypnotism.* 2nd Revised Edition, trans. C. A. Herter. New York: G. P. Putnam's Sons, 1889.

Bowen, Murray, "A Family Concept of Schizophrenia," in D. Jackson, *The Etiology of Schizophrenia*. New York: Basic Books, Inc., 1960.

———, "The Family as the Unit of Study and Treatment: Part I. Family Psychotherapy," Workshop, 1959, *American Journal of Orthopsychiatry*, XXXI (1961), 40–61.

Breger, Louis and McGaugh, James L., "Critique and Reformulation of Learning-Theory Approaches to Psychotherapy and Neurosis," *Psychological Bulletin*, 63 (1965), 338–59.

Breuer, J., and S. Freud, *Studies on Hysteria* (1893). Standard Edition, Vol. II, ed. and trans. by James Strachey. London: The Hogarth Press, Ltd., 1955.

Bromberg, Walter, *Man Above Humanity: A History of Psychotherapy*. Philadelphia: J. B. Lippincott Co., 1954.

Bugental, J. F. T., "Humanistic Psychology: A New Breakthrough," *American Psychologist*, XVIII (1963), 563–67.

Case, H. W., "Therapeutic Methods in Stuttering and Speech Blocking," in H. J. Eysenck, *Behavior Therapy and the Neuroses*. London: Pergamon Press, 1960.

Coghill, G. E., "The Biologic Basis of Conflict," *Psychoanalytic Review*, XX (1933), 1–4.

Conn, J. H., "The Child Reveals Himself Through Play: The Method of the Play Interview," *Mental Hygiene*, XXIII (1939), 46–49.

Coué, Emile, *How to Practice Suggestion and Autosuggestion*. New York: American Library Service, 1923.

Dollard, John and Neal Miller, *Personality and Psychotherapy*. New York: McGraw-Hill Book Company, 1950.

Dunlap, Knight, *Habits: Their Making and Unmaking*. New York: Liveright Publishing Corp., 1932.

Eiduson, Bernice T., "Intellectual Inbreeding in the Clinic?" *American Journal of Orthopsychiatry*, XXXIV (1964), 714–21.

Ekstein, Rudolf and Robert Wallerstein, *The Teaching and Learning of Psychotherapy*. New York: Basic Books, Inc., 1958.

Eysenck, H. J., "Learning Theory and Behavior Therapy," in H. J. Eysenck, *Behavior Therapy and the Neuroses*. London: Pergamon Press, 1960.

Ferster, C. B., "Positive Reinforcement and Behavioral Deficits of Autistic Children," *Child Development*, XXXII (1961), 437–56.

Foulkes, S. H., *Introduction to Group-Analytic Psychotherapy*. London: William Heinemann, Ltd., 1948.

Fraiberg, Selma H., "Psychoanalytic Principles in Casework with Children: Part I. Understanding the Child Client," *Social Casework*, XXXIII (1952), 374–81.

Franks, Cyril M., "Behavior Therapy, Psychology and the Psychiatrist," *American Journal of Orthopsychiatry*, XXXV (1965), 145–52.

Freud, Anna, *The Ego and the Mechanisms of Defense*. New York: International Universities Press, Inc., 1946 *a*.

———, *The Psychoanalytical Treatment of Children*. London: Imago Publishing Company, Ltd., 1946 *b*.

Freud, Sigmund, *Analysis of a Phobia in a Five-Year-old Boy* (1909). Standard Edition, Vol. X, ed. and trans. by James Strachey. London: The Hogarth Press, Ltd., 1955.

Gardner, George E., "The Supervision of Psychotherapy," *American Journal of Orthopsychiatry*, XXIII (1953), 293–300.

Gralnick, Alexander, "Family Psychotherapy: General and Specific Considerations," *American Journal of Orthopsychiatry*, XXXII (1962), 515–26.

Grossman, David, "Clinical Psychology: Comments and Suggestions," *American Psychologist*, XVIII (1963), 568–70.

Grotjahn, M., *Psychoanalysis and the Family Neurosis*. New York: W. W. Norton & Company, Inc., 1960.

Hall, G. Stanley, *Pedagogical Seminary*, I, No. 1 (1891), Editor's Preface.

Haworth, Mary R., ed., *Child Psychotherapy*. New York: Basic Books, Inc., 1964.

Jackson, D. D., "Family Interaction, Family Homeostasis and Some Implications for the Conjoint Family Psychotherapy," in Jules Masserman, *Individual and Familial Dynamics*. New York: Grune & Stratton, Inc., 1959.

Joint Commission on Mental Illness and Health, *Action for Mental Health*. New York: Basic Books, Inc., 1961.

Jones, H. G., "The Behavioral Treatment of Enuresis Nocturna," in H. J. Eysenck, *Behavior Therapy and the Neuroses*. London: Pergamon Press, 1960.

Jones, M. C., "Elimination of Children's Fears" (1924), in H. J. Eysenck, *Behavior Therapy and the Neuroses*. London: Pergamon Press, 1960.

Key, Ellen, *The Century of the Child*, trans. M. Franzos. New York: G. P. Putnam's Sons, 1909.

Klein, Melanie, "The Psychoanalytic Play Technique," *American Journal of Orthopsychiatry*, XXV (1955), 223–38.

Konopka, Gisela, *Social Group Work: A Helping Process*. Englewood Cliffs, N.J.: Prentice-Hall, Inc., 1963.

Krasner, Leonard, "Reinforcement, Verbal Behavior, and Psychotherapy," *American Journal of Orthopsychiatry*, XXXIII (1963), 601–13.

Kubie, Lawrence S., "The Pros and Cons of a New Profession: A Doctorate in Medical Psychology," in Molly Harrower, *Medical & Psychological Teamwork in Care of the Chronically Ill.* Springfield, Ill.: Charles C Thomas, Publisher, 1955.

——, in *The New York Herald Tribune*, Sunday, July 8, 1962. A letter to the editor.

Lazarus, A. A., "The Elimination of Children's Phobias by Deconditioning," in H. J. Eysenck, *Behavior Therapy and the Neuroses*. London: Pergamon Press, 1960.

Lehrman, L. J. et al., "Success and Failure of Treatment of Children in the Child Guidance Clinics of the Jewish Board of Guardians, New York City," *Jewish Board of Guardians Research Monograph*, No. 1, 1949.

Levin, Sidney, "Some Comparative Observations of Psychoanalytically Oriented Group and Individual Psychotherapy," *American Journal of Orthopsychiatry*, XXXIII (1963), 148–60.

Levitt, Eugene E., "The Results of Psychotherapy with Children: An Evaluation," *Journal of Consulting Psychology*, XXI (1957), 189–96.

——, H. R. Beiser, and R. E. Robertson, "A Follow-up Evaluation of Cases Treated at a Community Child Guidance Clinic," H. M. Forstenzer, discussant, *American Journal of Orthopsychiatry*, XXIX (1959), 337–49.

Levy, David, "Release Therapy in Young Children," *Psychiatry*, I (1938), 387–89.

——, "Trends in Therapy: III. Release Therapy," *American Journal of Orthopsychiatry*, IX (1939), 713–36.

Levy, John, "Relationship Therapy," *American Journal of Orthopsychiatry*, VIII (1938), 64–69.

Lowrey, Lawson, "Orthopsychiatric Treatment," in L. Lowrey and V. Sloan, *Ortho-psychiatry 1923–1948: Retrospect and Prospect*. Menasha, Wisconsin: American Orthopsychiatric Association, Inc., 1948.

Lubin, B., "Survey of Psychotherapy Training and Activities of Psychologists," *Journal of Clinical Psychology*, XVIII (1962), 252–56.

Lucas, Leon and Ruth Ochroch, "Psychotherapy by the Orthopsychiatric Team: A Review of the Literature." Paper presented at the Annual Meeting of the American Orthopsychiatric Association, Washington, D.C., March, 1963.

May, Rollo, "Contributions of Existential Psychotherapy," in Rollo May, Ernest Angel, and Henri F. Ellenberger, eds., *Existence*. New York: Basic Books, Inc., 1958.

Meiers, Joseph I., "Origins and Development of Group Psychotherapy," in J. L. Moreno, *Group Psychotherapy: A Symposium*. New York: Beacon House, 1945.

Meyer, Adolf, "Presidential Address: 35 Years of Psychiatry in the United States and our Present Outlook," *American Journal of Psychiatry*, LXXXV (1928), 1–32.

Mittleman, B., "The Concurrent Analysis of Married Couples," *Psychoanalytic Quarterly*, XVII (1948), 182–97.

Moreno, J. L., "Group Method and Group Psychotherapy," *Sociometry Monographs*, No. 5, New York: Beacon House, 1931.

——, *Group Psychotherapy: A Symposium*. New York: Beacon House, 1945.

Mowrer, O. H., "A Stimulus-Response Analysis of Anxiety and its Role as a Reinforcing Agent," *Psychological Review*, XLVI (1939), 553–65.

——, *Learning Theory and Personality Dynamics*. New York: The Ronald Press Company, 1950.

——, "Payment or Repayment," *American Psychologist*, XVIII (1963 b), 557–80.

——, *Psychotherapy: Theory and Research*. New York: The Ronald Press Company, 1953.

——, *The New Group Therapy*. Princeton, N.J.: D. Van Nostrand Co., Inc., 1963 a.

——, and W. M. Mowrer, "Enuresis: A Method for its Study and Treatment," *American Journal of Orthopsychiatry*, VIII (1938), 436–59.

Mullan, Hugh and Max Rosenbaum, *Group Psychotherapy*. New York: Free Press of Glencoe, Inc., 1962.

Oberndorf, C. P. "Folie à Deux," *International Journal of Psychoanalysis*, XV (1934), 14–24.

Rank, Otto, *Will Therapy*. New York: Alfred A. Knopf, Inc., 1936.

Redl, Fritz, "Crisis in the Children's Field," *American Journal of Orthopsychiatry*, XXXII (1962), 759–80.

Rioch, Margaret J. *et al.*, "National Institute of Mental Health Pilot Study in Training Mental Health Counselors," *American Journal of Orthopsychiatry*, XXXIII (1963), 678–89.

Rogers, Carl R., *Counseling and Psychotherapy*. Boston: Houghton Mifflin Company, 1942.

Sargent, Helen, "Methodological Problems of Follow-up Studies in Psychotherapy Research," *American Journal of Orthopsychiatry*, XXX (1960), 495–507.

Sheehan, Joseph G., "The Modification of Stuttering Through Non-reinforcement," *Journal of Abnormal and Social Psychology*, XLVI (1951), 51–63.

Slavson, S. R., *Analytic Group Psychotherapy*. New York: Columbia University Press, 1950.

———, *An Introduction to Group Therapy*. New York: The Commonwealth Fund, 1943.

———, *Child Psychotherapy*. New York: Columbia University Press, 1952.

Solomon, J. C., "Active Play Therapy," *American Journal of Orthopsychiatry*, VIII (1938), 479–97.

———, "Active Play Therapy: Further Experiences," *American Journal of Orthopsychiatry*, X (1940), 763–81.

Stein, Herman D., "Sociocultural Factors in Psychiatric Clinics for Children," *Social Service Review*, XXX (1956), 9–19.

Taft, Jessie, *The Dynamics of Therapy in a Controlled Relationship*. New York: The Macmillan Company, 1933.

Thom, D. A., *Habit Clinics for the Child of Pre-school Age: Their Organization and Practical Value*. Washington, D.C.: Government Printing Office, 1924.

Witmer, Helen L., *Psychiatric Interviews with Children*. New York: The Commonwealth Fund, 1946.

———, and Jane Keller, "Outgrowing Childhood Problems: A Study in the Value of Child Guidance Treatment," *Smith College Studies in Social Work*, XIII (1942–1943), 74–90.

Wolf, A., "The Psychoanalysis of Groups," *American Journal of Psychotherapy*, III (1949), 525–58.

Wolf, Alexander and Emanuel K. Schwartz, *Psychoanalysis in Groups*. New York: Grune & Stratton, Inc., 1962.

Wolpe, J., *Psychotherapy by Reciprocal Inhibition*. London: Oxford University Press, 1958.

———, "Reciprocal Inhibition as the Main Basis of Psychotherapeutic Effects," in H. J. Eysenck, *Behavior Therapy and the Neuroses*. London: Pergamon Press, 1960.

Woltmann, A. G., "Play and Related Techniques," in D. Brower and L. E. Abt *Progress in Clinical Psychology*. New York: Grune & Stratton, Inc., 1952.

Yates, A. J., "The Application of Learning Theory to the Treatment of Tics," in H. J. Eysenck, *Behavior Therapy and the Neuroses*. London: Pergamon Press, 1960.

15

WORK WITH PARENTS

No matter how important genetic, prenatal, and natal influences may be in the formation of personality, there is still a tremendous place left for the role of environment. One cannot question the principle that the parent's relationship with his child influences the child's mental health. In recognition of this, countless studies have been made of the relationships among child rearing practices, parental attitudes, and child behavior, and concerted efforts have been made to alter parental behavior through education, in the interest of preventing mental illness in children. It is generally recognized that helping children with problems will necessarily involve their parents, and much thought has been given to work with the parents in collaborative forms of treatment. In our earlier discussion of referral and diagnosis (see Chapter 4), we emphasized the parental defensiveness which arises from guilt. The parent who is able on his own to recognize emotional problems is especially likely to feel totally responsible for them.

Although this chapter is restricted to the general subjects of the role of the parents in affecting child development and their role in psychotherapy with children, one should bear in mind the previous consideration given to organic factors (see Chapters 7, 8, and 11),

constitutional sensitivities (see Chapter 13), fortuitous events (such as illness and surgery), unspoken fantasies (such as primitive concepts of sex differences and causality), and omnipresent genetic factors. The amount of attention given to the role of the parents does not represent the degree of their responsibility, even in theory. It is rather a question of therapeutic ambition: Of all the causative factors, the parental influences seem most susceptible to change. Sometimes, in their zeal to cure, professional workers may foster the impression that if parents will do the right things in the right spirit, their children will have no problems. This is by no means the opinion of the author, nor of most workers in this field.

On the other hand, the actions of parents make a real difference to their children. Nowhere is this more obvious than in the treatment of emotionally disturbed or handicapped children, when so much extra self-control, decision making, and understanding is required. Before considering the nature of guidance given to parents of children with special problems, the general field of parent education will be briefly reviewed, because most families coming for help have already been affected, directly or indirectly, by the current precepts of child rearing. And, since one of the chief objectives of general parent education is the amelioration or prevention of emotional problems, the degree to which it can be successful is of great interest to clinicians.

Trends and Techniques in Parent Education

History of Parent Education

There is nothing new about the idea of parent education; since the beginning of written history there have been commentators on the subject of parental duties. The history of efforts organized specifically to influence parents has been summarized by Orville Brim *(1959, Appendix)*. Early in the nineteenth century, magazines for parents made their appearance in the United States, and mothers' groups known as "Maternal Associations" met regularly to study child rearing problems. These early groups were much concerned with moral and religious issues, and relied heavily on Biblical materials. The nursery and kindergarten movement has been involved in parent education from the time of its inception, the middle of the nineteenth century.

The Child Study Assocation of America, founded in 1888 as the Society for the Study of Child Nature, and the National Congress of Parents and Teachers, formerly the Congress of Mothers, are the two major organizations devoted to parent education. Early in the twentieth century, there began to be considerable federal support for parent education. One of the early projects of the Public Health Service was the publication of a pamphlet, *The Care of the Baby*, designed primarily for parent consumption *(1914)*. In 1932, the Children's Bureau (established in 1912) took over publication and printed a new, revised edition entitled *Infant Care*. The tremendous expansion and increased professionalism of parent education

reached a peak in the early thirties. In 1929, a National Council for Parent Education was incorporated, and for five years published a professional journal, *Parent Education*. The Council supported several research studies, later published as monographs *(Witmer, 1934; Shirley, 1938)*; and it also granted fellowships for training and research. With the Council's demise in 1938, training for professional leadership of parent education programs suffered a setback.

Currently, the growth of parent education has been substantially aided by the financial support available for mental health programs. As Brim comments, "The shift in interest in mental health and other areas of human concern from treatment to prevention has been marked in the past decade, and parent education, primarily a preventive technique, has grown in wealth and recognition with this shift of emphasis" *(1959, p. 338)*. At present, parent educators come from many professional backgrounds—chiefly education, child development, home economics, psychology, social work, and public health nursing. Although these professionals are expected to be knowledgeable and interested in parent education, very little specific training is offered. The respective academic curricula contain much information about child development, and it is tacitly assumed that parent education consists of giving parents the same information in simplified and diluted form. Social work training is perhaps unique, in that considerable attention is given to the resistances and distortions in the way of simple teaching. Future caseworkers are taught how to gauge the client's readiness to accept new information and ways of working through the obstacles to his understanding new ideas and acting on them, but other professional workers are more likely to view parents simply as uninformed students waiting eagerly for nuggets of knowledge.

Changing Fashions in Child Care

This leads us to the question of the content of parent education. What do the experts offer the parents? Brim points out that the literature for parents, falls into two main categories: descriptive information regarding normal behavior and advice on handling practical problems *(1959)*. The descriptive publications usually emanate from child study centers, and the books and articles of Gesell and his co-workers at the Yale Clinic of Child Development are the best-known of these. Gesell and Ilg's *Infant and Child in the Culture of Today (1943)*, which was widely read by the lay public, included "behavior profiles" which described the feeding, sleeping, toileting, and play patterns of children of different ages. Suggestions were made about play equipment and daily routines, but little advice was offered about education or training. For example, referring to the difficult behavior of the normal 2½-year-old, Gesell and Ilg wrote, "He needs developmental time; he deserves discerning patience" *(1943, p. 180)*. The emphasis on inherent growth processes led to a laissez-faire approach which accorded with the trend toward permissive child rearing. Parents checked Gesell to see if Johnny was normal, and they usually found that he fit one or another of the developmental profiles. Some parents were relieved to learn that child development unrolled in a kind of inevitable pattern independent of their doing; others felt frustrated and helpless. (The importance of maturational concepts, brought to the fore by Gesell, was discussed in Chapter 1, and the dangers of overpermissiveness were discussed in Chapter 6.) Informing parents of what to expect from children at different ages is a useful first step in parent education, but now one also tries to define the role of the parents and their contribution to their child's maturity.

The many reviews of the literature on child management concur in highlighting the major changes in the past 60 years or so. Celia Stendler surveyed the articles on child rearing appearing in three women's magazines from 1890 to 1950 *(1950)*; Clark Vincent reviewed some 644 articles of this kind appearing in the same period *(1951)*; and Martha Wolfenstein *(1953)* analyzed the content of the editions of the Children's Bureau's *Infant Care* published in 1914, 1921, 1929, 1938, 1942, 1945, and 1951 *(1953)*. Recommendations regarding feeding schedules, age of toilet training, and manner of discipline, have undergone definite cycles; for 60 years, the pendulum has swung between the extremes of rigidity and permissiveness. Stendler terms the period between 1890 and 1910 as one of "sweet permissiveness," during which "mother knew best" *(1950)*. Around 1910 there was a period of rigid habit training which reached its peak in the twenties. *All* the articles written around 1920, which Stendler reviewed recommended rigid feeding schedules, and affection was to be conveyed with equal care and precision. All the details of child care were reduced to formulas and nothing was left to spontaneity. *Infant Care*, in 1921, advised the mother to take up the task of bowel training as soon as she recovered from her confinement and informed her that almost any baby could be completely trained by six months or the end of the first year, at the latest.

This rigidity, and even harshness, was relaxed in the early thirties, approximately one generation after the "sweet permissiveness" of 1890 to 1910. From 1942 to 1945, parents were advised officially that bowel training should commence at around eight or ten months and should not coincide with weaning, since one or the other might be hard for baby to accept *(Wolfenstein, 1953)*. The tendency to increased gentleness and leniency continued through the forties. The 1951 edition of *Infant Care* advised that bowel training be postponed until the end of the second year. *All* the articles written in 1948 that Stendler reviewed recommended feeding the baby on its own demand ("self-regulatory" schedules)—a complete reversal from the situation in 1920. This period has been called the "era of the baby," with the implication that the contentment and even the normal development of the baby required great parental self-denial.

In 1956, Anna Freud reviewed some trends in parent education as she had seen them from her vantage point as a child psychoanalyst. She pointed out that, while clinicians were pursing specific pathogenic factors, parents and teachers were eagerly waiting for advice: "they sometimes tore isolated bits of knowledge out of the hands of the analysts and applied them, not always with the best results" *(1956 a)*. Without giving dates, she described a number of successive phases. The first discovery of the importance of infantile sexuality led to the slogan of sexual enlightenment for children. The child was not only granted the right to know about sex, he also was very gradually given the right to indulge in physical gratifications. There was greater tolerance of thumb sucking, wetting and soiling, and masturbation. The second phase followed the realization of the importance of inner conflict in producing neurosis, particularly conflict between the wishes and the conscience. Parents then wanted to soften the child's conscience, and some went to extraordinary lengths to avoid an authoritative role and to try to establish a chummy, democratic family group, with no bosses. The third phase, following on the new emphasis given to aggression by psychoanalysts, was characterized by the slogan, "freedom for aggression."

All of these ideas fitted the permissive trends in child rearing. Parents and teachers were pumped full of notions about what they should not do, but given very little direction about what they should do in caring for children. In the end, neither the children nor their parents were happy about this. The children were flooded by naked impulses which made them unsociable, unlovable, unproductive, excited, frightened, and unhappy. Although the philosophy of permissiveness had been fed by a number of streams, the dissatisfaction with it became general. More and more, articles began to point out that children need parents who are authority figures, set limits, and make demands. Benjamin Spock gives, as one reason for revising his famous book on *Baby and Child Care (1946, 1963 a)* a "need to counteract a growing tendency toward overpermissiveness among certain parents, to buck up their self-assurance and authority, to help them to give firmer guidance to their children." He took great pains "to emphasize parents' rights to expect politeness and cooperation from their children. I stressed the point that children who are given firm leadership by their parents are not only much better behaved but much happier" *(Spock, 1963 b)*.

It is too early to have a historical perspective on the period since 1950. Those of us who have been intimately involved with child rearing since that date naturally tend to think that the golden mean has finally been found, but the next generation may see it differently. It should be pointed out that rules are always interpreted and applied by individuals; some people no doubt follow them slavishly but others modify them according to their own judgment. Christine Olden felt that America was particularly quick to "take over and misuse" the catchwords of psychoanalysis, and she attributed permissiveness to the cultural climate:

The [American] population was too diverse, too mobile, too oriented to the future to allow the gradual accretion of a national or even regional or local traditions. In the absence of such traditions the adult's normal insecurity with the child was left unsupported, and an inclination toward extreme permissiveness was the consequence. *(1952, p. 389.)*

She relates this to the history of America, a country in which the child needed to be independent as soon as possible and where he was expected to do better than his parents. She suggests that American parents equated independence with permissiveness. However, American parents are not equally affected by education; proportionately more middle and upper-class mothers are reached *(Boek et al., 1957; Anderson, 1936)*. There are also well-known relationships between social class and child rearing practices *(White, 1957; Littman, Moore, and Pierce-Jones, 1957; and Kohn, 1959)*. The lower-class mother is more likely to accept an authority close at hand, such as mother, husband, or neighbor, or to act on her own impulses, or to respond to necessity. She is unlikely to have either the time or the inclination to ponder over what she has done or to consult a book or a community agency to see what she ought to do in the future.

The undeniable contradictions in so-called scientific advice over the past 50 years have tended to make the child care experts more humble and less dogmatic. Vincent reviewed some 298 articles on the subject of feeding from 1920 through 1945, and found that approximately 75 per cent of those appearing in 1920 to 1925 offered "absolute" advice, compared with 17 per cent in 1945. Alternatives were suggested, and less dire consequences were threatened *(1951)*. At the same time, there was a growing effort to dethrone the experts and to restore the parents' self-confidence. Although himself a parent educator, Benjamin Spock, has this approach. In an address to parent educators, he stated that the "only question you have to ask yourself is 'Will this make them [i.e., parents] more comfortable or will it make them more guilty?' My impression is that you

rarely help them by making them guilty and that you always get a reflection of better management of the child by making them more comfortable" *(Spock, 1955)*. In the latest edition of his book, he urges parents to trust themselves: "It may surprise you to hear that the more people have studied different methods of bringing up children, the more they have come to the conclusion that what good mothers and fathers instinctively feel like doing for the babies is usually best after all" *(Spock, 1963 a, p. 4)*. He believes that the chief source of this "instinctive" feeling is the parents' memories of their own childhood, and that attempts to veer far from this half-remembered experience are fraught with anxiety, ambivalence, and hesitancy. Unfortunately, strict adherence to this philosophy would require the parent educator to use the weight of his training and experience simply to say that mother knows best, which would take us back to the turn of the century.

Aims of Parent Education

There is no gainsaying two facts: (1) research has shown conclusively that specific child care practices are less important than the spirit in which they are carried out (see Chapter 6); and (2) it is much more difficult to change attitudes than specific acts of overt behavior. Nonetheless, it is the author's conviction that parent education can be constructive.

There seem to the author to be five useful functions of parent education. First, there is the sharing of experiences in study groups or the vicarious sharing obtained by reading articles about children. Second, the mere fact that there are study groups and literature on this subject affirms the importance of child rearing and calls attention to the parental role. Third, factual information about behavior usual at different ages helps the parents to know what to expect. There is no reason to expect that the biological fact of parenthood makes people immediately comfortable with, or knowledgeable about, infants and children. Fourth, interpretive information tries to get under the surface and explain some of the whys of child behavior. Spock does some of this; for instance, in the following discussion of the contrariness of the two-year-old:

It looks as though the child's nature between 2 and 3 is urging him to decide things for himself, and to resist pressure from other people. Trying to fight these two battles without much worldly experience seems to get him tightened up inside, especially if his parents are a little too bossy. It's similar to the 6 to 9-year period when the child tries to throw off his dependence on his parents, takes over a lot of responsibility for his own behavior, becomes overfussy about how he does things, and shows his tenseness in various nervous habits. *(1963 -a, p. 353.)*

Some excellent examples of interpretive information are in Selma Fraiberg's book *(1959)*. She is particularly interested in the primitive or magical mental processes of the child under five. She points out that the "inner life of a very young child is often inaccessible to us. Because we cannot remember this time of life, we cannot easily enter his world and adult intuition and imagination often fail before the problems presented by the Pre-School child" *(1959, Introduction)*. Parent educators hope that explanatory information will help the parents to understand and communicate with their children, that the relationship between parent and child will be closer if the child is not a baffling mystery. Understanding should not be confused with permissiveness, however; one can understand exactly why a child is behaving in a certain way and still set about to change his behavior. Understanding should provide the basis for more effective action.

The fifth function of parent education is to offer recommendations on ways of handling children. This, of course, is what parents are looking for in books on child rearing. Many become impatient with normative descriptions and psychological explanations, and want to be told what to do and what not to do. These are the rules which have proven so treacherous in the past, but there still seem to be a few on which there has been general agreement. For example, it is considered unwise for the child to sleep or bathe regularly with his parents. The psychoanalysts would caution against risk of stimulating sexual feelings and fantasies and the learning theorists would point out the danger of reinforcing dependent behavior. Other rules are stressed more by one person than another. For instance, Spock warns against letting the baby get used to taking his bottle to bed because the subsequent attachment may delay weaning. However, "if you prefer the bottle in bed as a sort of sedative and won't mind continuing to give it through a good part of the second year, then there's no harm" *(Spock, 1963 a, p. 122)*. Selma Fraiberg is especially concerned about television viewing and warns that exposure to unselected programs may complicate the process of distinguishing between fantasy and reality. Other rules are more controversial. A good example is the uncertainty regarding the proper way for the parents to handle masturbation when it comes to their attention. It would be worthwhile to canvass parent educators and delineate the areas of complete or partial agreement. In this author's opinion, there is more agreement than is commonly believed.

Parent educators rarely make their theoretical assumptions explicit, and they do not give the steps that intervene between theory and practice. Although this is of little importance to parents who place their trust in the final judgment of the expert, deliberate attempts to connect theory and practice in scientific journals would perhaps prevent premature conclusions and a repetition of past mistakes. The simplification of the expert's opinion is probably inevitable; the parent is attracted by the simple, concrete suggestions, which are so plentiful in newspapers and magazines and so freely offered by neighbors, relatives, and even professionals. There is no easy way for the parent consumer to judge the expertness of the advice he reads and hears, authorities of one sort or another say almost anything.

Techniques of Parent Education

There are three main media of parent education: mass media, group discussions, and individual guidance. The first includes all material directed at an anonymous audience. The principal mass medium used by parent educators is the printed word—books, pamphlets, magazines, and newspapers. It is this material which was analyzed in the studies cited in the preceding section, and there is an immense quantity of it. Brim estimated that, in any given year, the number of available books on the subject numbers several hundreds, and that about 25 million pamphlets are distributed each year. Many newspapers, information agencies, and businesses have pamphlets which they routinely dispense to mothers of new babies. Examples are the "Pierre the Pelican" series, published by the Louisiana Society for Mental Health and the "Cradle Roll Bulletin" published by the Cleveland Press. Every kind of women's magazine carries material on children; there are magazines devoted to parent education (e.g., *Parents' Magazine* and the *National Parent-Teacher*); and there are several widely syndicated newspaper columns. Apparently literature of this kind has a large audience; it is doubtful that there would be so much of it if it were not profitable advertising or promotional material.

Another common educational device which Brim includes as a "mass medium" is the single lecture, because the lecturer does not know his audience.

The programs planned for Parent-Teacher Associations are largely of this order, but the speaker generally has the uncomfortable feeling that his audience has heard the same things over and over and that many of them have come out of a sense of obligation. The mothers often react with a vague sense of guilt to the lecturer's admonitions, a guilt which they neither deserve nor need; the irresponsible parents are comfortably at home or enjoying themselves elsewhere. However, to the extent that fathers (who ordinarily do not read the literature soaked up by their eager wives) attend, the PTA talks may have some value.

The next most impersonal method is *group discussion.* A differentiation should be made between the single meeting and the series of meetings in which there is some continuity of material. Probably the Child Study Association has had more experience with this particular method than any other organization. Aline Auerbach contrasts the character of present parents groups with that of past groups:

At first groups were conducted didactically with the leader acting as a teacher in the traditional academic sense. They then became lecture-discussions, with the leader acting as a speaker and answering questions in a discussion period. More recently they have taken the form of discussion groups, in which parents learn through participation in the group process. Here the leader uses his knowledge of the dynamics of individual behavior and of the inter-relationships of people in groups to help the parents to share their thinking and feeling about common problems, to examine the meaning of their common experiences and to build on their inner strengths as they take on a more integrated parent role. *(1953, p. 2.)*

Group discussions of this order can come close to group psychotherapy, and there have been many attempts to delineate the two *(Neubauer, 1953; Brim, 1959)*. S. R. Slavson distinguishes guidance from therapy in a number of ways. Therapy requires:

. . . an intensive transference relationship with a therapist, by self-confrontation and regression permitted by the therapist and by the patient's own ego and by acting out in a manner that ordinarily creates guilt and anxiety. This is of necessity a prolonged process . . . In guidance the aim is to affect specific attitudes which do not proceed from strong neurotic conflicts and compelling needs to behave in a particular manner; rather the behavior is a result of misconceptions of what the function of parenthood is, what the parent's role is in the development of the child, and of the rather universal lack of knowledge or misunderstanding of the needs of young children. (1958, p. 15.)

The decision as to what material can be covered in a group discussion is a matter of tact and skill in gauging what the parent can accept. The following example illustrates the different levels of interpretation which may be possible in a group discussion:

In the process of group discussions, it becomes apparent that a mother is often unreasonably irritable, critical, and aggressive towards her ten-year-old son. In order to reveal to her the role she is herself playing in these altercations, the leader wants to suggest that her reactions to her son's behavior must be displaced from some other source.

The leader may say something general, to the effect that when one is in a bad mood, everyone, including one's own son, "looks bad." The next level, a little more specific, might be that she takes out on her son a feeling of frustration that is primarily stimulated by someone else, perhaps her husband. The next level would be that she is irritated by her son just because he is like her husband. The next level would be the most general, and would probably refer to an unconscious attitude, namely, that she is angry at her son because he is a boy. This would put the problem squarely to the mother and would, in all likelihood, be felt as an accusation. It is unlikely that such an interpretation would be acceptable in an educational guidance situation.

The techniques used in discussion groups vary with the nature of the group and the training of the leader. Slavson reports that he takes only a passive role, even deliberately dozing, to leave the group to work out their own answers (1958). It is doubtful that anyone but Slavson could do that, and only with a group of well-educated, well-motivated parents. Excluding groups of parents of disturbed children, most parent groups are expectant mothers and parents of pre-school children (Barnes, 1952; Meyer and Power, 1953). They are usually young, inexperienced, perhaps feeling socially isolated by their pregnancy or by the small children who are always underfoot, and with a sense of the full weight of the responsibility of parenthood. The infant or pre-school child is growing so rapidly that his parents are constantly facing new problems and questions; this is much less true of the schoolchild. The role of the parent is more central in the development of the pre-school child than the child of any other age. Parents of normal adolescents also have many questions and problems, but they are much less likely to form discussion groups. For one thing, it is obvious that there are many factors influencing their children, so they feel less wholly responsible. It is interesting that parents of twins have felt that their problems are different enough to warrant forming separate groups (Plank, 1958).

Group guidance has also been widely offered to parents of mentally and physically handicapped children. Such groups are sometimes formed for public education and fund raising (Katz, 1961), but they often later become avenues for counseling. Harry Bice has described his experiences with mothers of cerebral palsied children (1952; 1955); their disbelief, bitterness, ambivalence, and uncertainty are common to all parents of handicapped children.

The importance of helping parents with these feelings has already been mentioned in connection with the retarded (Chapter 8), but there is some real advantage to group meetings. The parents have many of the same problems and the same emotional reactions, and they can help one another. Many of them have found practical ways of helping their children, of lightening their burdens, or of arranging their households which the professional could not imagine. Despite the emotional support and practical advice these parents can give each other, however, there is need for a professional leader who can control the parent who would dominate the group, who can help the parents maintain their individuality, and who can provide technical information. A recent, very perceptive book, *Understand Those Feelings,* is a useful basis for parent group discussions, if one likes to have some formal structure. Eugene McDonald, a speech therapist, writes in this book that a treatment program for handicapped children should include the family, that is, the program should be designed to help parents understand and manage their own feelings, as well as to treat their child *(1962).* This idea is becoming more and more accepted by speech clinics, facilities for crippled children, clinics and schools for the retarded, and so on. These programs are probably the newest development in group education for parents.

Individual counseling as a method of parent education is a natural part of the relationship between parents and members of many professions. The clergyman, the physician, the teacher are some who may become involved in parent counseling. Pediatricians have long recognized their potential value as mental hygienists; Spock has written:

If he [the physician] can think of the fully developed disease as the end result of commonplace, often innocent appearing deviations from healthy functioning, usually developing in the first years of life,

he may come to realize that he and not the psychiatrist has the greater opportunity to make contributions to mental health. *(Spock and Huschka, 1938, p. 757.)*

Lucille Blum analyzed the counseling practices of some 19 physicians caring for 81 babies in well-baby clinics of New York City, and found that relatively few mothers expressed their concerns to the physician. She suggested that mothers not be asked for yes-or-no answers by the physicians, but that the doctors phrase their questions "so as to reflect a general interest in the area to be investigated . . . [A] freer approach on the part of the pediatrician with respect to procuring information would undoubtedly encourage the mother to become a more active participant in the give-and-take of the pediatrician-mother relationship" *(1950, p. 95).*

Barbara Korsch described a program of training medical personnel in advising parents *(1956).* She points out that a doctor spends somewhere between 65 and 70 per cent of his day talking to patients, but that his training for this is relatively meager. The project, which extended over a number of years, offered training in (1) direct observation; (2) interview techniques, and (3) techniques of giving advice and reassurance. Despite the general acknowledgment of the importance of psychological skills, two factors militate against their incorporation into regular medical practice. The doctor must concern himself primarily with physical problems; that is his major responsibility. He can be forgiven (or forgive himself) for mishandling a psychological problem but improper treatment of physical disease is another matter. Moreover, particularly in clinics, there is a turn-over of staff personnel so that patient-doctor relationships do not become strong. And there are always patients waiting, often patients with critical physical problems. Since psychological investigation can be postponed, it usually is. The medical profession is by no means alone in neglecting such apparently simple activities as observing, interviewing, and advising normal people with normal problems. Clinical psychologists, who are exposed to a wide range of personality theories, learn a great deal about experimental design and statistical measurement, practice diligently with clinical testing devices, and have some supervised experience in treating emotionally disturbed adults or children, often do not know how to talk with a parent except in a formal therapy session.

Counseling by educators has been best developed in the nursery schools. Dorothy Baruch presents some lengthy protocols of individual counseling sessions with parents in a school situation (1939), and Margarete Ruben offers some very practical guidance on such matters as thumb sucking, eating, toilet training, aggression, timidity, jealousy, masturbation, fantasy, sleep, and jealousy. Her advice is designed for parent advisers on a nursery school staff. Most of the problems which she discussed often become manageable after one or two conferences with the parent, but she also suggests that some topics (e.g., masturbation) are more easily managed in small meetings, at which parental anxieties can be shared and during which the counselor can offer more general information (1960).

When the child enters school, counseling of parents becomes much less intense and less frequent, being almost entirely restricted to conferences with the grade school teacher if the child is considered normal. Such parent-teacher conferences are now routine in many school systems. They are usually half-hour conferences (although as little as five minutes is allowed in some cities), scheduled once or twice a year. They were established for two reasons: to give the teacher some insight into the home and family situation; and to give the parent a report of the child's progress at school. In the short time allotted, the two participants must become acquainted with one another, the mother must think about what to tell the teacher about the child's past life and home situation, and the teacher must inform the mother about the child's academic work and his social adjustment in the class. Besides, if there is any problem, however small or large, the teacher is supposed to make some recommendations for its solution! In the author's opinion, the most obvious way to increase the usefulness of these routine conferences is to be less ambitious and focus the interview on the child's academic and social progress in school. When there is a problem a second interview should be scheduled, one in which the teacher seeks, rather than gives, information.

Much of the material written to help teachers with parent conferences has emphasized the importance of having the facts about the child well prepared. There is also much information about the physical setting (lighting, ventilation, comfortable seating arrangements, quiet, and privacy). Much less is said about the psychological aspects of the conference. The excellent discussion of feelings contained in Grace Langdon and Irving Stout's book on teacher-parent interviews is exceptional (1954). The parent and the teacher have heard about each other from the child; moreover, each has her own background of experience, with teachers and mothers, respectively, both as adults and as children. The approaching conference reawakens old feelings toward school; as a result, the mother may be awed and deferential or resentful and defiant. The teacher, too, has feelings about mothers; she may expect criticism and be feeling defensive. If the child is not doing well, both are looking for a reason and both are hoping that they will not be held accountable. Of course, everything is lovely when the child is a superior student, happy in school, and a social leader.

The teacher, as the professional, should be able to achieve a degree of objectivity and control over her personal feelings. It is her job to put herself into the mother's shoes, to understand that the mother feels protective toward her offspring and defensive about her way of doing things, and to respect the mother's background, culture, and education. She should try to detect any worries that the mother may have (financial, health, or whatever) and try to enable her mother to speak frankly. There are three reasons why a mother hesitates: She is afraid of hurting a teacher's feelings or angering her, because the teacher is in a position to "take it out" on the child; she believes that the teacher would not be interested or that she would not understand; and she is afraid that the information will become part of the child's permanent record. This last point is a matter of concern to teachers as well. It is difficult to decide what should be recorded in the school files. From fear of unfair prejudice, many teachers like to start from scratch and make up their own minds, and this would be a laudable approach except that neither the child nor the mother *can* start from scratch. In order to evaluate the child's progress, or lack of it, one must compare the present with the past. And in order to appreciate the mother's reactions, one must have some insight into what she has been told in previous conferences. It is worth reviewing these previous interviews with the mother before launching into a new set of observations and recommendations. This follows the casework practice of finding out where the client is and starting from there.

When one starts to review the past, however, it is extremely important not to be drawn into a rehash of what was done wrong. It is seldom helpful to the parent to engage in a critique of her child's previous teachers, and it *never* helps to discuss the problems of another child or his parent. The teacher may think she is establishing intimacy, but the parent may lose confidence in the teacher in the process, fearing that the teacher will be equally confidential, perhaps about her, with some other mother. The ethics of interviewing bear considerable reiteration and cannot be overemphasized; they are far more important than the lighting or the ventilation.

Finally, one comes to the making of recommendations. Faced with a problem child and a hopeful mother, the teacher feels obligated to come up with a solution, little realizing how difficult this may be on the basis of her sparse information. The teacher should not feel that she should know all the answers, and she should put her recommendations in a tentative form: "Let's try this, and see." Above all, she should find out what the parents have already tried. Teachers are likely to decide, when a child is not doing well, that the parents are not taking enough interest or that they are pushing him too much, but the child's behavior is no evidence of its cause. This, of course, leads back to the problems of diagnosis and referral which were discussed in Chapter 4. In counseling a parent, the teacher must restrict her advice to those areas where she has specific information on which to proceed. This same general principle applies equally to other professional counselors in the schools—psychologists, guidance counselors, principals, and social workers.

Effectiveness of Parent Education

Brim has devoted considerable attention to the evaluation of the results of parent education (1959). Many of the issues involved are the same as those discussed in connection with evaluating psychotherapy. The first question is always how one judges success. Theoretically, since the aim is to improve the welfare of the child, the results should be assessed in terms of what happens to the child rather than what happens to the parent. However, Brim points out that the incidence of mental illness is a tricky measure. Incidence can change with new definitions, when diagnostic and treatment facilities are increased, or when parents, teachers, and physicians become more perceptive. An educational program for parents might effectively reduce the true incidence of mental illness in children, but produce an increase in the recorded incidence. He also points out that parent education might increase the well-being of children who were never sufficiently disturbed to be counted officially. Also, some emotional disturbances are largely the result of organic or constitutional factors. It is unlikely, for example, that parent education would affect the number of psychotic or retarded children, but it is possible that it would affect the number designated as "immature."

In view of such difficulties, researchers have resorted to evaluating the changes in the parents rather than in the children. The measures which have been used have often been chosen because of their ready availability rather than their proven validity. In addition, one needs a control group—not just a group who have had "no treatment," but an equally well-motivated and interested group, with the same social experience of meeting together, but without the special education. Of the 23 studies which Brim reviewed, only 11 attempted to compare an experimental group with a control group.

Virtually none of the investigations so far conducted has met all the conditions of reliable measurement of valid criteria and with adequate controls to evaluate the single factor of parent education. However, the evidence we have gleaned from the research we have is positive; it indicates that parents are significantly and desirably changed by participating in parent discussion groups and by being individually counseled.

Although scientists deplore the absence of clean research in parent education, as they do in psychotherapy, the clinicians are more concerned about their patients, their techniques, and their personal proficiency. They have no great need to prove the general efficacy of psychotherapy or of education. This is not because of sublime self-confidence; in fact, practitioners usually have fewer illusions about what they can do than people outside the field. Rather, it is confidence in the simple fact that people can and do change, that they continue to respond to external influences throughout their lives. The psychotherapist, or the educator, tries to provide something special in the way of an external influence, something which will give them new information about themselves or about their children on the basis of which they may, or may not, change their attitudes and behavior. The content of this information may change through experience and new observations about parents and children. Teaching parents about children is no different than other kinds of adult education, and it needs no more scientific validation than any other educational effort.

Parental Contributions to Psychopathology in Children

A major premise of parent education, as we saw in the previous section, is that there is a connection between parental and child behavior, and that influencing the parent influences the well-being of the child. In theory, parent education is designed for the normal parent of the normal child, and its goal is prevention. In the next section, we will discuss the role of the parents in the actual treatment of children with recognized emotional difficulties. In such guidance, one must be aware both of the parents' part in the causation or perpetuation of the child's disturbed behavior and the demoralizing effect of the child's problems on the parents. This section is a brief review of what is known about parental influences on the child's personality. The material is vast, and only representative studies will be mentioned.

Maternal Deprivation and Mental Health

It is logical to consider first the psychopathology resulting from the absence of parents, specifically the deprivation of maternal care in the first years of life. Such deprivation is graphically depicted in a film which the author recommends (Appell and Aubrey, 1951). J. Bowlby drew attention to this topic when he published his analysis of the many scattered studies reported as of that date (1951). He sorted the evidence into three main sources: direct studies of the mental health and development of children living in institutions, hospitals, and foster homes; retrospective studies which investigated the childhood histories of adolescents or adults who developed psychological illness; and follow-up studies of children who suffered severe deprivation in their early years. Our review is based on his classification.

René Spitz was an early contributor of direct observations of infants in institutions, and reported a considerable amount of data contrasting the development of infants in a foundling home with infants in a nursery connected with a prison, where the mother continued to care for her child. He described two kinds of psychiatric conditions: "hospitalism," by which he meant a vitiated condition of mind and body, generalized physical and mental retardation, and lack of responsiveness, which he felt resulted from prolonged institutional care (Spitz, 1945; 1946 a); and "anaclitic depression," by which he meant a specific reaction to separation which tended to occur when a good relationship between mother and infant had been interrupted. Some infants, after they lost their mothers, developed weepy, then withdrawn, then rigid behavior, and they became insomniac, ill and emaciated. They assumed a faraway, dazed expression, and screamed, and their disturbance increased when an adult approached them. Spitz found this distinctive clinical picture in 19 out of 123 infants. It occurred during a three-to-four month separation from the mother, and it disappeared after she returned (Spitz, 1946 b). Separation before the age of six months did not seem to evoke this acute depression. This, plus evidence from other studies (Rheingold and Bayley, 1959) indicates that there is a critical period (i.e., six to eighteen months) during which the infant is most vulnerable to separation. This coincides with our understanding of the timing of the child's recognition of and need for his mother and the development of the anxiety toward strangers usually seen around eight months (see Chapter 2). Although it is not easy, it is possible for conscientious, well-staffed, psychologically oriented institutions to provide adequate substitutes for the mother in the first four or five months and thereby prevent the early deprivational syndrome (Rheingold, 1956; David and Appell, 1961).

Other investigations have demonstrated the increasing importance of a single mother figure with whom the child can form a one-to-one relationship. Anna Freud and Dorothy Burlingham observed retarded verbal development in one to two-year-olds without families (1944). This was confirmed by Sally Provence and Rose Lipton, who found that "language development was the first area to be depressed in early infancy and remained the sector of greatest retardation as measured by the tests during the period of institutional living. It also took a longer period of family living for significant improvement to take place."[*] These authors, psychiatrically trained pediatricians, made repeated examinations of 75 children who were placed in an institution when they were less than three weeks old, and compared them with 75 children of similar backgrounds who were placed in foster homes in infancy

---

[*]Quoted from Sally Provence and Rose Lipton, *Infants in Institutions* (New York: International Universities Press, Inc., 1962) p. 149. Reproduced by permission.

and with 75 children who remained with their own families. They concluded that the institutionalized children were significantly retarded. Their developmental quotients dropped progressively during the first year (see Table 10).

Provence and Lipton also compared the infants' motor, social, and language development, and their responses to inanimate objects. Motor development was the least retarded. The infants' interest in inanimate objects was similar to their relationship with people who are, after all, animate objects. *(Provence and Ritvo, 1961)*. In their first few months, their visual and acoustic responses to toys, as well as the approaches to them and their grasping of them, were very similar to those of the normal infants. From this point, however, they displayed a decreasing interest in toys. They showed little displeasure when toys were lost, even toys which they had appeared to enjoy, and rarely tried to recover them. In the second year, their discrimination was inferior and their capacity to exploit toys was poorly developed. Provence and Lipton make some very interesting interpretations of the early interest in playthings. It is their view that the original source of interest in toys is the infant's personal relationship to his mother and that without this relationship, the toys are as interchangeable as the people around him.

Provence and Lipton made a careful analysis of the institutional environment of these infants, in order to un-

TABLE 10†

	Number	Median Developmental Quotient			Range of Developmental Quotient		
		14-26 Weeks	27-39 Weeks	40-52 Weeks	14-26 Weeks	27-39 Weeks	40-52 Weeks
Institutionalized Children	75	102	92	84	85-125	72-107	72-92
Foster-home Children	75	116	108	107	99-151	91-126	95-112

†Sally Provence and Rose C. Lipton, *Infants in Institutions* (New York: International Universities Press, Inc., 1962), p. 171.

TABLE 11†
Family versus Institution as Structural Models for Adult-Child Interaction

Factor	Family	Institution
Number of children per adult	Low	High
Continuity of adult-child interaction	High	Low
Specificity of adult-child emotional response	High	Low
Warmth and intensity of adult emotional response	High	Low
Adult approval and reward	High	Low
Gratification of tensions	Rapid, magical, achieved effortlessly	Unpredictable
Richness of environmental stimulation	High	Low
Stereotypy in environmental stimulation	Low	High

†W. Goldfarb, "Emotional and Intellectual Consequences of Psychologic Deprivation in Infancy: A Re-evaluation," in P. Hoch and J. Zubin, *Psychopathology of Childhood* (New York: Grune & Stratton, Inc.), p. 192.

derstand what was present and what was absent in the infants' experience. Their summary follows:

We believe that the poverty and the infrequency of the personal contact were the outstanding deficits in the experience of the institutionalized babies. It was a quantitative deficit in that there were not enough interchanges to promote development. It was also a qualitative deficit. While the attendants were pleasant to the babies and worked uncomplainingly and conscientiously, there was no relationship between nurse and infant that contained the variety and intensity of feelings a mother has for her own baby. The atmosphere as it appeared to the observer was mainly one of quiet, tranquility, and blandness.[*]

W. Goldfarb put much the same thing into tabular form (see Table 11).

In the second kind of evidence, follow-up studies, there is a long gap between infancy and the follow-up. Only 14 children were followed up by Provence and Lipton, and for less than five years, but the continuity of their observations is unique. After they were placed in foster homes, these infants made "dramatic gains" and "in many aspects of their development they looked sufficiently improved that they were not markedly different from their peers on superficial observation and casual contact."[**] On the other hand, their verbal recovery was slow. In Provence's opinion, there was other mental impairment resembling the concreteness of thought and intellectual rigidity often found in certain types of brain-damaged children. She mentions their impoverished imagination, which could be observed in their play, in conversation, and in their responses to questions.

The institutionalized infants in the Provence study quickly blossomed from their lethargy but tended to be indiscriminately friendly, which the authors interpreted as reflecting a lack of depth and specificity in the relationship. Even after many months with the same foster mother, the institutional children did not turn to her for comfort; in stressful situations, they more commonly regressed to the solitary behavior of their first year. The foster mothers did not report even the normal number of feeding or sleeping disturbances in these children; they ate and slept rather too much than too little. Initially, the babies were passive, uncomplaining, and undemanding, taking all that they could get that was freely offered to them.

Subtle qualitative differences have also been found by other researchers. Juanita Chambers compared a group of 28 children who had been placed in at least three different foster homes in their first three years with a matched group of children who lived with their families, on the single variable of their ability to conceptualize time. In three of four experiments adapted from Piaget, she found that the deprived group was significantly inferior *(1961)*. This is of theoretical importance in view of the connection between a sense of time and ability to defer gratification (also impaired in the Provence group).

The most frequently quoted follow-up study is that of Goldfarb who compared 15 institutionalized children with 15 children in foster homes. The first group had entered the institution at about 5 months of age and were transferred to foster homes at an average age of 3 years and 11 months. The control group, supposedly of a similar genetic background, had lived in foster homes since infancy. The children were studied in early adolescence, at a mean age of 12 years, the range being 10 to 14 years. The findings are shown in Table 12.

In summary, the institutionalized children were more retarded intellectually. There were also distinct emotional consequences, chiefly, the absence of a normal capacity for inhibition.

---

[*]Provence and Lipton, *op. cit.*, p. 47.
[**]Provence and Lipton, *op. cit.*, p. 158.

TABLE 12*

Function Tested or Rated	Test or Rating Method	Results Expressed As	Results Institutionalized Group	Foster Home Group
Intelligence	Wechsler	Mean I.Q.	72.4	95.4
Ability to conceptualize	Weigl	Mean score	2.4	6.8
	Vigotsky	Mean score	0.5	4.7
Reading	Standard tests	Mean score	5.1	6.8
Arithmetic	Standard tests	Mean score	4.7	6.7
Social Maturity	Vineland	Mean S.Q.	79.0	98.8
Ability to keep rules	Special experiment	Number of children	3	12
Guilt on breaking rules	Special experiment	Number of children	2	11
Capacity for relationship	Caseworkers' assessment	Number of children able to make normal relationship	3	14
Speech	Caseworkers' assessment	Number of children up to average	3	14

*Quoted from William Goldfarb, "Emotional and Intellectual Consequences of Psychologic Deprivation in Infancy: A Re-evaluation," in *Psychopathology of Childhood*, P. Hoch and J. Zubin, eds. (New York: Grune & Stratton, Inc., 1955), p. 109. Reproduced by permission.

The institutionalized group displayed extremely difficult behavior—hyperactivity, restlessness, inability to concentrate, and unmanageability. This description is reminiscent of the "Strauss syndrome." Furthermore, the institutionalized children seemed to have no genuine attachments, although they were indiscriminately and insatiably demanding of affection. This confirms, at a later age, the observations which Provence and Lipton made about younger children.

On the other hand, David Beres and Samuel Ober have given a somewhat more encouraging report of the status of 38 young adults who were separated from their mothers in infancy and placed in an institution for as long as four years. They found a variety of pathological conditions, but about half of the 38 were said to have made some degree of favorable social adjustment. These authors also commented on the ego growth that took place *after* the age of five years and rejected the spirit of therapeutic hopelessness which was evoked by the early reports on maternal deprivation *(1950)*.

The prototype of the retrospective study of the relationship between maternal care and mental health is Bowlby's monograph on 44 juvenile thieves *(1946)*. Of the total, 17 had suffered early or prolonged separation from their mothers or mother figures during their first five years, as compared with only 2 of the 44 control subjects (other children attending the same child guidance clinic). Of the 14 thieves considered "affectionless," 12 had experienced such separation, as compared with 5 of the remaining 30 thieves *(1946)*. The characteristics of this subgroup, "affectionless" delinquents, are the same as those ascribed to "psychopathic personalities" in Chapter 12.

A. M. Earle and B. V. Earle compared 100 adult patients who had suffered severe maternal deprivation, (longer than six months before the age of six) with 100 other patients, matched for age and sex, who had not been separated from their parents, as children. The group which had experienced maternal deprivation contained a greater number of "sociopathic personalities" and more history of "childhood behavior disorders" but there was no evidence that schizophrenia or other emotional illnesses were more prevalent (1961). Studies by S. and E. T. Glueck (1950) and C. J. Wardle (1961) tend to support the connection between separation and delinquency, but studies by R. G. Andry (1960) and S. Naess (1959) do not. Some of the disagreement may come from the selection of delinquents to be studied; Bowlby restricted his conclusion to the affectionless psychopath and did not generalize it to all delinquents. Some of the disagreement may also arise from differing definitions of "deprivation." One must ask at what age, for how long, for what reason the separation occurred and what substitute arrangements were made.

The retrospective study done by Hilda Lewis shows the complications in relating cause and effect in this area. Her study dealt with 500 children admitted to an English reception center. Some had had insufficient contact with their parents, some had had distorted relations with their parents, some had had discontinuous relations with their parents because of previous separations, and others had had a combination of these experiences. The children were classified according to their degree of disturbance, and also qualitatively, and attempts were made to connect specific features of their previous experience with specific features of their current behavior. Lewis found that a prolonged separation of the child from his mother before he was two was related to the degree of maladjustment but not to the specific form. This concurs with Bowlby's thesis. But her other findings have been used as refutation. Other kinds of separations did not correlate with serious maladjustment, and lasting separation before the age of two did not relate specifically to antisocial disorders. She also found many other factors which were related to the degree of maladjustment: lack of maternal affection, maternal overindulgence, maternal mental illness, paternal neglect,

paternal overindulgence, and prolonged public care (1954). In brief, she found that there are many adverse conditions which singly, or in combination, can produce emotional disturbances. Prolonged maternal deprivation in the first two years of life was only one such factor.

Even a cursory review of the literature indicates that a surprising amount of controversy was stirred up by Bowlby's monograph. To make sense out of the commotion, one must return to Bowlby's original conclusions:

Evidence that the deprivation of mother-love in early childhood can have a far-reaching effect on the mental health and personality development of human beings comes from many sources. . . . The extent to which these studies, undertaken by people of many nations, varied training, and as often as not, ignorant of each others' conclusions, confirm and support each other is impressive. What each individual piece of work lacks in thoroughness, scientific reliability, or precision is largely made good by the concordance of the whole. (1951, p. 15.)

There is no doubt that he hoped that his monograph would stimulate social action, and he may have pleaded his cause with unscientific eloquence:

The proper care of children deprived of a normal home life can now be seen to be not merely an act of common humanity, but to be essential for the mental and social welfare of a community. For, when their care is neglected, as happens in every country of the Western world today, they grow up to reproduce themselves. (1951, p. 157.)

It is highly instructive to examine what was made out of Bowlby's conclusions. The misinterpretations which ensued are classic examples of oversimplification and errors in logic. In 1962, the World Health Organization published a second monograph, containing a number of papers "reassessing the effects of deprivation of maternal care." In the paper which Dane Prugh and Robert G. Harlow wrote for this symposium, they enumerated three common misunderstandings. First, some understood Bowlby to say that *any* separation of the infant or young child from the mother necessarily results in serious emotional deprivation. This is not true; it is only prolonged separation followed by inadequate substitute care which creates serious consequences. Second, many have thought that the dire consequences were inevitable and universal, that all children undergoing early institutionalization or other sorts of gross maternal deprivation develop the picture of the "affectionless character" or retarded mental development. This also is not true, although the fact that there are differences in vulnerability does not refute the thesis of causality. Not every individual exposed to a virus falls ill of disease. Third, the inference has been made by some that every psychopathic or mentally retarded person suffered maternal deprivation in infancy. This also is not logical; as we observed earlier, many pathogenic factors can produce the same result. This is one of the ways in which physical and mental illness differ. Physical illness is likely to be more specific in its symptomatology and to be the result of more specific antecedents. Psychological disorders are less sharply delineated and result from multiple, rather than single, causes.

These errors have had their effect on clinical opinion and practice. Anna Freud has remarked that the realization that the capacity for attachment to other human beings can be definitely harmed in the first year of life has led educators to believe that it depends solely on the mother whether she has a normal or an abnormal child:

Very often when an ill child is brought to the child psychiatrist he shows no interest in the child—he looks for what is wrong with the mother. It is another slogan which has been coined out of this rather complicated psychological study of the first year of life, and that is the slogan of the so-called rejecting mother who harms her child because she does not comfort, love, satisfy it enough. *(1956- a, p. 15.)*

Later, she avers that a good mother-child relationship in the first year of life is a wonderful thing which provides an excellent basis for mental health, but adds that, in and of itself, it offers no guarantee of the child's mental health. Many things can happen which are not a direct influence of the mother's personality.

Prugh and Harlow object to the recent tendency to believe that any home is better than any institution. They point out that there can be "masked deprivation," that the child's needs may not be met by his family and that some children would be better served by removal *(1962)*. (Some of the pathological mother-child relationships which they term "masked deprivation" are discussed a little later, and the indications for removal from home are discussed in the next chapter.)

There is still another "error" which has been made regarding Bowlby's conclusions, particularly around the issue of the possible irreversibility of damage done by early deprivation. The evidence showing the lasting effects of early deprivation has been erroneously interpreted by some to mean that psychoanalysts believe that the personality is fixed by the age of three and that no further changes are possible. The normal child of three is reasonably plastic with a potential for a great deal of further learning and development. It is only under highly abnormal conditions that the potential for change is lost. A child who reacted to pathogenic deprivation is, indeed, scarred for life. Whether these scars are barely noticeable or a severe handicap will depend on circumstances and on the child's endowment.

The issue of reversibility comes up in some very practical situations. When social workers encounter disturbed or retarded children who are known to have severely deprived infancies, some adopt the position that nothing can be done. More frequently, they turn to a diagnostician and ask if the damage can be undone. Provence and Lipton describe the dilemma of the psychologist, psychiatrist, or pediatrician who is asked if it is "too late."

When an infant in an institution shows signs of retarded development, one cannot clarify the question of his basic endowment as long as he remains in a situation of deprivation. One of the aids to diagnosis in clinical medicine in general is that of response to the therapeutic trial. This procedure employs that principle: if the infant's improvement is adequate after the introduction of more adequate nurturing, one can exclude gross central nervous system damage or defects and gross congenital mental subnormality. One cannot exclude very mild degrees of equipmental impairment, however, because the residual effects of severe deprivation in infancy and the residual effects of minimal cerebral damage or dysfunction are similar in many ways.[*]

The treatment of Susan (see Chapter 8) illustrates the results of a therapeutic trial. This case demonstrated that the deleterious effects of early deprivation could be significantly altered (i.e., reversed) even at 21 months. It was theoretically possible that she was permanently retarded, but fortunately this assumption was not made. Until it is proved otherwise, one must proceed on the basis that an improvement in the environment will improve the child. This means undoing the trauma by supplying what has been missing, namely, the stable affection of a mother. Although there are scientific perils to the single case study, the opportunity to witness the blossoming of a child's mind and personality endows the concept of maternal deprivation with a significance which cannot be gleaned from tables, numbers, or semantic arguments.

---

[*]Provence and Lipton, *op. cit.*, p. 7.

Research on Parental Influences on the Child's Personality

Before examining the special problem of parental contributions to child psychopathology, we will summarize the major findings about parental influences on the personality of the *normal* child. The early research was largely stimulated by the desire to prevent behavior problems, and it was disappointing to find that this was not as easy as it first appeared. The first approach was an attempt to relate specific maternal practices to later behavioral symptoms, but research results provided no confirmation. Reviews of many studies conclude that no infant care practice bears a predictable relationship to later personality adjustment *(Orlansky, 1949; Frankiel, 1959).* (See Chapter 6.)

It became apparent to both researchers and clinicians that it was meaningful to study child care practices only in the context of the total mother-child relationship. A study by Marjorie Behrens *(1954)* attempted to do this. She investigated the infant rearing practices of families who were coming to a mental health clinic, and found no correlation between feeding, weaning, and toilet training practices and the child's adjustment at the age of three. She went on to evaluate what she considered to be the mother's underlying attitudes (i.e., character structure), her way of meeting the demands of maternity, and her observed conduct toward her child, and obtained correlations ranging between .69 and .93 between the adjustment of the child and the mother's attitudes. In studies of this sort, one must not confuse concomitance with causation. It may be that emotionally disturbed children evoke poor maternal behavior, rather than the other way around. However, there is no doubt whatsoever that it is futile to try to connect isolated bits of maternal behavior with the child's personality. It is not so much what the mother does (or says she does) as why she does it, under what circumstances, and how she does it.

The investigations into patterns of parental behavior and attitudes can be classified as "idiographic," that is, as employing the case history approach, or as "nomethetic," that is, involving the statistical treatment of a considerable number of subjects. The nomethetic studies can be further subdivided into those which utilize direct observation and those which rely on interviews, on questionnaires, or on ratings supplied by the parents.

One of the earliest observational studies was made by B. Merrill *(1946)*. Thirty mothers, together with their respective children (ranging in age from 3 to 5½ years) were observed for one-half hour sessions through a one-way vision screen. They were then divided equally into a control and an experimental group. Before the second session, the examiner told the experimental subjects that their child's play, in the first session had not "realized his capabilities." The control group behaved toward their children in the second session much as they had behaved in the first, but the experimental group became more interfering and more critical of their children. The change provided dramatic evidence of a conscientious mother's sensitivity to the advice and criticism of an expert. Perhaps it can give us some idea of what happens when a teacher tells a mother that her child is underachieving.

A large-scale research program has been carried out at the Fels Research Institute. From data collected during periodic visits to the homes of some 124 families, trained clinical workers prepared a summary. They also rated a series of 30 variables covering the major areas of parent-child interaction. The variables were intercorrelated, and clusters, or syndromes, of parental behavior were delineated. In the final form, the major clusters were identified as warmth, democracy, intellectuality, and indulgence *(Baldwin, Kalhorn, and Breese, 1945; 1949)*. These workers in-

vestigated the relationships of three clusters—democracy, warmth, and indulgence—to the behavior of the children. The subjects were 56 nursery school children who were observed both at home and at school. The children from the democratic and warm homes were found to be socially outgoing, in both friendly and hostile fashion, to be active in school activities, and to be generally assertive. The children from indulgent homes tended to be inactive, unaggressive, and socially unsuccessful. Baldwin pointed out, however, that the "democratic" parents and their children generally had higher IQ's and intellectual superiority might account for some of the differences. The Fels research illustrates the time and training required to make meaningful observations of how parents raise their children.

Most of the research on parental influence has been based on information supplied by the parents. An early example of a questionnaire and interview study with a limited aim is that of M. J. Radke. The mothers and fathers of 43 pre-school children completed questionnaires about their disciplinary practices and the way in which they used their authority, and were also interviewed. The items were arranged into four general scales: philosophy of authority, ranging from autocratic to democratic; parental restriction, ranging from strict and firm to lax and easygoing; severity of punishment, ranging from severe to mild; and parent-child rapport, ranging from good to poor. The particular purpose was to study the effect of authoritarian parents on the child's behavior in school. In general, children from restrictive homes, in which punishment was severe and control autocratic, were more unpopular, more quarrelsome, less emotionally stable, more daring, and less sensitive to praise and blame. Radke suggests that such children assume the behavior of their parents, acting toward the other children without sensitivity or consideration *(1946)*. If so, this is a good example of the importance of identification. The child does not learn simply how to behave from his parents; he also incorporates their method of teaching and does unto others as he has been done by. The design of this research reflects the interest in democratic versus autocratic group structures which was strong in the forties.

A more recent and more general investigation involving questionnaires and interviews was reported by R. R. Sears, Eleanor Maccoby, and H. Levin. The mothers of 379 five-year-olds were extensively interviewed regarding their feelings about marriage and motherhood, their child training practices, and their children's behavior. Five major factors were isolated: (1) permissiveness-strictness; (2) general family adjustment; (3) warmth of mother-child adjustment; (4) responsible child training orientation; and (5) aggressiveness and punitiveness. In discussing the effects of child rearing on the children, the authors emphasized the importance of maternal warmth and the negative effects of punishment and permissiveness. They found maternal coldness to be associated with feeding problems, bed-wetting, aggressiveness, toilet training problems, and slower development of conscience. Their observations on the effect of punishment have been widely quoted:

The unhappy effects of punishment have run like a dismal thread through our findings. Mothers who punished toilet accidents severely ended up with bed-wetting children. Mothers who punished dependency to get rid of it had more dependent children than mothers who did not punish. Mothers who punished aggressive behavior severely had more aggressive children than mothers who punished lightly. They also had more dependent children. Harsh physical punishment was associated with high childhood aggressiveness and with the development of feeding problems. *(1957, p. 484.)*

This provides yet another demonstra-

tion of the importance of identification. Like Radke's finding, that bossy children come from bossy homes, Sears, Maccoby, and Levin report that children who have been treated aggressively and harshly treat others in the same way.

A standard questionnaire, entitled "Parental Attitude Research Instrument" (PARI) was developed by E. S. Shaefer and R. Q. Bell *(1958)*. This instrument is based on two previous attitude scales. One of these was used to show differences between the mothers of normal children and those of hospitalized schizophrenics *(Mark, 1953)*. The other scale was used in a study that found that a questionnaire which measured dominant, possessive, and ignoring attitudes differentiated significantly between the parents of children referred for psychological assistance or known to the courts and mothers of children without such problems *(Shoben, 1949)*. Both these studies were made after the fact, so it is possible that the disturbance of the child changed the attitudes of the parents or that both the disturbed parental attitudes and the disturbed child resulted from a third factor (e.g., marital friction or economic deprivation).

The PARI consists of 23 five-item scales soliciting parental attitudes about marriage, child behavior, and child rearing. Statistical study indicated that two major dimensions, "acceptance-rejection" and "autonomy-control" were the crucial components of both maternal behavior rated by interviews and maternal attitudes rated by the PARI. The PARI has enjoyed great popularity as a research tool. It has been used: (1) to evaluate attitude changes resulting from treatment and education programs; (2) to examine the characteristics of the parents of normal children and those of children with various physical and emotional problems; (3) to explore the antecedents of various personality processes in normal children; (4) to study cross-cultural differences in parental attitudes; and (5) to predict parental behavior in other situations (*Frankiel, 1959*).

Misgivings have been expressed about the reliability of parents' retrospective reports. Taking advantage of an unusual research opportunity, Marian Radke-Yarrow studied 224 families who had sent their children to a research nursery school sometime between 1930 and 1958. When the mothers were interviewed for this study, their children were between 6 and 32 years of age. It was possible for her to compare the original data on each mother and child with the mother's retrospective report. Approximately 80 variables of maternal care and children's characteristics were investigated. The correspondence between the two sets of data was "disappointingly low." Even the recall of specific traumatic events was poor. With careful probing in the second interviews, a quarter of the mothers ignored, denied, or completely transformed the earlier experience, another quarter tended to remember it as a normal experience, and a small group intensified or exaggerated it. The two sources of data agreed closely only in 39 per cent of the cases. This study adds weight to the reservations that were voiced in connection with taking a history from parents (Chapter 4).

Radke-Yarrow also compared the interview data with observations made during the visit to the home and comments on the complexity and variability of observed maternal behavior compared with the interview material. There are important aspects of maternal behavior of which the mother is totally unaware and which she is therefore unable to report. The particular example which she gives is "facilitative behavior" —teaching, praising, encouraging. Most mothers are vague about the positive techniques which have become second nature.

Radke-Yarrow concludes that interview data are so fraught with error as to preclude much confidence in either the descriptive pictures they provide or the independent-dependent relationships obtained between mother and child behavior (*1963*). Obviously, such criticism of the personal interview casts even greater doubt on the written questionnaire. In the author's opinion, research linking disturbances in children's behavior with their parents self-evaluations will suffer the same fate as the earlier attempts to relate child rearing practices to disturbed behavior.

Studies Based on Case History Material

Most of the case histories used to demonstrate the role of the parents in the formation of the child's personality have been contributed by clinicians and deal with psychopathology. Of all the deviant parental patterns, *maternal rejection* is perhaps the most obvious, and it was one of the first to undergo examination. The term was widely used in the 1930's, and a number of investigators reported the ill effects of maternal rejection on the children (*Newell, 1934; 1936; Fitz-Simons, 1935; Symonds, 1939*). Parents rated as "rejecting" had children who behaved in an aggressive, attention-getting way.

Maternal rejection may be manifested by open hostility or by lack of interest, and it may stem from different causes. There are unwilling mothers, who never meant to have a baby or did not mean to have one at the time they did. The completely unwilling mother, however, usually relinquishes her baby for adoption. It is the ambivalent mother, who wavers between rejection and possessiveness, who exposes her baby to a full dose of maternal rejection. Another type is the conscientious, willing mother who has such a cold, rigid, and isolated character structure that she cannot respond to her infant. This is similar to the description Kanner (*1943*) gave of the mothers of some autistic children. A psychotic mother is, of course, ordinarily unable to care for a baby. Charles Goshen suggests that severe maternal depression during the first year of a child's life may be a frequent cause of mental retardation. He is particularly concerned with the mother's role in stimulating language. "Neurotic maternal attitudes which are characterized by a failure to stimulate and evoke meaningful signals during critical periods of life can result in failure on the child's part in grasping the significance of language, thus proceeding to a state recognizable as mental retardation" (1963, p. 174). Some rejecting mothers are so narcissistic and immature that they have nothing left over for their infants; they cannot tolerate a one-sided situation in which the infant does all the demanding and the mother does all the giving. Still another kind of maternal rejection occurs when other problems preoccupy the mother and drain her of emotional energy (e.g., when she is ill, or a close relative is ill, or when there is severe marital conflict).

Although "maternal rejection" is no longer a popular term, the concepts related to it have been subsumed under "deprivation." Prugh and Harlow (1962) call "insufficient relatedness" an example of "masked deprivation," and there is increasing awareness of the fact that a child may be deprived of maternal care within his own home and family. Like deprivation, rejection may lead to defects in social relationships (i.e., autism), in perception of reality (i.e., psychosis), in cognitive development (i.e., mental retardation), or in conscience (i.e., psychopathic personality). Still another possibility is that of physical injury. Pediatricians coined the phrase, "the battered child syndrome," to attract attention to physical abuse of children by parents or other adults. Katherine Bain (1963) points out that the volume of literature on the abused child syndrome, increased from one or two papers a year to about 15 papers in 1961 to 1962, although it is not possible to determine if physical abuse of children is actually increasing. However, it is no small problem. C. H.

Kempe *et al.* reported that there were, in one year, 302 cases from 71 hospitals and 447 cases from 77 district attorneys (1962). Although physicians are involved in the treatment of the injuries, they do not usually make a referral or report the case to legal agencies: ". . . even when strong evidence of this confronts the physician, he may find the idea that parents could abuse their children so abhorrent that he denies the facts" (Bain, 1963, p. 896). For the most part, the abuse takes place in early infancy, when the child is helpless to escape or complain. A social service home study of a number of infants seen at Children's Hospital in Pittsburgh revealed that the parents were impulsive and immature, ill-prepared for pregnancy, and often thought that their offspring was unhealthy, defective, or unusually troublesome (McHenry, Girdany, and Elmer, 1963). Gross physical abuse must be counted one of the possible results of parental rejection.

Granted that there are some wholly bad mothers and fathers, who give nothing and who endanger their children, nevertheless, workers have learned to be cautious about classifying a case as one of "maternal rejection." "Rejection" is an unprecise, vague term which covers too much psychological territory. It can take many forms, be recognized or unrecognized by the parents, be partial or complete, be verbal or behavioral, be subtly or overtly cruel, and so on. No parent is wholly loving at all times. The feelings of parents fluctuate, not only because of their own moods and preoccupations, but also because of the behavior of the child. Rose Coleman, Ernst Kris, and Sally Provence report that maternal attitudes vary with the phase of the child's development (1952). Some parents are comfortable with infants who are totally dependent on them, whereas others are uneasy in the face of such helplessness; some enjoy the burgeoning independence of the one to two-year-old, whereas others are irritated by their inability to control the toddler. A parent who might be deemed "rejecting" at one point might be classified as "accepting" at another. Similarly, a parent does not have identical feelings for all her children. She may be more congenial with a girl (or a boy), or with a child of a certain disposition.

Considering the variations which make up the range which we call "normal," clinicians hesitate to decide that a parent is rejecting unless there is overwhelming evidence of negative feelings or total lack of interest. Instead, the clinician tries to define precisely what is lacking in the relationship between parent and child, without fixing blame on one or the other. What part of her child does the mother reject? How does she show it? How does the child respond? Can the mother respond positively to affection from the child, or to signs of progress? Does the mother recognize her hostility and have any guilt about it? The answers to these questions can be much more helpful than a categorical judgment of "maternal rejection." Anna Freud sounds a note of caution when she writes:

But, whether owing to the fault of the analysts who were too emphatic in their statements, or owing to the fault of the caseworkers who were too bent on exchanging a multitude of causes of mental trouble for one single, simple causal factor, the idea of being "rejected by the mother" began suddenly to overrun the fields of clinical work and case work. . . . This caused much heart searching and also much self-accusation, especially among the mothers of abnormal children. (*1955, p. 8.*)

Historically, the next term to capture popular attention was *maternal overprotection*. At least one early worker, M. J. Fitz-Simons, viewed this as the diametric opposite of maternal rejection. On her scale of "acceptance-rejection," rejection was at one end and overprotection (i.e., "over-acceptance")

was at the other (*1935*). Dynamically, however, overprotection tends to be more closely related to rejection than to acceptance. M. F. Zemlick and R. I. Watson found that those women who demonstrated rejecting feelings before the birth of their baby were overindulgent, oversolicitous, and compulsive in caring for the infant. They conclude that "fairly convincing qualitative evidence is at hand to support the statement that symptom-oriented mothers who generally are rejecting frequently show their rejection through an overprotecting attitude toward the child" (*1953, p. 582*). There are different patterns of maternal overprotection, but excessive anxiety about possible danger, illnesses, and hurts can be understood as a reaction formation against unconscious hostility.

David Levy distinguished two types of maternal overprotection, one characterized by domination and the other characterized by indulgence (*1943*). Both had in common excessive contact between the parent and the child, prolongation of infancy, and prevention of independent behavior. But there were differences in the tone of the relationship, and the effects were not the same. The controlling, dominating form of overprotection led to submissive traits in the child (e.g., dependency and passivity). The indulgent form led to disobedience, tantrums, demandingness, and the general syndrome we have described as "immaturity" in Chapter 6.

Although the specific term "maternal overprotection" went out of style, the ideas connected with it remained. In discussions of specific clinical problems, repeated references were made to the mother who can not "let her child go." In its most extreme form, this results in a symbiotic relationship (see Chapter 11). Another form of oversolicitousness and overinvolvement of the mother can lead to a feeding problem or to obesity (see Chapter 6). The role of the mother's anxiety in the development of a school phobia was presented in Chapter 10. The relationship between immaturity and infantilization was mentioned in Chapter 6. The effect of the dominating, controlling parent who takes over for the child, leaving him no sense of volition or responsibility, has been discussed in the contexts of toilet training and learning inhibitions. The only clinical problems which seem to have little connection with maternal overprotection are delinquency and autistism.

Distortions in Parent-Child Relationships

Maternal rejection and maternal overprotection are general patterns of parent behavior. Distortions are more specific. The author has chosen to classify the common distortions as (1) misidentifications; (2) seductive relationships; and (3) sadomasochistic relationships.

Misidentifications occur when the parents are unable to see the child for what he is or is not. Their perception may be distorted for any one of a number of reasons. The child may be so identified with a sibling or with some other relative that the parents cannot see him except in this remembered image. Or the parent may view the child as a replica of himself, and react according to his self-concept rather than to the child. In some instances, the child is made to vicariously satisfy some need of the parents, regardless of his own interest or aptitude. The mother who tries to make her graceless daughter into a ballet dancer or the laborer who insists that his son become a professional, are simple examples. This, again, involves a question of degree. No parent is entirely objective about his children, but if his view is severely distorted, the child becomes nothing more than an appendage of himself, a figment of his wishes or fears, rather than a real person.

In *seductive relationships*, the child is unconsciously made a vehicle for his parents' sexuality. This is particularly likely to happen when the marital relationship is poor or nonexistent, so that the child becomes a companion, a substitute for the husband or wife. This can very well excite sexual fantasies and conflicts which are beyond the child's capacity to manage. In extreme cases, actual seduction (e.g., penetration, *fellatio*, or exhibitionism) may occur. Erna Furman reported the successful treatment of a little girl, seduced at a young age, who had a severe ego disturbance bordering on a psychosis. She was not only sexually excited, frightened, and confused by her experience, but her conflicts were increased by the fact that she was sworn to secrecy. This necessitated repression and the general defense of not knowing, and it was many months before the traumatic event was reconstructed in psychoanalysis (1956). Granted that it may be rare for an overt sexual act to occur, it is not uncommon for a parent to overstimulate a child by tickling, in wrestling, or when caring for him physically, without being aware of the erotic quality of such physical contact. Again, this is a matter of degree and judgment. Physical handling is an intrinsic part of taking care of small children and a certain amount of roughhousing goes on in every family. It becomes overstimulating as the child gets older, or when the parents continue in spite of the child's objections, or when it is continued to the point of frenzied excitement. Distorted relationships of this kind are likely to provide the subsoil for neurotic disorders.

Sadomasochistic relationships are characterized by a delicate balance between hurting and being hurt. The terms "sadism" and "masochism" refer to sexual perversions. Sadism is the obtaining of sexual pleasure by inflicting pain; masochism is the obtaining of sexual pleasure by experiencing pain. Sadism and masochism are, however, two sides of the same coin; by the process of identification, each partner enjoys the sensations of the other. Freud extended the concept of masochism to include a more general kind of suffering, a kind of irrational martyrdom which he termed "moral masochism" *(1924, 1961)*. The moral masochist seeks to suffer, and finds innumerable opportunities to be frustrated, disappointed, humiliated, treated unfairly, and so on. This is closely linked with the unconscious sense of guilt and need for punishment (see criminality from a sense of guilt, Chapter 12), but the moral masochist's behavior is exemplary, and he is punished by unfair persons or unjust circumstances. In reviewing the details, one finds that the masochist has been remarkably accepting of what has been done to him; and sometimes one can see that he has gone out of his way to be the "fall guy." Like Cinderella, who responded to hateful treatment with simple devotion, the true masochist turns the other cheek and prays fervently that goodness will be rewarded and that the attacker will be smitten by guilt or punishment from some higher source. Beneath his patient humility, he may entertain quite sadistic fantasies of revenge, not of course at his hands, but those of fate.

Margaret Brenman has written a vivid account of the illness and successful treatment of a paranoid 15-year-old girl with a long history of abnegation to her mother and older sister. She came into treatment after leaving a boarding school because of her abject misery over being chronically mistreated there. Brenman describes her as emotionally deprived and intensely demanding of attention from an early age. Her techniques for dealing with her deprivation and her rage took several forms: extreme self-sacrifice and abdication of personal achievement; presenting herself as a lovable clown while subtly mocking her parents; and fantasies of "victory in defeat," (i.e., of her own death, which would cause her mother great guilt). Brenman points out the use of denial, reaction formation, introjection, and projection in her masochistic character development *(1952)*. The

projection is particularly interesting; the masochist assumes that all people are as imperiously needy as he and that he must therefore be inexhaustibly giving, as he would unconsciously like to be given to.

In this context, we are concerned with interpersonal relationships of a permanent nature in which each person plays his sadistic or masochistic part in a kind of unspoken psychological contract. The classic examples are between marital pairs, but one also sees the same kind of interplay and perverse satisfaction between parent and child. It is possible for the parent to be the masochistic victim of the child's provocative, aggressive behavior, feeling that she must sacrifice her own feelings on some altar of maternity. However, it is usually the other way around. The parent's sadistic aggressiveness may take a physical form, rationalized as a necessary punishment, and in extreme cases may result in the "battered child syndrome." Children can acquire a taste for severe physical punishment and become quite adept at provoking it. Physically abused children do not always tell, partly because of fear, but also partly because they are so used to it. One also sees this even in ordinary spankings. Parents may suddenly realize that that spankings are not serving the deterrent purpose intended, but that the child actually seems to be asking for them and to be relieved by them. This observation is usually sufficient reason for most parents to look for some nonphysical punishment, but the sadistic parent may look for a more formidable physical punishment.

Like masochism, sadism does not require physical maltreatment. There are all degrees of mental cruelty, ranging from degrading and humiliating ridicule to playful teasing. After a time, the child obliges by living down to the views of those who degrade him, thus providing further justification for the parent's attacks. Loving and fighting get very much mixed up. The parent's attention is always of a negative sort but it is in these ways that he shows his love and interest. The child responds in a well-learned pattern to provoke this kind of attention. In the full-fledged version, both the parent and the child simultaneously suffer and cause to suffer.

It is very difficult to break into this closed system. The case of the L family illustrates the malignancy of the mutual satisfactions derived from this kind of perverted love:

Mrs. L sought help from many agencies for the troubles of her two sons, expressing great concern about their fearfulness, poor school performance, nervous habits, enuresis, and lack of friends. Each agency, in turn, learned a great deal about her marital difficulties. Mr. L was weak and ineffectual. He operated a business on the fringe of the law and was tied to his mother. He neglected his sons, was parsimonious with money, and treated his house as a place to eat and sleep. The parents had nothing to do with each other, sexually or socially. As she poured forth vituperative remarks about her husband, she constantly talked of divorce. There was nothing in the marriage for her, she said repeatedly. However, years went by and she made no move to improve or change the situation. It became increasingly clear that she needed her husband as a legitimate scapegoat for her aggression and that she also needed her sense of suffering from his neglect and mean ways.

This sadomasochistic attitude was carried over to her sons. She viewed them as replicas of her husband and loudly lamented their laziness and many failures, which she viewed as living proof of their father's poor example. She was persistent in her efforts to help them, medically, psychologically, and educationally, but nothing worked. Her reports were uniformly gloomy. Both boys were indeed lazy, thoughtless, and a great trial to everyone. She constantly berated them for their obvious faults, occasionally whipped them in a furious attack, and often threatened to leave them so they could see "what it would be like without

me." On first acquaintance, one sympathized with her unhappy lot.

During the ten years of the author's acquaintance, Mrs. L never indulged herself. She spent all the money she earned on the boys and denied herself almost everything. She rationalized this on the basis of her husband's penuriousness and what the boys needed. But she purchased a car for the older son on his sixteenth birthday, with the money she had saved for a vacation, a car casually mentioned to her by a distant relative. The son did not have a drivers' license, the car proved faulty, and she had to sell it at a considerable financial loss. She told about this to show how much she sacrificed for her boys and how little it was appreciated.

Consciously, Mrs. L was always trying to help and to do things for her sons; unconsciously, she was gratified by their failure and her role as martyr. After treatment was discontinued, she kept up a desultory contact with the author, but she never visited except to report bad news or a new catastrophe. At such times, there was a lift to her voice and an animation in her face which belied the words she spoke. At other times, she seemed mildly depressed. Her sadomasochism resulted in a peculiar mixture of rejection and overindulgence. The boys, although infantile, attached to their mother, and fearful of separation, related to her by teasing, provoking, and failing. The sadomasochism was shared equally by all four family members; no one could be successful or allow anyone else to succeed. The parents felt self-righteous about what they were doing for the children and the suffering they endured; the children felt indignant about their parents' maltreatment and vindicated by the punishment they received at the hands of their parents and other authority figures.

Teasing deserves special mention. Teasing stands somewhere between aggression and love; it can easily slip from good humor into ridicule or mockery. The person who is being teased stands somewhere between the clown who deliberately provides entertainment at his own expense and the cowering masochist who makes himself a natural butt for teasing. Parental teasing is not an uncommon way of demonstrating affection. Some of the confusion which this creates in the very young child was mentioned in Chapter 2, where it was pointed out that the child cannot distinguish between the possible and the impossible and gives everything equal merit. At a later age, the child learns to distinguish teasing from true statements, but parents often tease in a barbed way. This leaves the child hurt, confused, angry, and with little defense except to retort in kind. Rarely do parents appreciate teasing from their children.

Inconsistent Relationships between Parents and Children

Perhaps inconsistencies should not be considered separately. There are inconsistencies to be observed in rejecting, overprotective, and distorted relationships. However, it is also useful to look at the family in terms of more concrete aspects of overt behavior.

The deleterious effect of inconsistency was mentioned in Chapter 12, in our discussion of the Gluecks' finding that leniency versus strictness was not as important in conscience formation as consistency *(1950)*. There are a number of ways in which the parents can be inconsistent: they can disagree with each other; they can contradict their words by their tone and facial expression; they can have varying reactions because of changing moods or hidden personal reasons; and they can establish dual standards for themselves and their child.

There is little need to discuss the inconsistencies arising from marital disagreements. Everyone knows that the child will play one parent against another, if possible, and that he can escape a feeling of guilt or responsibility by getting one of his parents to take his side. In some families, inconsistencies arise from a genuine difference of opinion about child rearing, and if one parent attempts to compensate for what he considers the error of the other, the discrepancy can become very great. Such parents often derive considerable benefit from professional guidance. There is also, little need to elaborate the second inconsistency, that between the spoken word and the latent feeling. This idea was particularly developed in connection with superego lacunae by Adelaide Johnson and her colleagues, who illustrated the vicarious and secret gratification the parents derived from the misbehavior of their children *(1947)*. Children are very sensitive to underlying feelings and can see through subterfuges better than adults can.

The changing moods and attitudes of parents have been illustrated by Annemarie Sandler, Elizabeth Daunton, and Anneliese Schnurmann *(1957)*. Unfortunately, there are many opportunities to observe the illogical teaching of parents. They accept certain behavior when they are in one mood or situation, and punish it when their mood or the situation changes. No one can be perfectly consistent, but when there are frequent and intense changes of mood a parent's reaction may become entirely unpredictable to his child. As Sandler, Daunton, and Schnurmann point out, such children become anxious about the unpredictability of their mothers' reactions, and do not know how to predict anyone's reactions. This makes them anxious about new situations and new people. Not seeing any causal connection between their behavior and their mothers' response to it they honestly do not know what to expect, nor can they develop a basic sense of trust.

Mothers may be inconsistent in another way, adopting different attitudes toward certain behavior because of hidden, internal reasons. For example, a parent may be very seductive in bathing with a child, perhaps wipe him after toileting or undress in front of him, and yet be horrified if the child reaches out to touch some private part. Or the parent may be very receptive to the child's questioning until it touches a secret part of the parent's life. Ilse Hellman's clinical discussion of the guilty secrets of mothers of children with severe intellectual inhibition (see Chapter 9) illustrates this point *(1954)*. Such mothers use the mechanism of isolation, failing to see any similarity between the child's curiosity on one score and his curiosity on another score.

The double standard leads us to the problems of identification with parental examples. Sometimes the inconsistency is humorously blatant, as when a mother screams at her child, "Don't yell!" The parents may be doing the very thing for which they criticize their child, without knowing it, but more frequently the child's behavior is a transformation of the parents' example —not exactly the same thing, but a child's version of it. One father complained bitterly that his children never finished anything they started, especially their school work. He was very worried about them and spent hours explaining the importance of education to them. On the other hand, he himself had started innumerable ambitious projects (building a boat, a car, a radio, a television set) none of which he had completed. A mother complained about her teen-ager's childishness and vanity, yet she herself spent hours on her appearance and carried a picture of Rock Hudson in her wallet. Another mother wondered why her child had an obsession about possible poisoning, but she herself avoided public drinking fountains for fear of possible contamination and contact with germs. Such examples could be multiplied indefinitely. The parents fail to see the connection, partly because they cannot see themselves, partly because they think that the child learns only what they want to teach him, and partly because

the child does not behave in precisely the same way as the parent. Often, the parents' behavior is exaggerated and caricatured by the child. It is like the distortion of an image as it is reflected in water; it is the same thing only taking a different turn in the new medium.

The Role of Parent in the Psychotherapy of Children

In this section, we discuss work with parents of children with recognized emotional problems. The distinction we are making is between individualized parent education (e.g., by pediatricians or teachers) and therapy or casework with parents who are involved because their child is in some way different from most children of his age. Counseling parents of mentally or physically handicapped children is an admixture of informing and advising the parent, as well as dealing with the parent's feelings, and thus borders on both parent education and casework or therapy. Some attention was given to such counseling in the chapter on mental subnormality and in the discussion of parent groups earlier in this chapter.

Before proceeding further, the reader should review the remarks made in Chapter 4 about referring parents for psychiatric or psychological help and the difficulty of making the initial diagnostic evaluation. Common manifestations of guilt and defensiveness, and some ways of ameliorating these, have already been described. Parents' attitudes later in therapy are always colored by their first experiences, namely, the manner of referral and the history taking.

Professional Viewpoints

There is universal agreement that therapeutic work with children, at least on an out-patient basis, requires the cooperation of the parents—if only to transport the child to and fro, to pay the bills, and to give verbal allegiance to the idea of treatment. But there is considerable disagreement as to the extent and nature of the parents' participation beyond these areas. Helen Witmer reviewed some of the changes which occurred in the early history of child guidance. Initially, the parents were considered "givers of information and receivers of advice about their children" *(1946, p. 11).* This method was perhaps best used and best explained by child psychiatrists in private practice:

... the existing problem must be formulated to the parents frankly but tactfully, in simple and understandable everyday language, devoid of professional terminologies, in an inoffensive manner which would assume acceptance ... Treatment should be planned with the parents and not dictated to them. They are entitled to know why certain recommendations are made. *(Kanner, 1935, p. 127.)*

Child guidance workers did not find the authoritarian approach entirely satisfactory, perhaps because they dealt with less sophisticated patients, perhaps because they lacked the prestige of the private psychiatrist, or perhaps because they wanted to do more than eliminate symptoms. The strong influence of psychoanalysis in the 1930's and 1940's led them to look to the unconscious of the parents as the source of their difficulties. Thus, for a number of reasons, child guidance workers began to scorn an intellectual approach to parents and to assume that no mother could change her handling of her child without a basic change in her personality. Parents were thus viewed as patients and work with them was directed toward resolving some of their own emotional conflicts. David Levy's attitude therapy is one of the procedures by which social workers helped parents to discover the emotional origin of their negative feelings toward their children *(1937).*

In the early 1940's, child guidance work felt the impact of child psycho-analysis. More, and younger, children were subjected to intensive psychotherapy, and the emphasis shifted from the environment (i.e., the parents) to the internalized conflicts which were felt to create symptoms quite remote from reality. It was agreed that the parent needed help to permit and accept the treatment of his child, but no major changes were expected of him. Anna Freud describes the supportive role to be expected of the parents of a child who was being psychoanalyzed:

The patient's family cannot be excluded from the analysis. Insight into the seriousness of the neurosis, the decision to begin and to continue treatment, persistence in the face of resistance or of passing aggravations of the illness are beyond the child and have to be supplied by the parents. In child analysis the parents' good sense plays the part [which] the healthy part of the patient's conscious personality plays during adult analysis to safeguard and maintain the continuance of treatment. *(1945, p. 129.)*

Work with parents shifted away from therapy for them, but there was no move to return to the days when they were simply informers. The parents became partners in the therapeutic process. Child therapists wanted the parents to stimulate and sustain the child's interest in treatment and to encourage the change and growth in his behavior. These tasks sound simple, but they demand a great deal of insight and patience, and leave little room for a parent's neurotic involvement in her child's problems. Currently, the view is that different situations require different approaches. Nathan Ackerman suggests that "we may approach the whole matter of therapy for disturbed mothers in another way—by establishing a rough hierarchy of levels of contact, categories of psychotherapeutic process differentiated in accordance with the depth of influence to be exerted on the personality" *(1958, p. 285).* His first level is that of "guidance or re-education" and the deepest level is "reorganization of the unconscious functions of personality as they impinge on the integration of personality into the maternal role" *(1958, p. 285)*. Dorothy Burlingham, discussing the mother of the child in psychoanalysis, says that it is sometimes necessary for the mother to undergo simultaneous psychoanalysis "when the mother's neurosis overwhelmed the child, so that the child could not be made independent of her, or when the mother had an unconscious fantasy which the child had taken over from her" *(1951, p. 32)*. Slavson also speaks of differential handling of parents and distinguishes between guidance and therapy:

"The major differences between psychotherapy and therapeutic guidance are that in the first consideration is focused upon the past, while in the latter current events predominate; also instead of unconscious conflicts and preoccupations, overt difficulties and conscious problems are discussed."[*]

In guidance work, the therapist is much more active and directive than he is in true psychotherapy.

"Once the parent is treated as a patient, in contrast to his treatment as a parent, all the techniques of psychotherapy described in this book apply. The emphasis is not upon the relations with children and mates, but upon overcoming traumata and conflicts that result in poor parenthood, as a secondary outcome."[**]

Albert Cutter and David Hallowitz *(1962)* take the strong position that child guidance clinics should not regard the child as the primary patient, but should view the diagnosis and treatment of the parents as equally important. They propose seven treatment

approaches to the child and parents and offer some criteria for their selective application. Their family-oriented approach is similar to family therapy (see Chapter 14), which could be reconsidered here as work with parents. However, child guidance clinics do regard the child as the primary patient, and this usually accords with the parents' view. After all, they have been referred to, or have sought help from, a child facility because of their concern about the child, not because of themselves. It seems appropriate to retain this focus in each case until cumulative evidence makes it clear that the parents' problems would cause them unhappiness even if their child were fine. This, in general, is the position of the author. It is also the author's opinion that one cannot predict what course will be necessary in the work with the parents; this decision evolves gradually as one goes along.

Our discussion is organized in terms of the usual sequence of events, starting with the inevitable introduction to treatment and going as far in depth as proves necessary. The remarks are based mainly on the author's experience in multiprofessional clinics. Group guidance for parents of disturbed children has been described in the literature but is not discussed here *(Durkin, Glatzer, and Hirsch, 1944; Lowrey, 1944; Slavson, 1952, 1958)*.

Introduction to Treatment

The idea of treatment is introduced after the completion of some diagnostic process which has entailed a number of interviews and tests of parents and child. The parents have been in the position of giving information, and now they want to know what you think. In other words, they want information. If the diagnostic evaluation has led to the conclusion that the problem is treatable, and continued work is recommended, the parents will have a number of fears, questions, and natural

---

[*]Quoted from S. R. Slavson, *Child Psychotherapy* (New York: Columbia University Press, 1952), p. 271. Reproduced by permission.

[**]Slavson, *op. cit.*, p. 272.

resistances. In some ways, there will be a recapitulation of the anxieties which are normally aroused by the first suggestion that there is a problem and by the initial referral. The recommendation for treatment alarms most parents because of their hope that their child would be given a clean bill of health by the experts. Again they feel ashamed and guilty, as if they had received a failing mark in child rearing. The professional worker must take care to explain the nature of the child's problems, emphasizing the role of accidental circumstances, temperamental differences, the child's misunderstandings, and the internal conflicts born out of the child's ambivalent feelings. Even if the therapist has some clear ideas about the parents' contributions to the child's problems, these should be minimized. Just as if their child were physically ill, the parents can feel responsible for obtaining proper care without feeling responsible for the illness.

But to advance psychotherapy as proper care raises questions: "Exactly what will be cured?" and "What will happen without this treatment?" The parents want to know what they can expect if they agree and what they can expect if they do not. The answers must be realistic and honest. One should be sure that the parents have the same conception of the problems as the therapist. Perhaps the child has come in because of low school grades, and diagnostic study has revealed that he is depressed, anxious, passive, and of low average intelligence. The goal of treatment might be to improve his self-concept, and there would probably be some improvement in his marks, but perhaps the parents feel he should become a scholar. So before improvement is promised, there must be some agreement about what the child's difficulties are. Even then, one cannot specify the extent or speed of the cure; the parents must be able to tolerate slow change and some uncertainty about the outcome. But improvement is a safe bet, if the child is not psychotic.

It is not at all uncommon for parents to fear that their child will be made worse by psychotherapy. Usually, if they have this idea, it is because they consider treatment painfully difficult for the child or because they assume that the therapist will sanction any kind of expressive behavior. They may tell you about So-and-so, who had psychiatric treatment and ended up worse off, perhaps in an institution. About such fears one can, in all honesty, be reassuring. An experienced therapist doses the painful aspects of treatment so that they are not overwhelming to the child, and no therapist condones continued acting out. There may be setbacks and periods of aggressiveness, but these are temporary symptoms, not final goals. The bad cases which the parents cite may have had only a diagnostic study or would have fared badly under any circumstances. Treatment does not make a person more ill; at worst, it may have no effect whatsoever.

It often turns out that the parents fear insanity and believe that an emotional disturbance is the first step along this road. They wonder if their child is doomed to insanity if he does not get this treatment. Even at the risk of oversimplification, it is imperative to explain that psychosis and neurosis are two different kinds of psychological illness, with different causes and different treatments. One should not scare the parents with morbid predictions of what might happen if the child is not treated. In fairness, one must say that the child will probably change for the better in any event, but that treatment is a way of smoothing his path and freeing him of unnecessary conflicts so that he can grow up faster and happier. Not all child therapists agree with the author on this point. Many are inclined to stress to the parents the permanence of personality problems and their crippling effect on future social and work relationships. As a matter of personal style, the author would rather undersell than oversell therapy and avoid painting the situation in black and white. When treatment is described as a way of sparing the child superfluous anxiety and conflict and allowing him more opportunity for developing his potentialities and for enjoying people, most parents are interested in cooperating.

One should point out the secondary effects of the symptom or the problem behavior on the child's idea of himself and the extent to which it is handicapping him. Naturally, one must be specific about what this particular child feels about himself and how he is missing out on experiences which belong to his age. Sometimes a verbatim quote from the child helps the parents to see that he, too, is worried and unhappy. Parents are impressed by what you "got out" of their child and what you can contribute to their understanding of him. Intellectual abstractions are much less impressive than your ability to illuminate even some small aspect of their child's behavior.

Assuming that the parents are interested in proceeding further, they naturally want to know about the treatment—how often you will see the child, how long it will take, and what the treatment consists of. The frequency of interviews should be set at this point, and it is rarely good policy to change it radically after treatment is begun. Particularly when psychoanalysis is recommended, one should take care to inform the parents that the frequency of the sessions is not determined by the seriousness of the illness but rather by the nature of the illness and the goals of treatment (see Chapter 14). The length of time required should be overestimated rather than underestimated. Some professional workers put the best face possible on everything, including length of treatment, figuring that by the time the parents and child have been in treatment a few months, they

will be in a state of positive transference and better able to accept unpleasant facts. This is a dangerous assumption; it is much more likely that they will feel that they were misled or that the therapist is not competent.

One of the most difficult problems in child therapy is to schedule appointments without interrupting the school day or interfering with extracurricular activities. When this is not possible, one has to point out that the potential gain is greater than the present loss. The problem of scheduling often brings up the parents' concern about other people knowing that the child is to be treated. They may actually be more concerned about the school's opinion than they are about the missed work. One cannot deny the existence of prejudices, but the anxious parent often exaggerates them. All one can do is to foster their courage and honesty. It is a smart person who knows when he needs help and accepts it; the fact that other people may be ignorant about psychology or psychiatry should not determine a parent's decision. The therapist may offer to help in the necessary explanations, but the parents often prefer to do it themselves.

Parents' questions about the nature of treatment are difficult to answer satisfactorily at this juncture. Ordinarily, it is enough to assure them that they will not be left out of the treatment, that they will in fact, be an integral part of it and thus will come to know what happens as treatment progresses.

Division of Labor

The next problem is who is to treat the patient. If one of the diagnosticians also will be one of the therapists, the knowledge and the relationship gained during the diagnosis is retained. It is much more difficult if there is going to be a transfer to someone new, although this is often necessary.

Treatment for children under five is

usually begun with the mother alone; only at a later point is there direct treatment of the child, and usually with the same therapist. When children are over five years, parent and child are usually seen separately by different therapists. The adolescent is seen much more frequently than his parents, and almost invariably by a different therapist.

The form of collaborative treatment for the schoolchild deserves special attention because most of the children seen in child guidance clinics are in this age group and also because there are differences of opinion about having separate therapists for the parent and the child. The parent does not usually like this arrangement; she wishes to talk directly with the person who sees the child and may feel that she has been shunted off to a social worker. Actually, little professional time is saved by this division of labor, because both workers must find extra time to compare notes. However, to use the same therapist creates difficulties for the child. The child expects his therapist to tell his mother everything. He needs to be reassured that his therapist will tell her only those things which the child wishes told, and that the therapist and parent meet together in order for the therapist to help the parent to help the child. The child also expects his parents to do his talking for him, thereby absolving him of the necessity of reporting his own difficulties to the therapist. This, too, must be corrected; it is the child's job to bring in his problems to work on and he cannot rely on his parents to do the job for him.

When there is a hostile, distrustful, mutually rejecting relationship between parent and child, division of the case is probably essential. In Slavson's opinion, child guidance agencies err with astonishing frequency on this score:

Because of his suspiciousness and antago-nism the child would not confide in the therapist, partly because of resentment, but more often due to the fear that the therapist might pass on information to the parent. Due to his emotional deprivation, the child cannot share the therapist with anyone, especially one whom he distrusts and dislikes, in this case the parent.[*]

Establishing a Relationship

Although the child is the primary patient, the parent also wants to be understood and does not want to be regarded merely as part of the child's environment. Gordon Hamilton (1947) stresses the need for genuine and complete acceptance of the parent: "The first objective, and often the major one, is to make and keep the insecure and guilty parent secure with the therapist . . . Just as the child patient has to know that we do not think him all bad, so does the adult need to have his strengths as parent accredited" (1947, p. 284).

In all psychotherapy, transference provides a means of release, self-awareness, and a desire to make new efforts. Without a relationship, the therapist's advice and recommendations count for little. This relationship is best established by expressing an interest, not only in the child but also in the general family picture, and particularly in the stresses and strains which the child presents for the mother. A recognition of her resentment over the extra burdens created by the child's problems and treatment usually implies that it is normal and relieves her guilt. One proceeds cautiously with the first recommendations. If one is too quick, the mother feels that she was stupid not to think of something so simple herself; if one waits and listens too long, the mother gets the uncomfortable idea that she may be making a fool of herself. She needs the reassurance of knowing the worker's opinion even if

---

[*]Slavson, *op. cit.*, p. 279.

it is not in perfect agreement with hers.

The worker, as an authority concerned with children, invariably gets many of the old feelings which the parent had for his or her parents. Slavson makes the provocative statement that "the chief function of the therapist is to demonstrate to the parent what a good parent really is by acting it out toward the father and mother of the young patient."[*]

Frequently it is the parents' first experience with a person in a parental role who is calm, understanding, sympathetic, and kindly, though firm. The pattern thus set and the example supplied are of immense value in refashioning much of the habit-set behavior of parents.[**]

In the author's opinion, one should not try to exploit the parents' feeling of being a child again, even if one is being the perfect parent. Of course, one tries to demonstrate by one's own behavior tactfulness, interest, and consideration, but this is not the same as acting like an ideal parent of the parents. One is trying to help the parents feel like effective parents, not like dependent children.

There are some other technical dilemmas which arise out of the transference situation. Not much progress will be made unless the parent talks about herself and her feelings; on the other hand, one can drift into an unplanned, personal therapy. The situation can usually be controlled by always returning to the child's problems. If this leaves the mother feeling rejected, it may be wise to suggest treatment for herself. In the author's opinion, this should be done by a different therapist.

One of the questions frequently asked is how far to explore marital problems when one is working with a parent. Such problems, after all, impinge on the child's life and are usually suspected by him. After listening sympathetically, it is necessary to help the mother examine exactly what the child perceives or feels, what has been said in his presence, and how it may be affecting him. In the context of collaborative treatment, one can do little more than to help the mother and father see the need for some kind of resolution, or at least to help them to understand the indirect effects on the children. Sometimes, after listening to an outpouring of the parents' personal problems, and recognizing with them the effect that such problems have on their mood and their handling of the child, it is useful to recommend that they convey some of this recognition to the child. The parents can explain that sometimes they have personal worries which make them cranky or tearful, and for which the child is not responsible at all. So often a child who is in trouble assumes that he is the cause of everything wrong, and he may be relieved to know that his parents have some troubles which are not his fault.

Educational Explanations of Behavior

In the author's opinion, parents of emotionally disturbed children are no less in need of education than parents of normal children. These parents, too, can be led astray by misinformation or misapprehension as well as by their feelings. The worker can be very effective as a communicant between parent and child. The parents' feelings change as they gain insight into the child as well as into themselves.

In preparing educational explanations, one must apply *all* one's general knowledge to the specific case. With one's general background in child psychology and psychopathology, one learns to listen selectively and to ask questions which will confirm or rule out tentative hypotheses. It is a mistake to be too sure too soon. The following are sample "explanations" given at various points of parent guidance.

---

[*]Slavson, *op. cit.*, p. 259.
[**]Slavson, *op. cit.*, p. 260.

Explanation of normality. The mother of a 12-year-old boy sought help because of his poor attitude toward school, his belligerence, and his lying and cheating. The boy was not seen because considerable information was available from his school and the mother was an unusually good informant. In the first three interviews, she revealed her worry that the boy was trying to pull away from her and home. In the fourth interview she told about his practice of going to his friends' houses after school and said that he volunteered very little information about what they did. He wanted to pick out his own clothes and criticized her taste. She felt that he did not like her, that somehow she had failed.

A considerable amount of his behavior could be explained as the beginning of normal adolescent rebellion and not at all personally related to her. Spontaneously, she recalled her own adolescence, and her own resentment of her mother's interference. She had thought she would do better for her children, so that they would not be so resentful. This explained her keen reaction of guilt when her son behaved much as she herself had. With this educational information, and her own spontaneous insight, she was able to change her handling of the boy.

Explanation of a symptom. Ginny's mother was seen once a week by one therapist while her seven-year-old daughter was seen twice a week by another (to suit the mother's convenience). The daughter had a number of symptoms, including a throat-clearing tic and a disturbing habit of talking loudly to herself. She did neither of these during the therapy hour, but they were sufficiently disturbing in school that she was excluded. Her first few days in a new school were successful because so much attention was paid to her. On the third day, when she was supposed to settle into the normal routine, the throat clearing and talking to herself became so annoying that she was excluded from class.

On the basis of this and previous information, it was suggested to the mother that *one* reason for these symptoms was Ginny's desire for attention and that these symptoms always gained her this end. Further, it was suggested that Ginny was not of one mind about going to school, as she professed, but that part of her preferred to remain at home. This part "escaped" in the symptom which had the effect of reuniting her with her solicitious mother. The mother was able to accept this idea, although a few weeks earlier she had rejected any notion that Ginny could be ambivalent about going to school. She had, before this, interpreted the throat-clearing tic as a result of a postnasal drip and the child's talking to herself as a result of loneliness.

Explanation of a defense. The defensive use of aggression is often not clear to parents. Jim was one of twins, nine years old, with a number of problems, including frequent fights with other children at school. Many times these fights were unprovoked. His parents were very frightened by the idea that he was unable to control himself, and punished him severely for these fights.

There was other behavioral evidence to show that Jim had many fears and anxieties, which he hid by bravado. He told his father that his schoolmates would all "beat me up" if they got the chance. It became clear that he was following the philosophy that the best defense is a good offense, and that he was basically terrified of what they would do to him if he did not fight first. Of course a vicious circle, which provided some justification for his fears, resulted; but when his parents appreciated the underlying fear, they felt differently about his aggression and could help him to make friends.

In the examples given above, the explanation was based primarily on the worker's information about child development in general and on material from the parents' interviews. Little specific advice was offered, so that the parents could have the chance to figure out some plan of action for themselves, something which would feel natural to them. Usually, one follows explanations with recommendations, but it is good practice to give the parents some time to try to work out their own solutions. Invariably, they are more successful when they try out their own ideas rather than borrowing them from someone else.

It is more difficult to tell the parents something which the child has brought up. The ingenious worker tries to present such material indirectly, without saying, "Your child says such and so." The parent, too, has the uneasy feeling that the child is "telling" on him and needs reassurance that no one is spying or looking for secrets. It is more effective to selectively present the more general observations of the child's therapist; to say, for example: "In therapy, one sees that when the child is sad, he reacts with anger," or that "when he is frightened, he withdraws," or that "when he is frustrated, he regresses," and so on. One can say that the child seems to have been concerned about people getting angry at him, or leaving him, or whatever, but avoid naming a specific person as the cause of his concern, so that the parents cannot go back to the child and question him about a specific statement he made in treatment. Information from the child's therapy becomes part of the parent worker's armamentarium, and he draws on it to steer the parents into one channel or another.

Advice and Recommendations

As we mentioned earlier, parents expect some recommendations, but it is better not to be too ready to tell them what to do, lest they come to depend entirely on the worker's thinking rather than on their own. Advice can be very simple: "The skill of the social worker consists quite as much in knowing how to deal with simple things simply as how and when to go deeper when necessary" (Hamilton, 1947, p. 276).

Examples of simple advice would be helping a mother to choose toys, to find appropriate recreational activities, and to encourage activities which father and son, or mother and daughter, can enjoy together. Common areas of recommendation include: methods of discipline, allowing more or less freedom, detaching oneself from teasing interplay situations, eliminating ex-cessive stimulation (e.g., bathing, sleeping practices, or exciting physical play), management of the bickering between brothers and sisters, and helping the child to verbalize rather than to act out his feelings.

The most complicated advice is given when the *parent acts as therapist.* There are a number of such cases reported in the psychoanalytic literature, including the first example of psychoanalytic principles applied to young children (*Freud, 1909, 1955; Rangell, 1950; Bonnard, 1950; Jacobs, 1949; and Furman, 1957*). There are other examples of mothers helping children through crises with the help of psychoanalytic guidance (*Robertson, 1956*).

Of those cases which involved treatment of symptoms, almost all concerned children under five years of age. There is an especially close relationship between the mother and the child under five. Lydia Jacobs mentions the incompleteness of the young child's personality, which leaves him still very responsive to his mother's handling (*1949*). The child who is under five has not yet erected complicated defenses, and his thoughts and feelings are more exposed to his mother's view. Also, a correct interpretation produces results promptly, so that her guess can be quickly confirmed. Jacobs mentions a third factor which makes the mother a good therapist: namely, that the mother still regards such a young child as part of herself. Rarely has a mother established reactions so rigid or feelings so strong toward her young child that they cannot be changed. Furman also discusses the "uniquely close bond" between mother and young child, a bond which enables her to know things about her child intuitively (*1957*).

The cases described by Jacobs included feeding and sleeping problems during the first two years of life, training difficulties, and some early fears. Augusta Bonnard describes the mother as therapist in a case of a 4½ year old in a severe obsessional state (*1950*); Erna

Furman reports on a three-year-old girl with a mixture of problems including wetting and soiling, thumb sucking, and general babyishness. These authors also mention that some types of mothers are unsuitable: psychotic mothers or those with borderline conditions; extremely infantile mothers; mothers who maintain all-around sadomasochistic relationships; and mothers who do not themselves see the need for help for their child. Jacobs (1949) estimated that about 16 per cent of the mothers of children under five referred to her in two London clinics were unsuitable.

The following are brief examples of "the mother as therapist."

A child of two suddenly developed a fear of going to sleep, and also began waking during the night. Usually she demanded to be taken to the bathroom when she awoke, which her mother thought was simply a stalling technique or an excuse to get her to come. However, the child seemed quite unhappy and anxious, and the symptom persisted a number of weeks.

On inquiring, the worker learned that the symptom started soon after the girl had been toilet trained. It was suggested that she might be fearful of sleep for fear she would lose control and wet or soil her bed. The mother was reassured that this did not mean that she had been trained too soon or too harshly, and that no change should be made in their daytime habits. However, it was recommended that the mother take pains to reassure her that it did not matter at all if she had an accident during her sleep, and that she need not try so hard to keep dry. The anxiety immediately disappeared, and there was only the occasional wetting which one would expect from a child her age.

A little girl of four suddenly became very cranky and disagreeable with her mother, refusing to accept any suggestions and making life very difficult. Her mother tried to give her extra attention, thinking the problem had to do with jealousy of her year-old brother, but the little girl spurned her efforts at friendliness. On her own, she enjoyed rummaging in her mother's personal belongings and one day was observed trying on her mother's girdle.

It was suggested that the mother talk to her about her feeling jealous of all that her mother had—clothes, a husband, a baby, and so on. The little girl soon agreed that she had nothing and her mother everything; she also added, with emphasis, that she had made a baby *boy*, as if her mother had failed her in making her a girl. All in all, she held her mother responsible for her woefully impoverished state. Although the mother pointed out the reality of her blamelessness, she sympathized with her jealousy and resentment. She then tried to do things with her daughter of a more grown-up nature, away from the house, which showed some of the pleasures of growing up.

If the parents can intervene therapeutically, it saves a great deal of professional time. There is no need for the therapist to develop a relationship with the child, and the mother-child relationship is kept intact. Success of this kind always pleases a mother and heightens her enjoyment and understanding of the child. A good experience helps her to look again at the world through the eyes of the small child, and the benefits of this psychological awareness spread to other situations and other children.

There are two cautions worth mentioning in this connection. Many mothers, if they are able to see the source of the child's feeling, feel guilty and over-identify with the child. They want to *do* something (or undo something) to set things right, and it is hard for them to be content with just talking. However, it comes as a surprise to them to see what relief words can bring. Second, such therapy should be limited to a particular problem. One does not want to leave the parents with the impression that they should always be searching for hidden reasons and making these known to the child. Not only does this make for an intellectualized, artificial home atmosphere, but after a while, the child experiences such "instant psychoanalysis" as an aggressive attack. He feels that everything he does is interpreted. The schoolchild and the adolescent need their defenses, and interpretation of unconscious material is rightly regarded as an invasion of their privacy. In her comments on "A Mother's Observations on the Tonsillectomy of her Daughter" (*Robertson, 1956*), Anna Freud contrasts the usual role of the mother with that of the analytic therapist:

Mrs. Robertson helped her child precisely in this way: to meet the operation on the level of reality, to keep the external danger in consciousness to be dealt with by the reasonable ego instead of allowing it to slip to those depths in which the rational powers of the ego become ineffective and primitive methods of defense are brought into action. . . . Mothers—unless specially instructed and guided to do otherwise—should, as Mrs. Robertson has done, limit themselves to assisting the child's ego in its task of mastery, lend it their strength and help to guard it against eruptions from the id. Analysts work in the opposite direction. Under carefully controlled conditions they induce the child to lower his defenses and to accept the id derivatives in consciousness. (*Freud, 1956 b, p. 432.*)

Collaboration in Treatment

Returning to the more usual psychotherapeutic situation, namely, the schoolchild in direct treatment, the child's therapist would like more from the parents than passive cooperation. One needs information about the child's behavior at home and about events at home which might affect him. The child's behavior is used by the therapist like a psychological barometer. A child rarely says to his therapist, "You are so right"; at best, he meets an interpretation with silence. The therapist must judge the correctness of his interpretation by what happens at home as well as by what happens in the treatment sessions. Of course, the therapist would also like to learn of the child's remarks about the therapist and therapy, but

these are less important than the parents' observations about the child's behavior.

A second important role for the parent is to orient the child to therapy and to encourage him to bring significant feelings and events to the therapist. The parent has many more opportunities to observe the child's difficulties, and he can identify these for the child with the added suggestion that the therapist might be able to help with just these problems. There are two parts to this task—facing the child with reality and educating him to talk to the therapist.

The first part is more difficult than it seems. Many parents and teachers have the idea that therapy consists solely of sympathetic understanding, and that a child in therapy is fragile and should be treated with care. A private school for children with learning problems expressed the wish not to have their children in treatment simultaneously with enrollment in their school. It was the opinion of the director that therapy was all-permissive and that children could not then accept the restrictions of school. Also, she felt that they could not use their ordinary methods of discipline. In practice, the therapist wants the child to be treated exactly the same as anyone else; the goal of therapy is to help the child to adjust to reality, not the other way around, unless the child is mentally or physically handicapped or psychotic. If the child is spared ordinary frustrations, reprimands, or disappointments, he has little motivation to work on his problems. Without conflict, internal or external, there is no therapy.

Nancy, a very intelligent eight-year-old in psychoanalysis for daytime wetting and soiling, was an unusually insouciant patient. She developed a defense of denial regarding her symptom and rarely mentioned it. In school, everyone knew of her problems and special arrangements were made for her to go to the bathroom whenever she wished. Her friends were instructed to say nothing about it. Nancy coasted along with the happy illusion that everyone's silence meant they knew nothing about it. Her mother, who felt guilty about her earlier harshness was also sympathetic. One day when the girl had had three bowel movements in her pants, her mother said thoughtfully, "Nancy, dear, I think you must be worried about something." Another day, Nancy attended a Girl Scout meeting in soiled pants, but no one said anything to her, and she took this as proof that no one could tell. This kind of arranged reality, designed to protect her from painful awareness of her problem, impeded treatment.

Encouraging her child to bring his problems to the therapist means that the mother should not discuss the child's worries with him too much. She may also have to give him permission to talk about personal family matters.

Mother and therapist must also work closely together, so that the child cannot play one against the other. Children sometimes tell their mothers that their therapists have directed thus and so, which the mothers have not allowed. They can also do the reverse. The little girl, Nancy, informed her psychoanalyst that her mother was going out all the time and justifying it on the basis, "Well, your doctor goes out all the time too." The mother was genuinely surprised to hear about this, and further analysis proved that this was Nancy's oblique way of trying to find out something more about the psychoanalyst's home life.

It has been mentioned several times that, for the sake of the parents, the therapist must not condemn them or add to their guilt. However, it is also true for the sake of the child. He cannot live more easily with parents whom he feels are no good. They are a part of him and he of them, and they will be important figures for the rest of his life. Hilde Bruch states that "He [the child] needs to gain from treatment the conviction that his parents, in spite of their shortcomings and errors, are fundamentally good people"

(1948). The child can be helped to see his parents' problems and to be critical of one or another thing which they do, but he cannot be treated successfully if he lives with his parents and loses basic trust in them.

Finally, as collaborators, the parents must be prepared to tolerate temporary regressions and, even more important, to recognize and accept growth in behavior. As the child begins to verbalize his previously unconscious problems, the parents must see that this is growth process, even though it may be an unnerving kind of growth. The best examples are around the expression of aggression. The therapist may long have suspected aggression to be at the root of a symptom and be very pleased when the child finally puts it into words. But if the parents are not ready, their shocked reaction may reinstate the conflict and the symptom. The open expression of aggression or open masturbation are not the end-alls of treatment, but they are often significant forward steps. The same holds for sexual impulses. If a symptom is a substitute for masturbation, one can expect a period of ostentatious sex play to test the parents' attitudes. The therapist must predict this behavior, so that the parents are prepared for it. They are otherwise likely to view the child's changed behavior as evidence of their worst fears—that modern psychology approves of unleashed impulses.

In a good collaborative treatment situation the parents feel informed and important; they trust the understanding and good sense of the child's therapist. And the child feels he is amongst friends who are all aiming towards the same goal, despite their differences of opinion.

Obstacles to Progress

Parents are not always consistently cooperative, however, and may actually impede the treatment of the child. They may quibble or argue over every suggestion. Or they may resist more covertly—acquiesce, but then come back to say that the suggestions don't work or forget everything in between appointments so that the therapist feels she is pouring water into a sieve. At this point, the worker needs to take stock, and this may mark the beginning of a therapeutic relationship with the parent. It will be necessary to face the situation squarely and hunt for the cause, this time in the parent's emotional makeup rather than the child's.

This takes tact. Perhaps the best opening is some disarming statement such as, "You have patiently come so many times, and I wonder if it is fair to you to keep you coming. You have probably noticed, too, that we are not getting very far." If the parent wants to shift the blame to the child, the worker should be frankly skeptical and say something like "I think it is more a question of what is or is not going on with us." There are an infinite number of possible sources of resistance, but the following are among the more common.

Transference conflict. It was mentioned before that, in some ways, the parent in casework must be reminded of his childhood and of his parents. This may reactivate helpless, dependent, you-can't-expect-anything-of-me feelings. Or it may reactivate resentment toward authority, a resentment that the parent is afraid to verbalize or of which he is totally unaware. His resentment takes the form of "showing up" the therapist as ineffectual. He may have divided loyalties, and so be equally receptive to advice from his doctor, teacher, or some neighbor or relative. If the parent is listening to everybody, he listens to nobody. The parent must be helped to make a commitment to a single line of approach.

Resistance out of jealousy and rivalry. Sometimes the parent is well aware of the problem and remarks, "I know what I ought to do, but I just can't seem to do it." This betrays his ambivalence, perhaps toward the therapist but perhaps toward the child. Parents are uniformly ashamed to admit it, but they can be jealous of their own child, jealous of the therapist's attention to him, and jealous of all the understanding he is getting which they did not. This very naturally leads into a discussion of the disappointments of their own childhood, and ventilation of their bitterness is usually enough to help them rise above their human jealousy.

Resistance out of displacement. Sometimes the ambivalence toward the child is in part displaced from another member of the family, often the marital partner.

Resistance because of shared symptoms or defenses. This is one of the most difficult obstacles to overcome. Parents who either had or have the same symptoms as the child cannot be objective. They cannot help the child to lose the symptom or defense because it threatens their own psychological structure. Unless someone helps them with the anxiety which will follow the giving up of an entrenched symptom, they are helpless to help their child. This is one indicator of their need for treatment.

Resistance out of anxiety about results. Sometimes parents cannot put educational recommendations into effect because they are so terrified that nothing will work. They make only half-hearted efforts. For example, they are afraid to let the child choose what to eat, for fear that he will starve to death. Usually, when they are able to express their fears, they gain the courage to make more serious efforts.

Resistance out of a need to fail. This again is difficult to recognize and to overcome. If the mother is a truly masochistic character, only personal treatment will help, and that may be almost interminable! It is important to watch her reaction to small successes; if it is one of gratification, it is relatively easy to build up her confidence. Some mothers appear hopelessly masochistic when, in reality, they are so convinced of their incompetence that they cannot move. Here a positive transference is very helpful, because it allows the mother to borrow the worker's confidence until she has achieved enough successes to convince herself.

Termination of Treatment

A great deal was said about this as far as the child patient himself is concerned, but it is surprisingly difficult to terminate casework with parents. One of the problems is that the parents do not have a separate and specific treatment aim for themselves. The child may be very much improved, but the parent is not sure he is better. He is not convinced that he can carry on after the treatment stops and he gets the child back, so to speak. If the parent is a dependent character, he may require some continuing contact with the worker after the child is finished. Another problem is that the transference relationship is usually not a major topic of discussion in parent guidance, as it is in child therapy. The parent therefore has less insight and less opportunity to work through his feelings. He is also ordinarily ashamed of his sad feelings about separation, because they seem so childish, whereas the child has no such embarrassment. All in all, termination is likely to be troublesome and is best accomplished by tapering off and assuring the parent of one's continued interest.

Rose Green's remarks are especially appropriate to our conclusion:

Most clinics, I think, have moved away from the feeling of blaming parents, whether directly or subtly, that was perhaps a natural concomitant of the first insights into the importance of parent-child relationships. The feeling of blame came out of an acute awareness of the importance of the parental role. At first we were able to use that awareness only negatively; that is, by feeling that the parent ought to be different, and in actively trying to make him so. The last decade's exploration of the parent's role is opening up for the clinical team a way to use that role more constructively. *(1948, p. 446.)*

She suggests that many social institutions, such as the school, court, and some social agencies still express blame of parents directly and indirectly. People who choose to work with children have a professional bias toward the child and away from the parent, as if they were protagonists in the battle of growing up. The relative sparseness of the literature on working with parents of disturbed children attests to the relative lack of interest. Most workers admit that it is more than a necessary evil, but they are still unclear as to just how the parents can help in the treatment process. The analytic reports of treating a child through the parent are almost the only important exceptions to this general observation.

This neglect has arisen from a number of factors: (1) a conviction that parents cannot change their basic personalities, coupled with a distrust of lesser measures; (2) an awareness of the importance of internal factors; and (3) the preference of the therapists. Child therapists are not above the problems of countertransference, and those who are empathic and skillful with children often become impatient with parents who are less so. A review of the literature leaves one with the uncomfortable feeling that the guidelines for working with parents of emotionally disturbed children are still very hazy.

References to Chapter 15

Ackerman, Nathan W., *The Psychodynamics of Family Life*. New York: Basic Books, Inc., 1958.

Allport, Gordon. Talk given on November 8, 1963 at Allen Memorial Library, Cleveland. Sponsored by Western Reserve University, School of Applied Social Sciences.

Anderson, John E., *The Young Child in the Home: A Survey of Three Thousand American Families,* Report of the Committee on the Infant and Preschool Child, White House Conference on Child Health and Protection. New York: Appleton-Century-Crofts, Inc., 1936.

Andry, R. G., *Delinquency and Parental Pathology.* London: Methuen & Co., Ltd., 1960.

Appel, G. and J. Aubrey, "Maternal Deprivation in Young Children," 1951. A 16-millimeter sound film, distributed by New York University Film Library, New York.

Auerbach, Aline B., "Parent Discussion Groups: Their Role in Parent Education," Parent Group Education and Leadership Training. New York: Child Study Association, 1953.

Bain, Katherine, "The Physically Abused Child, *Pediatrics,* XXXI (1963), 895–97.

Baldwin, Alfred L., Joan Kalhorn, and Fay H. Breese, "Patterns of Parent Behavior," *Psychological Monographs,* LVIII, No. 3 (1945).

———, "The Appraisal of Parent Behavior," *Psychological Monographs,* LXIII, No. 4 (1949).

Barnes, Marion J., "The Educational and Therapeutic Implications in Working with Parent Study Groups Around the Problems of the Normal Preschool Child," *American Journal of Orthopsychiatry,* XXII (1952), 268–76.

Baruch, Dorothy W., *Parents and Children Go to School: Adventuring in Nursery School and Kindergarten.* Chicago: Scott, Foresman & Company, 1939.

Behrens, Marjorie L., "Child Rearing and the Character Structure of the Mother," *Child Development,* XXV (1954), 225–38.

Beres, David and Samuel J. Ober, "The Effects of Extreme Deprivation in Infancy on Psychic Structure in Adolescence: A Study in Ego Development," *The Psychoanalytic Study of the Child.* Vol. V. New York: International Universities Press, Inc., 1950.

Bice, Harry V., *Group Counseling with Mothers of the Cerebral Palsied.* Chicago: National Society for Crippled Children and Adults, Inc., 1952.

———, "Parent Education and Counseling," in William M. Cruickshank and George M. Raus, *Cerebral Palsy.* Syracuse, N.Y.: Syracuse University Press, 1955.

Blum, Lucille Hollander, "Some Psychological and Educational Aspects of Pediatric Prac-

tice: A Study of Well-Baby Clinics," *Genetic Psychology Monographs,* XLI (1950), 3–98.

Boek, Walter E. *et al., Social Class, Maternal Health and Child Care.* Albany, N.Y.: New York State Department of Health, May, 1957.

Bonnard, Augusta, "The Mother as Therapist, in a Case of Obsessional Neurosis," *The Psychoanalytic Study of the Child.* Vol. V. New York: International Universities Press, Inc., 1950.

Bowlby, J., *Forty-four Juvenile Thieves: Their Characters and Home Life.* London: Bailliere, Tindall & Cox, Ltd., 1946.

———, *Maternal Care and Mental Health,* 2nd Edition. World Health Organization Monograph Series, No. 2. Geneva: World Health Organization, 1951.

Brenman, Margaret, "On Teasing and Being Teased; and the Problem of 'Moral Masochism,'" in *The Psychoanalytic Study of the Child.* Vol. VII. New York: International Universities Press, Inc., 1952.

Brim, Orville G., *Education for Child Rearing.* New York: Russell Sage Foundation, 1959.

Bruch, Hilde, "The Role of the Parent in Psychotherapy with Children," *Psychiatry,* XI (1948), 169–75.

Burlingham, Dorothy T., "Present Trends in Handling the Mother-Child Relationship During the Therapeutic Process," in *The Psychoanalytic Study of the Child.* Vol. VI. New York: International Universities Press, Inc., 1951.

Buxbaum, Edith, *Your Child Makes Sense.* New York: International Universities Press, Inc., 1949.

Chambers, Juanita, "Maternal Deprivation and the Concept of Time in Children," *American Journal of Orthopsychiatry,* XXXI (1961), 406–20.

Children's Bureau Publication Number 8—1963, *Infant Care.* Eleventh edition, Washington, D.C.: United States Department of Health, Education, and Welfare (1963).

The Cleveland Press, "Cradle Roll Bulletin," Cleveland, Ohio.

Coleman, Rose W., Ernst Kris, and Sally Provence, "The Study of Variations of Early Parental Attitudes," *The Psychoanalytic Study of the Child.* Vol. VII. New York: International Universities Press, Inc., 1952.

Cutter, Albert V. and David Hallowitz, "Different Approaches to Treatment of the

Child and the Parents," *American Journal of Orthopsychiatry,* XXXII (1962), 152–59.

David, M. and G. Appell, "A Study of Nursing Care and Nurse-Infant Interaction," in B. M. Foss, *Determinants of Infant Behavior.* London: Methuen & Co., Ltd., 1961.

Durkin, H. E., H. T. Glatzer, and J. S. Hirsch, "Therapy of Mothers in Groups," *American Journal of Orthopsychiatry,* XIV (1944), 68–75.

Earle, A. M. and B. V. Earle, "Early Maternal Deprivation and Later Psychiatric Illness," *American Journal of Orthopsychiatry,* XXXI (1961), 181–86.

Fitz-Simons, M. J., *Some Parent-Child Relationships as Shown in Clinical Case Studies.* Contributions to Education, No. 643. New York: Bureau of Publications, Teachers College, Columbia University Press, 1935.

Fraiberg, Selma, *The Magic Years.* New York: Charles Scribner's Sons, 1959.

Frankiel, Rita V., *A Review of Research on Parent Influences on Child Personality.* New York: Family Service Association of America, 1959.

Freud, Anna. Comments in Joyce Robertson, "A Mother's Observations on the Tonsillectomy of her Four-Year-Old Daughter," *The Psychoanalytic Study of the Child.* Vol. XI. New York: International Universities Press, Inc., 1956 *b.*

———, "Safeguarding the Emotional Health of our Children," *Casework Papers,* 1954, from the National Conference of Social Work, Family Service Association of America. New York: Columbia University Press, 1955.

———, Talk given September 20, 1956 *a,* at Severance Hall, Cleveland.

———, and Dorothy Burlingham, *Infants Without Families.* London: George Allen & Unwin, 1944.

———, "Indications for Child Analysis," *The Psychoanalytic Study of the Child.* Vol. I. New York: International Universities Press, Inc., 1945.

Freud, Sigmund, *Analysis of a Phobia in a Five-year-old Boy* (1909). Standard Edition, Vol. X, ed. and trans. by James Strachey. London: The Hogarth Press, Ltd., 1955.

———, "The Economic Problem of Masochism" (1924), Standard Edition, Vol. XIX, ed. and trans. by James Strachey. London: The Hogarth Press, Ltd., 1961.

Furman, Erna, "An Ego Disturbance in a Young Child," *The Psychoanalytic Study of the Child,* Vol. XI. New York: International Universities Press, Inc., 1956.

———, "Treatment of Under-Fives by Way of Parents," *The Psychoanalytic Study of the Child,* Vol. XII. New York: International Universities Press, Inc., 1957.

Gesell, Arnold and Francis L. Ilg, *Infant and Child in the Culture of Today: The Guidance of Development in Home and Nursery School.* New York: Harper & Row, Publishers, 1943.

Glueck, S. and E. T. Glueck, *Unraveling Juvenile Delinquency.* Cambridge, Mass.: Harvard University Press, 1950.

Goldfarb, W., "Emotional and Intellectual Consequences of Psychologic Deprivation in Infancy: A Re-evaluation," in P. Hoch and J. Zubin, *Psychopathology of Childhood.* New York: Grune & Stratton, Inc., 1955.

———, "Infant Rearing and Problem Behavior," *American Journal of Orthopsychiatry,* XIII (1943), 249–65.

Goshen, Charles E., "Mental Retardation and Neurotic Maternal Attitudes," *Archives of General Psychiatry,* IX (1963), 168–75.

Green, Rose, "Treatment of Parent-Child Relations," *American Journal of Orthopsychiatry,* XVIII (1948), 442–46.

Hamilton, Gordon, *Psychotherapy in Child Guidance.* New York: Columbia University Press, 1947.

Hellman, Ilse, "Some Observations on Mothers," *The Psychoanalytic Study of the Child,* Vol. IX. New York: International Universities Press, Inc., 1954.

Jacobs, Lydia, "Methods Used in the Education of Mothers: A Contribution to the Handling and Treatment of Developmental Difficulties in Children Under Five Years of Age," *The Psychoanalytic Study of the Child,* Vol. III/IV. New York: International Universities Press, Inc., 1949.

Johnson, Adelaide, "Sanctions for Superego Lacunae of Adolescents" (1947), in K. R. Eissler, *Searchlights on Delinquency.* New York: International Universities Press, Inc., 1949.

Kanner, Leo, "Autistic Disturbance in Affective Contact," *The Nervous Child,* II (1942–1943), 17–50.

———, *Child Psychiatry.* Springfield, Ill.: Charles C Thomas, Publisher, 1935.

Katz, Alfred H., *Parents of the Handicapped.* Springfield, Ill.: Charles C Thomas, Publisher, 1961.

Kempe, C. H. *et al.,* "The Battered Child

Syndrome," *Journal of the American Medical Association,* CLXXXI (1962), 17–24.

Kohn, M. L., "Social Class and Parental Values," *American Journal of Sociology,* LXIV (1958–1959), 337–51.

Korsch, Barbara Maria, "Practical Techniques of Observing, Interviewing and Advising Parents in Pediatric Practice as Demonstrated in an Attitude Study Project," *Pediatrics,* XVIII (1956), 467–90.

Langdon, Grace and Irving W. Stout, *Teacher-Parent Interviews.* Englewood Cliffs, N.J.: Prentice-Hall, Inc., 1954.

Levy, David M., "Attitude Therapy," *American Journal of Orthopsychiatry,* VII (1937), 103–13.

———, *Maternal Overprotection.* New York: Columbia University Press, 1943.

Lewis, Hilda, *Deprived Children (the Mershel Experiment): A Social and Clinical Study.* London: Oxford University Press, 1954.

Littman, R. A., R. C. A. Moore, and J. Pierce-Jones, "Social Class Differences in Child Rearing: A Third Community for Comparison with Chicago and Newton," *American Sociological Review,* XXII (1957), 694–704.

Louisiana Society for Mental Health, "Pierre the Pelican" series, New Orleans, Louisiana.

Lowrey, L. G., "Group Treatment for Mothers," *American Journal of Orthopsychiatry,* XIV (1944), 589–92.

McClure, Dorothea and Harvey Schrier, "Preventive Counseling with Parents of Young Children," *Social Work,* I (1956), 68–80.

McDonald, Eugene T., *Understand Those Feelings.* Pittsburgh: Stanwix House, Inc., 1962.

McHenry, Thomas, Bertram R. Girdany, and Elizabeth Elmer, "Unsuspected Trauma with Multiple Skeletal Injuries during Infancy and Childhood," *Pediatrics,* XXXI (1963), 903–8.

Mark, J. C., "Attitudes of Mothers of Male Schizophrenics toward Child Behavior," *Journal of Abnormal and Social Psychology,* XLVIII (1953), 185–89.

Merrill, B., "A Measurement of Mother-Child Interaction," *Journal of Abnormal and Social Psychology,* XLI (1946), 37–49.

Meyer, Marguerite S. and Edward J. Power, Jr., "The Family Caseworker's Contribution to Parent Education through the Medium of the Discussion Group," *American Journal of Orthopsychiatry,* XXIII (1953), 621–28.

National Society for the Study of Education. Twenty-Eighth Yearbook. *Preschool and Parental Education,* G. M. Whipple, ed. Bloomington, Ill.: Public School Publishing Co., 1929, pp. 275–353.

Neubauer, Peter B., "The Technique of Parent Group Education: Some Basic Concepts," *Parent Group Education and Leadership Training.* New York: Child Study Association, 1953.

Newell, H. W., "A Further Study of Maternal Rejection," *American Journal of Orthopsychiatry,* VI (1936), 576–89.

———, "The Psychodynamics of Maternal Rejection," *American Journal of Orthopsychiatry,* IV (1934), 387–401.

Naess, S., "Mother-Child Separation and Delinquency," *British Journal of Delinquency,* X, No. 22, 1959.

Olden, Christine, "Notes on Child Rearing in America," *The Psychoanalytic Study of the Child.* Vol. VII. New York: International Universities Press, Inc., 1952.

Orlansky, Harold, "Infant Care and Personality," *Psychological Bulletin,* LXVI (1949), 1–48.

Plank, Emma N., "Reactions of Mothers of Twins in a Child Study Group," *American Journal of Orthopsychiatry,* XXVIII (1958), 196–204.

Provence, Sally and Rose C. Lipton, *Infants in Institutions.* New York: International Universities Press, Inc., 1962.

———, and Samuel Ritvo, "Effects of Deprivation on Institutionalized Infants: Disturbances in Development of Relationship to Inanimate Objects," *The Psychoanalytic Study of the Child.* Vol. XVI. New York: International Universities Press, Inc., 1961.

Prugh, Dane G. and Robert G. Harlow, " 'Masked Deprivation' in Infants and Young Children," in *Deprivation of Maternal Care: A Reassessment of its Effects,* World Health Organization, Public Health Papers, No. 14. Geneva: World Health Organization, 1962.

Radke, M. J., *The Relation of Parental Authority to Children's Behavior and Attitudes,* University of Minnesota Institute of Child Welfare Monograph Series, No. 22. Minneapolis: The University of Minnesota Press, 1946.

Radke-Yarrow, Marian, "Problems of Methods in Parent-Child Research," *Child Development* XXXIV (1963), 215–26.

Rangell, Leo, "A Treatment of a Nightmare in a Seven-Year-Old Boy," *The Psychoanalytic Study of the Child.* Vol. V. New York: International Universities Press, Inc., 1950.

Rheingold, H. L., "The Modification of Social Responsiveness in Institutional Babies," *Monographs of the Society for Research in Child Development,* XXI, No. 63 (1956).

———, and N. Bayley, "The Later Effects of an Experimental Modification of Mothering," *Child Development,* XXX (1959), 363–72.

Robertson, Joyce, "A Mother's Observations on the Tonsillectomy of her Four-Year-Old Daughter," *The Psychoanalytic Study of the Child.* Vol. XI. New York: International Universities Press, Inc., 1956.

Ruben, Margarete, *Parent Guidance in the Nursery School.* New York: International Universities Press, Inc., 1960.

Sandler, Annemarie, Elizabeth Daunton, and Annaliese Schnurmann, "Inconsistency in the Mother as a Factor in Character Development: A Comparative Study," *The Psychoanalytic Study of the Child.* Vol. XII. New York: International Universities Press, Inc., 1957.

Sears, R. R., Eleanor E. Maccoby, and H. Levin, *Patterns of Child Rearing.* New York: Harper & Row, Publishers, 1957.

Shaefer, E. S. and R. Q. Bell, "Development of a Parental Attitude Research Instrument," *Child Development,* XXIX (1958), 339–61.

Shirley, May, *Can Parents Educate One Another?* New York: National Council of Parent Education, 1938.

Shoben, E. J., Jr., "The Assessment of Parental Attitudes in Relation to Child Adjustment," *Genetic Psychology Monographs,* XXXIX (1949), 103–48.

Slavson, S. R., *Child-Centered Group Guidance of Parents.* New York: International Universities Press, Inc., 1958.

———, *Child Psychotherapy.* New York: Columbia University Press, 1952.

Spitz, René A., "Anaclitic Depression," *The Psychoanalytic Study of the Child.* Vol. II. New York: International Universities Press, Inc., 1946 *a.*

———, "Hospitalism: A Follow-up Report," *The Psychoanalytic Study of the Child.* Vol. II. New York: International Universities Press, Inc., 1946 *b.*

———, "Hospitalism: An Inquiry into the Genesis of Psychiatric Conditions in Early Childhood," *The Psychoanalytic Study of the Child.* Vol. I. New York: International Universities Press, Inc., 1945.

Spock, Benjamin, *Baby and Child Care,* Revised Giant Cardinal Edition. New York: Pocket Books, Inc., 1963 *a.* A new version of the *Pocket Book of Baby and Child Care,* originally published as *The Common Sense Book of Baby and Child Care,* published by Duell, Sloan & Pearce, Inc., New York, 1946.

———, "How my Ideas have Changed," *Redbook,* CXXI, No. 6 (1963 *b*).

———, "Values and Limits of Parent Education," in *Communication in Parent Education: Proceedings of the Ninth Annual Institute for Workers in Parent Education.* New York: Child Study Association, 1955.

———, and Mabel Huschka, "The Psychological Aspects of Pediatric Practice," *Practitioners Library of Medicine and Surgery,* Vol. VIII. New York: Appleton-Century-Crofts, Inc., 1938.

Stendler, Celia B., "Sixty Years of Child Training Practices: Revolution in the Nursery," *Journal of Pediatrics,* XXXVI (1950), 122–34.

Symonds, P. M., *The Psychology of Parent-Child Relationships.* New York: Appleton-Century-Crofts, Inc., 1939.

Vincent, Clark E., "Trends in Infant Care Ideas," *Child Development,* XXII (1951), 199–210.

Wardle, C. J., "Two Generations of Broken Homes in the Genesis of Conduct and Behavior Disorders in Childhood," *British Medical Journal,* II (1961), 349–52.

Whipple, G. M., *Preschool and Parental Education,* Twenty-eighth Yearbook of the National Society for the Study of Education. Bloomington, Ill.: Public School Publishing Co., 1929, pp. 275–353.

White, Martha Sturm, "Social Class, Child Rearing Practices, and Child Behavior," *American Sociological Review,* XXII (1957), 704–12.

Witmer, Helen L., *Psychiatric Interviews with Children.* New York: The Commonwealth Fund, 1946.

———, *The Field of Parent Education: A Survey from the Viewpoint of Research.* New York: National Council of Parent Education, 1934.

Wolfenstein, Martha, "Trends in Infant Care," *American Journal of Orthopsychiatry,* XXIII (1953), 120–30.

Zemlick, M. F. and R. I. Watson, "Maternal Attitudes of Acceptance and Rejection during and after Pregnancy," *American Journal of Orthopsychiatry,* XXIII (1953), 570–84.

16

TREATMENT AWAY FROM HOME

When the patient is a disturbed child in a disturbed family, removal from home seems an obvious solution. However the observations on institutionalized children, particularly young children, demonstrate the importance of the personal relationships which are so hard to maintain in an institution. And the child who is placed outside his home is by no means guaranteed a more stable life; more than likely, he will have to endure a succession of foster homes, placement agency workers, and institution staff. In addition to these external difficulties, placement also puts an additional strain on the child. The placed child feels rejected, guilty, and unworthy, and expects a repetition of the experience. He cannot help but blame his parents for their desertion, and one can readily imagine the problems which this angry, disappointed, and guilty child will bring to the substitute parents. His sense of identity is shaken by the loss of his parents and, all in all, his emotional turmoil is exacerbated by the separation. Some child care workers have therefore come to think that his own home, no matter how bad, is still preferable to placement. Separation from the parents is truly major surgery, well deserving the coined name "parentectomy." Like any other radical therapy, however, there are times when the long-range goals warrant the risks and pain.

Diagnostic considerations, choice of placement facility, preparation of parents and child, and legal and financial arrangements are very much in the domain of social work. Partly this is because financial assistance is almost invariably needed; partly because the parents are often not psychologically capable of making the decision and working through the involved steps leading to an appropriate placement. Without the stabilizing effect of a social work agency, the child can be tossed around from home to home. The problems and techniques of child placement have been extensively described in the social work literature, and such classics as Esther Glickman's book *(1957)* should be carefully read by anyone recommending placement or working with children living away from home.

Placement Facilities

Before instituting placement procedures, it is imperative that the diagnostician or referring person know what facilities are available. The psychological needs of the child must be met realistically, not by some theoretical ideal concocted by the child care worker. Accordingly, we start with a

456

brief inventory of the kinds of placement facilities now in existence
throughout the country. Glickman
(1957) differentiates two major types of
arrangements for the care of children
who must live apart from their own
families: (1) the substitute family
plan; and (2) the group plan.

Substitute family plans. Substitute
family arrangements are of several
kinds:

Adoptive homes, in which permanent
placement is expected.
*Free permanent homes or private foster
homes* are arranged for by the child's
family. Since all foster homes are required
to have a state license to board a child,
however, there is some surveillance by
public agencies of the general physical
and moral fitness of the foster home.
Boarding homes are usually for adolescents who do not need close supervision
but who are not ready to live independently.
Professional foster homes may or may
not be owned by a social agency. "The
characterization of the foster parent as
'professional' means that he accepts more
training and supervision than the average
foster parent in providing the specific care
required by a given child."*

Social agencies try to train foster
parents, especially for the care of infants, young children, and children
who have emotional or physical problems.

Group homes usually care for six to
ten children. The group home may
serve as a small residence club for adolescents who need some supervision but
who do not require the psychological
intimacy of one-to-one relationships
with parental figures, it may be designed for children who are so disturbed that they cannot tolerate such
relationships, or it may be used for

children who maintain considerable
contact with their own families and
therefore do not need substitute parents.

Group plans. Groups plans are also
of several major types:
Boarding schools are arranged for by
the parents, and the children come
home for the usual school vacations.
Most boarding schools are planned for
educational enrichment, but there are
an increasing number for the "exceptional" child. (Each year a *Directory
for Exceptional Children* is published
by Porter Sargent, of Boston. In 1965
some 450 schools were listed.) Schools
define "exceptionality" in educational
terms, that is, as mental retardation,
underachievement, or giftedness. Boarding school is usually not thought of as
"placement," and therefore it is sought
by many parents who see it as a way
of rectifying educational mistakes,
rather than as a reflection on their own
training. However, a boarding school
certainly is a kind of placement when
it operates 12 months a year, as do
most schools for the mentally retarded.
*Institutions for the care of dependent
children* are the orphanages of yester-
year. They house children whose parents are dead, ill, or incapable of caring
for them. There is a definite trend away
from institutions of this kind and
toward foster or group home plans for
children simply "in need of parents"
(Maas and Engler, 1959).
*Institutions for long-term or perma-
nent care of severely handicapped children* are usually state institutions
designed for psychotic or retarded children, for whom life-time planning is
required. The children may go from
the institution to foster homes, but they
usually remain under the aegis of the
state agency.
Medical treatment centers may be
attached to hospitals, or they may be
separate institutions, under medical direction. These units may be planned

---

*Quoted from Esther Glickman, *Child
Placement Through Clinically Oriented Casework* (New York: Columbia University Press,
1957), p. 71. Reproduced by permission.

for physically handicapped or chronically ill children, although there is a trend toward treating such children as outpatients, to avoid the trauma of separation. Some institutions, however, consider separation almost part of the treatment as, for instance, the Children's Asthma Research Institute and Hospital in Denver, Colorado. Most of the medical treatment centers, however, provide short-term diagnostic study or care for psychotic and severely disturbed children.

Residential treatment centers are usually operated by a social work agency. Many of these have been converted from obsolete orphanages to modern treatment centers for emotionally disturbed children who are usually not as sick as those cared for in medical settings but more sick than those placed in foster homes. However, this is not always true: The Orthogenic School in Chicago, for example, accepts children who are as disturbed as any found in a hospital ward.

One cannot determine the kind of institution from the official name. The Orthogenic School and the Southard School of the Menninger Clinic, in Topeka, Kansas, are for very sick children even though they are called "schools." Anyone in the placement business needs a first-hand acquaintance with the facilities, and placement workers generally check with the intake department of the facility before discussing specific possibilities with the parents.

Our inventory does not include the specialized institutions for delinquents which were described in Chapter 12. Placement in such institutions is primarily a legal matter, and the family, the youngster, or the child care worker have little choice. Such separation is undeniably a punishment, no matter what other purposes it may also serve. This fact colors the entire rehabilitation program, although many of the treatment principles are the same as for children who are not in trouble

with the law. Institutions for delinquents, also, are primarily for adolescents (with the exception of Pioneer House) whereas our focus is on the treatment of younger children. In this chapter, little will be said about the intricacies of adoptions, the care of dependent children, or provisions for the physically or mentally handicapped. Our primary concern is with children in need of placement because of their behavior or emotional problems.

Diagnostic Decision and Preparation for Placement

Diagnostic Considerations

The decision to remove a child from his home is properly based on three variables: (1) the psychopathology of the child; (2) the family situation; and (3) the available resources. The great majority of the children who are living outside their own homes are doing so because of the inadequacies or pathology of their families, rather than because of the severity of their emotional disturbances. Some of the more purely social reasons for placement will be noted in the section on foster homes; this section is devoted to a discussion of the psychological factors which lead to placement, usually in a residential treatment center.

Psychopathology of the child. Almost any psychological disturbance, if sufficiently chronic and severe, can be the basis of placement. Such chronicity and severity of the child's disturbance usually also bespeak some parental pathology, but for the moment we will focus on the child. Severity may be the degree of intolerability to the parents or to the community; the potentiality of self-destruction or of permanent handicap to the child; and his inability to form interpersonal relationships.

Symptoms so severe that they cannot be tolerated by the parents or the community are usually aggressive or acting-out behavior. The aggressive adolescent runs afoul of the law, and his repeated antisocial acts culminate in his removal from the community because he is a danger to the life and property of others. The adolescent has the physical and mental wherewithal to constitute a real hazard to others if his energies are aggressively directed against society. But even the younger child who consistently defies authority and who fights with other children is intolerable. His behavior frightens and enrages his antagonists, and strong punitive measures are inevitably taken. The parents have to live with this provocative child twenty-four hours a day, and school teachers must consider his effect on the other children who have come to school for an education. Often, like John, such children are effectively bringing about the very things they are trying to safeguard themselves against:

John, aged seven, lived with his mother, an older brother, a step-sister, and assorted relatives who came and went as their fortunes changed. His mother worked full time, and his care fell to relatives or whoever was convenient. He endured more than the usual number of separations, although his mother was not aware that he had any special reactions to them. On first starting school, he seemed withdrawn and was temporarily excluded. He was started in psychotherapy and efforts were made to stabilize his home environment. When he started school again, his behavior was less bizarre, and he definitely related to the children and teachers. However, he was obstreperous, demanded attention, raced around, and sang loudly. Efforts to control him were met with increased defiance and provocativeness, and a power struggle ensued between John and the adult involved. The other children were attracted by his bravery, and imitated his teasing.

It became necessary to exclude him again, although for different reasons. On first hearing the news, he showed genuine sadness, sobbing and saying, "I can't help singing those crazy songs." Soon, however, he resumed his "I-don't-care" and "You-can't-make-me" attitudes, which were so convincing that both his mother and teachers were convinced that he had no other feelings. For example, when his mother was planning to move to a new house, John declared that he was going to throw her away and live alone. The mother concluded that she meant nothing to him, and felt very hurt and rejected. Accordingly, she sent him off to visit some grandparents, thus confirming his unconscious fear that he would be left behind in the imminent move. One task of psychotherapy was to help John give up the madness which covered his sadness, and another was to help his mother to see through his veneer of not caring. Unfortunately, John's defense of rejecting before he was rejected tended to bring about the very thing he most feared.

Acting out may lack conscious aggressive intent and still be intolerable. Any child who requires constant attention will prove unmanageable, particularly in school. The incessant and attention-getting talking of Julie Ann resulted in her exclusion from both regular and special school. The school situation is especially vulnerable to certain kinds of behavior disturbances, and exclusion is a frequent precipitating reason for placement. Obviously, children excluded from school need a placement facility which offers schooling as well as a therapeutic environment.

The second set of psychological reasons for placement has to do with the effect of the symptom on the child's future. Potential self-destruction was mentioned. Anorexia nervosa, some of the psychosomatic disorders, and possible suicide (usually of adolescents) threaten the very life of the child and may require treatment in a hospital setting. Other symptoms may become so restrictive that the child is deprived of opportunity for growth and development. It is possible for a learning inhibition to be so severe, for example, that the child cannot profit from any modification of normal public schooling. Phobic and obsessive-compulsive neuroses can become so severe that the child cannot attend school. Ken was so weakened by anxiety that continued school attendance became impossible for him, even though the school authorities had only praise for his conduct.

Ken first became known to a child psychiatry clinic when he was four. He seemed strange and different, poorly related to other children, and unable to enjoy himself. He was tense, fearful, and had a marked speech impediment. He had low-average intelligence. His mother, a war bride, was diagnosed as having anxiety hysteria, with symptoms of moodiness, irritability, and headaches.

With speech therapy and remedial work in the schools, Ken seemed to settle down, and he learned surprisingly well. However, he remained anxious and isolated from the other children.

As he approached adolescence, a new set of symptoms appeared. He developed a serious eating inhibition, fearing that any food not prepared by his mother was contaminated. He feared one fatal disease after another. He worried constantly about his school work and had to be restrained from studying day and night. He could not tolerate the "roughness" and "crudeness" of the other boys, and was sickened by the school gym's showers and by undressing in the gym lockers. Although much of his behavior was praised by his parents and teachers, his fears finally became so excessive that he was in a constant panic, and his anorexia weakened him so much that he was unable to participate in many of the school activities. It became impossible for him to go anywhere.

Outpatient treatment was considered, but only if his mother was interested in simultaneous treatment. Unfortunately, she considered her own troubles physical and rejected the suggestion. She agreed with many of Ken's fears, although she felt that perhaps he went too far. After a stalemate of some months, Ken was referred to a residential treatment center, a decision which he and his parents accepted out of desperation.

A child cannot remain out of school for a prolonged period of time. He misses too much, socially as well as educationally, and a tutor cannot restore this loss. Of course, schools have different standards, and exclusion from school should never be the sole reason for placement. The usual history involves repeated exclusions, failure of outpatient psychotherapy, *and* pathogenic influences in the home situation which are impervious to change.

The third diagnostic factor we mentioned was inability to relate. The autistic child is an extreme example (see Chapter 11). Left at home, he may be ignored and so become increasingly withdrawn, for it is an unusual parent who will continue to expose herself to hurt by making affectionate overtures to a child who seems to have no use for her. The institution, however, is more impersonal, and the staff can pay attention to such a child without feeling personally rebuffed. Miriam Dettelbach makes the important point that for the withdrawn child, the more diluted emotional atmosphere of the institution with its less provocative stimuli and more limited demands for interpersonal response may be a necessary preparation for psychotherapy (1955). The so-called psychotic child cannot accept love or information from other people. He may be knowledgeable beyond his chronological age, but his thinking is egocentric, or primitive. For him, things are what he wishes them to be, and he believes that everyone shares his thoughts and feelings, for he makes no distinction between himself and others. He baffles his parents, who often alternate between irritated criticism and helplessness.

The effect of the child's problems on other members of the family plays an important part in the decision to remove him from home. Some families are able to live comfortably with a disturbed child and meet his requirements without undue sacrifice (see the case of Ralph). The well-being of the brothers and sisters must be considered.

If the needs of the disturbed child are excessive, they may take such a toll of his parents' energy that the other children suffer. The irritability he stimulates may be vented on the well children, or they may suffer actual neglect, or they may be asked to make extraordinary sacrifices. However, one should not make the assumption that this is the case, nor should one assume that all the problems engendered by the disturbed child will be solved by his removal. The brothers and sisters will react to his departure with confusion and anxiety, fearing they will be the next to go, or with guilt about their responsibility, imagined or real. In some rare instances, the parents' preoccupation with the sick child is a blessing in disguise to the others. If the parents are so disturbed that they require a partner in their pathology, they will substitute another child who will then bear the full brunt.

Psychopathology of the Parents. Children are placed either because they are so disturbed or handicapped that the parents and local community resources cannot cope with them, or because the home situation is so damaging. A decision of either kind involves the most careful study of the parents' personalities.

Glickman states that there is no distinctive psychological mechanism or specific character structure in parents of placed children. The families who are seen in placement agencies differ, "first in the quantity of the disturbance and in its lack of compensations, and second, in the location of the pathology in the parents' personality or family relationships."[*] For example, maternal depressions can range from mild to severe and from occasional to constant. Even when they are severe and frequent, however, some families can manage without placement because of their financial resources or because of the strength of the other parent or some close relative who can fill in the breach. By "location," Glickman means the particular role functions involved in the parent's pathology. There is no complete correspondence between the degree of the parent's neurotic disturbance and his adequacy as a parent. Some people who float around irresponsibly and unproductively find fulfillment in their children. Some women may have severe marital difficulties and still be able to manage their children. As "an illustration of the diagnostic differential in the factors of compensation in the emotional economy and in the location of pathology which can avert placement," Glickman cites the classic, hard-working, long-suffering wife of the chronic alcoholic:

The mother, however, has learned to handle her husband when he is intoxicated and to protect the children from him at such times. She works outside the home for the family's support, at the same time keeping house for the family. With these compensations, even though they stem from her neurotic needs, this parent keeps the family together. Her ability to prevent her husband's abuse in his drunken rages from seriously affecting the children physically and her explanation to them of their father's drinking as an illness keeps his disturbance out of the parent-child relationship sufficiently to allow the children to escape from gross damage from it. The mother's masochistic needs are met in the marital relationship and are therefore usually less exploitive of her relationship with the children.[**]

The converse is also true. Some people function adequately in society, but do not trouble themselves about care of their children. Such individuals are narcissistic, pleasure-loving, and incapable of making personal sacrifices. The selfishness of these parents tends to irritate agency workers, but moral censure of the parent does not help the child who, if he is not abandoned,

---

[*] Glickman, *op cit.*, p. 23.

[**] Glickman, *op. cit.*, p. 29.

identifies with his parents and grows up to be a replica of them.

The extreme form of any of the pathological parent-child relationships described in Chapter 15 can necessitate removal of the child for effective treatment. It is very difficult to determine the degree of pathology in a short intake study, and it is better to give the parents the benefit of the doubt until they are known to be incapable. Such proof is therapeutic failure (assuming that the therapist is competent) and the detailed knowledge of the parent which only comes from lengthy acquaintance.

Available Resources. The importance of knowing what the available resources offer cannot be overstated. It is not enough to be familiar with their intake policies (i.e., what age their patients are, of what mental level, and what kinds of problems they have); one also should know about:

1. Living arrangements
2. Policies with respect to visiting and to working with pàrents
3. Average length of stay and usual disposition after discharge
4. Educational arrangements
5. Kind and number of professional staff
6. The types of children who do and who do *not* fare well in the institution.

Some boarding schools which do not claim to offer psychological treatment nevertheless have outstanding success with certain problems, and some facilities with reputations for treatment may have very little to offer because of curtailment of funds or loss of staff. Placement agencies acquire a great deal of information from following their children in various settings, which is one good reason for using these resources rather than to make an occasional independent placement.

The case of Ralph illustrates a poor placement recommendation, poor because it was based on only one of the three diagnostic considerations, namely, the degree of pathology in the child.

Ralph was first seen at a child psychiatry facility when he was five. He had been late starting to talk, would not attempt to do things for himself, and screamed at the least provocation. He had had two hospitalizations, one for eye surgery and another for spinal meningitis. At the time of the first evaluation, he was terrified and could not stand frustration or delay. He used only the simplest language, with frequent echoing. His performance on mental tests was very erratic and his IQ was 51. He could not adjust to regular school and was transferred to a special school for brain-damaged children. His parents were interested in him, cooperative, and surprisingly calm. His mother could sense when he was ready to blow up, and could divert him or soothe him in a fairly short time. She accepted his limitations and cooperated with the agency.

Four years later, his parents consulted a specialist at the school's request. The school staff felt that he had made good progress in learning, but that he was restless, hard to manage, and that his relationships with other people were very weak. On seeing Ralph for the first time, the specialist recommended that he be placed in a nearby hospital for mentally ill children. His parents returned to the original facility on their own. Ralph's Stanford-Binet IQ was now 76 and his WISC IQ was 70. He was also much better able to cooperate with the examiner and to converse in a social way. His mother reported that he did not have tantrums or obsessive fears and that he was beginning to play with neighborhood children, although for short periods.

Placement seemed a poor recommendation because of the impressive signs of progress, the family's ability to manage Ralph without undue sacrifice, and the treatment that would have been available in the hospital. As so often happens in public institutions, this hospital was suffering from a curtailment of staff which left them operating on a custodial maintenance program. There was no psychologist, social worker, psychiatrist, or teacher in residence. A year later, Ralph was reported as having made a satisfactory adjustment to special classes in public schools. He was still somewhat isolated, but he was making good progress in behavior control and academic learning. Considering his history, his achievements were genuinely gratifying.

Preparatory Phase

The preparation for placement differs when it is voluntary rather than the result of court action. In either case, however, some time usually elapses between the moment of decision and the carrying out of the final arrangements. It is better if the child can wait in his own home rather than in a detention institution of some kind. The time can be effectively utilized to work through some of the feelings of both parents and child. Glickman points out that "nonetheless, caution should be taken that not too much time is spent in handling the parents' feelings before action is begun, as again the matter of placement may become a theoretical exercise, or the anxiety and tension over the placement's hanging fire will be increased."*

Preparation for placement can serve five purposes: (1) It can help the parents to wait for a good placement rather than to act impulsively; (2) it can prevent a last-minute change of mind; (3) it can prevent a loss of interest in the child after placement; (4) it can encourage the parents' participation in the planning, a foretaste of their later participation in the planning of his return to them; (5) it can help the parents to prepare the child for the separation.

None of this can be accomplished if the parents are considered hopeless cases and are ignored by the placement agency. Many of these parents appear dull, irresponsible, and unfeeling (therefore the recommendation for placement), but a caseworker who is genuinely interested in the parents as *people* can often find untapped reservoirs. As one can imagine, most parents react with mixed feelings to the recommendation of placement: On one hand, it is a relief; on the other hand, it

heightens their feelings of inadequacy and worthlessness. Emily Smith, Betty Ricketts, and Sarah Smith described the reactions of one mother who "spoke of leaving her interviews at the psychiatric clinic and the placement agency feeling withered, as if she were totally inadequate and so inferior that the professional staff could not communicate with her" *(1962, p. 45)*. If only one child is being removed from the family (usually because of the severity of his disturbance), it is extremely important to support the mother and to help her regain her self-respect so that she can allay the fear and guilt of the other children. A guilt-ridden, depressed mother cannot do this. Finally, the continued interest of his parents may make the difference between a destructive or constructive placement.

After the diagnostic evaluation, the selection of a facility, and the preliminary work with the parent, comes the all-important step of telling the child. This is usually done during an appointment with the agency worker or with someone in the institution. Unfortunately the parents may have previously threatened to send the child away. It is important to know what has already been said in order to understand the reactions of the child.

Glickman feels that it is important to make it clear to the child that the worker is not taking him away from his helpless parents. In her words,

"the placement worker's making his first contact with the child by coming to his home for the purpose of eventually removing him will most likely leave a strong impression with the child that the worker is an invading enemy. Thus is created a barrier which will impede the worker's further attempts to help the child both in the process of separation and in later adjustment."*

One would expect the child to blame the worker, but this hostility becomes a

*Glickman, *op. cit.*, p. 109.

*Glickman, *op. cit.*, p. 119.

resistance against accepting help or forming new relationships, and for this reason the responsibility must be clearly established. When the child is placed in a foster home, it is usually because of a difficulty in the family situation; when he is placed in a residential treatment center, it is usually because of a combination of reasons, not the least of which is the child's problem. The record must be kept factually clear for the child, although his displacements, denials, projections, and repressions will come up time and time again during the course of treatment.

There have been some interesting controversies regarding techniques for preventing separation trauma in child placement. One of the issues has been whether it is better to place the child in a temporary home before he is placed in his adoptive or foster home. It has been suggested that an emotionally undemanding interim eases the transition for the child *(Taylor, 1937)*. In the "functional theory" espoused by the University of Pennsylvania School of Social Work, the point is also made that the child must participate in the placement and view himself as having some control over the situation *(Pile, 1946; Gennaria, 1939)*, but this seems far-fetched when one realizes that the theory is to be applied to babies and young children.

Margaret Gerard and Rita Dukette take strong issue with these points, citing evidence that the child tenaciously resists the second separation *(1954, p. 113)*. They feel that "such evidence certainly contradicts the theory as described by Helen Baum *(1937)* that the consciously planned temporary placement is a solution for the pain involved in the first separation and in the assumption of new permanent parents" *(1954, p. 116)*. They recommend, instead, a "transition method of placement" where the aim is to place the child in a new home only after he has developed some familiarity with it and gives evidence of affection for the new parents. "The slogan 'be off with the old love before one is on with the new' is reversed to 'Be off with the old love only after one is sure of the new'" *(Gerard and Dukette, 1954, p. 117)*. Although most of this controversy revolves around techniques of moving a child from one home to another, it has some applicability to moving him from his own home to a residential treatment center. Most of the modern treatment centers encourage preliminary visits by the child and make no effort to curtail visits from his parents after he has been admitted. These children are usually older than those who move into adoptive homes, and therefore can make more use of language and symbols to maintain contact with the old and to get ready for the new. More and more workers are seeking techniques which will mitigate the child's shock and surprise and so reduce the trauma of separation.

Work with Parents after Placement

In former years, workers in the child placement agencies or residential treatment centers had little contact with parents after the child was placed. The therapeutic focus was exclusively on the child and his new environment, as if his old ties were gone and were best forgotten. So much energy was poured into the placement process that nothing was left with which to anticipate its termination and the possible reunion of family and child. The parents of children in foster homes were left to fend for themselves, regarded as something of a nuisance if they showed up, and were allowed to drift away. Recent studies have shown that the disappearing parent leaves the child in a kind of limbo, belonging nowhere and to no one. Eugene Weinstein found that even those children who were placed in infancy had greatest "well-being" when they received regular visits from their natural parents. This was the case even in long-term foster care during which the foster children made a meaningful identification with their foster parents: "Our data strongly suggest that continuing contact with the natural parents has an ameliorative effect on the otherwise detrimental consequences of long-term foster care" *(Weinstein, 1960, p. 18)*. Glickman encourages contacts between family members even when they do not have an altogether favorable influence.

The child's longing for the parent persists whatever the parent is like. Such longing may be based on illusions out of the wish to belong, but the child cannot make new ties while still committed too intensely to old ones through this longing. The working through of these neurotic ties to gain some freedom from them is helped by the child's testing them by experiencing them in reality. The parent realizes how difficult it would be to care for the disturbed child after a few hours' visit, and the child can discern the parents more clearly as being not as glamorous as fantasized, or in some instances, not as formidable as imagined. The inevitable frustration of the child by his parents is thus brought out into the open to help him bear it.*

When parents are very disturbed, their visits with the children are held in the agency's office or with the worker present. But any visit at all may have a demoralizing effect on the foster parents, and care must be taken to minimize the friction between the two families lest the child be caught in the crossfire. The placement worker usually acts as arbitrator and interpreter between the two sets of parents and arranges that they have as little direct exchange as possible.

There is often the possibility that work with the parents can lead to the rehabilitation of the family and the return of the child. This goal is most possible when the placement was occasioned by situations which may change in time or which may be changed by one of the parents. When the child is placed in a residential treat-

ment center, he is even more likely to return home than is the child in a foster home, because it was as much the child's problem as his family's which prompted the placement and one expects him to improve markedly. Marie McCann, Catherine Berwald, and Keith Eldridge describe some of the principles of working with parents in a residential setting, including the important one that it be institution staff who work directly with the parents *(1961)*. As might be expected, one of the important problems is dealing with the parents' feeling of guilt, which they often handle by denying that their child has any problems or by projecting the responsibility for the problems onto something or someone else. The institution staff also try to maintain and improve the relationship between parent and child, and to help the parents to understand the child's behavior. The importance of adjunctive work with the parents is a strong argument for placing children in local institutions. This requires, however, that more institutions be strategically located so they can care for children from smaller geographical regions than is now the case.

There are times when the child cannot return home and placement is terminated only by his coming of age. Then the agency must make sure that the child is clearly aware of its functions and of its responsibility for him. The agency remains a parent figure, and the young adult who leaves should have the feeling that the worker and the agency will always have a friendly interest in him.

"Since these children are often lone individuals who have no kin or none on whom they can fall back, it helps them to know they can come back to the agency, even if the worker is no longer there, if they find themselves in an extremity and desperately in need of help."*

The picture of a young adult obtain-

---

*Glickman, *op. cit.*, p. 372.

*Glickman, *op. cit.*, p. 418.

ing references from an agency, sending holiday messages and marriage and birth announcements to an agency, and returning to an agency office on furloughs and the like is a sad one when one thinks of the inevitable turnover in staff and the impersonality of the contact. The need for parents is not suddenly ended when one comes of age.

Foster Home Care

Social Factors Leading to Placement

The proportion of children in the United States who live outside their own homes has been sharply reduced since the beginning of the twentieth century. The decline in the number of orphans is most striking *(Schudde and Epstein, 1955).* Henry Maas and Richard Engler state that the number is less than one-sixteenth what is was in 1920! However, although they are fewer, the number of children living in other than their own homes is still impressively large. At the time of their study *(1959),* Maas and Engler estimated that some 268,000 children were in foster care, including about 44,000 in preadoptive homes.

As one would expect, there is abundant evidence that social factors create much of the need for placements in foster homes. These are usually complicated by psychological factors, but sometimes they result from relatively basic conditions, such as economic distress. A study of some 4,281 children residing in nine different communities in the United States, carried out for the Child Welfare League by Maas and Engler, showed that one of every four children was placed in foster care because of death, illness, or economic hardship *(1959).* For these children at least, some other solution should have been found. The nine communities varied considerably in their attitudes and social work facilities, and these differences were reflected in the reasons for foster home placement. The

number of placements made because of the psychological problems of parents increased with the complexity of the community and the professional character of the social services provided. On the whole, the economic level of the parents was not very different from that of the community at large, but less than a third of the parents were still married to each other. Leon Eisenberg found, in a foster home population of 4,409 (in the State of Maryland, 1959), that only 18 per cent had been living with both parents at the time they entered the agency, and that 36 per cent had been living with someone other than a parent. Regarding a subgroup of this total population (those referred for psychiatric evaluation), Eisenberg adds the following observations:

But mere tabulation hardly conveys the life circumstances of these children: slum dwellings; irregular and inadequate meals with resulting malnutrition; nomadism; strife, alcoholism, promiscuity, and crime among the adults in the household; inconsistent and often brutal punishment . . . what information we did have was replete with accounts of children who witnessed promiscuous sexual behavior between parents and transients in the household, of others seduced by adults and older children, and of a few who had been forced into prostitution. Several of our children had seen a parent murder or be murdered. *(1962, p. 7.)*

Although these observations do not pertain to all those in foster care, it is nonetheless obvious that foster children endure much more than a normal quota of traumatic experiences *before* the specific trauma of separation. This is the natural consequence of the reasons for placement, i.e., family breakdown or parental inadequacy and irresponsibility.

Common Experiences of Foster Children

The following facts emerge, largely from data gathered by Maas and Engler for the Child Welfare League

(1959). The median age of children in foster care was about 11, and the majority had first been separated from their parents as pre-schoolers. Most children remained in care from two to five years, about 20 per cent leaving within a year. However, the average stays in the nine communities ranged from 1.2 to 8.0 years. Those who remained beyond a year and a half were much less likely to be adopted or to return home. Only about 25 per cent returned to their own homes (usually within a year and a half) and about 67 per cent remained in foster home care throughout their lives. Perhaps the most surprising figures concern the number of moves: in six of the nine communities, 25 per cent or more of the children in public foster care had experienced not less than four moves! This led Eisenberg to remark that "permanence is the fiction of foster care" *(1962, p. 15)*.

Psychopathology in Foster Children

Foster home settings have been used as part of the treatment plan for severely disturbed young children *(Kaplan and Turitz, 1957)* but our discussion is concerned with the behavior disturbances of the run-of-the-mine foster children, rather than with a group selected because of their special emotional difficulties.

It is difficult to obtain an over-all picture of the adjustment of foster children, but Eisenberg estimated that the admission rate to psychiatric clinics is about 30 per thousand (as compared to 3 per thousand for the total child population). Eisenberg is careful to point out that "we do not know, for either the general or this foster population, what ratio obtains between referred cases and all existing cases so that this cannot be considered a statement of the relative prevalence of psychiatric disturbance in the two populations" *(1962, p. 13)*. In the League study, Maas and Engler found that symptoms of disturbance were re-

ported of 40 to 60 per cent of the foster care children in each of the nine communities involved *(1959)*, as compared to 10 per cent in the general school population *(Abrahamsen, 1955; Goldfarb, 1960)*. An even higher figure was suggested in an informal study by Abraham Simon. Of 95 children accepted for placement by the Jewish Child Welfare Association of St. Louis, 93 per cent were judged to have below-average or inferior personality adjustment *(1950, p. 299)*. Eisenberg was the only one to specify the symptoms these children show. Aggressive behavior, persistent and severe, was far and away the major reason for referral (70 per cent). The mean IQ of the 119 children who had WISC scores was 83, and only 6 had IQ's above 100; and their academic retardation was even greater. Inarticulateness, a poor sense of time as well as of place and person, apathy, mistrust, and disorganized habits were frequent characteristics.

There is little doubt that foster care children have more psychopathology than children remaining in their own homes. The reasons can be subdivided into pre- and post-placement factors. Eisenberg compared his group of referred children with other children in foster care, and found that the referred children had been more often abandoned by their parents than the average foster child; at the time of placement only 42 per cent had been living with one or both parents, compared with 64 per cent of the state-wide foster population. The other variables studied are post-placement factors: Two of these seem very significant. First, symptomatic behavior is positively associated with the number of different moves made, not with the length of time in foster care *(Maas and Engler, 1959)*. Eisenberg found that 36 per cent of his referred sample had moved four or more times, as compared with 8 per cent of the state-wide foster population. To some extent this resulted from the children's disturbed behavior, but not entirely. Second, symptomatic behavior seems to be associated with the continued interest of the child's own parents. Weinstein studied 61 children, none of whom was mentally retarded or emotionally disturbed, who had been placed for at least a year by the Chicago Child Care Society. A Total Well-Being Scale was rated by caseworkers, and the children were interviewed on 20 open-ended items designed to elicit responses in three broad areas: the child's conception of his situation *vis-à-vis* his own family and his foster family; his conception of the role of the agency and its relationship to him; and the pattern of his identification with either his own or foster parents. About half of the group were semi-adopted, that is, they had been placed in infancy and had never been visited. Eleven of the 61 used the last name of their foster parents. It was found that the average well-being for those with mixed identification was the lowest; of those identifying with the foster parents, the next lowest; of those identifying with natural parents, the highest. Even those children who identified chiefly with the foster parents had greater well-being if there were regular contacts with the natural parents.

The results indicate a good deal of internal consistency in the children's overt responses. The child who identifies with his natural parents tends to defend his being in placement as necessary, more frequently expects to return home, more frequently identifies himself as a foster child, more frequently expresses a difference between being in a foster home and living with natural parents, and tends to have a better understanding of his foster status. *(Weinstein, 1960, p. 51.)*

This finding seems paradoxical. One might think it better to let children forget their good-for-nothing parents and attach themselves wholeheartedly to their new parents. But this would be to ignore the fact that the differences between the status of the foster child and the natural or adopted child are very real and cannot be hidden. The differences are both legal and psychological. This requires work with the foster parents as well as with the foster child. The foster parents may be tempted to register the child in school under their name, to tell him and others that he is adopted, and to explain away the rare visits of the parents with some fiction.

The foster parents are indeed in an anomalous position. They are reminded that this is not their own child and that his stay is indefinite and temporary, and yet they are asked to take care of him just as they would their own. The agency must not only find the home and match the child to the family, the agency worker must maintain contact with the foster parents in order to give them the external support they need for their difficult task.

In Glickman's opinion, *all* placed children require treatment. Attempts should be made to help every child with the conflicts which attend separation as well as those which are derived from damage done before the placement. The normal conflicts which accompany growing up are complicated by his confusion about his identity. She feels that the placed child can never have the whole or normal personality described in the textbooks, but that good experiences in foster care, *plus* psychotherapy, can redress some of the damage. "With skilled help, his bitterness toward his family, apparent or submerged, will be softened, his loyalties become less conflicted, and with understanding, his hopes for himself in the future be less blighted, in fact, even lighted."[*] Prevention of psychological disturbances in foster children would require:

1. Avoidance of unnecessary separation by careful diagnostic evaluation and provi-

---

[*]Glickman, *op. cit.*, p. 331.

All citations should be settle withing five (5) days since failure will constitute grounds for dismissal and/or cancellation of Vehicle Registration. Fees should be paid at the College Police Department.

ENFORCEMENT AND PENALTIES FOR VIOLATIONS:

1st Citation - $1.00 if settled within 5 days. After 5 days, fee will be $2.00

2nd Citation - $2.00

3rd Citation - $3.00

4th Citation - $4.00 - Subsequent, additional $4.00 per ea.

Students who have accumulated five (5) violations during a school year will be referred to the Dean of the College for disciplinary action and may be denied the use of an automobile on the campus. All fees must be paid before a student may receive his or her transcripts or be permitted to enroll for the next semester. Students who have unpaid fees will not receive transcripts of their work, nor will transcripts be sent to other universities and colleges until such fees are paid.

TEXAS SOUTHMOST COLLEGE
CAMPUS POLICE DEPT.
BROWNSVILLE, TEXAS

I.D. _____

Date _12/3/85_

N° 26192

TRAFFIC CITATION

NAME: _____

MAKE _Chevrolet_ MODEL _SW_

LIC. PL. NO. _2QT 444_ ST _TX_ YR _86_

LOCATION _Library_ TIME _9:54pm_

FACULTY _N/a_ STAFF _____ STUDENT _____

PERMIT NO. _____ EXPIRED _____

VIOLATIONS

☑ No Parking Permit
☐ Improper Parking
☐ Entering Restricted Area
☐ Obstruction of Sidewalk
☐ Parked or Stopping in Service Drives
☐ Blocking Traffic
☐ Expired Permit
☐ Parking in Faculty
☐ Parked in "No Parking Zone"
☐ Parking on Lawn or Turf or in Construction Area
☐ Parked so as to obstruct the Servicing of a Trash Container
☐ Parked in Handicapped
☐ Parked in Visitors

_____
Officer's Signature

sion of needed assistance to the intact family

2. Careful preparation for placement
3. Work with foster parents to provide what is desirable and to keep the reality clear
4. Work with natural parents to maintain some interest
5. Work with the foster child
6. Work to return the child home or to help the parents relinquish him for adoption if they have no interest at all

One cannot help but feel that if all placements were done in the thorough, sophisticated manner described by Glickman, the sorry aftermaths would be much reduced. Unfortunately, most public placement agencies are understaffed and underfinanced, and fall far short of this ideal. We cannot continue to restrict our interest to the neurotic child of the middle or upper-class family. In terms of prevention of mental illness in the next generations, one must remember that "these children grow to father others they cannot rear" *(Eisenberg, 1962, p. 5).* Without experiencing good family care, these children cannot provide it for the next generation. The harsh realities of contemporary foster care should force us to reevaluate public services and to place new emphasis on ways of assisting deprived families in the disadvantaged urban centers.

Residential Treatment Centers

After all that has been said about the emotional problems of foster home children, both before and during placement, it may appear contradictory to speak of residential treatment centers as reserved especially for emotionally disturbed children. Reflecting on the changes in the past decades, Martin Gula commented that:

. . . community resources are absorbing larger and larger numbers of younger, less disturbed, or less retarded children who can be cared for while living at home or in foster homes. In turn, this means that the more severely disturbed, aggressive delinquent, and severely retarded children are squeezed to the top and referred to institutions. *(1958, p. 4.)*

Gula describes the criteria by which agencies decide between foster family and institutional care as "fuzzy," but there is no question that the institutions are taking the more disturbed children. Other factors are the age of the child, the resources of the community, and the attitude of the parents. Some parents will accept the total care program of an institution but will not accept foster family care. The possibility that the child might make a satisfactory adjustment with another set of parents is a threat, and the idea that the child needs specialized care around the clock, and a special school (an integral part of most residential treatment centers), is less damaging to the parents' self-esteem. Parents may admit their helplessness but still not want to relinquish the child to another set of parents. Their greater desire to maintain their parental status helps to explain why more institutionalized than foster children return to their own home.

Child-care institutions vary widely in form and functions. Joseph Reid and Helen Hagan made a study of 12 representative institutions for the Child Welfare League *(1952).* Seven were medical units administered by physicians, including closed wards in a general psychiatric hospital, and five were social agency units administered by social workers. Most of the medical units were relatively small, for 12 to 20 children; the social agencies cared for more children. The largest of these was Hawthorne Cedar Knolls School, run by the Jewish Board of Guardians, which had 200 children. A half-hour film, "Boy in the Doorway," portrays the program at Bellefaire which is one of the foremost social agency residential centers.

The annual per capita costs, as of

1952, ranged from $2,099 (in Arthur Brisbane, a state-operated treatment center) to $8,079 (at Southard School in Topeka, which was primarily supported by patients' fees). For its 57 children, Arthur Brisbane had one professional director, three nurses and two teachers; Southard School, for 20 children, had six full-time psychiatrists, psychologists, and social workers, and five full-time teachers.

Clearly, the treatment programs and type of children served will vary with the setting and with the institution's budget, professional staff, and so on, but all the institutions utilize: (1) individual psychotherapy with the child and his parents; (2) remedial education; and (3) a therapeutic way of life designed to restore the child to mental health and return him to the community. It is the last, the design for living, which is the unique feature of the institution. The emphasis on the importance of the institutional environment gave rise to the concept of "milieu therapy" *(Bettelheim, 1948; Bettelheim and Sylvester, 1949).* Fritz Redl points out that a great number of factors can be subsumed under "milieu" *(1959).* The following is an admittedly crude division of the major ones: (1) the institutional staff; (2) the management of daily activities; and (3) the role of the group.

The Institutional Staff

Besides the professionals whose function is to diagnose, treat, and educate the children (i.e., the psychiatrist, psychologist, social worker, and teacher), there is a large staff of administrative, child-care, and group work personnel.

The role of the child-care worker is perhaps the least well defined, despite the general agreement about its crucial importance. These are the people who live with the child, take care of getting him up and putting him to bed, and supervise his meals, dressing, and his other everyday activities. Herschel Alt

has described some of the variations in qualifications and titles for those persons responsible for the child-care function *(1953).* The qualifications which the centers have established are directly related to their treatment program and the place these workers are given in that program. The child-care worker may be a substitute parent, functioning under the general guidance of the therapist (usually a psychiatrist or a social worker) or he may share the responsibility for the therapy and the management of the child's daily activities. When he functions *in loco parentis,* he is usually called a "cottage parent" and is expected to be a particularly mature and stable person. There is a trend toward enlarging the cottage parents' range of responsibilities and prerogatives, as well as their status *vis-à-vis* the other professionals in the institution. In many places, they participate in treatment conferences, become acquainted with the child's history and his treatment record, make observations, and contribute to the planning.

In an institution, there is a multiplicity of relationships between the children and the adults—at school, at play, in the cottage, and in the clinic—and it is difficult to design a situation which helps the child to identify a particular person as a parent figure. Married couples could serve as substitutes for both mother and father, but it is difficult to find well-suited couples. Compromise arrangements include employing a wife whose husband is employed elsewhere and who returns in the evenings, like most fathers, and single persons of both sexes. Another practical complication is the need to have the cottage parents work in shifts, in order to have a reasonable work week.

The child himself is probably in conflict about his own parents and distrustful of new people who want to step into their shoes. For his own reasons, he will be slow to attach himself to a mother or father substitute. But despite all the practical and psychological problems, most residential therapists would probably agree with Alt in feeling that:

. . . each child must be given the opportunity to develop a meaningful substitute parental relationship with a particular adult in the institution, so that when he is ready to enter into such relationship, he may do so. If we accept such a thesis, we come to the heart of the problem and a central dilemma in residential treatment: that this goal could be achieved only if we were able to find ideal, or nearly ideal, cottage parents.*

It is difficult to define the degree of authority which the cottage parents should exercise over the immediate lives of the children. If they are to function as parent surrogates, they should have the right not only to limit and deprive, but also the right to give and to provide satisfaction. They must be able to determine on the spot what each child should be permitted or forbidden, and to choose the proper reward or punishment. They should be sufficiently well-informed about each child to give him individual care, yet they must remain aware of the group as a whole. Parents do not find this easy with relatively normal children in the smaller unit of the family, so one can imagine the practical problems encountered by cottage parents. Every residence tries to provide support and some professional supervision, usually from psychiatric social workers who have had experience in cottage management and cottage living. It is equally important that the cottage parents have direct contact with the administrator, in order that they can function as agents of that authority. When the therapist requests individualized treatment which is demoralizing

to the other children, the cottage parents may find themselves opposing him.

Eva Burmeister discussed some of the practical questions raised by cottage parents, including the problem of seeming to show favoritism. If the special treatment arises from a need or prejudice of the houseparent, then it is favoritism; if it arises from a special need of the child, it can be properly interpreted to the other children, who should all experience special treatment from time to time. Her hints and suggestions on discipline are interesting because they could be applied by any parent:

1. Set limits which are definite and consistent.
2. Allow verbal expression of feelings in place of acting out behavior.
3. Stick to what you have said.
4. Watch for behavior which is due to fatigue and malaise.
5. Avoid charts, star systems, etc. because it is too difficult to classify behavior as "good" or "bad" and it is better to use your relationship.
6. Overlook what you can, such as nail biting, dirty hands, etc.
7. Allow for natural exuberance.
8. Do not use as punishment those things he should be able to count on such as food.
9. Don't assign extra work as punishment.
10. Be sure that the punishment has some logical connection with the wrongdoing.
11. Don't use deprivation of home visits as punishment.
12. Avoid unnecessary irritants such as parade of visitors through the cottage, a bus conspicuously labelled with the name of the home, etc.
13. Avoid comparisons between children.*

A different kind of institution and another point of view regarding childcare workers are represented by Bruno Bettelheim, director of the Sonia Shank-

*Quoted from Herschel Alt, *Residential Treatment for the Disturbed Child* (New York: International Universities Press, 1960), p. 100. Reproduced by permission.

*Quoted from Eva Burmeister, *The Professional Houseparent* (New York: Columbia University Press, 1960), p. 126. Reproduced by permission.

man Orthogenic School since 1944. This is a smaller institution, for younger and more severely disturbed children than those at the Hawthorne Cedar Knolls School. Most of them have a diagnosis of schizophrenia, including autism *(Bettelheim, 1955, p. 498),* whereas a minority of the children at Hawthorne are considered schizophrenic *(Alt, 1960, p. 40).* There is no attempt to reconstruct the family; six to eight children live in a dormitory, and three counselors and one teacher are in charge of each group. Bettelheim feels that the children who need his program are not ready for a relationship as complex as that with a substitute parent:

Therefore the newcomer in the School is not expected to seek and find parental figures and to relate to them. Instead, he is offered casual acquaintance with various people who provide him with whatever he needs, including respect for his need for privacy and non-interference. If he succeeds in relating to them, well and good; if not, little damage has been done since they need not become important to him.*

The counselors are graduate students and persons with varied backgrounds; they may hold degrees in anthropology, education, human development, medicine, nursing, psychology, social work, or sociology. The Orthogenic School is an integral part of the University of Chicago, and this may account for the availability of interested graduate students.

The role of the counselor is no less difficult or ambiguous than that of the cottage parent. Most of the weight of the treatment program is on her shoulders. For different children and at different times, the counselor performs the following: (1) need fulfillment at the most primitive levels; (2) acceptance of primitive expression of need

and feelings from the child; (3) working through some conflicts in "marginal interviews"; and (4) working through other problems in specially scheduled individual interviews. The treatment philosophy at the Orthogenic School lays great stress on the necessity of providing immediate gratification of the child's wishes, if they do not interfere with his own well-being or that of other children. In Bettelheim's opinion, these are ungratified children, and it is necessary to provide compensation:

In helping to bring order into the child's personality we rely mainly on his desire to get along in a world that provides him with ample satisfaction of all, or almost all, of his needs and not only the ones that are commonly accepted by adults as legitimate. We feel that before anything else a child has to be utterly convinced that—contrary to his past experience—this world can be a pleasant one, before he can feel any impulse to get along in it.*

Bettelheim's counselors are not expected to function like parents. Their need-fulfillment function involves freely giving the child whatever food he wants, whenever he wants it, and standing ready to satisfy the child's desires, however regressive (e.g., providing a bottle, dressing him, or bathing him). The counselor accepts primitive expressions of needs and feelings:

"It is best if the counselor suffers the child's aggressions quietly and submits—as far as he can realistically do—to the child's hostile whims."**

Particularly in the initial stages, the counselor's chief aim is to convince the child, by every means possible, that he is loved and accepted *no matter what* he does. This philosophy of deliberate indulgence and permissiveness follows from the basic premise that these are deprived children. One therefore tries

---

*Bettelheim, *op. cit.,* p. 27.
**Bettelheim, *op. cit.,* p. 93.

to go back to the beginning to establish, on the basis of total gratification, a relationship which will lead to identification and to a desire to please. There is no attempt to provide a single all-giving mother; the counselors are expected to coalesce into one in the child's mind.

In the course of treatment, there is a gradual movement towards verbal expression, both by the child and the counselor. This starts with on-the-spot problems, which are handled by what has been termed the "marginal interview":

Anxieties that center around cleanliness or elimination are handled more directly and more easily with these children while they wash, or resent taking a bath, than by discussing their feelings in play sessions where the real experience can only be re-enacted by play dolls or toys. . . . Therefore we try to deal with anxieties around cleanliness in the settings in which they arose; that is, in the bathroom and the toilet. By the same token, oral disturbances can be dealt with much more directly in the dining room than in the treatment room, and so on round the clock.*

The marginal interview is a conversation which may be directed toward clearing up an anxiety, warning the child of an unavoidable outcome of his behavior, or explaining something that he seems to have misunderstood. Although Bettelheim relies heavily on the various relationships between the children and the staff members and on the therapeutic possibilities of everyday activities, he retains the more traditional, private treatment session. A large number of the children are seen by their counselors, who thus perform yet another professional function. He comments that these individual sessions closely resemble any other form of child therapy based on psychoanalytic principles except that the therapist is also involved with all the child's activities at the school. However, Bettelheim's description of some of these sessions leaves one with the impression that the relationship is stressed more than the interpretation of unconscious conflicts or ego defenses *(1950; 1955)*.

The contrast between the approach of the Orthogenic School and that of the Hawthorne School (though both are psychoanalytically oriented) is undeniably great. This makes it important to match the child and the treatment. Bettelheim's program is for the extremely disturbed or psychotic child who shows "incongruous development, misinterpretation of reality and a weak level of self-control."* There are many less disturbed children who also need residential treatment, though of a different kind.

Management of Daily Activities and Out-of-School Time

More than half the child's time is spent outside of the school and therapy sessions. Daily routine, and group activities are therefore extremely important in every residential treatment center. Bettelheim's classic description of the psychological processes going on inside a child as he tries to get up in the morning shows how complicated these mundane events can be. How much time should be allowed for dressing? How frequent should baths be? How much leeway should be allowed about getting to meals on time? When should bedtime be? What about table manners and personal appearance? How available should snacks be? Should the child take care of his own belongings? These are all vital questions. Ultimately, the answers depend on the individual needs of the child and the major premises of treatment. Children need some kind of regularity, and institutions must be run on some sort of schedule, so even the most permissive centers have limits to their flexibility.

*Bettelheim, *op. cit.*, p. 34.

*Bettelheim, *op. cit.*, p. 37.

Such considerations are part of establishing a therapeutic milieu, and the decisions are no easier to make in an institution than in a private home.

The recreational program varies from one center to another. Some institutions view it as a way of keeping the children busy and out of mischief. Others view it as part and parcel of the treatment plan and give careful thought both to the activities and to the composition of the recreational groups. The activities are intended not only to provide enrichment and pleasure for the child, but also to help him become self-confident, whether through sports, dramatics, arts and crafts, or special interest clubs. When the children are aggressive or psychotic, a great deal of attention is given to matters of space, equipment, and physical environment. Schools for older and less disturbed children pay more attention to grouping. The recreational activities help in building relationships among the children and with the leader. Specially selected workers, who combine group work skill and clinical insight, may interpret the child's social difficulties to him as they arise (Konopka, 1954). The treatment center offers a natural setting for the practice of the "activity group psychotherapy" (Slavson, 1952) discussed in Chapter 14.

At one time, children in orphanages and training schools were an important part of the institution's labor force. Later, such work was viewed as slave labor, but it became respectable again because it was felt to have positive value for the child. It is now recognized that adolescents, particularly, need a sense of purpose and identification with the adult world, and that this is better achieved through a job than through school or play. Alt, of the Hawthorne School, offers the following observations:

The relatively naive emphasis on useful occupation as a medium for learning good habits has given way to a concept of work as a medium for building a sense of achievement as well as a bridge to meaningful interpersonal ties between child and adult. . . . It is important to make sure, however, that the work is not only useful in itself but that the child should understand how it contributes to the well-being of his immediate community as well as the general community. It should also, as far as possible, be educational in the sense of enhancing skills.[*]

At Hawthorne, all the children have household chores in their own cottages; at Orthogenic School, maids make the beds. This is still another reflection of the differences engendered by the types of children served and the theoretical basis of the treatment.

The Role of the Group in Residential Treatment

The older and the less disturbed the population, the more important is the influence of the group. For adolescents, especially, the group organization has a great potential for both health and pathology. Institutions which are sufficiently large form groups not only on the basis of sex and age, but also in terms of personality characteristics, to achieve a balance and to avoid the traumatization of the weak by the powerful or further consolidation of antisocial behavior. In cottage life there are cliques, leaders, followers, isolates, preferred cottage parents, indigenous leaders, scapegoats, mascots, and so on. The cottage group operates like a well-developed social organization—a gang, if you will—and certain children control others in very decisive ways. In the tight little island of an institution, the clusterings and social hierarchies operate around the clock, providing more than the usual motive for conformity.

There is still a lot to learn about how to manage these groups in order to produce a healthful environment. Parents fear that their child will be

---

[*]Alt, op. cit., p. 117.

influenced for the worse by the others, and this may happen. It also happens that a child on his way to recovery accepts and supports a newcomer, but the empathy of one disturbed child for another is an uncertain thing, more dependent on identification with some counselor or therapist than with the other child. The child's desire to belong to the group is good, and useful in treatment, but only if the group's values are good. Jealousy, competitiveness, psychological ascendancy, and the feeling of injustice when one child is treated differently from the others are very real problems, and formidable to one who is used to working with patients on an individual basis.

The Role of the School in Residential Treatment

Almost all children in residential treatment had serious difficulties in school. Indeed, the referral is often precipitated by exclusion from school or by chronic failure. Many of them were truants, disrupted their classes, flaunted the teacher's authority, or failed to learn. Alt *(1960)* reported an average academic retardation of approximately three years (average age, 15; average academic achievement, sixth grade). The average figures can be misleading: There is always a small group whose emotional problems did not affect their ability to function effectively in school. At least half of the children were more than three years retarded.

The learning problems of institutionalized children differ mainly in degree from those described in Chapter 9. Some are paralyzed by a fear of failure and by their conviction that defeat is inevitable; some are paralyzed by the fear of success and the independence and increased responsibility it will bring. Some are emotionally exhausted, and come to class in an apathetic lethargy; others are in an overactive whirl. Some fail to learn as a way of defeating adults, primarily teachers and

parents, and this may be further complicated if the academic failure is a masochistic self-punishment or relieves unconscious feelings of guilt. And all the time, time is passing, the gap between the patient's achievement and his age widens, and his shame and embarrassment increase.

It is obvious that the teacher in an institution school cannot follow an orthodox curriculum. Nor can she follow any standard pedagogical procedure, such as the project method, unit organization, or the core curriculum. Very little specific guidance is offered the teacher of emotionally disturbed children, except that she should "individualize" her instruction. The literature is replete with such recommendations as "the experiences provided children should be derivative from an understanding of their nature and needs" *(Rabinow, 1955, p. 685);* "an adequate educational program must be based on an adequate evaluation of the individual child and his total dynamics" *(Hirschberg, 1953, p. 684);* and "the understanding derived from full study of the child—not only his personality deviations and strengths, but also his educational capacities and disabilities—constitutes the foundation for the design of the individual child's educational program."* There is agreement that the teacher must work closely with the therapist and other staff, but that she must not merge her role with that of the therapist. She makes a deliberate effort to communicate new facts or skills to the child, which means that he is asked to learn something new, something about which someone else knows more than he. He has to have the desire, the ability, and the concentration to assimilate new facts, and he has to have the willingness to accept them from an external source, whether this be the *Encyclopaedia Britannica*, the teacher, or another child.

The specific material to be learned

---

*Alt, *op cit.*, p. 108.

can be jointly determined by the child and by the teacher. But to learn anything, the child must look or listen. And he must digest the information and make it his own, so he can use it later. The teacher can only go so far when there is an inhibition of learning, and then she must await the results of therapy. On the other hand, accomplishment in the classroom can give the child a feeling of confidence which may accelerate his treatment. The chance that this will happen is increased when he is set goals which are within his reach and not left to drift in an undemanding atmosphere of games and fun. There is a need for structure, albeit individually tailored. Even in the permissive climate of the Orthogenic School:

When the child enters the classroom, he finds his work all laid out for him by his teacher. He knows exactly how much he is expected to do and whenever possible the teacher gives him help as soon as he asks for it so that no frustration over a difficult problem will accumulate.*

Teaching in a residential treatment center differs in many ways from teaching in a public school. The children are more disturbed and academically retarded. The classes are smaller, from eight to twelve children. The academic expectations are lower, and the teacher has the support of the therapy staff, who can provide many reasons for the child's failure to learn. The clinical staff can explain the symbolic significance of the teacher's role, and what she means to a given child, and this understanding helps her to bear the hostile attitudes transferred to her from other adults in the child's past. Without some clinical understanding, the child's slow progress and frequent belligerence would certainly discourage any conscientious teacher.

However, the clincial staff is usually not so helpful in advising the teacher

as to what she should do. She must be able to keep order in the classroom— that is, she must prevent dramatic incidents and violent conflicts. She must not be afraid of the children. She must be able to portray a positive future for them, even when they don't see one. If all the children were simultaneously in the initial stages of treatment, it is doubtful that the teacher could bear it. Fortunately, the progress of the recovering child helps her to find the tolerance and patience she needs to deal with the one who is still negativistic and disinterested.

Education in a residential setting has the same goal as education anywhere, namely, preparation for a productive and satisfying life as an adult in the community. It may be preparation for vocational training or it may be preparation for college. Most children spend a period of time in extramural work or in school, as a transition between living in the institution and returning to the community. This step on the way back is a crucial one, because school looms so large in a child's life. Ruth Newman describes the factors which determine the success or failure of this extramural education as: (1) the moment in treatment when it is attempted; (2) the selection of an appropriate school; and (3) the communication between the school and the institution (1960). A similar situation obtains for the first extramural job.

The Place of Individual Treatment

Most residential treatment centers provide individual psychotherapy or casework, although they do not always consider it appropriate for all the children in residence. The same people who are responsible for therapy are usually also responsible for the diagnostic evaluation at the point of intake and discharge, for work with the parents, and for the coordination between cottage, clinic, and school. The problem

---

*Bettelheim, op. cit., p. 153.

which usually arises is how much responsibility the clinical staff should have for the actual handling of the child. Alt proposes that "if the clinician can achieve the required understanding of the child management and educational functions, in addition to mastery of clinical procedures *per se*, then it becomes desirable to have the clinician control all phases of the treatment."* However, this is a big "if"; it requires that the clinician have extensive experience in the residential setting.

Treatment itself does not differ markedly from the description given in Chapter 14. Compared to outpatient treatment, there is relatively little interpretive therapy, because the majority of the children in residential treatment do not suffer from the internalized conflicts which characterize neurosis. There is relatively more "ego supportive" and relationship therapy, because most of the children suffer from character defects which hark back to distorted relationships with parent figures or to identifications with poor adult models. Augusta Alpert coined the term "corrective identification" for a therapy which emphasizes "a second infancy, a chance to repeat and relive the developmental process around a corrective identification" (1957, p. 256). This sounds like the basic philosophy underlying the milieu therapy of the Orthogenic School, but the stratagems are different. In Alt's opinion, treatment at Hawthorne School follows Alpert's thinking. He feels that these children are first and foremost at odds with their environment, and only secondarily at odds with themselves. Accordingly, one provides an external structure to support the weak ego, and one provides a long and intimate relationship with *one* adult, to work through present, real problems rather than to uncover unconscious conflicts. The Orthogenic School emphasizes need fulfillment in the "second infancy" they provide

whereas Hawthorne School emphasizes constancy of a relationship to provide the corrective identification.

Only a very few centers, among which are Bellefaire and the Children's Aid Society in Cleveland, have attempted classical psychoanalysis, and they have found that it requires modifications which have yet to be clearly defined. It remains to be seen whether their therapeutic success warrants increased use of psychoanalysis, but there is no doubt that the psychological information they derive will be helpful in understanding what goes on in the individual in a treatment milieu, surrounded by disturbed companions and many adult authorities, and separated from his family.

Follow-up and Evaluation

If one thinks about the severity of the emotional disturbance of the children who enter residential treatment centers, one becomes curious about their fate after discharge. Professional workers want to know if it was possible to help these children, whether their separation from home was warranted, and whether residential treatment is economically defensible. But despite widespread interest in follow-up studies of residentially treated youngsters, there is no standard design for such studies. They are subject to all the criticisms levelled at evaluations of outpatient psychotherapy (see Chapter 14). The matter of suitable controls is particularly difficult. The children accepted by an institution are markedly different from those who are rejected, and they cannot be compared at some later date on the theory that the intervention of treatment is the only significant variable.

In discussing the Bellefaire follow-up study, Melvin Allerhand, Ruth Weber, and Norman Polansky remark:

One must bear clearly in mind that to study and "measure" a group of patients at

---
*Alt, *op. cit.*, p. 77.

some point in time after a specific treatment has ceased is by no means the same thing as evaluating that treatment. No matter how carefully one conducts his research, there is simply no way of knowing what would have become of these patients had the treatment not been applied. *(1961, p. 7.)*

Prima facie evidence provides considerable support for one's personal conviction that the residential treatment improved the child's condition more than could be expected from maturation alone, but there is no way of establishing this beyond a shadow of a doubt because the same child simply cannot remain at home and be in an institution, simultaneously.

The follow-up studies range from informal reviews of clinical case reports by the therapy staff to formal measurement by a research staff working independently of the treatment staff. The therapists use such criteria as "good, fair, or poor adjustment" or "cured, much improved, moderately improved, or no change," or "successful, partially successful, unsuccessful" *(Herzog, 1959)*. In his second book, Bettelheim reviews the status of the 31 children discharged from the Orthogenic School in the five years from 1948 to 1953. He describes 15, or 48 per cent, as "doing well" or "cured"; 11 as "much improved"; 13 as "moderately improved"; and 2 as showing "no change." In addition, he presents four detailed case reports so that the reader can judge for himself the nature and efficacy of the treatment *(Bettelheim, 1955)*. The fact that even some of these psychotic, or near-psychotic, children could be restored to normal functioning is undeniably impressive. He also mentions that a number of children are discharged after a brief trial period as "untreatable," and it would be interesting to know more about them. One would like to know how the determination is made. It would help practitioners to make referrals and perhaps relieve some of the vague sense of guilt

which one has about the severely disturbed youngster for whom this treatment is not available. It is not enough to describe the successes; information about the "rejectees" and "failures" would be equally helpful.

The Bellefaire follow-up study, which actually comprises a number of investigations, is a good example of formal research. The sample consists of the first 50 boys discharged after January, 1958. They were followed up one year after their discharge, and 25 of the boys were seen again between two and two and a half years after they were discharged. Their average age at admission was 12 years and 11 months, and their average age at discharge was 16 years and 7 months. Their mean IQ on the Wechsler Intelligence tests when they were admitted was 103, and the range was 67 to 137. At the time of the first follow-up, 4 were in another institution; 6 were in foster homes or group homes; 4 were at colleges or schools; 1 was in the Armed Services; and 35 were living with their families or independently.

Data were collected in the following areas: (1) the original treatment plan formulated at the time of entrance; (2) the verbal accessibility of the child during his stay; (3) his adaptation at the time of discharge; and (4) his adaptation at the time of follow-up. Scales were developed to measure adaptation in terms of: (1) self-expression through investment of energy outside of self (energy); (2) achievement or accomplishment of the mastery of reality (achievement); (3) compliance to the needs and expectations of others (social acceptability); and (4) situational variables (e.g., school or occupation, community, leisure, and physical condition) *(Allerhand, Weber, and Polansky, 1961)*. Norms with which to compare the boys' ratings were established by a group of experts. The follow-up survey included: (1) unstructured interviews with both subject and mother or mother substitute by the research investigator; (2) an interview with the therapist; and (3) a series of psychological tests, including selected cards from the Thematic Apperception Test. In the interviews, data were collected on each boy's experiences after he left Bellefaire, his current situation, how he usually spent his day, his family life, his friendships, his opinion of himself and of his life, his view of the future, and his reminiscences about Bellefaire. From the interview data, an "adaptation profile" was drawn up.

The Bellefaire workers divided "success" into a number of parts, big and little (as contrasted with Bettelheim's more general evaluations). The major areas were: (1) behavior at the time of discharge (14 scales); (2) the staff's evaluation at the time of discharge; (3) the child's view of the help he received; (4) the parent's view of the help received by the child; (5) the adaptability scales; and (6) socially valued achievement (11 items). This method of calculating a "success profile" exemplifies the current trend toward devising criteria which range from the abstract to the concrete and from the whole to its parts, the parts becoming progressively more specific and subject to independent verification. There is, however, a danger in over-refinement:

Big criteria have little criteria upon their backs to bite 'em
The small ones have still smaller, and so on ad infinitum. *(Herzog, 1959, p. 17.)*

All the factors comprising the success profile show that the majority of the children function adequately after residential care. There was close agreement among the various measures used and, on virtually every measure, more than half the children were rated "successful." For example, a child was considered successful in *socially valued achievement* if there was 60 per cent or more positive accomplishment in

those of the 11 specific areas which were applicable to him. By this criterion, two-thirds of the Bellefaire children were "successful." The most conservative figure came from the parents. The 39 parents who were interviewed rated 44 per cent of the boys as "considerably helped" and 31 per cent as "helped some." One suspects that even at the late date of the discharge, many parents were still smarting over their personal sense of failure and were reluctant to admit that someone else succeeded in their place. The boys' self-evaluations were more positive and were significantly related to other success factors. This led Allerhand to suggest that greater credence should be given to the client's self-evaluation than is commonly done in research with children.

The rating on "verbal accessibility" proved to be highly related to later adaptation. The term refers to the readiness of the child to discuss his important attitudes and feelings. Five areas of "freedom to communicate feelings" were rated: (1) feelings toward other adults in the institutional setting; (2) feelings toward the caseworker; (3) painful feelings in general; (4) feelings toward oneself; and (5) feelings toward one's family. The boys were relatively most free in communicating their feelings toward adults in the institution and least free in discussing their feelings toward their parents. "The net restraining force against communication varies as the content to be communicated, and it does this in a manner which is reasonably similar among all the children in our sample" *(Polansky, Weiss, and Blum, 1961, p. 160).* That is, the disclosure of certain feelings creates more anxiety than the disclosure of other feelings, and resistance increases with the anxiety. Feelings toward the parents, being most deeply imbedded, are particularly intense. Their intensity makes them dangerous, and the danger is increased when the parents are absent. Many children hesitate to express anger against someone who is absent, because there is no way of being sure that the hostility does not harm the absent person.

The positive relationship between a boy's verbal accessibility and his later adaptation ratings supports the idea that children who can disclose their feelings tend to relate better to other people and to adapt better to an institution than those children who conceal their feelings *(Allerhand, 1962; 1963)*. This finding also supports the clinician's assumption that "just talking" about feelings helps to modify behavior.

Another contribution of the Bellefaire study is the analysis of situational factors and their bearing on the boys' adaptation. The living situations of 34 of the 50 boys were described as "supportive" or "partially supportive," and 16 were deemed to be in "stressful" environments. Their home lives were extremely important in sustaining their ability to adjust, particularly for those boys whose ability to adapt was considered limited. Those who had successfully adapted to community, school, or work during their stay at Bellefaire seemed to have gained enough strength to be relatively impervious to their later milieu. Those who had exceeded or fallen short of the staff's expectations were boys whose environment was unusually good or unusually poor, respectively.

The findings of the Bellefaire investigation thus show the importance of carrying out the institution's discharge recommendations. All children from Hawthorne receive supervision from one to three years after they are discharged, and this after-care service is given by the staff who knew the child in residence. Alt remarks:

We have learned that the kind of disturbed and delinquent youngsters we now undertake to treat need help in varying degrees over a long time and that for many of them it is unrealistic to think in terms of two or three years of care. While the institutional period may not need to be much longer than it is at present, a responsible agency must continue with the youngsters for a long time, perhaps as long as a decade. It is important not only to make aftercare services available to them for an extended period, but also to establish machinery for periodic assessment of their progress. Only in this way can we evaluate the effectiveness of our work with them.[*]

Community Planning for Care of Children

The psychological plight of the child who must be cared for outside his home should impel any community to take a close look at its child welfare facilities. The principle stated in the 1909 White House Conference Report, that no child should be removed from his own home merely because of poverty, should be acted on. This means that public assistance programs and social services must be adequate. Outpatient treatment facilities should be made available to the child who remains at home, and the concept of outpatient treatment must be broadened to include more than the conventional psychotherapeutic hour for the group or individual. There is, already, a gratifying increase in homemaker services, day-care centers, day hospitals, and school programs for emotionally disturbed children who cannot be contained in regular classes. Such programs are not only psychologically sound; they are also economical.

Although a sufficient number of these programs would decrease the number of children requiring foster home or residential care, there will still be children and families who cannot remain together. The best placement and guidance should be provided for those children, not only to salvage them but to prevent sorrow in the next generation. We know that the primary basis for successful parentage lies in being a loved child. Harlow's study of mother love in monkeys showed that the mon-

---

[*]Alt, *op. cit.,* p. 83.

keys who were brought up by inanimate, terry-cloth figures later rejected their babies and could not care for them *(Harlow and Harlow, 1962)*. Mother love is not instinctive; even subhumans learn to love by being loved. Children who have been badly treated by their parents are likely to become bad parents themselves unless they have had corrective experience.

There is, at present, a dearth of facilities for children in need of residential care. Alt estimated the number of disturbed children in need of residential care to be about 600 youngsters per million. He also estimated that not more than 25 per cent, and probably as few as 10 per cent, of the 100,000 children in institutions in 1960 were receiving the kind of care they needed *(Alt, 1960)*. We need more institutions, sufficiently diverse to serve the needs of the children. The institutional program should be planned so that there is continuity of the care of the child before, during, and after placement. Most institutions now encourage social intercourse between the children and the communities in which they are located. There are boards made up of local representatives, volunteers who come to the institution, and "big brothers" who take the children home for visits; the libraries, cultural resources, the schools, and jobs are made available to the children as they become ready to use them.

A final note of caution should be given the professional worker in the community who is eager to solve a problem by sending the child somewhere. The decision to place a child should rest on the best of our diagnostic skills whereby we judge the following:

. . . whether the negatives outweigh the positives in the family for giving a child parental care; whether the child will gain more from placement than by remaining in the troubled home; whether it is necessary that he live elsewhere so he can have treatment for some serious emotional and mental disturbance which is more handicapping than the scars of separation and the unknowns of placement; and whether there are reality factors which make it impossible for the child to be cared for in his family.*

After a thorough exploration of these questions, and only then, should one proceed to investigate the available resources and their suitability for the child. There are no magic cures. Treatment away from home is hard work, requiring the collaboration of a large number of highly trained and dedicated professional workers who are receiving adequate financial and community support.

---

*Glickman, *op. cit.*, p. 22.

References to Chapter 16

Abrahamsen, D. *et al.*, "Status of Mental Hygiene and Child Guidance Facilities in Public Schools in the United States," *Journal of Pediatrics*, XLVI (1955), 107–18.

Allerhand, Melvin E., "Success: A Many-Splendored Thing." Paper presented at the National Association of Social Welfare Meetings, Cleveland, 1963.

———, "The Grand Puzzle: Does Helping the Closed Self Become Open Result in More Adaptive Behavior?" Presented at the American Psychological Association Meeting, St. Louis, 1962.

———, Ruth E. Weber, and Norman A. Polansky, "The Bellefaire Follow-up Study: Research Objectives and Method," *Child Welfare*, XL (September, 1961), 7–13.

Alpert, Augusta, "A Special Therapeutic Technique for Certain Developmental Disorders in Pre-Latency Children," *American Journal of Orthopsychiatry*, XXVII (1957), 256–70.

Alt, Herschel, *Residential Treatment for the Disturbed Child*. New York: International Universities Press, Inc., 1960.

———, "Responsibilities and Qualifications of the Child Care Worker," *American Journal of Orthopsychiatry*, XXIII (1953), 670–75.

Baum, Helen, "Function as an Integrating Force in Child Placement," *Journal of Social Work Process*, I (1937), 41–53.

Bettelheim, Bruno, "Closed Institutions for Children?" *Bulletin of the Menninger Clinic,* XII (1948), 135–42.

———, *Love is Not Enough.* New York: The Free Press of Glencoe, Inc., 1950.

———, *Truants From Life.* New York: The Free Press of Glencoe, Inc., 1955.

———, and Emmy Sylvester, "Milieu Therapy," *The Psychoanalytic Review,* XXXVI (1949), 54–68.

Boy in the Doorway. Film written by Basil Beyden, directed by K. Elmo Lowe. Produced at Cleveland, Ohio: Bellefaire, 22001 Fairmount Blvd., by Cinecraft Productions, Inc., 1957.

Burmeister, Eva, *The Professional Houseparent.* New York: Columbia University Press, 1960.

Dettelbach, Miriam H., "The Role of Residential Treatment For Children," *American Journal of Orthopsychiatry,* XXV (1955), 669–78.

Eisenberg, Leon, "The Sins of the Fathers: Urban Decay and Social Pathology," *American Journal of Orthopsychiatry,* XXXII (1962), 5–17.

Gennaria, Marion R., "Helping the Very Young Child to Participate in Placement," *Journal of Social Work Process,* III (1939), 29–59.

Gerard, Margaret W. and Rita Dukette, "Techniques for Preventing Separation Trauma in Child Placement," *American Journal of Orthopsychiatry,* XXIV (1954), 111–27.

Glickman, Esther, *Child Placement Through Clinically Oriented Casework.* New York: Columbia University Press, 1957.

Goldfarb, A., *Evaluation of Children's Behavior by Teachers and Psychiatrists.* Baltimore: Baltimore City Health Department, Division of Mental Hygiene Research, 1960.

Gula, Martin, *Child-caring Institutions.* United States Department of Health, Education and Welfare, Children's Bureau Publication No. 368. Washington, D.C.: Government Printing Office, 1958.

Harlow, H. F. and M. K. Harlow, "Social Deprivation in Monkeys," *Scientific American,* CCVII (November, 1962), 136–46.

Herzog, Elizabeth, *Some Guide Lines for Evaluative Research.* United States Department of Health, Education and Welfare, Children's Bureau Publication No. 375. Washington, D.C.: Government Printing Office, 1959.

Hirschberg, J. Cotter, "The Role of Education in the Treatment of Emotionally Disturbed Children through Planned Ego Development," *American Journal of Orthopsychiatry,* XXIII (1953), 684–90.

Kaplan, Lillian K. and Lilly L. Turitz, "Treatment of Severely Emotionally Traumatized Young Children in a Foster Home Setting," *American Journal of Orthopsychiatry,* XXVII (1957), 271–85.

Konopka, Gisela, *Group Work in the Institution: A Modern Challenge.* New York: William Morrow & Co., Inc., 1954.

McCann, Marie, Catharine D. Berwald, and Keith Eldridge, "Work with Parents in a Residential Treatment Center," *Child Welfare,* XL (March, 1961), 9–16.

Maas, Henry S. and Richard E. Engler, Jr., *Children in Need of Parents.* New York: Columbia University Press, 1959.

Newman, Ruth, "The Way Back: Extramural Schooling as a Transitional Phase of Residential Therapy," *American Journal of Orthopsychiatry,* XXX (1960), 588–98.

Pile, Florence M., "Helping the Baby to Move into the Adoption Home," in Pennsylvania School of Social Work, *The Role of the Baby in the Placement Process.* Philadelphia: University of Pennsylvania Press, 1946.

Polansky, N. A., E. Weiss, and A. Blum, "Children's Verbal Accessibility as a Function of Content and Personality," *American Journal of Orthopsychiatry,* XXXI (1961), 153–69.

Rabinow, Barney, "The Role of the School in Residential Treatment," *American Journal of Orthopsychiatry,* XXV (1955), 685–91.

Redl, Fritz, "The Concept of a 'Therapeutic Milieu'," *American Journal of Orthopsychiatry,* XXIX (1959), 721–36.

Reid, Joseph H. and Helen R. Hagan, *Residential Treatment of Emotionally Disturbed Children.* New York: Child Welfare League of America, 1952.

Schudde, Louis O. and Lenore A. Epstein, "Orphanhood: A Diminishing Problem," *Social Security Bulletin,* XVIII (March, 1955), 17–19.

Simon, Abraham J., "Social and Psychological Factors in Child Placement," *American Journal of Orthopsychiatry,* XX (1950), 293–304.

Slavson, S. R., *Child Psychotherapy.* New York: Columbia University Press, 1952.

Smith, Emily A., Betty M. Ricketts, and Sarah H. Smith, "The Recommendation for Child Placement by a Psychiatric Clinic," *American Journal of Orthopsychiatry,* XXXII (1962), 42–49.

Taylor, Mary N., "The Temporary Home as an Integral Part of Adoption Procedure," *Journal of Social Work Process,* I (1937), 67–84.

Weinstein, Eugene A., *The Self-Image of the Foster Child.* Philadelphia: Russell Sage Foundation, 1960.

White House Conference Report, *Proceedings of the Conference on the Care of Dependent Children,* January 25–29, 1909, United States Senate Document, No. 721. Washington, D.C.: Government Printing Office, 1909.

17

PREVENTION

Definition of the Problem

Extent of Mental Illness in Children

After looking at the pound of cure necessary to change an established condition, it is customary to look for the ounce of prevention. The exact size of the problem to be cured, or prevented, is elusive; quantitative estimates vary with the definitions used, the particular population studied, and the specific methods applied. It has been known for a long time that the problem of mental illness is both large and important. The greater consciousness on the part of the general public in recent years should not be confused with any real increase of mental disorders. In 1931, the National Committee for Mental Hygiene estimated that "the chances of developing a psychosis or severe incapacitating neurosis (whether the person is sent to the hospital or not) are about 1 in 10" *(1931, p. 5)*. Their statement about the mental health of children was even stronger: "In early childhood—even as early as 4 years of age—about 1/3rd of apparently normal children of self-sustaining families, average in intelligence, have behavior problems sufficiently marked to necessitate treatment" *(1931, p. 5)*. The *1964 Fact Sheet* published by the National Association for Mental Health reiter-

ated that 10 per cent of our adults need psychiatric treatment and added that at least half of all the millions of medical and surgical problems treated by private doctors and hospitals are complicated by mental illness. These estimates are staggering; perhaps, because the problem is so all-encompassing that it seems virtually hopeless, they have done a disservice to the cause for mental health. In some localities, it would appear, a small fraction, around 20 per cent of the population, would be caring for the other four-fifths who are "mentally disturbed" *(Srole et al., 1962)*. This is so patently impractical that it can serve as an excuse to do nothing.

Some of the difficulties of differentiating the normal from the abnormal were discussed in Chapter 4. This problem is by no means unique to the field of mental illness; in their study of organic illness in the home, John Dingle, George Badger, and William Jordan discuss at length the problem of defining an "illness" in any given individual *(1965)*. It is even more difficult to find an operational definition for mental illness. The person may not be a reliable judge of his own condition and those closest to him have no way of judging. So it is imperative to examine the definition used when cases are counted. One of the best programs for detecting emotional disturbance in children was conducted by E. M. Bower and by his associates in the California school system. *(Bower, Tashnovian, and Larson, 1958; Bower, 1961).* They used three evaluative instruments: a self-rating by each child; a rating of each child by the other children in his class; and a rank ordering of the emotional status of the children in each class, by their teacher. The composite score on the three tests was used to identify those children to be called "emotionally disturbed." A sample of this disturbed population and a control sample of the unidentified school population were interviewed by psychiatrists and psychologists to validate the screening procedure. By those means, approximately 5 per cent of the population were identified as in need of special help.

Other surveys of the mental health of school populations have used simpler ratings, with similar results. In Middlesex County, New Jersey, nearly 9 per cent of elementary school children were rated as poorly adjusted, and 3 per cent were adjudged *very* poorly adjusted *(Gordon, 1965).* In Los Angeles County, 2.4 per cent were classified by teachers as severely disturbed, and 7.3 per cent as "demanding a disproportionate share of the teachers' time" *(Welfare Planning Council, Los Angeles Region, 1960).*

These are surveys of the prevalence of emotional disturbance—that is, both old and new cases are counted together —and they give no idea of the duration of the disturbed behavior. An indeterminate number, at any given time, have problems which will be spontaneously resolved. Unfortunately, there are few longitudinal studies of children with problems so there is no "natural history" for emotional disorders to compare with the "natural history" for organic illnesses. J. W. MacFarlane, L. Allen, and M. Honzik evaluated the adult adjustment of more than 200 individuals who had been studied in childhood (21 months to 14 years) as

"normal" research subjects. In general, they found that the clinical predictions based on childhood behavior problems had been too pessimistic. The majority of the group got along far better than expected. By the very nature of their work, clinicians are familiar with those children who do *not* cope successfully, and whose problem behavior represents the first symptoms of chronic difficulties.

Anna Freud illustrated the problems of prediction with the analogy of a traveler on a walking tour through the city. Looking backward, one can retrace his steps from his starting point; given only the starting point, one cannot foretell which of many possible paths he might trace. Psychological problems are different from organic problems because they involve such complicated interactions between the individual and his environment. Mental illness is not contained within the person's mental structure to the same extent that physical illness is contained within the person's body. This warning of the riskiness of making psychological predictions is given only to lighten the prospective load of mental health workers. Not every child who is shown in a survey to have a behavior problem requires psychotherapy.

The Nature of the Problem

In the 1950's, and more so in the 1960's, attention turned from the individual's psychological conflicts to the reality in which he lives. The term "social psychiatry" describes this new approach.

The first major study on social class and mental illness *(Hollingshead and Redlich, 1958)* was done in New Haven. It revealed that poor people tend to have more psychoses, and that they receive radically different medical and psychiatric care than do the wealthy and the moderately well off. This was followed by a study made in midtown Manhattan *(Srole et al., 1962),* which resulted in a grim report of a "mass of mental morbidity." Only two out of ten subjects were found to have optimal mental health. Approximately half had "significant loads of pathology-denoting symptoms," and the mental health of the remaining quarter was signficantly impaired. One may question the definition of "mental health" which led the authors to such a conclusion, but the relationship between demographic variables and mental health is well documented. Like Hollingshead and Redlich, Srole *et al.* found social disorganization to be associated with a significantly higher prevalence of mental illness.

The growing recognition of the importance of social factors in the production of mental disorder has led to some reformulations. Mental illness has been detached from medicine and brought into the sphere of education, psychology, and sociology *(Szasz, 1961)*. George Albee suggested a theoretical model which might be termed the *social-learning theory* of mental disorder. In his view, mental disorder is much more akin to an educational failure than to a physical disease:

In very general terms this approach suggests that most emotional disorders are complex learned behavioral patterns, the origins of which are to be found in unfortunate emotional conditioning during the first few years of life in social interaction with significant adults, usually the parents. It is held by a growing number of behavioral scientists that most emotional disorders are acquired defects in *social* interactions and *social* participation. Evidence continues to accumulate from the laboratory, from psychoanalysis, and from psychotherapy in general that socio-cultural conditions which influence the stability and strength of the social world of the infant and child have profound effects on the rate and kind of subsequent emotional disorder. *(1965, pp. 6, 7.)*

Social psychiatry called attention to

the deprivations of infantile experience, to the transmission of mental disorder by *social* inheritance, and to the inequities of child care. It increased the sense of community responsibility and modified some concepts of prevention and treatment. But none of this invalidated the findings which came from individual case studies; rather, it illuminated the legion who stand behind the few cases which one comes to know personally. The opinion read by Frederick Allen before the Philadelphia Pediatric Society in 1928 is essentially the same as that expressed by Albee nearly 40 years later:

The important point to realize is that a large proportion of these sources [of behavior difficulties of children] are a part of the child's own life and are avoidable. The degree to which they will be avoided depends on the insight, intelligence and objectivity of those who make up the early world of the child; on their ability to keep the child more or less free from their own emotional entanglements, and on their realization that the goal to be attained is the development of a new healthy individual in society capable of standing on his own feet and having confidence in his own capacity to live, to produce, and to develop harmonious relations with his fellow beings. *(Allen, 1963, p. 59.)*

Levels of Prevention

In 1928, and for some time thereafter, problems between parents and their children were studied and treated on an individual basis. The families were chiefly those with the insight and motivation to ask for help from family agencies, child clinics, and private practitioners. But conventional modes of referral and office treatment were insufficient to reduce the prevalence of mental disorder in the community as a whole. Motivated by a sense of urgency and an ambition to reach the unaware and apathetic, mental health workers have borrowed concepts from the field of public health in order to organize more widespread social action.

The first level of prevention, *primary prevention,* is aimed at *reducing the incidence* (i.e., the occurrence of new cases) of mental disorders of all types. *Secondary prevention* is aimed at *reducing the duration and prevalence* (i.e., the total number of cases) of those disorders which do occur. *Tertiary prevention* is aimed at *reducing the impairment* resulting from mental disorders. Primary prevention is prevention in the traditional sense, that is, reaching the basic cause and preventing the initial occurrence. Secondary prevention (almost a synonym for treatment) is instituted with the expectation that it will shorten the duration of the disorder (i.e., cure it). Tertiary prevention also implies some treatment, but it is closer to the traditional idea of rehabilitation, that is, of helping a person to live as full a life as possible despite some degree of permanent handicap. A good example of this is helping the mentally retarded to achieve some measure of economic and social independence despite their limited capabilities.

In this chapter, we will stress the practical application of the principles of prevention of psychopathology in childhood, starting with proposals for mass action and proceeding to specific actions proposed for special groups, "populations at risk" known to have a greater vulnerability to mental health problems.

Primary Prevention

Mass Social Action

The children most likely to develop emotional disturbances are those in unfavorable circumstances—that is, circumstances which are inadequate for their proper development or traumatic, or both. The inadequacy may be physical or psychological; more often than not the two go hand-in-hand. Leon

Eisenberg described the *deprivation syndrome* as "a complex of intellectual retardation, personality defect, and social maladaptation, observable in children who may or may not exhibit central nervous system impairment" *(1962 b, p. 817).* The pathogenesis is a sequence of limiting conditions—maternal ill health, complications at birth, nutritional deficiencies, postnatal infections, intellectual understimulation, noxious interpersonal experiences, and maternal deprivation—and all of these factors have been shown to be positively related to class status. Helen Wortis and Alfred Freedman, in an anterospective study of development of premature children of low social class, documented the interrelationship between neurological defect and poor environment *(1965).* Prematurely born children have more neurological defects and lower IQ's than children born at term, and they are more likely to be born to women of low social class *(Knobloch, Rider, and Harper, 1956).* Wortis and Freedman compared 215 prematurely born babies with term children of the same economic status, and found the usual relationships between weight at birth, social conditions, and subsequent neurological abnormalities, which suggests that poor environment affects the organism before birth. Furthermore, continued poor environment apparently had a more depressing effect on the IQ's of the premature children (at 2½ years) than of the term children. The authors suggest that "infants who have a defective or vulnerable nervous system may be especially sensitive to poor environment, and disturbing factors may more readily elicit abnormal patterns of development in defective children" *(Wortis and Freedman, 1965, p. 65).*

There is other evidence that the deficiencies which abound in the impoverished lower socioeconomic classes increase the risk of organic deviations which, in turn, reduce the child's resistance to trauma and his ability to cope with the inadequacy of his environment.

Prevention requires some form of mass social action like the "war on poverty" of the Johnson administration. Prospective mothers must have good food and good obstetrical care, regardless of their ability to pay for it. Their children must be given equitable educational opportunities, and this may well require pre-school programs. Job opportunities must be increased, not only to increase the family income but also to provide a working parent with whom the growing child can identify. Discrimination based on color will only perpetuate the disproportionate rates of delinquency and serious illness among minorities *(Clark, 1957; Coles, 1964)*.

Primary prevention also requires that more money be available for public agencies to employ more professional workers. Public welfare agencies are not given a chance to prove what could be done because they are always working with too little and too late. In the field of public health many measures are supported by legislation and finances. For instance, it is considered a crime to refuse to have a child vaccinated against smallpox, but some types of neglect in mental health should be regarded as equally criminal. To move a pre-school child from one foster home to another, or to hold him in a detention home for months is to expose him to a mental illness he will escape only with luck. Yet these things are done with impunity *(Eisenberg, 1962 b)*. Our government is responsible, as are the taxpayers, and even the mental health professionals who eschew practical politics and take refuge in private practice or in theoretical research. There is an important place for such activities, but not if they insulate the professional conscience. The professionals should be creating a clamor and insisting that practices injurious to the mental health of our children be stopped forthwith.

Identification of Specific Target Groups

The data showing relationships between social conditions and mental disorder should not obscure the fact that a significant amount of disorder occurs in all socioeconomic classes. Low social class does not exert its influence in any mysterious way; it involves a concatenation of more adverse circumstances with fewer resources for assistance. When we look for children in traumatic circumstances, we find that these circumstances are more common in, but not exclusive to, the economically deprived population.

In Table 13, we have listed groups of children who run a special risk of incurring mental disorder, primarily because of the problems of their parents.

Some of the high risk groups listed in Table 13 would come to the attention of mental health workers only because of the needs of their parents. Considering this, one is surprised at how little clinical research has been done with children selected on the basis of their parents' problems. Most of the research showing the relationships between child and parental psychopathology starts with emotionally disturbed children and proceeds to an evaluation of their parents. Surveys of the offspring of disturbed parents have been cited mainly to support a genetic theory of the origin of psychosis. For example, F. J. Kallman reported that schizophrenia could be expected in about 16 per cent of the children of one schizophrenic parent and in about 68 per cent of the children of two schizophrenic parents *(1959)*. There has been little effort to discover the effect of the adequacy of mothering by the schizophrenic mother or her substitute, the impact of separation, and the child's fantasies regarding the allegedly hereditary illness.

The proposals for community mental health centers contained in federal legislation *(Public Law 88–164, 1963)*

TABLE 13

Risk Group	Who Knows Them	Relevant References
Abused children	Medical clinics and hospitals Protective services in child welfare agencies	Chapter 15
Foster-home children	Child placement agencies	Chapter 16
One-parent families* Out-of-wedlock children Divorced parents Deserted children Orphaned children Parent in jail	"Parents without Partners" Services for unwed mothers Domestic relations courts Juvenile courts Church and clergy Correctional institutions Public welfare agencies (ADC)	Chapters 12, 16
Children of chronically ill parents	Physicians Convalescent hospitals	Chapter 15
Children of parents with serious mental disease, including alcoholism	Psychiatrists Mental clinics and hospitals "Alcoholics Anonymous"	Chapter 15

*According to data from the 1960 Census, 9 per cent of the population under 18 years of age lived with one parent only, and 3 per cent lived with neither parent.

emphasize the dangers of long-term institutionalization of the adult mental patient, and encourage keeping him in close contact with his home and family by means of day hospital care, increased outpatient services, drug therapies, and short-term hospitalization to remove visible symptoms. Judiciously employed, these more flexible patterns of caring for the patient are a significant step forward.

However, rehabilitative efforts are often directed toward the patient's ability to hold a job, his social acceptability, and the removal of his outward symptoms; and scant attention is paid to his capacity for rearing his children. Eisenberg has asked: "If patients previously hospitalized are now kept afloat in the community although psychologically impaired, may there not be a potential for damage to children reared by disturbed parents?" (1962 a, p. 816). A preliminary study of the adjustment of children of psychotic mothers in the home is optimistic in its conclusions. James Sussex, Frances Gassman, and S. C. Raffel did not find any "marked evidence of being adversely affected by

the presence of a psychotic in the home" (1963, p. 854), but they studied only 16 children between the ages of 6 and 10, of 10 different mothers. Their initial sample contained 17 mothers, of whom 4 refused to participate and 3 failed to continue, and they were probably left with the more cooperative and concerned psychotic mothers. There is a pressing need for more such research, with larger groups, with children with a wider range of ages, and over a longer period of time.

The adult patient's capacity to be an adequate parent should be as carefully considered as his capacity to hold a job, and there must be closer collaboration between workers with children and adults and between their respective clinical facilities. Those who work with adult patients should also be trained in child development and psychopathology, so that they can help the family to maintain a normal environment for the children and help the children to understand what is going on. It would undoubtedly take a tremendous increase in homemaking and day-care services to provide children with the stable environment which is absolutely vital to their mental health. Helen Arnstein's pamphlet for the Child Study Association contains some useful advice for the worker who is concerned with the effect of a parent's illness on his child *(1960)*.

Parent Guidance

The preventive possibilities of parent education programs have already been discussed in Chapter 15, and the difficulty of reaching parents who do not attend parent discussion groups or read educational publications was pointed out. Written material should be easy to read, with lots of pictures, and be distributed to clinic waiting rooms, laundromats, and bus terminals

—any place where people gather and wait. Any method of spreading such information through the mass media should be encouraged.

There are times in a parent's life when he is especially receptive to suggestions, when he can more easily be influenced. A person is likely to pay more attention to someone else when he has a problem, is lonely or worried, and so on. These occasions usually arise in the wake of some event which is unusual and upsetting, and which requires some solution. The crisis need not be earthshaking, as long as it is unusual for the participant. In Table 14 we list some common examples, some of which have happened to everyone, but rarely.

TABLE 14

Crises	Responsibility for Guidance or Referral
Direct Impact on Parent; Indirect Impact on Child:	
Birth of a premature baby	Medical personnel
Diagnosis of handicapped child	Medical personnel; special services
Bereavement	Medical personnel; clergy
Direct Impact on Both Parent and Child	
Hospitalization of child	Medical personnel
Child's entry into school	Educational personnel
Pubescence	None established
Direct Impact on Child; Indirect Impact on Parent	
Birth of sibling	None established
Family Move	None established

The concept of "crisis counseling" evolved from observations of adults, particularly of the reactions to bereavement among the survivors of those killed in the Cocoanut Grove night-club fire *(Lindemann, 1944)*. Another kind of crisis which has been clinically investigated is the birth of a premature baby *(Caplan, 1960; Kaplan and Mason, 1960)*. Interestingly enough, the women who were most upset at first survived the crisis best, while those mothers who had initially denied the danger of losing their babies were still in a state of emotional turmoil two months after the danger had passed.

Other studies of mothers of abnormal infants, and of families in which someone contracted tuberculosis also confirm Lindemann's impression, that the best way to survive a crisis is to acknowledge the facts, and one's feelings, when the crisis occurs.

Caplan describes three aspects of crisis particularly significant for primary prevention:

1. The outcome of a crisis is in most cases *not* determined by its antecedent factors, such as the nature of the hazard or the personality or bio-psychosocial experience of the individuals . . .

2. During the crisis, an individual experiences a heightened desire for help and the signs of his distress evoke a helping response from those around . . .

3. During the disequilibrium of the crisis, a person is more susceptible to influence by others than during periods of stable functioning. When the forces are, as it were, teetering in the balance, a relatively minor interference may weight them down to one side or the other.*

The very nature of a crisis makes it imperative that the mental health worker be responsive and available when he is most needed—when the crisis is imminent or has just occurred. And someone who can take a child's eye view of the situation has to be available. Many of the crises listed in Table 14 require sensitive medical personnel who will initiate psychological intervention. Crisis counseling in these situations requires a close partnership between the people in charge of the physical emergency and the people who will be concerned with its long-range consequences.

Events which may be commonplace to an adult are easily misinterpreted by a young child.

"I think that we cannot overestimate the importance for management of crisis of the child's capacity for understanding at the time. . . . Helping mothers to understand the great importance of communication from earliest infancy on is a major need."**

Unfortunately, the younger the child, the less able he is to announce his concern or to ask questions. He is also less likely to receive any explanations, because he is considered too young to

understand (see Chapter 2). Encouraging parents to talk to a young child, even at the risk of putting ideas into his head, is a general service which counselors of parents provide.

It is important to keep in mind that crises cannot be avoided, and that they may be constructive rather than traumatic. Through experience, the child learns to handle anxiety, sadness, and anger without resorting to the more pathogenic defenses of denial and projection. Murphy discusses the educational possibilities of crises:

The problem of prevention, then, is one of assessing the external and internal factors in the child's experience of stress and crisis and the child's capacities to deal with it; then finding ways to support the child's efforts towards mastery. This can include both medical, social, and psychological help (giving him usable knowledge and insight where he can use it, as before an operation; comfort in the terms that can help him; support for mastery in his terms; compensatory gratifications that have value for him; opportunities for discharge of tension; help in communicating his experience of stress; doses of challenge, reality testing, and stimulus to give up unconstructive defenses at a pace he can manage; appreciation of his efforts to cope and progress in coping). This can go parallel to management of the environment to prevent the child from becoming overwhelmed by stress with which he cannot cope.*

Primary Prevention in the School Setting

Medical and social agencies intervene on the child's behalf primarily through the parents, by providing substitutes for the parent when necessary, and by supplying the child's basic needs. The institution with the greatest opportunity to work directly with children on a preventive basis is the school, and the implications of this are slowly dawning on mental health practitioners and professional educators. The relationship

---

*Quoted from Gerald Caplan, *Principles of Preventive Psychiatry* (New York: Basic Books, Inc., 1964), p. 53. Reproduced by permission.

**Quoted from Lois B. Murphy, "Preventive Implications of Development in the Pre-School Years," in G. Caplan, ed., *Prevention of Mental Disorders in Children* (New York: Basic Books, Inc., 1961), p. 231, 243. Reproduced by permission.

---

*Murphy, ed. by G. Caplan, *op. cit.*, p. 228.

between intellectual development (the unquestioned province of education) and personality development (the concern of mental health personnel) is well described by Barbara Biber:

In the light of knowledge available to us from the behavioral sciences and the theoretical and applied contribution of clinicians, it is no longer feasible to dichotomize the learning functions (mastery of symbol system, processes of reasoning, judging and problem solving, acquisition and ordering of information, etc.) on the one hand, and the processes of personality formation (self-feeling and identity, relatedness potential, autonomy, integration, creativity, etc.) on the other. It is therefore no longer an open question as to whether or not the school is overextending its function when it concerns itself in personality issues.*

There are two general areas of interest: the *curriculum* and the *teacher*. About the curriculum, Biber writes:

It is assumed that schooling will contribute to ego strength to the extent that learning can be made viable, that learning power can be enhanced by basing curriculum content and method on knowledge of capacity, interests, drives, and motivations of children at successive stages of development.**

Biber also gives examples of educational material which ties in with psychological issues specific to different phases of normal child development:

For example, with preschool children, *origin* is a theme that has basic meaning on a psychodynamic level in terms of the child's highly motivated interest in his own origin. To study "where did the carrots come from?" is not a cold intellectual

inquiry; it interacts with the deeper question: "Where did I come from?"*

In the same fashion, the efforts of the nursery school or kindergarten teacher to teach the concept of similarities and differences—by matching similar things and discovering common attributes on the basis of which things can be classified—overlap with the child's search for sexual identity. The kindergartner wants to know how *all* human beings are the same, how the sexes differ, and how children differ from grown-ups. In all of this, of course, he wants to find his place. The teen-ager's interest in revolutionary periods of history is, similarly, partially fired by his personal rebellion against established authorities. An appreciation of the conflicts and anxieties which belong to normal phases of development can enable the educator to frame formal learning situations which help the youngster to organize some of his feelings into communicable thoughts.

There are some curricula which are explicitly designed to deal with emotional problems. Many schools offer formal sex education, usually in the upper elementary grades. Some parents support this wholeheartedly, feeling that it saves them an embarrassing task; other parents feel it is unwise to talk to ten or eleven-year-olds about sex. Although such courses are only a small part of sex education, school administrators should work to improve this instruction and make it more widely available. Many secondary schools have experimented with courses in "personal adjustment," "family life education," or "human relations" *(Hertzman and Mueller, 1958)*. The spirit is a good one, but it is hard to know how effectively it is executed. Not everyone can teach such a course, or wants to. The teacher must be convinced of its value, and must be care-

---

*Quoted from Barbara Biber, "Integration of Mental Health Principles in the School Setting," in G. Caplan, ed., *Prevention of Mental Disorders in Children*. (New York: Basic Books, Inc., 1961), p. 324. Reproduced by permission.
**ibid., p. 331.

---

*ibid., p. 334.

fully chosen and carefully prepared. It is hard to give official credits for courses of this nature because it is virtually impossible to assign grades to the students. Prestige accrues to these educational offerings only because they are taught effectively.

Another approach to curriculum has been suggested by Ralph Ojemann. In connection with the teaching of the social sciences, he and his co-workers at the State University of Iowa prepared discussion material to help children think about the whys of human behavior—causal thinking rather than judgments of good or bad. The material was introduced at the upper elementary school level, and Ojemann's evaluation indicates that it produced significant differences in certain psychological measurements (1961). Although his postulated connection between a "noncausal orientation" and the development of emotional disturbances sounds plausible, the preventive value of his material remains to be documented. However, the teaching of cause-and-effect relationships, of the relation between evidence and proof and between fact and opinion is intrinsically valuable, whether it is applied to psychology (with a possible subsequent reduction of mental disorder) or to the physical sciences.

Teachers

No curricular innovations can be successful per se; the teacher makes or breaks the material she handles. The role of the teacher is described by Biber as follows:

It is assumed that the teacher–child relationship, through which learning in school is mediated, can contribute toward the maturing of positive feelings toward self and others, deepen the potential for interpersonal relatedness, and increase the flexibility of the adaptive process.*

_____
*ibid., p. 337.

Some educational objectives can be achieved by impersonal fact giving, even by teaching machines, and through reward and punishment meted out as simple conditioning. Attitudes and feelings, however, are modified mainly through social and personal relationships, from which the child absorbs the attitude of an outside person, usually someone of whom he is fond, but sometimes a person of whom he is afraid (see Chapter 3, on identification with the aggressor). Like the parent, the teacher influences the personality of her pupils by the model which she offers for identification. In the presence of the children, she is always on display and can never turn off the teaching which goes on.

Some aspects of the teaching situation are particularly relevant to mental health—for example, the matter of discipline. There must be some control in a classroom and the rules of order are largely established by the teacher. One cannot rely solely on the children's zest for learning or on democratic procedures of self-government. The limits set by the teacher should be clear, consistent, reasonable, and the minimum necessary for group functioning. Even so, there will be infractions—minor crises, actually. A variety of punishments are used: sitting in the hall, being sent to the principal's office, being temporarily banished to a lower grade, having one's knuckles rapped, being paddled, being detained after school, being shown how it feels to be poked or bit, getting extra homework, missing recess, being threatened with exclusion from school, punishment of the whole class when one child has made trouble, sarcasm, and so on. Teachers try to apply some kind of pain (humiliation, physical discomfort, or embarrassment) to extinguish the undesired behavior. Without quarreling with the need to bring the disruptive behavior to an immediate end and restore order, one wonders why teachers make so little use of the relationship to establish positive motivation for future good behavior. It is possible to go on record as being against certain acts and yet go on record as being for the child. Quiet, private inquiry about the why of the misdemeanor probably will not elicit a logical reason from the child, but it will convey the teacher's interest and concern. She can go into partnership with the child against the behavior problem, be it pestering the other children, talking out of turn, restlessness, daydreaming, impudence, or whatever.

It is often said that punishment is necessary in the classroom, not to change the misbehaving child but to discourage the other children from following suit. There is some validity to this argument, but it is a double-edged sword. All people become anxious when they are part of a group of which some member is clearly out of control. At such times it is necessary for someone to assume leadership, but it is important to remember that all the children are reacting to the punishment of the single offender. Teachers are well aware of the demoralizing effect of a problem child, but they often see this as the direct influence of the offending child on the others, without appreciating their own role. If the teacher becomes very angry, punitive, or threatening, or tearful and upset, all the children become vicariously involved. The well-behaved child may become frightened or angry by the teacher's behavior toward the offending child. Even the best-behaved child has some feeling of kinship for the bad child in his midst. Teacher training should include as much exposure to the dynamics of group psychology as to the dynamics of individual psychology.

Another aspect of the teacher's role which has implications for mental health is her handling of individual differences in learning ability. It is natural for her to favor those who respond with enthusiasm and comprehension. The dull pupils are a source of concern and frustration to the conscientious teacher, and she may show this in any number of ways. His classmates will usually ignore the dullard. Most of the students not chosen for the class play, in E. M. Bower's study, for example, were slow learners or were retarded *(1961)*. One solution is to divide the children into classes of supposed homogeneous mental ability, but it is not possible to eliminate gradations of success in any classroom of normal size. A teacher who is genuinely friendly, respectful, and accepting, yet realistic toward her less gifted students will teach the others a great deal about tolerance, understanding of human behavior, empathy, and responsibility for others.

A third aspect of the teacher's role which has direct consequence for mental health is her use of praise and criticism, expressed in words or in grades. Biber expressed the problem as follows:

On the preventive side, there is the important matter of how constructively and objectively the functions of criticism and evaluation are handled, how free they are of the destructive elements of sarcasm and other forms of *ad hominem* humiliation. There is a difficult, technical problem involved: how to evaluate children's work in terms of concrete assessments, using individual capacity as the reference point, and yet satisfy the child's need for evaluations in peer-comparative terms. This is an area of active experimentation, of trying to find methods that will support children's realistic self-perception and evaluation and avoid fixed self-typing.*

Many other examples could be given to show how the teacher affects the child's self-concept, his ability to control himself, and his capacity for understanding others—in other words, his mental health. In view of this, it is remarkable that so few observational studies of teachers have been made. Maternal behavior has been subjected

---

ibid., p. 339.

to close scrutiny (see Chapter 15), and the same techniques could well be employed in the teaching situation, *except* that teacher subjects are hard to find. Most teachers would feel threatened by such microscopic examination, for their training does not emphasize the minutiae of behavior. This is in marked contrast to social work training, in which words, gestures, facial expressions, and tones used in the interview situation are a matter for supervision. One of the few extant classroom studies of teachers' methods of coping with children was done by Kenneth Davidson and S. B. Sarason, both psychologists *(1961)*. Their on-the-job observations raised serious questions about the value of conventional teacher training for preparation for the manifold duties involved in teaching young children in public schools. Preparation for some activities is totally lacking—talking with parents, for example. Sarason, Davidson, and Burton Blatt point out that teachers are expected to talk with parents in order to affect the behavior and performance of the children, but that such conferences are by no means simple *(1962)*. The relationships between parents and teachers are often complicated by unconscious rivalry, defensiveness, misunderstanding, and so on. Part of the effort being made to upgrade the schooling of children of lower socioeconomic levels includes finding new ways to strengthen parental support of the child's education. Communication between teacher and parent is one of these, but the teacher is given little opportunity to observe such interviews or to profit from supervision of the interviews she conducts. Teachers are asked, quite casually, to discharge a function which is accorded a great deal of respect by mental health practitioners (see Chapter 15).

Sarason, Davidson, and Blatt have more general criticisms of the colleges' preparation of teachers. The training is highly verbal, involving extensive reading and formal lectures but a minimum of participation or discovery on the part of the student. We are well aware of the fact that parents bring up their children largely as they were brought up; similarly, teachers teach much as they were taught. This is yet another example of the theorem that some very important learning takes place by identification with the model.

Watching the teacher work reminds one that the school is a complicated social institution. For instance, "teacher-child relations reflect teacher-principal relations as well as teacher personality."[*] The principal sets the tone of the school and determines the values by which his teachers will be judged. He has the unenviable job of juggling rivalries and jealousies, praising and criticizing, encouraging and discouraging, weighing the needs of individual children against those of the group, and relating to the parents, the teachers, the children, the administrators, and the public. His way of handling his problems will be emulated, and will influence the teachers' handling of the children and of their own conflicts of interest.

Specific opportunities for preventive work in the schools arise at certain points of crisis. One which has been investigated with some care is entry into kindergarten. In their study of 46 families, Donald Klein and Ann Ross found that the tension of the first few weeks was manifested by the children in various ways:

1. Physical reactions, such as loss of appetite, fatigue, stomach upsets;
2. Intensification or resumption of previous behaviors such as bedwetting, increase in thumb-sucking, dawdling, etc.;
3. Increased irritability, expressed in hitting out at siblings or other children, uncooperativeness, freshness with parents;
4. Increased dependence on mother;
5. Generalized signs of tension, expressed in such things as "keyed-up" behavior; a "worried" expression, increased

---

[*] *ibid.,* p. 329.

talkativeness or reticence, reluctance to go to school. *(1958, p. 64.)*

The signs of tension were accompanied by signs of growth; the children were growing up at the same time as they showed signs of regression. A particularly interesting part of the study concerned the reactions of the parents. Although the mothers were ashamed to admit it, most experienced an unexpected feeling of loss. All of them had a feeling of anxiety about the child's performance in school: "I've been spending five years doing my job. Now everyone will soon see whether I'm a success or not!" *(1958, p. 66)*. Many expressed conflict and uncertainty about the new triangle formed by teacher, child, and parent. In many ways, the mother is displaced by the teacher (much as the child is displaced by the birth of the siblings). She is ill-informed about what is going on at school, and she must share her authority with a stranger. The following incident illustrates a temporary tangle of differing views.

During a mild skirmish for seats for a television program at home, a quiet, conscientious, five-year-old boy suddenly burst out at his parents. "You don't care about anything," he complained, "you always let me sit cross-legged. You don't care what happens to me." When they asked, he explained that his kindergarten teacher had warned the class that poor sitting posture would "ruin their backs." The boy felt that his parents had been seriously remiss in not warning him about this.

The appreciation of the importance of a good start in school has led to a number of projects. The Sumter Child Study Project was one of the few which was designed to permit an evaluation of the effectiveness of the interventions *(Newton, Brown, and Crumley, 1965)*. All children entering the first grade of six schools were given a check-up in the spring prior to entry. Those entering the three experimental schools received recommendations for increasing their readiness. Summer programs were organized for special groups; parent guidance was offered to others; and a continuing consultation service for parents and teachers was established. Other projects have involved screening of the children for early detection of later problems, particularly in learning *(Fite and Schwartz, 1965)*. Here one can see how thin the line between primary and secondary prevention is. Presumably the screening finds children who are already different. In a sense, they already have some identifiable problems, so that subsequent action is treatment for the existing problems as well as prevention of later problems.

Changing schools is another crisis situation, particularly for the child who is transferring because his family is moving. It is the exceptional child who does not need some extra support from the adults in school to become acclimated. There is some recognition of the strain in changing from elementary to junior high school; in fact, the junior high school was largely designed as a transition between the self-contained elementary school classroom and the impersonal, large high school. In view of the fact that the children are entering a developmental stage no less anxiety-producing for the adolescent and his family than the entry into school ten years earlier, surprisingly little attention has been given to primary prevention in the high school. Considerable attention has been given to the secondary school curriculum, to make it meaningful for *all* children, whether or not they are college-bound. The extension of universal education to 16, 17, or 18 years has forced educators to reconsider the goals of secondary school education, but the extent to which we fall short of our goal is indicated by the number of dropouts. Some authors quote figures as high as 40 per cent

(Lichter et al., 1962), and an Ohio study made in 1962–1963 indicated that one out of seven students who begin the ninth grade drops out before finishing the twelfth *(State of Ohio, 1965)*.

Unfortunately, most of the time of the guidance counselors and psychological consultants in high schools is absorbed by serious problems and emergencies, and little is left for the normal problems of the normal adolescent. There is often a subtle shift in the school's attitude which brings it into opposition with the adolescent. Parents, school, and the law all become concerned with the enforcement of rules and regulations. Publicity about juvenile delinquency heightens the anxiety level of the adult authorities and leads them to try to tighten the reins. One high school junior, commenting on the plethora of rules regarding proper school dress, said "The teenager is in an impossible situation. It doesn't matter what he wears, he still looks like a juvenile delinquent to some people." Teachers who loudly lament the shallowness or amorality of the younger generation should not be assigned to high school teaching. It is not easy to empathize with the smart-alecky adolescent, but educational personnel must be able to recognize that a facade of bravado often hides inner feelings of insecurity. The accumulation of rules and enforcement methods only tempts the adolescent to try to outsmart the grown-ups.

Most adolescents respond well to people who genuinely like, respect, and trust them. In their struggle for emancipation from the family circle, they seek out new models. They are famous for their "crushes." The right teachers can have a profound effect on the adolescent without ever knowing it, because the "cool" adolescent hides his feelings. The psychology of adolescence deserves attention by itself and should not be tacked on as a postscript to courses in child development, and the same can be said about the psychopathology of adolescence. Training of secondary school teachers should include a special course on adolescence, and continuous in-service seminars should be available.

Secondary Prevention

Child Disorders Related to Adult Disorders

What may be secondary prevention for the child may be primary prevention for the adult he will become. Patricia O'Neal and Lee Robins studied the adjustment, 30 years later, of a large group of children seen in a court child guidance clinic, and found significantly more major psychiatric disability than in a control group drawn from the same schools. Only 21 per cent of those who had been child patients, as compared with 60 per cent of the control subjects, were free of psychiatric disease *(1958)*. This may seem to contradict the findings of McFarlane, Allen, and Honzik, which were cited earlier, but the difference can be explained by the original selection of subjects. Careful study of unselected children uncovers problems which are not highly visible and which resolve themselves; but those children whose problems are so extensive, chronic, and serious that they are referred to a child guidance clinic run a high risk of becoming mentally ill adults.

There is also an impressive array of studies indicating the relationship between academic achievement and later adjustment. When E. Ginzberg *et al.* studied the ineffective soldier in World War II, they found that the lower the educational level, the higher the prevalence of emotional disorders. Ginzberg described the escalating effect of poor achievement on mental health as follows: "a disturbed childhood is likely to be reflected in learning difficulties; children who do poorly in school are likely to develop emotional problems" *(1959, p. 118).*

The Dilemma of Early Detection

Experts argue for early case findings, on the premise that the earlier treatment starts, the briefer and more effective secondary prevention will be *(Caplan, 1964).* This involves using the mass screening procedures mentioned at the beginning of this chapter. Such procedures pick up children who have visible problems, and they imply that the problems will continue or will lead to others at least equally serious.

In the author's opinion, early detection can be dangerous. Without treatment, it can lead to a self-fulfilling prophecy. If, during a project to identify mild mental retardation, one informed the parents that they have a retarded child, but then dismissed them to raise the child without further help, one would be doing more harm than good *(Oppenheimer, 1965).* Alerting parents or teachers to possible future difficulties (emotional or intellectual) naturally increases their anxiety and this will reduce their effectiveness unless they are given some direction. In a project designed to predict reading difficulties, the investigators instituted special educational instruction and parent counseling *(Fite and Schwartz, 1965).* Such efforts at treatment need not interfere with the scientific goal of checking on the predictive validity of the original screening techniques if a control group is anonymous and untreated. Without any promise of treatment, early diagnosis may only compound the problem and prove to be a curse in disguise.

Referral for Diagnosis

Granted that the largest majority of disturbed children can be identified early by their teachers, this is only a first step—usually the first step in the referral of the child for individual study. Such study may be conducted either by the school or an outside agency. The diagnostic process was discussed in Chapter 4 from the viewpoint of the individual; in this chapter, diagnosis will be discussed in the context of the efficient use of professional time and its value to the referring person.

The *First National Report* on patients in mental health clinics indicated that the admission rate of children is less than 1 per cent of the population *(Bahn and Norman, 1959).* Every clinic must have a waiting list *(Gordon, 1965)* or close its intake periodically for weeks or months. There is an ever-widening gap between the number of applications for help and the staff time available, and disappointed pediatricians, teachers, and parents are likely to turn their backs on the community clinics when no help is forthcoming. This is one reason to take a hard look at the use of professional time. In the child guidance clinic, diagnosis consumes 15 to 20 hours of staff time, and it is questionable that it is helpful to the patient:

A clinic which in most instances limits itself to two choices—"psychotherapy," or, rather "psychotherapy waiting list," and "rejection," or, euphemistically, "referral to another agency"—could save a great deal of staff time usually devoted to analyzing the intricacies of the patient's history, psychic structure, personal and social relationships, and the like. Although the eliciting and recording of such details may give the staff a satisfying sense of professional accomplishment, they do the patient no good. If he is put on the treatment waiting list, the psychotherapist who commences the treatment a year or two later rarely pays much attention to the record; and, if the patient is accepted by another agency, the whole diagnostic process will probably be repeated anyway.*

This criticism does not negate the value of the complete diagnostic study, with a complete psychosocial history

---

*Caplan, *op. cit.,* p. 96.

and a battery of psychological tests, but it suggests that diagnosis should be related to disposition. If one is ready to begin treatment, the more complete and recent the diagnostic study, the better. Since most child guidance clinics are also professional training grounds, complete studies and conferences of the entire staff are educationally important. But the educational value is soon exhausted unless there is a follow-up of the predictions made at the time of the diagnosis. Only one-fourth of the cases studied are treated *(Bahn and Norman, 1959)*, so the follow-up on the other cases must be in the form of brief contacts with parents and teachers. If the diagnostic process is detached from disposition and treatment (as is often the case for the psychologist on the team), there is little further for him to learn after the first dozen or so cases. When he is beyond the initial practice phase, the psychologist should ask himself: What questions am I trying to answer with this test? What difference can the answers make for the patient? Am I doing this for myself and, if so, will it really increase my fund of knowledge and understanding?

Partly because of the waiting lists at community clinics, there has been a trend toward establishing mental hygiene clinics and diagnostic facilities within the school system. It was hoped that this would be more efficient, and that better communication would result. However, the psychological diagnosis and consultation offered by the schools has also been subjected to considerable criticism:

It has been said that school psychologists spend 90 per cent of their time diagnosing problems and 10 per cent of their time doing something about them. Whether or not this accurately describes the activity of any given school psychologist, there is no gainsaying that the language of the typical psychological report made after studying a child usually contains dynamic descriptive and diagnostic information—but very few specific sug-

gestions for follow-up ideas directed to the teacher who must continue to carry on with the education of the child under study. And summary recommendations contained in the report are often in the "further information" or "further diagnosis" category. *(Lambert, 1964, p. 36.)*

School psychologists are likely to fall into one of two categories: those who are organically minded and want further neurological examination to check on "minimal brain damage," and those who are psychoanalytically minded and want psychiatric consultation or projective tests to check on "passive aggressive tendencies" or "underlying homosexual trends." Again, we are on the horns of a dilemma: on the one hand, we train psychologists to be cautious and thorough, especially with regard to possible medical complications; on the other hand, we want them to be able to make independent decisions.

Translating diagnostic information into useful recommendations is probably an art. Here, the skills and training of social work have a major contribution to make, but of all the mental health professionals, the social workers are perhaps in shortest supply and very scarce in school situations. Rather than hopelessly trying to fill all the positions themselves, social workers should be employed as supervisors and consultants in the very tricky business of interviewing and advising parents.

With respect to the help given to teachers, Ralph Ojemann remarks that "much of the resistance appearing in work with teachers arose from the frustrations a teacher feels when he learns about a child's needs but does not see how these can be met under classroom conditions" *(1961, p. 388)*. In some respects, teacher guidance is like parent guidance. One hopes to explain the child's behavior in a way that helps the parent, or the teacher, to empathize *and* to take constructive action. The action required may be educational—that is, teaching the child that certain behavior is no longer acceptable and helping him to stop gradually; it may be reassuring—that is giving the child a sense of security which will decrease the bad behavior which stems from his anxiety; and it may be interpretive—that is, explaining or clarifying some area of confusion for the child. Other possible actions include forms of environmental manipulation: arranging special activities or special help, changing schedule or classes, and so on. Modifications of the environment are the concrete suggestions that teachers expect, but much guidance should be devoted to improving communication with the child. Both parents and teachers consistently underestimate the value of listening, and the power of well-chosen, well-spoken, and well-timed words.

Another purpose of the interpretation of the diagnosis is to relieve some of the anxiety and guilt felt by the parent or the teacher. In Chapter 4, we discussed the guilt of parents. In their description of an observational seminar for education students, Sarason, Davidson, and Blatt discuss a similar phenomenon in teachers:

A third reason for structuring the seminar as we did had to do with the self-attitudes of teachers, more specifically, the marked tendency among teachers to view themselves in their professional role in a derogatory manner. There are many reasons for such devaluation, but one of the most important is based on the implicit assumption that the teacher should be adequate, or equally effective, with all children and all problems in her class. In our opinion, this is as presumptuous an expectation as one could make and, in our experience, is not made for any other profession. It is difficult, and frequently impossible, for a teacher to say—to other teachers, administrators, and lay people—that there are children and problems to which she feels inadequate and ineffective. Aside from contributing to an unhealthy professional attitude, this situation frequently inhibits the teacher from seeking

the kind of consultative help she needs. *(1962, p. 80.)*

A lot of attention is given to helping children recognize the limits of their knowledge and competencies so that they can say, "I don't know," without shame. We try to teach children that there is nothing wrong in not knowing, and that the admission of ignorance is a first step in learning. At the same time there is some mystique about the teacher. She is supposed to know everything, and many a teacher, at all levels of education, is trapped into trying to live up to this fanciful illusion.

Treatment Priorities

Only a minority of the children referred will be treated. To some extent, the selection of patients depends on the competencies and interests of the therapist, which is eminently sensible. To some extent, it depends on the known treatability of the condition. Especially in conditions in which anxiety is a prominent symptom (e.g., school phobia), there is a striking relationship between remission of the acute symptoms and the promptness with which treatment is begun *(Waldfogel and Gardner, 1961)*. Treatment of phobias proceeds much more quickly and surely than that of learning disorders, for instance. Some referrals should be put ahead of other cases which require more involved and prolonged treatment, but it is more common to refer the seriously and chronically disturbed children first, because of the reality problems they create and because there is no longer any question about the permanence of their problems.

Eisenberg and Ernest Gruenberg made a strong case for determining treatment priorities on the basis of information regarding treatability with current methods, as opposed to value judgments:

To take an outstanding example, it is not uncommon for child guidance clinics to have an over-all policy of refusing treatment to brain-damaged or mentally defective children. Yet the implication of present information is that perhaps more can be offered certain brain-damaged or defective children than bright but severely neurotic or psychotic children. This is not to suggest that treatment be refused the latter group but that priority for treatment be assigned on the basis of careful review of what treatment can contribute to community health rather than biases against certain clinical entities or predilections for others. *(1961, p. 363.)*

Educational Treatment

Schools are, to an ever-increasing extent, being required to provide appropriate education for all children regardless of their mental, physical, or emotional disability. In many states, the education laws have been amended to qualify emotionally disturbed children for such special services as transportation, home instruction, and special classes, which are provided other handicapped children. The educator's first thought is often to establish special classes. This makes the children more visible and makes it easier to obtain financial support.

Segregation into special classes creates problems of stigmatization, group contagion, and reintegration, however. Many emotionally disturbed children would profit from a less total measure. Mortimer Schiffer has described a different program, involving group therapy once a week, utilizing the activity group techniques developed by Slavson (see Chapter 15), with teachers serving as group leaders *(1958)*. N. M. Prentice and Bessie Sperry have developed techniques for therapeutically oriented tutoring of children with learning inhibitions. They discuss the differences between a tutor and a therapist, and the limitations of having only a tutor whose help is based on the hypothesis of neurological and pedagogical etiologies or only a therapist whose help is based on the hypothesis that unconscious conflicts need to be made conscious (see Chapter 9). The potentialities of therapeutic tutoring of children with psychogenic learning problems have hardly been scratched, perhaps because of the disdain for treating just a symptom. Therapeutic tutors would need to have special training and supervision, but the technique sounds like one which could be developed almost like speech therapy.

Tertiary Prevention

Tertiary prevention is based on the improbability of total cure, and is an attempt to find ways to improve the person's ability to function. Gerald Caplan contrasts treatment attitudes in the United States with those prevailing in Europe, remarking on the "unconquerable optimism of our culture, which maintains that no problem is impossible if we devote sufficient time, energy, and intelligence to its solution."[*] The difference is particularly marked in the treatment goals set for severely neurotic patients or those with chronic personality disorders. The European psychiatrist is content to terminate the treatment when the patient returns to his pre-morbid condition, without attempting any radical reconstitution of his personality. In the United States, treatment of such patients is likely to be prolonged in pursuit of the ephemeral goal of complete mental health.

The same attitude is demonstrated in the treatment of children. Except when the child is mentally retarded or has organic brain damage, therapists are likely to expect total cure and to be intolerant of residual symptoms. The case of Bobby, quoted in Chapter 11, is an example: At the age of four, Bobby had no speech, would not meet another person's eye, and could neither participate in a group nor relate to an individual. Four years later, he was speaking well, was cooperating in a

---

[*]Caplan, *op. cit.*, p. 109.

special class program, and was able to play or work with someone, although under direction. He continued to be a proficient reader. Someone who had never before known Bobby observed him in class, described him as "socially withdrawn," and referred him for psychiatric study—another 15 hours of professional time! True, Bobby was far from normal. He looked very different from the other children in his special class. But there was a failure to appreciate the strides he had made and a reluctance to accept the probable limitations of treatment.

One of the essential ingredients of a sound preventive program is humility, a recognition of our limitations. In physical rehabilitation, some disability often remains. Even when it is not apparent, the patient may be more susceptible than others to a recurrence of, for instance, a heart attack, tuberculosis, cancer, and so on. Somehow, people expect more from psychological treatment than they do from physical treatment. If the patient continues to have some difficulties or needs treatment again, the original treatment is regarded as a failure. Mental health professionals are sometimes guilty of a narcissistic overevaluation of treatability. Each worker (or each agency) secretly believes that his methods are better, and he is intrigued by the apparent failure of someone else. This unconscious competitiveness may in part explain the results of a recent survey of mental health agencies, which revealed that a significant proportion of staff time was taken up by useless diagnostic investigations of patients who shuttled back and forth between them *(Ryan, 1962)*. The other reason, of course, is the disappointment of the patients or their families when no miracle cure has been achieved. Perhaps if agencies were more realistic about what patients could expect, some of this shopping could be eliminated. Some of the shuttling, however, is what

Caplan calls "dumping" (although professionals call it "referral"):

Because of an inevitable shortage of resources, all community agencies are likely to feel over-burdened. This leads to a natural tendency to "dump" particularly troublesome patients. Into that category often fall the mentally disordered, especially those with chronic problems. "Dumping" usually involves categorizing the patient or client as unsuited for care in one's own agency and then referring him to another agency and forgetting about him. [*]

Needless to say, troublesome patients are troublesome wherever they go. Child care agencies are likely to dump children with impossible parents by sending them to a family agency. The parents are miffed because, in their view, the child was the one with the problem, and the family agency inherits an unwilling and resentful patient. Referral is sometimes tantamount to rejection. These problem families are likely to take up a disproportionate amount of the total time available in the community, to the satisfaction of no one. If one agency accepted responsibility for them, and other agencies consistently referred them back to this agency, there would be some continuity of support for the family and less wasted time.

Treatment of children with probably permanent handicaps offers the possibility of primary prevention elsewhere within the family. A problem child affects his parents and siblings, whether he remains at home or not. All too often, the parents' concern for the disabled child and their bewilderment and depression lead them to neglect the others in the home. The normal children may bear the brunt of the parents' frustrations or be asked to carry too heavy a load of responsibility. The parents find it hard to discuss the

---

[*]Caplan, *op. cit.*, p. 153.

situation with their other children or to protect their rights against the overwhelming needs of the seriously disturbed or limited child. On the other hand, placement creates guilt and anxiety in the other children (see Chapter 16). Treatment of the handicapped child should be planned in terms of the whole family, and due consideration should be given the feelings and basic needs of all.

Philosophical Issues in Prevention

Evaluation and Research

Those who are engaged in applied psychology are repeatedly asked to prove their case, and prevention programs are no exception. Starry-eyed, utopian programs which set out to "eliminate mental illness" are doomed to failure. Prevention is *not* possible if one defines the goal as the eradication of all social, mental, and emotional handicaps. There are too many diverse disorders in this basket. Prevention *is* possible if one attacks specific conditions; and the more it resembles a physical disease, the more likely it is that the condition can be prevented in the forseeable future. For example, it is easy to imagine a scientific breakthrough which would pinpoint the cause of the failure of fusion which results in the extra chromosome responsible for Mongolism (Down's syndrome). The consequent mental retardation is the direct result of the biology of the individual; there is little, if any, relationship to environmental factors. However, most mental retardation has no known organic etiology. The retarded are simply the bottom of the heap, so far below average that they have little chance to compete. This disadvantage creates secondary problems—for the individual, his family, and society. When the retardation is mild, the incompetence is based on the prevailing societal norm rather than on biological fact. As society raises its standards, individuals who could previously have performed adequately become deficient. Society is past the point where it can operate on the Darwinian principle of survival of the fittest, and we must assume responsibility for the least of our members.

Other examples of the differences in preventability can be cited. For instance, it is conceivable that childhood psychosis will become preventable as research into its causation proceeds. Psychosis is detectable at an early age; it is an extreme deviation from normal; it is not outgrown. The etiological factors, although they may depend on the host as well as on the environment, should become equally identifiable. We know something about the origins of psychoneurosis, and if timely intervention at crucial points of development and crisis were available, most of the psychoneurotic disorders could probably be prevented. In contrast, one cannot be very optimistic about learning disorders or juvenile delinquency. As we ask more and more children to learn more and more, we will find increasing numbers who resist or fall by the wayside. The increase in learning problems arises from the increasing ambitiousness of our educational institutions. Some teen-age problem children, such as dropouts and runaways, were not problem children 50 years ago, when most 16-year-olds left home and went to work. The extension of the period of compulsory education may elevate the citizenry in general, but it prolongs the dependency of the adolescent and delays his emancipation. And now we are hearing about the college dropout. Only in an advanced society could there be legitimate anxiety about them.

Some of the same reasoning can be applied to juvenile delinquency. In Chapter 12, we pointed out that there is more juvenile delinquency in the more industrialized, so-called civilized societies. There are more laws, better enforcement, better records, and fewer direct action outlets for the adolescent. A juvenile delinquency program should not be evaluated in terms of over-all court statistics or police arrests, but rather in terms of reduction of specific crimes—particularly the more serious offenses against persons.

Evaluation and research cannot be delegated to a research team which comes in from the outside. Experts in research design, statistical methods, and evaluation techniques are extremely helpful, but the task of evaluation belongs as much to the practitioner as to the researcher. Research is a state of mind, briefly described as objective, but many times, in order to sell a program to the public, the professional promises too much. There is a danger of a backswing when the public is disappointed, but perhaps greater danger lies in the self-delusion of the practitioner. If he has committed himself to a particular stand, he may have fenced himself in so that he is no longer able to learn from his experience.

Professional Roles in Prevention

Although the controversy about the medical versus social nature of mental disorder continues (*Ward, AMA Position, 1965; Albee, 1965*), its prevention is unquestionably everyone's domain. There is no place for territorial struggles under the euphemism of "delineation of professional roles." Questions about hierarchical relationships among the psychiatrists, pediatricians, clinical psychologists, social workers, educators, and clergy should not be allowed to occupy important time and energy. There is a desperate need for the coalescence of all their efforts.

The problem of coordinating these efforts and of finding better ways to communicate is the important issue in prevention. It is the author's opinion that there should be more sharing of pre-professional training, in the hope that students who learn together may be able to work together. This is not to suggest a new mental health profession, but rather that professional schools let down the structural barriers and encourage their students to take courses outside their own field. This is different from inviting outside lecturers in to the professional schools to expose the student to other points of view. It would be more useful if medical students, psychology students, and speech, social work, and education students were to take some courses in common and share a basic core of knowledge. Obviously, such general courses would not replace their specific professional training, but they would create more mutual respect. Often students are unaware that students in another field are also taught about human behavior. At the outset of this text, we discussed some competing theories and emphasized the great need for the integration of knowledge. The dangers of professionocentrism are as great, or greater, in practice as they are in theory.

Decisions for the Individual Mental Health Professional

The only commodity which the mental health professional has to market is his time, and how he is to use it most effectively is a question for the individual as well as for the agency which employs him. Teaching, research, consultation, supervision, writing, reading, community organization, diagnosis, and treatment all vie for one's time.

One of the knottiest problems is the selection of patients for service. Clinics and practitioners have been sharply castigated for selecting only those who are most motivated and perhaps the least disturbed. Rema Lapouse has asserted that the greatest proportion of the treatment time of psychiatrists goes to the healthiest patients (*1965*). On the other hand, it would be absurd to think that we can treat everyone. Each worker selects those patients whom he understands and with whom he can reasonably expect to have some success.

Ideally, each practitioner can give a range of treatment, from intensive, long-term therapy to supportive hand-holding. If he restricts himself to a single type of practice, he should be knowledgeable about and respectful of other methods. Nor should he apologize for realizing his limitations; one who fancies himself the rescuer of all troubled mankind will waste a good deal of time and frustrate himself in the end.

The mental health practitioner is faced with another recurring problem: He must find some middle ground between critical, objective self-evaluation and the self-assurance he needs to make decisions and to instill confidence in others. Repeatedly, he must make recommendations when his knowledge is incomplete; he has to recognize this and yet decide that his knowledge is sufficient for the particular recommendation. If a case is ambiguous, he must still be able to take a position, but he must also be able to change it later when new facts become available.

Public Resistance

We have described the dilemmas and soul-searching of the individual mental health professional. Programs aimed at improving mental health are only as good as the people who operate them. People and programs, however, need the help of tremendously increased public support. There are foci of resistance against mental health in public opinion which should be counteracted with public education. Much of the resistance against mental health activities takes one or another of the following forms.

Denial. Some people simply deny the size of the mental health problem. They dismiss the figures quoted by professional persons as biased estimates, almost suggesting that the professional persons themselves were creating a problem by calling attention to it.

Despair. At the other extreme, some people feel that the problem is so overwhelming, nothing can be done and there is no use trying. The control of such common afflictions as smallpox and bubonic plague must have appeared equally fanciful to the average person living·in the Middle Ages.

Simple Solutions. The general public offers many simple solutions such as old-fashioned discipline, returning the patient to the home, full employment, more education, and so on. In most cases, there is some value to the proposed solution, but the danger remains that one will be disappointed when no panacea emerges.

Scientific Scepticism. Some intellectual persons complain that the mental health professions are not scientific enough and that they lack sufficient knowledge and proof of their theories. One can agree in part with this view, but knowledge is acquired through doing; without activity there can be no advances in science or practice.

Political Fears. Since many of the current mental health programs are intimately involved with government agencies, some persons have been fearful lest they lead to a welfare state. To date, the federal government has been more responsive to these problems than local governments, but this need not be the case. When everyone feels an equal involvement, a great variety of solutions should emerge.

The promotion of mental health is the task of our age and the key may be found in services to our children. All who undertake to treat and to prevent mental disturbance—whether as individuals, professions, or agencies—must have opinions on which to base constructive action without allowing their positions to become congealed. The knowledge which we now have about child development, normal and pathological, should be more widely disseminated and more effectively utilized. Information from all sources should be pooled in a search for areas of agreement and methods to settle basic differences.

The quickening of interest in mental health stimulated by the federal legislation of the Kennedy and Johnson administrations must be kept alive. The new social concepts and patterns of comprehensive care suggested therein have a great deal to offer, but there is a danger that the needs of children will continue to be slighted in favor of the adult patient. In a speech given in February, 1965, to the Conference for Planning Comprehensive Community Mental Health Services, Nicholas Hobbs, President-Elect of the American Psychological Association, had this to say:

The great, persistent, and inexplicable neglect in the planning of community mental health programs is of children. In the eleven model programs studied, the editors conclude: "hardly a beginning has been made in providing children's services adequate to the need . . ."

Rationales and technologies for working with children are seriously underdeveloped . . .

I would urge that fully 50 per cent of funds, facilities, and personnel be invested in programs for people under the age of 20. A 75 per cent allocation would be more far-sighted but it is possibly politically inexpedient. Programs should concentrate on children, children and their parents, children and their teachers, and children and their communities.

We must have an array of services for emotionally disturbed children and adolescents, to include: consultation for teachers, welfare workers, and parents; special classes in public schools; daycare centers; residential schools such as those in project Re-Ed; short-term and long-term camping programs; programs in churches and community centers and for neighborhood playgrounds; intensive diagnostic and treatment centers in settings that show that the designers have considered the needs and interests of growing children; and, unhappily, we shall need places for children who cannot respond to our best efforts to help them.[*]

References For Chapter 17

Albee, George W., "Needed: A Conceptual Breakthrough," Chapter prepared for a book to be published under the auspices of the California Medical and Educational Research Foundation, 1965.

Allen, Frederick H., *Positive Aspects of Child Psychiatry*. New York: W. W. Norton & Company, Inc., 1963.

Arnstein, Helen S., "When A Parent Is Mentally Ill: What to say to the Child." New York: Child Study Association, 1960.

Bahn, A. K. and V. B. Norman, *First National Report on Patients of Mental Health Clinics*, Public Health Reports, LXXIV (1959), 943–56. United States Public Health Service, United States Government Printing Office, Washington, D.C., 1959.

Biber, Barbara, "Integration of Mental Health Principles in the School Setting," in G. Caplan, *Prevention of Mental Disorders in Children*. New York: Basic Books, Inc., 1961, pp. 323–52.

Bower, E. M., *Early Identification of Emotionally Handicapped Children in School*. Springfield, Ill.: Charles C Thomas, Publisher, 1960.

——, "Primary Prevention of Mental and Emotional Disorders," *American Journal of Orthopsychiatry*, XXXIII (1963), 823–32.

——, "Primary Prevention in a School Setting," in G. Caplan, *Prevention of Mental Disorders in Children*. New York: Basic Books, Inc., 1961, pp. 353–78.

——, P. J. Tashnovian, and C. A. Larson, "A Process for Early Identification of Emotionally Disturbed Children," *Bulletin of the California State Department of Education*, XXVII, No. 6 (1958).

Caplan, Gerald, "Patterns of Parental Response to the Crisis of Premature Birth: A Preliminary Approach to Modifying Mental

---

[*]Quoted from Nicholas Hobbs, "Conference for Planning Comprehensive Community Mental Health Services—Comments." Paper presented to the Conference for Planning Comprehensive Community Mental Health Services, February 18, 1965, Washington, D.C. Reproduced by permission.

Health Outcome," *Psychiatry,* XXIII (1960), 365–74.

———, *Principles of Preventive Psychiatry.* New York: Basic Books, Inc., 1964.

———, ed., *Prevention of Mental Disorders in Children.* New York: Basic Books, Inc., 1961.

Clark, Kenneth B., *How to Protect Children Against Prejudice.* New York: Child Study Association, 1957.

Coles, Robert, "Psychiatrists and the Poor," *Atlantic Monthly,* CCXIV, No. 1 (July, 1964), 102–06.

Davidson, Kenneth S. and S. B. Sarason, "Test Anxiety and Classroom Observations," *Child Development,* XXXII (1961), 199–210.

Dingle, John H., George F. Badger, and William S. Jordan, Jr., *Illness in the Home: A Study of 25,000 Illnesses in a Group of Cleveland Families.* Cleveland: Western Reserve University Press, 1964.

Eisenberg, Leon, "Possibilities for a Preventive Psychiatry," *Pediatrics,* XXX (1962 *a*), 815–29.

———, "The Sins of the Fathers: Urban Decay and Social Pathology," *American Journal of Orthopsychiatry,* XXXII (1962 *b*), 5–17.

———, and Ernest M. Gruenberg, "The Current Status of Secondary Prevention in Child Psychiatry," *American Journal of Orthopsychiatry,* XXXI (1961), 355–68.

Fite, June H. and Louise A. Schwartz, "Screening Culturally Disadvantaged First Grade Children for Potential Reading Difficulties Due to Constitutional Factors: A Preliminary Report." Paper presented at the American Orthopsychiatric Association, Annual Meeting, New York, March, 1965.

Fitz–Simons, Marion J., "The Predictive Value of Teachers' Referrals," in M. Krugman, *Orthopsychiatry and the School.* New York: American Orthopsychiatric Association, 1958.

Ginzberg, E. *et al., The Ineffective Soldier: Lessons for Management and the Nation.* New York: Columbia University Press, 1959.

Gordon, Sol, "Are We Seeing the Right Patients? Child Guidance Intake: The Sacred Cow," *American Journal of Orthopsychiatry,* XXXV (1965), 131–37.

Hertzman, Jack and Margaret L. Mueller, "The Adolescent in the School Group," in M. Krugman, *Orthopsychiatry and the School.* New York: American Orthopsychiatric Association, 1958.

Hobbs, Nicholas, "Conference for Planning Comprehensive Community Health Services —Comments." Paper presented to the Conference for Planning Comprehensive Community Health Services, February, 1965, Washington, D.C.

Hollingshead, A. B. and F. C. Redlich, *Social Class and Mental Illness: A Community Study.* New York: John Wiley & Sons, Inc., 1958.

Kallman, F. J., *The Genetics of Schizophrenia.* Locust Valley, N.Y.: J. J. Augustin Publisher, 1938.

Kaplan, D. M. and E. A. Mason, "Maternal Reactions to Premature Birth Viewed as an Acute Emotional Disorder," *American Journal of Orthopsychiatry,* XXX (1960), 539–52.

Klein, Donald C. and Ann Ross, "Kindergarten Entry: A Study of Role Transition," in M. Krugman, *Orthopsychiatry and the School.* New York: American Orthopsychiatric Association, 1958.

Knobloch, H., R. Rider, and P. Harper, "Neuropsychiatric Sequelae of Prematurity," *Journal of the American Medical Association,* CLXI (1956), 581–85.

Kubie, L. S., "The Future of Preventive Psychiatry," *Mental Hygiene News,* XXIV (April, 1948), 1–7.

Krugman, Morris, ed., *Orthopsychiatry and the School.* New York: American Orthopsychiatric Association, 1958.

Lambert, Nadine M., "Applications of the Taxonomy of 'Strens' in Specific School Situations," in *The Protection and Promotion of Mental Health in Schools.* Mental Health Monograph, No. 5, United States Department of Health, Education and Welfare, Washington, D.C.: Government Printing Office, 1964.

Lapouse, Rema, "Who is Sick?" *American Journal of Orthopsychiatry,* XXXV (1965), 138–44.

Lichter, S. *et al., The Drop-Outs.* New York: Free Press of Glencoe, Inc., 1962.

Lindemann, Erich "Symptomatology and Management of Acute Grief," *American Journal of Psychiatry,* CI (1944), 141–48.

MacFarlane, J. W., L. Allen, and M. Honzik, *A Developmental Study of the Behavior Problems of Normal Children between Twenty-one Months and Fourteen Years.* Berkeley, Calif.: University of California Press, 1954.

Murphy, Lois B., "Preventive Implications of Development in the Pre-School Years," in G. Caplan, *Prevention of Mental Disorders in Children*. New York: Basic Books, Inc., 1961, pp. 218–48.

National Association for Mental Health, *1964 Fact Sheet: Facts about Mental Illness*. New York: National Association for Mental Health, 1964.

National Committee for Mental Hygiene, *Mental Hygiene Bulletin*, IX, Nos. 1, 2 (1931).

Newton, M. R., Racine D. Brown, and James Crumley, "Crisis Intervention in Preschool and Early School Years: The Sumter Child Study Project." Paper presented at the American Orthopsychiatric Association, Annual Meeting, New York, March, 1965.

Ojemann, Ralph H., "Investigation of the Effects of Teaching Understanding and Appreciation of Behavior Dynamics," in G. Caplan, *Prevention of Mental Disorders in Children*. New York: Basic Books, Inc., 1961, pp. 378–97.

O'Neal, Patricia and Lee N. Robins, "The Relation of Childhood Behavior Problems in Adult Psychiatric Status," *American Journal of Psychiatry*, CXIV (1958), 961–69.

Oppenheimer, Sonya *et al.*, "Prevalence of Mental Retardation in a Pediatric Out-Patient Clinic Population," *Pediatrics*, XXXVI (1965), 922–29.

Prentice, N. M. and Bessie M. Sperry, "Therapeutically Oriented Tutoring of Children with Primary Neurotic Learning Inhibitions," *American Journal of Orthopsychiatry*, XXXV (1965), 521–30.

Public Law 88–164. "Mental Retardation Facilities and Community Mental Health Centers Construction Act of 1963," *United States Statutes at Large*, LXXVII (1963), 282–99. Washington, D.C.: United States Government Printing Office.

Ryan, W., Report of the Boston Mental Health Survey to the Advisory and Steering Committees. Sponsored by the Massachusetts Association for Mental Health, Massachusetts Department of Mental Health, Division of Mental Hygiene and the United Community Services of Metropolitan Boston. Boston: 1962.

Sarason, Seymour B., Kenneth Davidson, and Burton Blatt, *The Preparation of Teachers: An Unstudied Problem in Education*. New York: John Wiley & Sons, Inc., 1962.

Schiffer, Mortimer, "The Therapeutic Group in the Public Elementary School," in M. Krugman, *Orthopsychiatry and the School*. New York: American Orthopsychiatric Association, 1958.

Srole, L. *et al.*, *Mental Health in the Metropolis: The Midtown Manhattan Study*, Vol. I. New York: McGraw-Hill Book Company, 1962.

State of Ohio Comprehensive Mental Health Planning Project, *Emotionally Disturbed Children*, Staff Report, No. 5. Columbus, Ohio: Department of Special Education, 1965.

Sussex, James N., Frances Gassman, and S. C. Raffel, "Adjustment of Children with Psychotic Mothers in the Home," *American Journal of Orthopsychiatry*, XXXIII (1963), 849–54.

Szasz, T. S., *The Myth of Mental Illness: Foundations of a Theory of Personal Conduct*. New York: Paul B. Hoeber, Inc., 1961.

Waldfogel, Samuel and George E. Gardner, "Intervention in Crises as a Method of Primary Prevention," in G. Caplan, *Prevention of Mental Disorders in Children*. New York: Basic Books, Inc., 1961, pp. 307–22.

Ward, Donovan F., "AMA Position: American Medicine's Stake in Expanded Mental Health." *Psychiatric Spectator*, II, No. 2 (1965), Hanover, N. J.: Sandoz Pharmaceuticals. A paper presented at the American Psychiatric Association Conference, February, 1965.

Welfare Planning Council, Los Angeles Region, *The Mental Health Survey of Los Angeles County: 1957–1959*. Los Angeles: State of California, Department of Mental Hygiene, 1960, pp. 307–14.

Wortis, Helen and Alfred Freedman, "The Contributions of Social Environment to the Development of Premature Children," *American Journal of Orthopsychiatry*, XXXV (1965), 57–68.

NAME INDEX

Abraham, Karl, 103, 126
Abrahamsen, D., 467, 481
Abt, L. E., 83
Ack, M., 335, 336, 362
Ackerman, N., 387, 391, 392, 394–95, 406, 439, 440, 451
Ackerson, L., 92, 98
Actus, W. D., 206, 224
Adler, Alfred, 7, 16
Aichhorn, A., 323, 328
Albee, G., 261, 294, 397, 406, 486, 504, 506
Aldrich, C., 102, 126
Alexander, Franz, 352, 353, 362–64
Alexander, I. E., 164, 367
Allen, Doris, 81, 83
Allen, Frederick, 310, 311, 373–77, 384, 406, 485, 506
Allen, L., 84, 99, 127, 485, 507
Allerhand, Melvin, 477, 478, 480, 481
Allinsmith, Wesley, 58, 66
Allport, Gordon, 202, 224, 451
Alpert, Augusta, 477, 481
Alpert, Richard, 224
Alt, Herschel, 470, 471, 474, 475, 477, 480, 481
Anderson, Joan E., 414, 452
Anderson, L., 152, 161
Andry, R. G., 426, 452
Angelino, H., 66
Ansberry, M., 165
Anthony, E. J., 81, 83
Appell, G., 422, 452, 453
Arnstein, H. S., 490, 506
Arthur, Bettie, 157, 161, 360, 363
Arthur, Helen, 381, 406
Ashley-Montagu, M. F., 356, 363
Atkin, E., 304, 330
Aubrey, J., 422, 452
Auerbach, Aline, 416, 452
Axline, Virginia, 376, 377, 406

Babcock, H., 156, 161
Babinski, J., 245, 257
Badger, G., 484, 507
Bagby, E., 235, 236, 257
Bahn, A. K., 498, 499, 506
Bailey, Percival, 280, 292

Bain, Katherine, 432, 452
Baker, C. T., 212, 226
Baldwin, A. L., 429, 452
Baller, W. R., 122, 126, 184, 196
Bandura, A., 315, 317, 318, 326, 328
Barbara, D., 137, 161
Barker, R. G., 342, 363
Barnes, M. J., 417, 452
Barrett, Henry O., 206, 224
Baruch, Dorothy, 376, 406, 419, 452
Baum, Helen, 464, 481
Baumgartner, Bernice B., 182, 196
Bayley, Nancy, 422, 455
Beck, H. S., 157, 159, 161
Beck, S. J., 80, 83
Beers, Clifford, 370, 406
Behrens, M. L., 428, 452
Beiser, H. R., 393, 394, 408
Bell, R. Q., 430, 455
Bellak, L., 81, 83, 261, 292
Bellak, S. S., 81, 83
Beller, E. K., 76, 77, 83, 88, 89, 91, 92, 98, 100, 114, 126
Belmont, L., 152, 161
Bender, Lauretta, 81, 83, 93, 98, 130, 151, 152, 161, 246–48, 257, 263, 264, 266, 267, 276, 278–80, 285, 288, 291, 292, 349, 364
Bender, M. B., 156, 162
Bender, R., 162
Bene, E., 81, 83
Benjamin, Anne, 176
Bennett, Ivy, 311, 328
Benoit, E. Paul, 173, 199
Benton, Arthur L., 148, 162, 178, 196
Bentzen, F., 115, 116, 126
Beres, David, 281, 292, 425, 452
Bergman, L., 282, 284, 292
Bergmann, T., 363
Berko, M. J., 157, 158, 162
Berkowitz, P. H., 280, 292
Berlin, I. N., 109, 126
Berman, L., 390, 406
Bernheim, H., 245, 257, 369, 406
Berrestford, K., 128
Berwald, Cathe, 465, 482
Bessemer, D. W., 225
Bettelheim, Bruno, 470, 472, 476, 478, 482

509

SUBJECT INDEX